Papermaking

The Dard Hunter Paper Museum of the Massachusetts Institute of Technology

PAPERMAKING

The History and Technique
of an Ancient Craft

BY

DARD HUNTER

SECOND EDITION, REVISED AND ENLARGED

LONDON

PLEIADES BOOKS

MCMXLVII

RAGS MAKE PAPER,

PAPER MAKES MONEY,

MONEY MAKES BANKS,

BANKS MAKE LOANS,

LOANS MAKE BEGGARS,

BEGGARS MAKE

      RAGS.

(Author unknown, *circa*
eighteenth century)

Foreword

FOR more than forty years I have been assembling material relating to the ancient craft of papermaking, and my researches have taken me to all parts of the world, travelling hundreds of thousands of miles in this elusive study. During this period a dozen books have been compiled on this much-neglected subject. For the most part these books were expensively printed upon handmade paper in limited editions and were sold at extravagant prices. All of these volumes, from both my own and other presses, are now out of print and not easily obtained.

The present book embraces a selection of material from the expensive editions, but is issued at a modest price. This compilation is not a reprint of any previous volume, but it draws from many of them, with a store of material not previously used. It is the aim of this book to give accomplished bibliophiles and amateur booklovers an insight into the methods employed by the makers of paper in all parts of the world and from all periods; also it is the desire to interest and instruct papermakers, workers in watermarking, etchers, engravers, printers, bookbinders, paper salesmen, and all users of paper.

Inasmuch as I have made use of material from my former books it is only proper that credit be given the publishers: The Mountain House Press, Chillicothe, Ohio; William Edwin Rudge, New York, N. Y.; Elmer Adler, Pynson Printers, New York, N. Y.; McGraw-Hill Book Company, New York, N. Y.; and the Manual Arts Press, Peoria, Illinois.

After more than four decades of interest in the craft of papermaking it is only natural that my association with the world's historians of paper and papermaking has been considerable. This affiliation and correspondence through the years has been a source of constant inspiration, and my knowledge and understanding of paper and allied subjects has materially broadened through contact with makers and collectors of paper in every part of the world. It would not be possible to set down the name of every person who has given generous help; there have been thousands, of every religion and nationality; all interested in the one elusive subject — Paper. A partial list of my friends and correspondents will not only express my esteem and affection, but will serve as a record of my contemporaries who have long been devoted to the ancient industry of papermaking. To these workers I am grateful and appreciative: Elmer Adler; Lennart Åkesson; Henri Alibaux; François Angeli; Harold Bayley; Martha T. Bennett; Raffaello Bertieri; André Blum; Hans H. Bockwitz; Yun Ts'ung Chao; Bodil Christensen; R. H. Clapperton; Georges Degaast; Harrison Elliott; Peter Franck; Yasunosuke Fukukita; Henri Gachet; Emile P. Gaillet; Andrea Gasparinetti; Jack Green; Victor von Hagen; Hellmut Lehmann-Haupt; Bunsho Jugaku; Perm Kumpangtong; E. J. Labarre; Hans Lenz; Rosamond B. Loring; Leopoldo Marzano; F. A. McClure; Shigeo Nakane; C. Pels; Marius Péraudeau; Joseph J. Plank; Jan Poortenaar; Piero Rambaudi; Sarangu Madhawa Rao; Armin Renker; Alfred Schulte; T. Seki; Peter Sinclair; F. Bailey Vanderhoef, Jr.; Tekumalla Venkajee; I. Waite; Adolph Waller; R. E. Wedgwood; Theodore Weiss; William Bond Wheelwright; Y. F. Woo; S. Yamada; Ruth Yantai.

Dard Hunter

Massachusetts Institute of Technology
Cambridge, Massachusetts, U. S. A.

Contents

Illustrations

V

VI

VII

VIII

IX

XI

XII

XIII

XIV

XV

Papermaking

I

Before Paper

THE WRITING SUBSTANCES OF THE ANCIENTS

THE PROGRESS of man through the myriad centuries may be divided into three dominant fundamental steps, or stages, of development, each transition extending through periods of hundreds or even thousands of years. These stepping-stones in the growth of man may be categorically classified under these broad headings: *Speaking — Drawing — Printing*.

The first of these evolutions — Speaking — has existed from the commencement of time and constitutes the primary and fundamental form of expression. Prehistoric man early mastered a positive method of oral communication by the use of guttural sounds that conveyed intelligible meanings among the peoples of primitive tribes; in the beginning there was no means of transferring ideas save through the human voice.

But in the second phase or stage of development of civilization — Drawing — there evolved a method of communication that raised man's intellectual powers to a vastly higher plane than could have been achieved through the mere utterance of vocal sound. Even the most crude and distorted portrayal of objects and devices and the drawing of embryonic hieroglyphics, symbols, and signs required unprecedented ingenuity and facility, employing skills unknown throughout the word-of-mouth epoch. With the drawing or writing method of thought-communication it was expedient that first a pointed drawing stick be devised and in turn guided by hand so that the desired characters or emblems might be scratched in simple outline in the ocean sands; or a marking tool or implement be provided for portraying pictures upon the inner walls of caves, like the ancient bison of the Altamira caverns. Long after the period of drawing in the sands and upon the walls of caves, came the more workable materials such as wood, metal, stone, ceramics, leaves, barks, cloth, papyrus, and parchment as basic surfaces upon which to incise or inscribe hieroglyphics and characters, each of these substances, for want of a more flexible and pliable material, faithfully fulfilling its individual requirements through the centuries. Then in 250 B.C. the Chinese savant Mêng T'ien invented the camel's-hair brush, an innovation that not only revolutionized the writing of Chinese characters, but was instrumental in the further development of woven cloth as a writing material, a substance which, along with the papyrus of Egypt and the parchment of Asia Minor, made possible the manuscript scroll, the first form of book in its true sense.

The rapid development of calligraphy by archaic Chinese scholars and their spontaneous adoption of the camel's-hair brush and fluid pigment brought forth the exigency for a writing substance that was cheaper and more practical than woven textile. It was this urgent need for a totally new writing surface that inspired the Chinese eunuch Ts'ai Lun A.D. 105 to proclaim his marvellous invention of true paper — a thin, felted material formed on flat, porous moulds from macerated vegetable fibre. With the advent of paper the art of calligraphy as originally conceived by Ts'ang Chieh in 2700 B.C. had its real impetus and the brush-written manner of recording history and setting down accounts upon paper was destined to supersede all other methods.

It is incomprehensible that the third step in the development of civilization — Printing — was so long retarded after the invention of paper, for it was not until A.D. 770 that the first text printing upon paper was finally completed. While this original printing of Empress Shōtoku's million dhāranī took place in Japan the accomplishment was, nevertheless, of Chinese conception, and its execution was made possible only through Chinese ingenuity and influence. If man may now be considered as having reached a high state of civilization his gradual development is more directly due to the inventions of paper and printing than to all other factors.

Most of the crafts — including feltmaking, weaving, ceramics, papermaking, printing — now so much taken for granted and with but little veneration, were laboriously developed over long periods of time; for the most part their origins are enshrouded in obscurity. This obscurity is particularly applicable to the methods of early papermaking technique. Although the inventors of paper, the Chinese, were imprinting their skilfully executed engravings of religious subjects as early as A.D. 868, these dextrous people did not deem it expedient to render delineations of the papermaking craft until the Sung Ying-hsing wood-block prints appeared in 1634 — more than fifteen hundred years after paper had been first fabricated in the Celestial Empire. Likewise in Europe this same lack of concern for a workaday craft is manifest, for while paper-making was introduced into Spain as early as the middle of the twelfth century, no representation of a papermaker at work was attempted until 1568, when there appeared in a little book of trades the exquisite, although somewhat indefinite woodcut of *Der Papierer* by the inimitable Jost Amman. With the unhappy absence of contemporary technical illustrations in both Orient and Occident relating to the early centuries of papermaking, it is indeed fortunate that through the efforts of archæologists a number of actual specimens of original papers have been unearthed, embracing the product of practically every century from the original invention by Ts'ai Lun in China, A.D. 105, onward through the introduction of papermaking in the Occident and its eight hundred years of history in Europe. From these precious sheets and fragmentary bits of paper bearing impressions of the woven cloth, bamboo, grass, and metal wire moulds upon which they were formed, historians of the papermaking craft have been able to piece together the actual technique employed by those patient artisans of archaic times.

Paper is defined by Noah Webster as "a substance made in the form of thin sheets or leaves from rags, straw, bark, wood, or other fibrous material, for various uses."

To be classed as true paper the thin sheets must be made from fibre that has been macerated until each individual filament is a separate unit; the fibres intermixed with water, and by the use of a sieve-like screen, the fibres lifted from the water in the form of a thin stratum, the water draining through the small openings of the screen, leaving a sheet of matted fibre upon the screen's surface. This thin layer of intertwined fibre is paper. This was the manner in which the Chinese eunuch Ts'ai Lun formed the first paper 105 years after the birth of Christ, and in our own time the most ponderous and most efficient papermaking machine employs precisely this same principle. The actual fibre formation of paper has undergone no change in almost two thousand years.

Long antedating paper came papyrus, but this substance was not formed from macerated fibre and therefore is not true paper, such as was conceived by Ts'ai Lun. Papyrus is a laminated substance made by cutting or slicing the stalks of the plant from end to end with a stone or metal knife and pasting the thin delicate "boards" together, in much the same way as a carpenter or cabinetmaker builds up sheets of laminated wood.

The tapas of the South Pacific islands are not made from macerated fibre and again, as in the case of papyrus, we have another method of creating a thin substance that has a surface resembling paper, but is not true paper; the fibres are not reduced to individual units.

The so-called "rice paper" of Formosa is a misnomer in every sense as this substance is not made from rice nor is it paper. This smooth, white material, so admired by Chinese painters, is cut spirally from the pith of the *Fatsia papyrifera* tree, and, like papyrus and tapa, is not a macerated fibre material and cannot be classed as true paper.

Genuine parchment and vellum were made from the skins of animals, and while they both have the feel and appearance of paper and were used in lieu of this fibrous substance, they have no other relation whatever to paper fabricated from macerated vegetable fibres.

In the United States in the year 1943 the amount of paper produced for each individual of the population was 287.5 pounds, with an estimated consumption for 1944 by the American Paper and Pulp Association of 284.1 pounds.* It has been stated that the

---

* For the year 1937 the per capita use of paper in the United States was 248.2 pounds. By way of comparison the following figures for 1937, except where otherwise noted (the latest figures available), of the per capita production, exports and imports, of paper in other countries are enlightening. These figures are from the U. S. Department of Commerce, Bureau of the Census:

1. United States	248.2	5. Australia	128.4
2. Canada	167.6	6. Newfoundland	109.7
3. United Kingdom (1935)	152.8	7. New Zealand	108.7
4. Sweden	149.6	8. Denmark	103.6

civilization of a country may be determined by the amount of paper consumed, but this is hardly conclusive when we consider the tremendous quantities of paper and boards used in the United States for industrial and utilitarian purposes — paper that has no real relation to the cultural development of a country. In the United States during the year 1943 the production of paper used in wrapping, in packaging, for cartons, building, and binding, was about three times the tonnage consumed in the printing of books and newspapers and for writing-purposes.

With the abundance of paper used today throughout the world in books, magazines, and newspapers and for writing, it is difficult to conceive that there was a period of thousands of years when true paper did not exist. At the present time it would be impossible for civilization to endure, even for a day, the total lack of paper — a material that is as little understood by the average consumer as it is indispensable.

Paper was invented in China about A.D. 105 and for fully five hundred years thereafter the ingenious Chinese reserved for themselves a monopoly in its fabrication. Long before the invention of printing, ancient civilization made use of many different substances for imparting its thoughts and ideas by means of hieroglyphics and characters, and in the portrayal of their plans and pictures. Although this book deals primarily with paper and papermaking, it will not be too remote from the subject to trace briefly the use of various materials that were ages ago used to convey word-pictures and calligraphy before the advent of paper:

9.	Germany	102.9	26.	Costa Rica	8.1
10.	Norway	100.4	27.	Peru	7.3
11.	Austria	97.7	28.	Mexico (1933)	7.2
12.	Belgium	84.8	29.	Panama (1934)	6.9
13.	Netherlands	79.6	30.	Colombia	5.2
14.	Finland	71.0	31.	Philippines	4.7
15.	Czechoslovakia	36.9	32.	Ecuador (1935)	2.8
16.	France	36.4	33.	Venezuela	2.8
17.	Argentina	29.6	34.	Salvador	2.8
18.	Italy	26.5	35.	Guatemala	2.5
19.	Union of South Africa	25.3	36.	Honduras	2.2
20.	Cuba	24.2	37.	Nicaragua	2.2
21.	Japan	23.6	38.	Netherlands Indies	1.8
22.	Uruguay	22.2	39.	Bolivia	1.7
23.	Chile	15.9	40.	British India	1.1
24.	U. S. S. R.	12.1	41.	China	.8
25.	Brazil (1938)	8.2			

Fig. 1   *Egyptian   obelisk brought to Central Park, New York, in 1880. Before the advent of paper the ancients wrote upon stone.*

Fig. 2   *The Rosetta Stone is a piece of black basalt found in 1799 near the Rosetta mouth of the Nile. It bears a trilingual inscription in hieroglyphics, demotic characters, and Greek. It was this stone that gave M. Champollion his original clue in deciphering the Egyptian hieroglyphics.*

Stone: It is thought that stone was the first material upon which effigies and, later, characters and letters were graven, and through this medium of expression countless historical facts have been our inheritance. The learned men of Egypt with sharp chisels carved hieroglyphics in monuments of stone, called obelisks, and from these word-pictures scholars of the present day are able to decipher the writings of these archaic peoples. The obelisks are four-sided shafts, gradually tapering as they rise, and terminating in an abrupt pyramid. The sides of these monuments were skilfully carved with symbolic devices which conveyed meanings to the Egyptians, just as words and figures written upon paper are intelligible today. In 1877 one of these great stone obelisks was transported from Egypt to London and its incised hieroglyphics may be interpreted as it stands on the Thames Embankment. Another of these ancient monuments, known as "Cleopatra's Needle," standing seventy feet in height, is in Central Park, New York City, having been brought from Alexandria, Egypt, to America in 1880 (Figures 1 and 2). It was through mediums such as these great stone pillars that ideas were first transferred from one person to another, from one generation to another, and from one period to another.

Bricks: The ancient Chaldeans engraved their characters or letters upon bricks or tablets of various sizes made of clay. After each individual character had been incised into the soft clay, presumably with a stylus or stamp, the bricks were baked until hard, then the tablets were passed from one person to another, just as letters and accounts written upon paper are transferred today. These blocks of clay (Figure 3), with their arrow-like characters, are called Babylonian tablets, and it is from these old blocks, or bricks, that the modern word "tablet," meaning a block of paper, has been derived.

Brass, Copper, Bronze, and Lead: The employment of these substances for preserving documents and writings was not unknown to ancient civilization. History records that sheets of lead and other metals were used for preserving treaties, laws, and alliances, and even in the Bible there is a reference to the use of lead for enduring writing.* Bronze as a substance upon which to write was used among the Romans in recording their memorials (Figure 4). The Roman soldiers, also, when on the field of battle, were privileged to write their wills on their metal buckles or on the scabbards of their swords.

Wood: Table-books, composed of pieces of wood, were employed long before the time of Homer (ninth century B.C.), the principal material used being from box and citron trees. The slabs of wood were usually covered with a thin coating of wax, chalk, or plaster, and the writing executed by scratching the letters or marks into the coating with a metal or bone stylus. With this man-

---

* The Book of Job, xix, 24. It is recorded that the works of the Greek epic poet Hesiod (fl. 776 B. C.) were written on leaden tablets and preserved in the Temple of the Muses, and when shown to Pausanias, the noted Greek traveller and topographer, the lead had become corroded with age. In early writings the term *charta plumbea* (leaden paper) is not uncommon and some writers have concluded that lead was actually made into paper, but these references concerned tablets of lead, such as used by Hesiod.

FIG. 4   *Text upon metal. A Roman military diploma on bronze,* A.D. *246.*

FIG. 3   *Before the invention of paper, baked clay tablets were used in transmitting texts. Clay cylinder of Sennacherib, 686* B.C.

ner of writing, the letters could be erased by resurfacing the wooden boards. The separate boards were fastened together with thongs and really composed a book, called a *codex.* Some of these wooden boards must have been of great size, for in the works of Plautus, a Roman dramatist (254–184 B.C.), a schoolboy of seven years is represented as breaking his master's head with his table-book. These table-books seem to have remained in use long after the invention of paper, for their existence is recorded on the continent of Europe as late as the beginning of the fourteenth cen-

FIG. 5   *Manuscript written with a stylus upon sixty palm leaves. This manuscript is in the Singhalese (Ceylon) script and consists of parts of the* Dhammacakkappavattanasutta *or* Dhammacakkasutta *from the* Samyuttanikāya *of the* Suttapitaka *of the Pali Buddhist Canon. Early nineteenth century.*

tury, and, according to Chaucer (1340?–1400), they were not entirely laid aside in England in the late fourteenth century.

Leaves of Trees: A number of ancient nations made use of the leaves of trees for the transmission of their thoughts and ideas. In speaking of the Egyptians, Pliny, Roman naturalist (A.D. 23–79), says that men first wrote on leaves of palm trees (Figure 5). Diodorus Siculus, Roman historian (first century B.C.), relates that the judges of Syracuse were accustomed to write, on olive-tree leaves, the names of such persons as were condemned to banishment. This sentence was termed "petalism," from the Greek word meaning "leaf."

Writing on palm and other species of leaves was practised until recent times in some parts of India and Ceylon. The Ceylonese sometimes used leaves of the palm tree for their writings, but more often the leaves of the talipot tree (*Corypha umbraculifera*), as these were broad and long and well suited to the purpose. In Assam the leaves of the aloe (*Aquilaria agallocha*) were used, while in other parts of India the leaves of the palmyra (*Borassus flabelliformis*) were well adapted for calligraphy — the art of writing with a stylus, brush, or quill. From the large palmyra leaves the people cut strips of any desired length, about two inches in width. After being written upon, each leaf was pierced with two holes and as many leaves as required were strung together with

FIG. 6   *A book inscribed on folds of tree bark and bound in heavy wooden boards. The origin of this book is unknown, but it was procured in the remote hills of Sumatra.*

cords, making a book. The writing was applied by means of a stylus, or metal pencil, which cut into the leaves. The scratched lines or crevices were then filled with a black pigment mixed with water, which made the letters discernible and distinct. It is from the use of leaves of trees for the making of books in ancient times that we now use the word "leaf" to designate a page in a modern book.

Bark of Trees: The bark of certain trees has been used as a material upon which to write in every period and locality (Figure 6). The ancient Latins used the inner bark, which was known as *"liber."* This word in time was used to denote a book itself, and from it our word "library" is derived. The American Indians wrote their sign language with wooden sticks and crude liquid pigment upon the immaculate bark of the white birch tree (Figure 7), this substance — a product of nature — being admirably adapted to the purpose of writing, and answering almost as well as paper. The aborigines of Mexico, Central and South America have at one time or another made paper by beating the inner bark of moraceous trees; but the aborigines formerly inhabiting the territory that now comprises the United States and Canada never made any material that even resembled paper (Figure 8).

Parchment and Vellum: The use of parchment as a writing material also antedates paper, the name "parchment" being derived from Pergamum, an ancient city of Mysia in Asia Minor. Although parchment was probably used as early as 1500 B.C., the King of Pergamum (197–159 B.C.) is usually credited with the invention of this material and it is thought that the invention was brought

FIG. 8   *The American Indians never made any type of paper, but made use of birch bark and animal skins for their picture writing.*

FIG. 7   *The North American Indians used birch bark for their writing. Unlike the Indians of Central and South America the aborigines north of the Rio Grande never made paper.*

about through a desire to produce a writing substance that would rival the papyrus of Egypt. During the second century the Egyptian rulers would not allow their writing material, papyrus, to be exported.

Parchment is made from the split skin of the sheep. The grain, or wool, side of the skin is made into skiver, a strong leather; the flesh, or lining, side of the skin is converted into parchment, provided the skin is suited to this exacting purpose. If the lining side is not adapted to the requirements of making the more expensive parchment, it is used for the cheaper chamois or suède.

Vellum is usually calfskin prepared by a lengthy exposure in lime, and finally scraped with a rounded knife and rubbed smooth with pumice stone. Vellum, as a general rule, is manufactured from the entire skin; the skin is not split into two layers as with

Der Permennter.

Ich kauff Schaffell/Böck/vñ die Geiß/
Die Fell leg ich denn in die beyß/
Darnach firm ich sie sauber rein/
Spann auff die Ram jedo Fell allein/
Schabs darnach/mach Permennt darauß/
Mit grosser arbeit in mein Hauß/
Auß ohrn vnd klauwen seud ich Leim/
Das alles verkauff ich daheim.
55

Fig. 9   *The parchment-maker scraping the skin held in a framework. From the book of trades illustrated by Jost Amman, with poems by Hans Sachs. Frankfurt am Main, 1568.*

Fig. 10   *A Hebrew scroll written on parchment, showing one of the two rollers. From the original in the Pierpont Morgan Library, New York.*

parchment made from sheepskin. The skins usually employed in making vellum are those of the calf, goat, and lamb. In many instances vellum may be distinguished from parchment by the grain and hair marks producing a somewhat irregular surface. Parchment does not have these elusive characteristics (Figure 9).

The present-day method of treating parchment and vellum is carried out in the following rotation: washing the skin, rubbing it with lime, removing the hair, scraping the skin with a curved knife, and again washing. The partially cleansed skin is then stretched tightly, by use of leather thongs, in a four-sided wooden frame,

FIG. 11   *Manuscript volume on parchment, from the fifteenth century, entitled* Hours of the Virgin, *Netherlands (Tournay, Belgium). From the Pierpont Morgan Library, New York.*

and the scraping is continued to pare away any irregularities in the skin, leaving it of an even thickness throughout its entire surface (Figure 10). Lastly the skin is dusted with powdered chalk and laboriously rubbed with fine pumice. The modern method of treatment of parchment and vellum is almost identical with that employed by the ancient European parchment-makers.

Neither parchment nor vellum is tanned and therefore these writing materials are not true leather; they are prepared with lime, which renders a more paper-like feel and surface than would be the result of tanning. In many European manuscript books executed by monks upon parchment and vellum (Figure 11) a difference between the hair side and the flesh side of the pages is noticeable, the latter being somewhat whiter in appearance. This difference is more encountered in old than later books as the latter-day workers used more chalk and pumice on the hair side of the skin than was the custom in earlier years. Before writing upon the skins the monk scribes selected their material with care so that the variation between the opposite pages of a book would not be too pronounced. In making up the books it was their practice to place the hair side of the parchment facing the hair side, and flesh side against flesh side, so that the difference in tints and textures would not be so discernible.

Even after the advent of printing in Europe from wood-blocks and movable metal type the use of parchment continued, and it is said that to produce a single copy of the Gutenberg Bible on this material required the skins of three hundred sheep. The employ-ment of parchment for book-printing in Europe did not survive to any extent beyond the year 1500, but for the purpose of cal-ligraphy and for printing documents and diplomas this durable material is in demand even to the present day. The documents covering patents issued by both Great Britain and the United States were printed and inscribed on parchment until the first part of the nineteenth century.* It was paper, however, that gave print-

---

* The officially signed Declaration of Independence was engrossed upon parchment by order of the Congress of July 19, 1776. The single sheet which contains its text was signed on August 2 by most of the members, and by the others during the following few months. Unfortunately, the records of ex-penditures of the Congress were not minutely kept, and those now extant do not give the name of the person from whom the parchment was pur-chased. From all present indications the document was originally kept rolled, as there are no creases that would suggest that it had ever been folded. Previous to 1841 the parchment had been carelessly rolled and unrolled so many times that the writing ink of the heavy engrossing at the top had be-come cracked and the text and signatures damaged to such an extent that at the present time the fine lines of the document are barely discernible.

The original Declaration was adopted on July 4, 1776, and on the same day the Continental Congress directed that copies be printed for distribution to official bodies in the various states, and to the Continental Army. These broadsides were made by John Dunlap, official printer to the Congress, on the evening of July 4 or the morning of July 5. An examination of a copy in the Library of Congress shows that the paper is watermarked "J. Honig & Zoonen," well-known Dutch papermakers of Zaandyk, Holland. The first newspaper announcement that the Declaration had been adopted appeared in the *Pennsylvanischer Statsbote* of July 5, 1776. Its text was first reproduced in a newspaper in the *Pennsylvania Evening Post* of July 6, 1776.

The paper used by Thomas Jefferson in writing the "First Ideas" of the Virginia Constitution, 1776, measures 7¾ by 12¾ inches and is watermarked "L V G." This paper was no doubt of Dutch origin and was probably made by one of three prominent papermakers of the period: Lubertus van Gerre-vink of Egmond a/d Hoef, North Holland, Lucas van Gerrevink of Alkmaar, or L. van Groot (or van Grooten). It is stated that James Whatman, the cele-brated papermaker who established "Turkey Mill," Maidstone, Kent, Eng-land, in 1731, learned his trade from Lubertus van Gerrevink. Whatman at one time used the initials "L V G" in his English-made paper, probably in honour of his master.

Thomas Jefferson's "Rough Draft" of the Declaration of Independence is written on four pages of Dutch paper, each measuring 7⅞ by 12⅜ inches.

ing its real impetus, for had the expensive parchment been the only material available the craft of printing could never have developed.

Papyrus: Although papyrus is not paper in the true sense, it was the first writing material to assume many of the properties of the substance we now know as paper. The words "paper," *papier, papel,* etc., are, of course, derived from the Greek and Latin words *papuros* and *papyrus. Bubloi* was the Greek term used to denote the inner fibre of the papyrus plant, and writings on sheets of papyrus were known as *biblos,* in Latin as *biblia* — hence the name Bible.

As outlined at the beginning of this chapter, papyrus (Figures 12, 13, 14) is a laminated material; true paper must necessarily be made from disintegrated fibre. It would be possible to manufacture true paper from the papyrus plant inasmuch as it has considerable cellulose in its structure. Before the Christian era the

---

This manuscript is on the well-known "WRYHEYT" paper which bears the watermarked lettering "PRO PATRIA EIUSQUE LIBERTATE" in an oval border surrounding a lion, all capped by a crown. This watermark was commonly used by Dutch papermakers and may have been from any of a dozen mills, including Blauw, Van der Ley, and Pannekoek, all renowned paper mills of the period. (See *Watermarks in Paper,* by W. C. Churchill; Amsterdam, 1935.)

The earliest attempts in the making of reproductions of the Declaration of Independence were by Benjamin Owen Tyler in April 1818 and by John Binns in November 1819. Binns had been working on his quasi-facsimile since 1816. The appearance of the Tyler copy previous to the Binns version caused a heated controversy between the two publishers as to priority rights. In 1818 during the course of this controversy Tyler published a pamphlet in which he stated that the paper used for his facsimile was made by Messrs. Gilpin, Pennsylvania papermakers. According to Tyler, "the paper was worth $200.00 a ream and will be superior to any paper ever made in this or any other country." A description of the paper used by Binns was given in the *Democratic Press,* April 30, 1817, and reads: "We have this day received from the paper mill of Mr. Thos. Amies (Lower Merton, Montgomery County, Pennsylvania), the paper on which we intend to print the splendid edition of the Declaration of Independence, which, for fourteen months last past, has been under the graver. The paper is believed to be of a size and quality *superior* to any ever manufactured in the United States. The moulds, felts, &c. were all of the best kind, and manufactured for the purpose. The paper weighs *one hundred and forty pounds,* and the price is *one hundred and twenty-five dollars* a ream. Cotton rags were altogether excluded, and the finest linen only has been worked up. The size is rather more than 36 by 26 inches. We flatter ourselves that the paper is such as will do credit to the state of the art of papermaking in the United States."

FIG. 12   *In this example of unwritten papyrus the built-up, laminated structure is evident. Papyrus is not paper, as true paper must be made from disintegrated fibre.*

FIG. 13   *A section of a Greek papyrus order for payment, seventh century* A.D. *The construction of the material is well defined. Pierpont Morgan Library, New York.*

papyrus plant (*Cyperus papyrus*) grew profusely in Egypt, but in modern times it is almost extinct in that country. It now grows in some other parts of north Africa and to some extent in Sicily. In Egypt in ancient times the papyrus plant grew along the Nile, the stalks reaching six to ten feet in height, the root embedding itself in a horizontal position in the marshy ground. To the ancient Egyptians the papyrus plant was as useful and indispensable as the bamboo has always been to the Chinese. Not only were the stalks of papyrus used by the Egyptians in making a writing substance, but it served them as a building material and for the making of boats, mats, cords, and sandals.

The most interesting and informative contemporary description of the preparation of papyrus is that given by Pliny the Elder, the Roman naturalist and author who lived A.D. 23–79. Pliny had apparently never made papyrus himself, but the process had been explained to him. The following description of papyrus and its making is taken from *The Historie of the World: commonly called, The Naturall Historie of C. Plinius Secundus.* Translated into Eng-

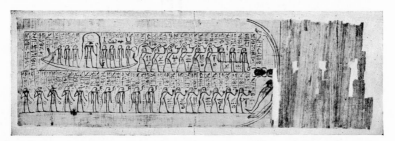

FIG. 14   *Egyptian papyrus written in hieroglyphic characters, with vignettes. This papyrus contains the text of the twelfth hour of the Book of Amy (or Imy) Ducrt. The vignette shows the sun-god being drawn through the last section of the underworld before sunrise. Egypt, XXVIth Dynasty.*

lish by Philemon Holland, Doctor of Physicke. London, printed by Adam Islip, 1635. The text is given verbatim, but it must be remembered that in the translation the Latin word "papyrus" has been changed to the English word "paper," and, as previously explained, the two commodities are of a totally different formation. The translation is set down in its original spelling and phraseology:

The best sheets or leaves of paper be those which are set out of the very midst or heart of the stem or stalk of Papyrus: and so consequently better or worse, according as they be nearer or further from it. In ancient time the principall paper and the largest was called Hieratica, (i. sacred or holy) as being imployed only about religious and divine books. But afterwards the flatterers of the Emperor *Augustus* named those of the best sort Augustae: like as the second Liviae, after the name of his wife. And hereupon it came that the paper Hieratica was set in a third ranke. Next to them in goodnesse was reputed the paper Amphitheatrike, which name was given unto it of the place where it was made. The polishing and trimming of this paper *Fannius* undertooke, who set up a shop in Rome for the selling of it: and so skilfull was he and curious in the handling and dressing thereof, that by the time hee had done withall and brought it to a perfect finenesse, hee made the same of a course and common paper, to be royall, & fit for the best persons that should use it: in such sort, as there was none in any request to speak of, but it: and called after his name it was Fanniana. As for that which passed not thorow his hands, nor had his workemanship, it retained still the old bare name Amphitheatrica.

After this kind of paper followed that which they called Saitica, of a towne or city in Egpyt, where great abundance was made thereof of the courser pieces and refuse of the said Papyrus. And yet there was another paper, towit Taniotica, so called of a place neere adioyning, made of the grosser part neere to the bark and outside: and this they sold for the weight and no other goodnesse that it had besides. As for the merchant Paper or shop-paper, called Emporetica, it was not for to write in, onely it served as wast Paper for sarplers to wrap and packe up wares in: also for coffins or coronets to lap spice and fruits in, and thereupon merchants and occupiers gave it that name. And with this, the very cane itselfe is to be seene clad outwardlt: and the utmost coat thereof is like a reed or bulrush, fit for no purpose but to make cordage of: and not very good for that use neither, unless it be for the water only, which it wil abide very wel. Now the making of all these Papers, was in this sort, namely, upon a broad bord wet with the cleare water of Nilus. For the fatty and muddie liquor thereof serves in stead of glew, wherwith at the first the thin leafe of the cane Papyrus, slived from the rest, and laid upon the bourd to the full length (in manner of the warpe) according as the trunke will give leave, being cut off at both ends, namely, toward the top and the root, is wet and besmeared: then is there another laid overthwart it, after the order of the woofe, with a crosse graine to the other: and so is the web (as it were) of the Paper performed. Pressed afterwards it is in certaine presses, that both leaves may sticke together: and then the whole sheets are dried in the Sun. Which done, they be so couched together, that the best and largest lie first, and so consequently in order as they be worse and of lesse size, untill you come to the worst. And one scape or trunke lightly of the cane Papyrus, yeelds not above 20 such sheets. Great difference there is in them for the breadth, notwithstanding the length be all one. The best, namely which were taken out of the heart of the cane, bare 13 fingers in breadth. The Hieratica Paper wants two of that number. The Fannian is but ten fingers broad. The common Paper Amphitheatrica, but nine. Saitica yet fewer, and will not beare the stroke of the hammer. And as for the merchants Paper, it was so short and narrow, that it went not above six fingers. Moreover, in Paper these 4 things must be considered, that it be fine, well compact, white, and smooth. Howbeit, *Claudius Caesar* the Emperor abated the credite of the Paper Augusta, that it was no more accounted the best: for indeed so thin it was, that it would not abide the dent of the pen: besides, it would not hold inke, but shew the letters on the other side; and was evermore in danger of blurring and blotting, specially on the back part: and otherwise, unsightly it was to the eie, for that a man might so easily see thorough it. And therefore he devised to fortifie and strengthen the said Paper, and laid another course or coat (as it were) over the former, in manner of a double woofe. Hee enlarged also the breadth of the Paper: for hee caused it to be a foot broad, yea, and some a foot and an halfe, I meane that kind which was called Macrocola, or large Roiall Paper. But herin was a fault, and reason found it out: for if one leafe of this large Paper were plucked off, the more pages took harm thereby, and were lost. And therefore the former Claudian Paper, which had but 3 leaves of Papyrus, was preferred before all the rest. Howbeit, that which was named Augustane bare the name for letters missive, and the Liviane continued still in the owne credite, having no property of the first and principall, but all in a second degree. The roughnesse of Paper is polished and smoothed either with some tooth, or else with a Porcellane shell: but the letters in such slick Paper, will soone fade and decay. For by polishing, it will not receive the inke so deepe as when it is not smoothed, although otherwise it will shine the better. Moreover, it falls out many times, that if the humor be not artificially laid, the Paper is very stubborn: but this fault is soon found out at the very first stroke of the hammer, or else discovered by the smell, especially if good heed were not taken in the tempering therof. As for the spots and speckles, the eie will quickly spie them: but the long streaks, and veines lying close couched between the pasted places, can hardly be discerned before that the letter runs abroad, and shewes how in the spongeous substance of the Paper wanting that past, the ink will sinke thorough, and make blots; so deceitfull is the making of this Paper. What remedie then? but to be at a second labor to past it new againe another way, towit, with the common past that wee use, made with the finest floure of wheat, and tempered with hote scalding water, and a little vinegre mingled therwith. For the joiners glue and that made of gums, is brittle, and will not abide the rolling up of these sheets into quiers. But they that wil go more surely to work, and make an exquisite past indeed, boile the soft and tender crums or leavened bread in seathing water, and then let it run thorough a strainer, which they use to this purpose. For besides that the Paper hereby will be more firme, and have lesse flawes, it surmounts also in sweetnesse the water of Nilus. Moreover, all kind of past whatsoever for this effect, ought neither to be staler than a day old, nor yet fresher and under that age. After that it is thus pasted, they beat it thin with the hammer: and a second time runne lightly over with new past: and then being thus knit & bound fast again, it is made smooth and void of wrinckles, and finally beaten even with the hammer, and driven out in length and breadth. After this manner was that Paper made, wherin were written the bookes and records of the two *Gracchi, Tiberius,* and *Caius,* with their owne hands, long agoe: the which I saw in the house of *Pomponius Secundus,* a noble citizen of Rome, and a renowned Poet, almost two hundred years after their death. As for the writings of *Cicero,* of *Augustus* late Emperour of famous memorie, and of *Virgill,* we daily see and handle them, by the meanes of Paper (Papyrus) so good and durable.

According to this learned naturalist the stalks of the plant were cut just above the root. The tops, or flower heads, and the parts nearest the root were discarded as unfit for making into the writing substance. The remaining stalks were cut into pieces about two feet long and split down the centre. The parts nearest the middle were naturally the widest and most refined and were therefore best suited for making into sheets for writing. The strips nearest the outside of the stalks were rejected as too narrow and too tough for use. After the strips had been cut in tissue-thin sections they were laid side by side on a board. The material was then covered on the upper side with a thin paste of wheat flour and the muddy water of the Nile, and, according to Pliny, mixed with vinegar. Another layer of strips was laid across in the opposite direction, and the two layers pressed or hammered together. This formed a laminated substance which could be written upon, but the making of which was totally unrelated to the technique of papermaking. Papyrus fabrication more closely resembles delicate carpentry, while the making of paper is the process of matting or felting individual fibres, suspended in water, into sheets. Papyrus and paper have been used for the same purposes, but the method of making them is totally different. Papyrus was used in Egypt centuries before Christ and at later periods in Greece and Rome. The material actually was in use until the tenth century, but by the twelfth century other writing material had almost entirely taken its place.

In 1908 I travelled along the Nile seeking the papyrus plant, but none could be discovered; on a later journey the sedge was found in other parts of north Africa and in Sicily. In the United States papyrus may be seen growing in the Southern and Far Western states as an ornamental plant, but the clumps are insignificant compared to present-day African growth. In the glasshouses of several Northern universities the plant has grown to a

FIG. 15   *The papyrus plant was as useful to the ancient Egyptians as the bamboo has always been to the Chinese.*

FIG. 16   *The "rice paper" plant of Formosa, known in China as Kung-shu (Tetrapanax papyriferum). The Chinese worker is cutting the "paper" spirally from the inner pith of the tree. This material is not true paper; it is a product of nature, not manufactured from disintegrated fibre.*

height of eight or ten feet, but the stalks are thin and lacking in substance. In experimenting in the preparation of sheets of papyrus from plants grown in the hothouses of Ohio State University, Columbus, and Massachusetts State College, Amherst, it has been found that the stalks lack firmness of body and cannot successfully be made into sheets that resemble closely the papyrus of the ancients. In an endeavour to make papyrus from the African-grown plant, however, the experiments have been more encouraging and sheets have been formed that more nearly emulate the papyrus used by the ancient scribes (Figure 15).

Rice Paper: This material is not of ancient origin, but inasmuch as it is a product of nature and could have existed before the invention of paper, it may be classified with other pre-paper writing materials. The so-called "rice paper" used for Chinese paintings is, like papyrus, a substance unrelated to true paper. The thin sheets of "rice paper" are cut spirally from the inner pith of the *kung-shu* (*Tetrapanax papyriferum*), formerly *Fatsia papyrifera,* a plant that grows in the hills of northern Formosa (Taiwan) (Figure 16).

Sheets of the *Fatsia* pith beautifully embellished with Chinese paintings of birds, fish, butterflies, trades, and costumes were first seen in England and in the New England states when sea captains and sailors brought many specimens to the Occident (Figure 17). The Europeans and Americans thought the material genuine paper and, being puzzled as to the material used in its making, called it erroneously "rice paper," a misnomer that still lingers.*

---

* Even the author of the earliest Chinese treatise on the subject of paper-making was evidently confused in regard to the making of the so-called "rice paper." In the three-volume work dealing with Chinese occupations by Sung Ying-hsing entitled *T'ien kung k'ai wu,* published in 1634, the manner used in making the "rice paper" is erroneously described, the author thinking the "paper" was fabricated by macerating the pith and spreading it into sheets.

In Europe as late as 1888 it was stated that "it is only within a few years that the true nature of this brittle 'paper' has been ascertained." In China the tree is sometimes called *"kung-shu,"* or hollow plant. The young trees grow with a single stem, but after flowering two or more branches are produced; the tree increases in size until it reaches a height of twenty to thirty feet. Inasmuch as the pith deteriorates in the parts of the tree that have become old, the trees are usually cut before they reach ten or twelve feet in height. The large leaves, resembling the sycamore, crown the slender stem, the flowers being wand-like bunches of small, light yellow blossoms. The stalk, or stem, of the slight tree is covered with a thick bark; the wood is hard and durable. For making into "rice paper" the stalk of the tree is usually cut in lengths of about twelve inches. The white pith is about two inches in diameter and is of uniform texture, except in the centre, where it is broken into a series of double concave cavities. In extracting the pith a rounded stick is forced into one end of each twelve-inch section and the pith pushed out by pounding the stick against the hard ground. The extracted pith is next placed in hollow sections of bamboo, where it is allowed to swell to the size of the inside of the bamboo. With this treatment the pith dries in a straight cylinder. The pith is then skilfully cut by a worker who holds a sharp knife against the cylindrical pith and turns the pith round and round against the sharp edge of the knife. The paring is continued until the inner broken pith is reached. Each pith section is capable of producing a smooth continuous scroll about four feet long, the width being determined by the length of the pith section, usually twelve inches. The scrolls are finally flattened in a pile and cut into sheets of the required size. The sheets of "rice paper" that reach

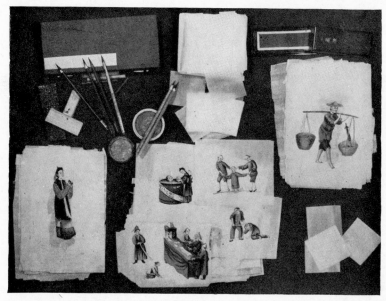

Fig. 17   *"Rice paper" is a product of nature and has no relation to true paper. The so-called rice paper is cut spirally from the pith of the* Fatsia papyrifera *tree and is used by the Chinese for painting.*

The sheets of pith when dry are quite brittle, but when saturated with water the material becomes tough and somewhat pliable. Since about 1830 this material has been used in the Occident for making artificial flowers, the pith taking colour readily. It is recorded that the Empress Charlotte of Mexico once paid seventy pounds for a bouquet composed of various kinds of flowers made from the *Fatsia papyrifera.*

Huun and *Amatl:* Somewhat related to the papyrus of the Egyptians, Greeks, and Romans was the writing material of the Maya and Aztec peoples. A remnant of this ancient craft as practised hundreds of years ago in the Western Hemisphere exists to the present day in the work of the Otomi Indians of southern Mexico. Bark-beating among the tribes of Middle America is perhaps as ancient as is this aboriginal civilization. Before Christopher Co-

America from Formosa and are used in the making of artificial flowers are usually of comparatively small size, but in China the "paper" may be as large as twelve inches square.

lumbus set foot in the Lesser Antilles, thus bringing to a close the
isolation of the Americas, a substance resembling paper was in use
by the Maya, the foremost tribe of the Yucatán peninsula. The
making of this beaten bark material, which was known as *huun,*
went hand in hand with Maya intellectual development and finally
with the advent of hieroglyphic writing; these ancient peoples actually constructed books.

The Maya made these hieroglyphic charts for centuries, even
through the period of decline. When Maya civilization revived
again in the tenth century, they had already begun to fold their
huun paper into book form. In this period they produced a sacred
almanac of forty-five pages still extant and known as the Codex
Dresdensis. This remarkable polychromic book, its characters and
figures set down by some anonymous astronomer-priest of Maya-
pan, was fashioned somewhere between A.D. 900 and 1100 (Figures 18, 19). If we can rely upon the Spanish chroniclers, this
Codex was far from being the only manuscript produced by this
ancient civilization; the Maya had many books; in fact, even extensive libraries. The Spanish missionary Diego de Landa, of the
Monastery of Izamal, Yucatán, writing in the sixteenth century,
said: "We found a great number of books written with their characters, and because they contained nothing but superstitions and
falsehoods about the devil, we burned them all. . . ." It was the
Aztec, following the Maya, however, who developed the beating
of bark into paper from a minor craft to a sizable industry. The
Aztec peoples termed their beaten papers *amatl.**

More than forty years ago I visited the Otomi papermakers in
southern Mexico and saw the procedure of their bark-beating in
detail, but as this method of making "paper" is only remotely related to true paper formed from disintegrated fibre upon moulds,
it will not be necessary to venture beyond an outline of the process. The bark, an inch or more in width, is taken from the trees in
as long strips as possible. The dark outer bark is then removed,
leaving the fibrous inner bark as the usable material. The inner

---

* The *amatl* paper was made from the inner bark of a moraceous tree;
of these trees there are 55 genera and over 700 species, of wide distribution,
nearly 600 being comprised in the single genus *Ficus.* The family also in-
cludes the important genera *Morus* (mulberry), *Cannabis* (hemp), etc. Several of the species used for making paper were *Ficus padifolia, Ficus involuta,*
and *Ficus petiolaris.*

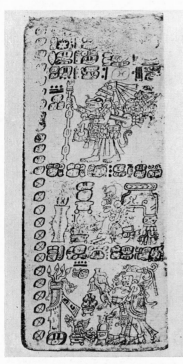

FIG. 19   A section of the Codex Telapalco, Valley of Mexico, from about 1530. The original paper roll measures 5½ by 61 inches. (Museum of the American Indian, New York)

FIG. 18   A "page" from the Dresden Codex. This polychromic book, called analteh by the Maya, is eight inches high, twelve and a half feet long, and is folded screenwise to form distinct pages. It is written on huun paper made from the inner bark of the Ficus. The book was made between 900 and 1000 A.D.

bark is boiled over a slow fire in a home-made cauldron containing water and wood ash. If the fibres are old and hard, a liquid residue obtained from cooking corn is used. (In this process the Mexican technique differs entirely from that employed in the Pacific islands, since the Polynesians do not resort to the boiling of the bark, as will be explained later.) The Mexican papermaking is done by women, as the men feel such work beneath their dignity;

Fig. 20   *The tools used by the Otomi Indians, Mexico, in mak-*
ing their paper. The grooved stones are of serpentine marble, and
those with rounded handles are gabbro. The cut amatl-*paper images*
(muñeco) *are used in the practice of sorcery.*

the men, however, do strip the bark from the trees. After boiling,
the strips of bark fibre, having become disintegrated to some extent, are laid side by side upon a rectangular board that is a little
larger in size than the dimensions of the paper being made. The
strips of bark, each strip slightly overlapping the next, are then
pounded and smoothed with a stone (Figure 20), or in some localities a smoothing tool is made by burning a corncob until it
becomes hard. After the strips of bark have been beaten and
united into a sheet (Figures 21, 22), the board with its deposit
of crude paper is placed in the sun to dry, when the stratum of
fibre can easily be removed (Figure 23). Of all the primitive
papers produced in the world, those of the Otomi Indians, Mexico, are perhaps the most crude. It does not require much imagination to liken the making of Mexican paper to the process used in
fabricating papyrus; also, to a limited degree the making of the

Fig. 21   An Otomi Indian
woman, San Pablito, Mexico,
placing bark fibre on a board
ready for beating with a stone
such as is shown in Figure 20.
(Photographs: Bodil Christensen)

Fig. 22   Beating bark fibres
into a sheet of paper. Sheets of
paper are drying upon boards
at the side of the worker; the inner bark of the Ficus involuta
hangs on the line.

Otomi paper is not unlike the beating of tapa. If we are not to be too particular in our generalization, we may loosely place papyrus, *huun*, *amatl*, and tapa in the same category — at least none of these substances is true paper made from disintegrated fibre upon porous moulds, the technique conceived and used by the Chinese Ts'ai Lun.[1]

Tapa, or the Bark Paper of the Pacific Islands: It is not possible to examine the fine old bark papers of many of the islands of the Pacific Ocean without a sincere regret that these localities ever came under the influence of white men. This is especially true of the beaten bark papers produced many years ago by the Hawaiians, as these islanders were more adept in this craft than any other Pacific peoples. The old Hawaiian bark papers (called *ka pa*, meaning "the beaten") preserved in museums and private collections show perfection of workmanship that skilled technicians of the present day would have difficulty in duplicating. In Hawaii, as in the other island groups of the Pacific, the natives made their beautifully decorated bark papers for clothing and for use in their

---

[1] Notes, mostly of a bibliographical character, referred to by a superior figure in the text are to be found at the end of the book.

Fig. 23   *A sheet of* amatl *paper being lifted from the board after drying in the sun. Otomi Indians, southern Mexico.*

homes and for many domestic purposes. It was an important material with them as they had no cloth or textiles, and the garments of tapa constituted their main article of dress. After the advent of white men with their prosaic manufactured tools and printed woven cloth, the art of making tapa, or beaten bark paper, was soon cast aside, so there has been no craftsmanship of this kind practised in these islands for more than a hundred years. Today in this highly commercialized locality not a vestige of anything relating to this age-old industry remains, and, aside from exhibits in museums, it might never have existed (Figure 24).

Not only did the Hawaiians make and decorate bark paper, but

FIG. 24   *The finest bark paper of the entire Pacific Ocean was at one time made in the Hawaiian Islands, but there has been no work of this kind done there for more than a hundred years. The specimens shown in this photograph date from the year 1843.*

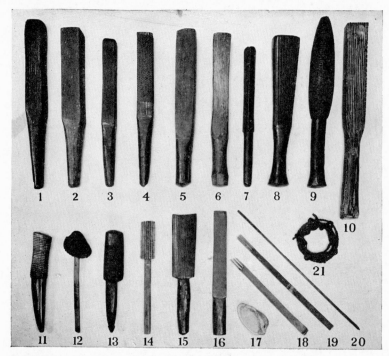

FIG. 25   *Tapa-beaters formerly used in the beating of the primitive mulberry-bark papers:* (1) *Hawaiian* ie kuku, *11* hoopai *marks, weight 26 oz., length 15 in.* (2) *Hawaiian* ie kuku, *44* hoopai *marks, weight 26 oz., length 14 in.* (3) *Hawaiian* ie kuku, *22* hoopai *marks, weight 14 oz., length 14 in.* (4) *Hawaiian* ie kuku, *two sides* hoopai, *one side* halua koeau, *one side* maka upena, *all designs forming "watermarks" in the paper, weight 20 oz., length 20 in.* (5) *Tahitian* tupai, *18* hoopai (ao) *marks, weight 38 oz., length 14 in.* (6) *Marquesan beater, 22* hoopai *marks, weight 26 oz., length 14 in.* (7) *Fijian* iki *or* samu, *5* hoopai *marks on each of the three sides, weight 8 oz., length 13 in.* (8) *Tongan* ike *or* tata, *Samoan* ie *or* ietosi, *9* hoopai *marks, weight 34 oz., length 13 in.* (9) *Loyalty beater, crossed lines, weight 28 oz., length 15 in.* (10) *Bark-paper beater of unknown origin (procured in Tahiti), weight 28 oz., length 18 in.* (11) *Belgian Congo (Stanley Falls) bark-paper beater, ivory carved with cross lines, weight 14 oz., length 9 in.* (12) *New Britain beater, shells with handle of bamboo, weight 9 oz., length 10 in.* (13) *Southeast New Guinea beater, 27 carved lines running around the implement, weight 8 oz., length 10 in.* (14) *Javanese* deloewang *paper-beater, grooved brass with handle of bamboo, weight 18 oz., length 11*

the craft was almost universal throughout the Pacific. Each island group, separated by hundreds of miles of ocean, had its own form of beating tools (Figure 25), its own technique of operation, and its own school of design. The principle of the operations, however, was the same throughout all the island groups. It is not known when this craft had its beginning; no records exist, its remote origin is shrouded in mystery.

The making of the beaten bark "papers" of the Pacific islands has no *precise* counterpart; these beaten tapas stand practically alone as an individual technique. Owing to the increasing present-day interest in the making of this material, I will set down extracts from my own observations as written almost twenty years ago after a year's travel in dozens of the islands and atolls of the great Pacific Ocean. In the course of my investigations relative to the making and decorating of tapa I travelled many thousands of miles, visiting the Society group, the Hervey Islands, Hawaii, and other frequented localities of the Pacific. In these islands nothing could be found of the old craft and I became apprehensive that I had arrived seventy-five or a hundred years too late to see the making of bark paper undisturbed by the march of civilization, which always deals a death-blow to fine aboriginal craftsmanship.

Upon reaching New Zealand I learned that if the art of tapa-beating was practised in its original state anywhere, it would be in the Tongan or Friendly Islands, which lie to the southeast of the great Fiji group and off the regular line of travel. The Tongan Islands embrace about one hundred and fifty islands and islets

---

in. (15) *New Hebrides beater, 14 widely spaced* hoopai *marks, weight 12 oz., length 11 in.* (16) *Solomon group beater, 15 rough* hoopai *marks, weight 17 oz., length 12 in.* (17) *Samoan shell* (asi) *used in the preparation of the mulberry bark* (tutuga) *for the making of bark paper.* (18) *Hawaiian bamboo liner used in decorating bark paper by dipping in dye and drawing across the material as a pen would be used.* (19) *Hawaiian bamboo liner which made six heavy lines, while the other tool* (No. 18) *made nine thin lines across the tapa.* (20) *Hawaiian bamboo stamper or printing stick* (ohekapala) *used many years ago in decorating paper.* (21) *Hawaiian braided coconut-fibre rope employed in the ornamentation of tapa; used as a carpenter uses a chalked cord. These tools were collected by me almost twenty years ago in the various localities where they were used.*

with a territory of 256 square miles; the population, about thirty thousand. I was aware that tapa was still made on the island of Savaii, of British Samoa, and also on Taviuni, of the Fiji Islands, but only in small pieces and in a form different from the ancient.

On the last day of March 1926 I left Auckland for the Tonga Islands, via Fiji, and after eight days on a small ship arrived at Nukualofa, the chief village on the island of Tongatabu — that is, Tonga the Sacred. This island, the largest of the group, and the seat of the original government, is shaped like an irregular half-moon, with the villages of Nukualofa about the centre and the hamlets of Hihifo and Hahake at the extremities. The islets of Ata, Malinoa, Tau, Euaiki, and Eua surround the larger island, forming one of the most picturesque groups in the Pacific. I visited numerous islands of the Tongan group, and saw practised the old craft of tapa-beating and tapa-decorating, much as it was in the days of the early English explorer Captain James Cook. It is my desire to enter into rather minute detail regarding Tonga tapa-making, as it will be only a few years before these island people, like those of the more frequented localities, cease this work entirely, and no first-hand records of a technical nature exist.

Upon reaching Tongatabu I went to the Wesleyan Mission House, as I had a letter of introduction to the Reverend Roger Page, an Australian, who had been among the Tonganese for over nineteen years and spoke the native language fluently. I found him a kindly and obliging gentleman, who, unlike the early missionaries of Tahiti, had tried to foster the old crafts and customs and had given every encouragement to the natives engaged in the making of bark paper. He acted as interpreter and arranged for me to see the entire process of making and decorating tapa.

The raw material being the most important item in the work, we first visited the outlying districts where the paper mulberry (*Broussonetia papyrifera*) was growing and saw its preparation by native women for use in papermaking. The trees do not appear to grow wild, but are cultivated in small clumps near frequented paths and roads accessible for working. The trees sprout from shoots, which are carefully planted and kept weeded until the stalks have reached a height of from twelve to fifteen feet, the trunks of the trees being slender and devoid of branches. The leaves are large and hairy on the under side, growing in clusters at the top of the slight stalk, and having much the appearance of the ornamental eucalyptus.

When the trees have reached the proper height and circumference for making into tapa, they are cut at the base, and after the leaf clusters are removed, the sticks are tied in bundles of a size suitable for conveyance. These bundles are soaked in a running stream or in a pool of fresh water until the outer bark becomes soft, when it is scraped away by the use of shells, leaving exposed the soft inner bark (*fetaaki*), clean and yellow-white. Next, each stick is cut perpendicularly from end to end, which allows the thin inner bark to come free from the stalk in a narrow strip, tapering from about three inches at the base to less than one inch at the extreme tip. The strips of inner bark are then laid upon the grass to dry and bleach. After sufficient exposure to the sun, the strips are made up into coils with the concave side of the bark outermost, which causes the material to assume a flatness that it would not otherwise have. In this form the bark is ready for the first beating, which is accomplished by heavy wooden mallets, called in Tonga *ike*. The prepared bark (called *pakoko* or *hiapo*) in rolls about twelve inches in diameter, each containing the inner bark of several trees, is distributed among the workers throughout the islands, who have had no part in the cultivation or preparation of the raw material.

In Tonga the growing of the bark and the making of the finished tapa (*gatu*) are more or less religious obligations, and the completed product is at present taken to the churches, where it is divided among the workers who had a part in its production. Unlike the Fijian and Samoan material, the Tongan tapa is rarely sold, and it is hoped that the making of this superior bark paper will never become commercialized.

The beating is undertaken by individual women artisans, who work before their huts in good weather and under shelter during the rainy season. While the old Hawaiians used a hand-hewn anvil, or beating-block, of symmetrical shape and studied form, the Tonganese, like the Javanese, have always employed a simple log, about fifteen feet in length, flattened along the top and supported at each end upon stones. The log, known in the Tongan language as *tutua*, remains in place from day to day as part of the furniture of the homestead. In Tahiti, Rapanui, and Samoa the wooden anvil is also called *tutua,* and in Fiji *dutua,* which may show a common origin of the terms. This would also apply to other appellations of Polynesia and Melanesia in the making of bark paper.

The beaters or mallets (*ike*) of Tonga are identical with those of Samoa, where they are known as *ie,* and are made of heavy, dark-brown, close-grained wood (see Figure 25, tool No. 8). The Tongan-Samoan mallets differ in shape from all others and contain fewer grooves for the width of the faces than those of any other Pacific islands. I was told that the men made the beaters, but I have never seen or heard of a Tongan man beating bark. One old man near Neiafu, Vavau, told me he liked the sound of the beating, but he could not perform the task himself as it was too steady and too hard.

The Tongan women beaters sit before the log anvils, cross-legged, upon banana leaves or grass mats. Around the logs are strewn leaves and grasses to keep the beaten bark from being soiled by coming in contact with the dirty ground. The constant tap, tap, tap, a hollow resonant sound, can be heard throughout the inhabited sections of Tonga, and I was able to trace in this way the location of any number of scattered workers (Figure 26). The first woman I found beating was sitting well out in her yard in front of a small thatched hut, amid naked children, mangy dogs, and lean pigs. I watched her at work for three or four hours, and during this time she never ceased the constant beating. A strip of bark that had been soaking in water was laid on the log anvil and was struck at right angles, the mallet falling squarely upon the material. As she beat, the bark was pushed away from her over the anvil, falling in folds upon the leaves. At each stroke of the beater the bark became wider, and when twice its original width, the material was doubled and tripled and again beaten, being kept sprinkled with fresh water during the entire pounding. The woman would then take the material apart and put it together again in different order, beating all the while, either straight with the bark or at right angles. As she pulled the bark apart it would stick and sometimes tear, and she would mend the holes as she went along by beating small pieces of bark over them. This folding and beating was continued for hours, until the bark, which in its original state was barely three inches wide, had assumed a

FIG. 26   *Polynesian women beating the bark of the* Broussonetia papyrifera *into small sections, which will later be made into large pieces of* tapa. *Tongan, or Friendly, Islands, South Pacific Ocean.*

width of eighteen to twenty inches. Beating the bark in one layer would never have made this width; it was the lapping together of the narrow folds that caused the bark to become wider when the mass was beaten together. This action naturally reduced the length of each strip. Before one piece was beaten to its entire width, the worker would start a fresh strip, apparently allowing the former one to dry a little before continuing the beating. Water was used sparingly, as the bark was only lightly sprinkled every few minutes. I tried the beating and found it difficult and exceedingly severe on the wrist, owing to the vibration of the long wooden anvil. (The Tongan beaters, called *ike* or *tata*, measure thirteen inches in length and weigh thirty-four ounces.) The women are ambidextrous and use both hands with equal facility, constantly changing when either arm grows tired. In Tongatabu I saw a dozen or more women at work beating tapa, and as many more on the island of Vavau. The workers were all aged women and were dressed mostly in tapa, with gaily coloured seed-pods and leaves about their bodies. They were kindly and seemed desirous of showing me the entire operation of their work, although somewhat curious regarding my interest. They gave me custard apples, coconuts, and pieces of tapa, and always invited me to sit before them on the banana leaves. One extremely ancient artisan had a mallet so scarred and marked with usage that I wished to purchase it, but she insisted that I be content with a newer and less worn one that was lying unused at her side. No amount of persuasion could induce her to part with the old beater; she had used it many years, she explained, and it had become a favourite tool, one that her hands had grown to fit. After learning this I did not press her further, as I could appreciate her affection for the implement; I have favourite tools myself, although of a different nature. On my visits to Lifuka, of the Haapai group, and also Niuafoöu, I could find no trace of tapa-making in these islands, although I found the decorated bark paper in use as wearing apparel and bed-clothing.

Of the several methods employed in the decoration and ornamentation of bark paper the method used by the Tonganese is the most ingenious and artistic, and is less contaminated by outside influence than any other means of decoration in the South Sea Islands. It was my rare good fortune to see this work being done on the island of Tongatabu, for the decorating, unlike the beating, is practised only at certain times and upon special occasions, as a great amount of beaten bark must first be made before any decorating is undertaken. I was on the island when the natives were making preparations for the celebration of the one hundredth anniversary of the founding of the Wesleyan Mission, in 1826, and many arrangements were being made for the festival. To see the complete process of tapa-making, a fairly long residence in the islands is necessary, as it is impossible to determine just

Fig. 27   *Coconut-fibre printing mats* (kupesi) *made near Nukua-lofa, Tongatabu, Tongan Islands, South Pacific. These mats are used in the decoration of tapa and each measures 6 by 19 inches. The lettering on the two outside mats reads:* Koe maka fakamanatu eni o sii tahine ko Meleami — *"this stone is in memory of the dear girl Miriam."*

when the natives will be working on the material. When, for instance, a Tongan chief dies, all tapa-beating and decorating is suspended for a period of three months, and as there are numerous deaths, the work is constantly interrupted.

For the decoration of Tongan bark paper the old-time *kupesi*, or vegetable mats, are the principal implement employed. These mats (Figure 27) are made from several kinds of dried plants, which act as printing surfaces in producing designs on tapa, in much the same manner as an impression of a coin is made on a piece of paper by rubbing with a lead pencil or chalk. These mats are of various shapes and sizes. The backings are composed of the flat leaves of either the coconut or the *Pandanus odoratissimus,* over which the mid-ribs or stems of coconut leaves are sewed to form designs by the use of the thin fibrous threads of the *fau* (*Hibiscus tiliaceus*). The mats, with their slightly raised, designed surface, are made up in innumerable shapes and patterns and are sufficiently flexible to bend in any form desired. From the illustrations of these *kupesi* the mode of their construction will be obvious, and while the method is primitive, their making is a difficult and tedious process. While in Nukualofa I called upon the native Queen's old aunt, who makes the printing mats for the island, and she very thoughtfully explained the process of sewing and gave me numerous specimens of her work. She is an adept worker in this material, and when she is gone, there will be no one so skilled to carry on her occupation. The young Tongans do not bother with the making of bark paper, as they prefer the gaily coloured Manchester cotton to the beautiful bark material that played such an essential part in the lives of their ancestors.

When the time for decorating tapa arrives, the pieces of bark paper that have been beaten over a period of many months by the old women in different parts of the island are brought in great bundles to a central meeting-place (*kokaagas*), where the innumerable small pieces are formed into immense sheets and the ornamentation applied. The single sections as originally beaten by the individual workers are in the embryo state and are seldom used in this form except when a small, white, filmy tapa is required. The community house that I visited stood at the corner of two roads, in an open field, amid a few scattered grass houses, where naked children played with sore-eyed cats and dogs. The house was about forty feet square and open to the roof, and with its wooden floor about two feet from the ground, suggested that it had been built by the mission or by someone interested in fostering and preserving the native arts. These central houses were no doubt in use in the old days, for then, as now, considerable space and many workers were required in forming the large sheets of tapa and applying the decorations. The building was without decoration except for a native portrait of Queen Salote Tubou, the successor to the throne of her father, George II, but upon the rafters of the building there were stored huge rolls of completed tapa, called *tukui gatu,* some of which would measure dozens of yards square. These rolls had been made for the centennial of the mission and were so heavy and bulky that I saw two strong women fall under the weight of one when they attempted to carry it.

When I entered the community house on a cool morning in April, I saw six or eight women arranging many printing mats upon two long half-cylinder benches in preparation for the decorating of the bark paper. Each of these wooden benches was about twenty-four feet in length and thirty inches at the base, supported by short, stout legs which held the curved bench about six inches from the floor. The women told me that their ancestors had used a large log for this purpose, and that the introduction of the more symmetrical table composed of smooth, regular boards was the only innovation in tapa-making since ancient times. As I watched the workers, each half-cylindrical bench was being covered, with the exception of about two feet at each end, with the vegetable-fibre mats, forming one large pattern made up of separate units. The small mats were applied to the curved benches, and over each unit was laid a thin piece of bark paper, cut in the shape of the mat, but with about two inches of margin on all sides. The whole was then fastened to the wooden form by the use of Polynesian arrowroot (*Tacca pinnatifida*). The margins of the bark paper on each section lapped over the adjoining mats, but owing to the thinness of the paper they did not interfere with the use of the raised design of the mats in printing. Dozens of these small *kupesi* were carefully applied to the form, and much measurement and calculation were exercised by the women in getting so many different sizes and shapes to fit correctly. The margins of the bark paper at the under edge of the half-cylinder were turned under the bench and held in place with the arrowroot paste. The women worked all day in covering the two large curved forms, and when the work was completed the appearance was exceedingly precise, each half-cylinder suggesting a huge printing block. The covered tables were to be used the following day for forming the beaten-bark sections into large sheets and adding the decoration. To prevent the mats from drying out and coming loose during the night, a dampened piece of plain tapa was thrown over each form.

The next day when I entered the community hut, there were thirty-five women at work, and also a number of men, including several chiefs with their wives. They all sat cross-legged upon the floor, clapping their hands and swaying back and forth, at the same time singing in their native tongue. The party was more festive than it had been on the previous day, and much kava was being drunk in the accustomed ceremonious fashion. Several women sat upon the floor at either side of each bench, so that their bodies were close to the curved printing tables and they could easily reach the tops. The small pieces of beaten bark that had been collected from the individual workers throughout the district were in great heaps upon the floor, the mass representing months of tedious beating. The pieces were from twelve to twenty inches wide and from four to six feet long; some of the small sections had been pasted together, forming strips of the same width, but about twenty feet in length. Both the small pieces and the long strips are essential in the building up of the large finished tapa.

The first operation was to place over the forms small pieces of the beaten bark which were fastened together at the edges by boiled arrowroot. In using this paste the skin of the tuber is cut as a lead pencil is sharpened. The root is the shape of the sweet potato, but of a grey colour when boiled, extremely glutinous, with tough, fibrous threads running from end to end. After one covering of bark paper had been laid over the design-form, another layer was applied, directly over the first, but joined at different intervals. The second thickness was pasted over the entire surface and any holes or tears were patched with small bits of the material. Each time a layer of bark paper was applied, the women would rub the outer surface with a dauber dipped in dark-red dye, which was rendered from the bark of the *koka* tree (*Ficus prolixa*). This process brought out the design of the mats in an all-over pattern, at first quite faint, but clearer upon drying; the design retaining a hazy, undefined appearance that gives the Tongan tapa such an artistic quality.

When the form was completely covered with two or three thicknesses of the small sections of beaten bark, one of the long, narrow strips was stretched over the top, reaching from one end of the form to the other. This was also fastened down with the arrowroot paste and rubbed over with the dye. The entire covering was then lifted from the curved bench and laid in the laps of the women who were on the receiving side of the table. To the edges of the completed piece next the form were then pasted other small pieces, until the form was again covered in the same manner as at first, making one continuous sheet. Every covering of the form table increased the length of the main tapa by about four feet, or the width of the table top. Each time the form was covered, one of the long, narrow strips was applied as described. These strips, running parallel with the length of the table, served not only as binders but as marks to determine the size of the finished tapa, for every time one of these long strips was added, the women would mark its ends with a figure or hieroglyphic, so that they were able to tell, as the work progressed, just how many strips had been applied, thus giving a rough estimate of the length of the tapa. By the curved-table method of Tonga the sheets of the tapa can be made endless in length, as it is simply a matter of the number of small beaten sections at disposal and the amount of wear the vegetable printing mats will endure. As the tapa grew longer it stuck more and more to the curved form, and after the decoration of a hundred or more feet of the material the mats had become well saturated with the arrowroot paste and the dark-red dye. Following the building up and staining of a large section of tapa, the printing mats are removed and repaired, then used again, but as they would seldom be laid against the curved table in the same rotation, each tapa would bear a varied series of designs.

After the bark paper has been completely formed and decorated, it is spread in the sun until the arrowroot paste and colouring pigment have dried; it is then folded along its width, rolled into a large bundle, and laid away until the finishing touches can be added. The pasting of the small pieces is performed with such perfection that the completed tapa appears to have been composed of one continuous piece of beaten bark and only a close examination will reveal the lapping of the numerous sections.

For the final treatment the tapa is again spread on the ground and held in place by stones. The barefooted women walk over it, adding free-hand lines around the dyed designs, detracting from rather than enhancing the soft beauty of the all-over pattern. These lines, about half an inch in width, are drawn with pieces of glass, bits of slate, or bamboo sticks dipped in dark-brown dye made from the charcoal of the shell of the candlenut, called in

F_IG. 28   *During the hundredth anniversary of the founding of the Wesleyan Mission, 1926, in Tongatabu, the native women were engaged in making and decorating unusually large and exceptionally fine pieces of tapa. The piece of rolled tapa in the foreground of the photograph measured 20 by 210 feet.*

Tonga *fukai tuitui* (*Aleurites triloba*). This dye produced a shiny or glossy surface in contrast to the hazy all-over pattern imprinted by the vegetable mats. The large pieces of tapa are cut to suit the requirements of different individuals and are made in great sizes to expedite the manufacture, much as cloth is woven in large sections and cut to suit the purchasers. The labour required in the preparation of the bark, and in the beating and forming of a piece of decorated Tongan tapa twenty by one hundred feet, is tremendous, as it would require the time of thirty-five women at least two and a half months to perform the complete operation (Figure 28).

During my voyage in the Pacific Ocean almost twenty years ago it was my privilege to see tapa being beaten and decorated in the

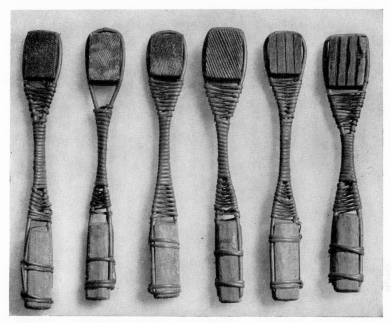

FIG. 29   *The bark-beaters of the Celebes are different from those of any other Pacific islands, being made of cut stones laced to wooden handles with rattan. The marks, or grooves, in the surface of the stones produce line markings in the bark papers.*

islands of Tonga, Fiji, Samoa, and Celebes (Figures 29, 30), but in all other islands where I had hoped to find at least a remnant of the craft I was disappointed. In each of the island groups the beating-mallets are of a different form and weight and the mode of applying the decoration to the bark paper varies to a marked degree; but, as previously mentioned, the principle of the operation and the type of bark used are almost identical throughout the Pacific. The methods employed in the Tongan group a quarter century ago were least contaminated by outside influence and therefore the most enlightening and interesting.

Although this chapter is headed "the *writing* substances of the ancients," the *amatl* paper of the Otomi Indians of Mexico and the bark-paper tapas of the Pacific islands have never been used for calligraphy. The Otomi paper, unlike that of ancient Maya and Aztec civilizations, upon which technique it is founded, is used

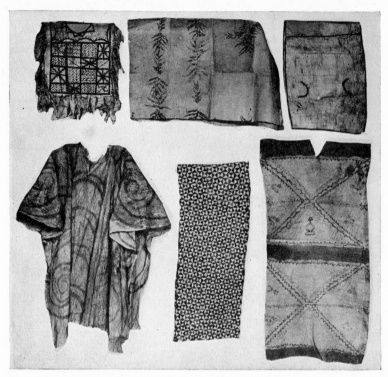

Fig. 30   *Primitive paper clothing made by beating the moistened inner bark of the mulberry tree until the narrow strips are widened into thin sections. Although this material is not true paper, it is nevertheless more closely related to paper than it is to cloth. These six specimens of "bark paper" or tapa were made in Samoa, Tahiti, and the Congo and date from 1868 to 1883.*

in witchcraft and black magic. The Otomi Indians cut images (*muñeco*) in their paper and use them in many different ways of sorcery. To cite but one observation: when I visited among the Otomi Indians more than four decades ago, the quiet village was in subdued commotion and I could sense that something was being concealed from me. I learned that one of the young Otomi men had been accused of an unpardonable crime and the authorities had taken him to the town for trial. Throughout their village the relatives and friends of the young malefactor were secretly making *amatl*-paper images of the judge who was to pronounce the sentence; the mouth of each paper doll was sewed tight shut with the idea that this would prevent the magistrate from uttering the verdict of guilty. Paper among the Otomi Indians does not concern the intellectual; it is devoted entirely to sorcery, superstition, and demonology (Figure 20).

The bark papers of the intelligent Pacific islanders found no ill or profane uses; the Polynesians and Melanesians made good use of their beaten-bark material for practical, utilitarian purposes. These bark papers, however, like those of the Otomi Indians, were never used for calligraphy, as the peoples of the Pacific had no written languages previous to the coming of the religious missionaries.[2]

II

Ts'ai Lun and the Invention of Paper

THE INFLUENCE OF CALLIGRAPHY UPON PAPER AND
THE INFLUENCE OF PAPER UPON PRINTING

BEFORE the invention of paper the Chinese scribes wrote with a
pointed stylus upon strips of wood or bamboo,[1] but this material
was difficult to write upon and difficult to store, for the wooden
strips tied into bundles for the orderly preservation of records
were cumbersome and consumed much space (Figure 31).

After many centuries of use by the Chinese scribes the strips
of bamboo were succeeded by woven material as a writing substance, especially after the introduction of the hair brush, an invention attributed to Mêng T'ien in the third century B.C.[2] The
cloth adapted itself readily to the purpose of calligraphy, or writing with a brush in the Chinese manner.[3] (Even in Europe and
America at the present time it is not unusual to employ cloth for
both writing and printing, the material being entirely practical
for these uses.) The Chinese made books and scrolls of woven
cloth, and as there was much waste when the textile was cut and
trimmed, it is only natural that an ingenious artisan conceived the
idea of beating the discarded cloth into fibre and forming sheets
that could also be used for writing. Cloth was expensive and even
in ancient times, as at present, there was a desire to produce necessary material quickly and cheaply. It was probably the narrow
strips of waste woven fabric trimmed from the edges of the pri-
meval manuscripts and documents that first suggested to the ever
practical Chinese mind the idea of making paper. It is possible
that the Chinese conceived the thought of matting and intertwin-
ing the fibres into sheets of paper through their knowledge of feltmaking, a craft which antedated even that of weaving.

The date usually given for the actual invention of paper is

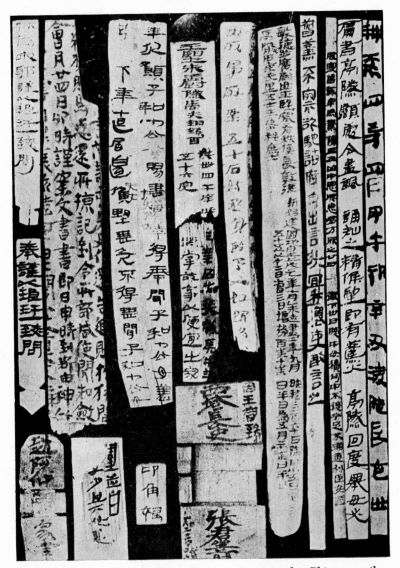

FIG. 31   *Long before the invention of paper, the Chinese scribes wrote upon strips of bamboo. From the ruins of the Niya and Lop-Nor sites, and from the Tun-huang Limes. (Reproduced from* Ruins of Desert Cathay, *by Sir Aurel Stein; London, 1912.)*

A.D. 105, but this date is chosen rather arbitrarily, since the first experiments in papermaking from disintegrated fibre probably extended over a long period before the process was actually brought to any degree of perfection and publicly announced. The date A.D. 105 is usually cited as the time of the first papermaking because in that year the invention was officially reported to the Emperor by the eunuch Ts'ai Lun (Figure 32). It is not known whether Ts'ai Lun was the actual inventor or simply the court official who became the patron of the invention, but with the Chinese people themselves the name of Ts'ai Lun will always be closely identified with the beginning of papermaking. Every schoolchild in China is familiar with the couplet: "Ts'ang Chieh * made characters and Ts'ai Lun made paper."

An ancient Chinese scholar has this to say about the illustrious Ts'ai Lun: "Under the reign of Ho Ti † (A.D. 89–105), Ts'ai Lun, of Lei-yang, conceived the idea of making paper from the bark of trees, discarded cloth, and hemp well prepared; the paper was then in use in the entire universe." The following biography of Ts'ai Lun was compiled in the fifth century of our era by Fan Yeh ‡ and appeared in the official history of the Han Dynasty:

At the close of the reign of Yen P'ing (A.D. 106), Ts'ai Lun was employed at the court and later he was made a member of the Imperial Guard. The Emperor Ho Ti, upon his accession, learning of Ts'ai Lun's superior qualities and talents, named him private counsellor and he was not spared by His Majesty in either praise or criticism. In the ninth

---

* Ts'ang Chieh is the mythical inventor of Chinese characters, about 2700 B.C. (See *The Evolution of Chinese Writing*, by G. Owen, King's College, Oxford; London, 1910; page 6.)

† 和帝

‡ The Chinese scholar Fan Yeh (范曄), who was born A.D. 398, prepared at least two sections of the *History of the Later, or Eastern, Han Dynasty* (*Hou Han Shu* 後漢書). Fan Yeh was responsible for the memoir of Ts'ai Lun (蔡倫) (Ts'ai Lun, chüan 8), a chapter containing biographical sketches of certain eunuchs, of which the inventor of paper was one. The writings of Fan Yeh were not incorporated in the famous history until after his death, A.D. 445. The *Hou Han Shu* is one of the original twenty-four official histories of the dynasties prepared under government supervision, and to a great extent the 120 volumes were compiled by individual Chinese scholars such as Fan Yeh. The books, covering the period A.D. 25–220, were annotated by Li Hsien, heir to the throne of T'ang, A.D. 651–684. The books were printed by Imperial order, A.D. 990–994.

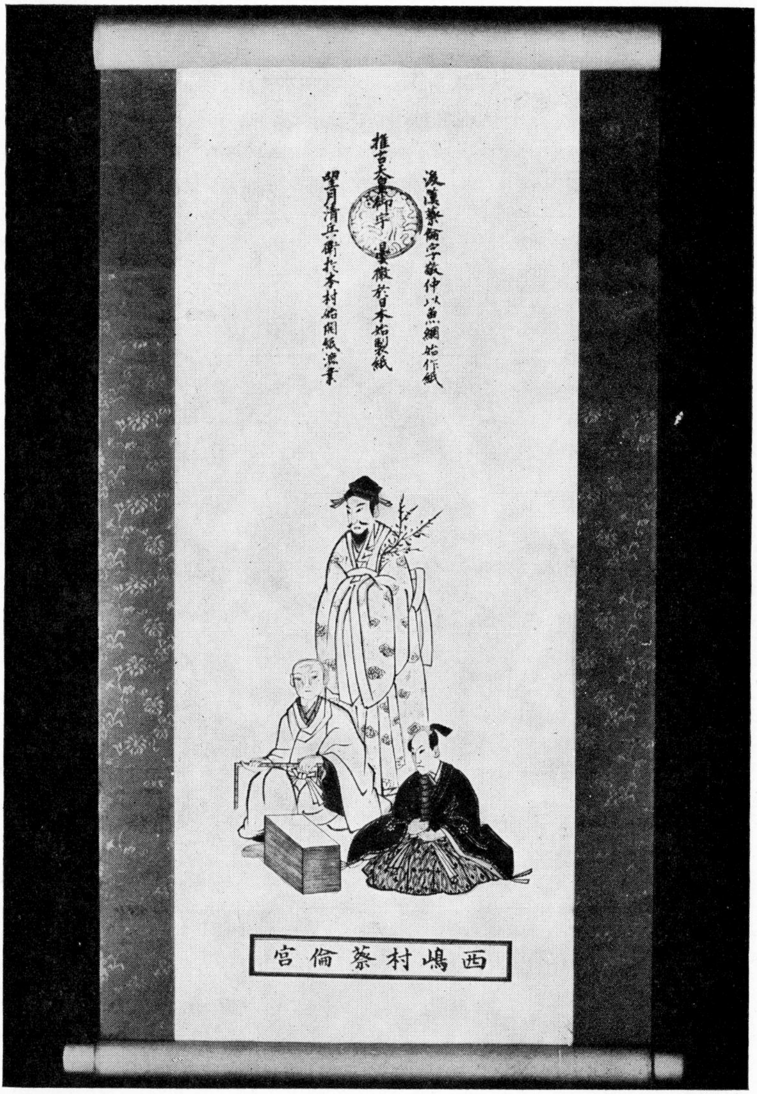

FIG. 32   Ts'ai Lun, the inventor of paper, A.D. 105. From a kake-
mono *produced by a Japanese artist in memory of Seibei Mochizuki,
who established papermaking in Hishijimamura, Japan, in 1572. Of interest because it depicts, along with Mochizuki, the imaginary portraits
of Ts'ai Lun and Dokyo, the Korean monk who introduced paper into
Japan. Ts'ai Lun, in conventional dress, stands in the centre, Dokyo
(left) is shown as a Buddhist monk, and Mochizuki, in formal costume,
is holding a "laid" mould-cover. No authentic portrait of Ts'ai Lun exists.*

year of the reign of Yung Yüan (A.D. 97), Ts'ai Lun was made inspector of works and through his efforts the engineers and workmen by the use of fine materials and skill produced swords and arms that served as models for future generations.

In ancient times writing and inscriptions were generally traced upon pieces of bamboo, or upon strips of silk, which were given the name *chih* (paper). But silk being costly and bamboo heavy, these two materials could not be used conveniently. It was Ts'ai Lun who conceived the idea of making paper from the bark of trees, hemp waste, old rags, and fish nets.

He made a report to the Emperor, the first year of the reign of Yüan Hsing (A.D. 105), upon his researches in papermaking and was highly commended upon his competency. In the first year of the reign of Yüan Ch'u (A.D. 114), the Imperial Mother gave Ts'ai Lun the honourable title of Marquis for his lengthy service at the palace; the government accorded him the ground-rent taxes and the proceeds from three hundred dwellings. Later Ts'ai Lun became one of the chiefs of the palace.

In the fourth year of his reign (A.D. 117), the Emperor, finding that there were some faults in the books of history, ordered two competent scholars to attempt the correction of these faults, according to the rules adopted by the Han Dynasty. It was Ts'ai Lun who was placed in charge of this important work of correction.

Ts'ai Lun received of the Empress To a secret order to invent slanders against a member of the Imperial family. After the demise of the Empress the successor to the throne was an Emperor of less animosity and he ordered Ts'ai Lun to give himself up to the Minister of Justice so that he might be judged. Ts'ai Lun experienced such profound remorse and shame that after bathing and dressing himself in his finest and most elaborate robes, he drank poison.

Ts'ai Lun's residence was situated in the district of Lei-yang, which belongs today to the department of Hengchow, province of Hunan. Early writers relate that near the home of Ts'ai Lun there was found a pool, and south of the pool, at the west of the house, there could be seen the stone mortar that had been used by Ts'ai Lun in the maceration of his material for papermaking. This mortar was offered to the Emperor in payment for some ground rent and he had it placed on exhibition in the Imperial Museum. It is said that this mortar was still preserved as a curiosity in the T'ang Dynasty (A.D. 618–907). The honour tendered such a modest appliance spoke highly of the esteem in which Ts'ai Lun and his invention were held by the Emperor. Improvements in the process of papermaking were advanced by Tso Tzŭ-yi, a young apprentice to Ts'ai Lun, and the craft of forming sheets of paper spread throughout the Empire. The records of following centuries contain many references to the use of paper, not only for writing and bibliographical purposes, but for ornamental use in Chinese houses and temples.

The people of Japan had communication with Korea from early centuries and it was from that locality, then part of China, that the Japanese, at the beginning of the seventh century of our era, gained their first knowledge of paper when sheets of this substance in the form of manuscript books fabricated from the bark of the paper mulberry (Broussonetia papyrifera) were brought to Japan by Buddhist monks. Ancient records inform us that the Japanese began the craft of papermaking about A.D. 610, over five hundred years after Ts'ai Lun had conceived the art in China. It is thought that a Buddhist monk named Dokyo was the actual person who brought papermaking to Japan. Dokyo was learned in painting, ink-making, and papermaking, and aside from these accomplishments he was a physician. This versatile monk eventually became chief physician to Empress Shōtoku and within a short period after his appointment he gained unusual influence over the Empress, being made her most trusted adviser. While paper had its origin in China, the first printing was actually accomplished in Japan; and, what is more surprising, the original printing was sponsored, perhaps invented, by a woman, the Empress Shōtoku. (See Chapter iii for account of the world's first printing.)

From China, by way of Korea, the Japanese received their knowledge of the arts, and of agriculture, religion, philosophy, ethics, medicine, and science. The Japanese did not even possess a written language until the third century, when Chinese characters and literature were introduced to them by Atogi, a son of the King of Korea, who visited the court of Japan about A.D. 286.[4]

After the Chinese artisans imparted their knowledge of papermaking to the Japanese, the craft spread rapidly in the Island Empire and during the Nara period (A.D. 708–806) paper was being made in nine different provinces, and in the Heian period (A.D. 806–1155) forty provinces of Japan were engaged in this manufacture.[5] By the eighth or ninth century the Zushoryō (department

of the library where the books, drawings, and paintings belonging
to the Emperor were stored) had set up a paper mill with a guild
of four expert papermakers. This establishment was created with
the hope of influencing papermaking in Japan. In the year 807
this guild introduced papermaking in the neighbourhood of Kyōto, always one of Japan's great artistic centers. At the close of
each year the various mills that had been established contributed
20,000 sheets of the finest plain paper to the Kuraryō, the keeper
of the Imperial storehouse where the Emperor's personal clothing, gold, silver, and curios were housed. This tribute paper, along
with 4,600 sheets of coloured paper from the ancient papermaking
province of Mino, was used by the Imperial court.

With the decline of the whole central administration during the
Heian period the Zushoryō ceased to have such extensive importance and the slave-like guild of papermakers, which had heretofore been kept apart from their contemporaries, gradually merged
with the common people and it was not long before the entire Imperial staff was reduced in number and talent. Because of the absence of materials, paper, and skilled workers, the owners of private estates began the erection of small paper mills and they
endeavoured to induce the former Zushoryō papermakers to resume their work for them in the fabrication of paper. Up to this
time about the only materials used for the making of paper in
Japan were the mulberry, gampi (*Wikstrœmia canescens*), and
hemp (*Cannabis sativa*), but as early as 1031 it was recorded that
waste paper became a useful material for remaking into sheets of
paper. The Chinese, no doubt, had used the method of reclaiming
material much earlier, and inasmuch as the Japanese received
nearly all of their ideas from China it is reasonable to surmise that
there was no exception in this instance. In Japan the remade paper
became the sole commodity of the paper-shops (*kamiya*) and was
known by the name of *kamiya-gami,* literally paper-shop paper.
The reclaimed material used in the making of the *kamiya-gami*
was charged with ink and pigment and therefore the paper manufactured from the used material was of a grey tone. It has been
stated that even books from the Imperial Library were macerated
into pulp to be formed into sheets of the *shukushi* paper, always
of a dull colour due to the writing on the paper from which it was
fabricated. The demand for this paper continued, and to meet this

need in the fifteenth century, guilds, called *za*, were established. In 1522 there were the upper and lower *shukushi-za*, the upper headed by the Togai family and the lower by the Osaji family. Both of these families were hereditary officials of the Zushoryō, or Imperial Library, and they no doubt had access to quantities of old manuscript books and written papers, which were rebeaten into pulp for use as papermaking material in their mills. In the Edo period there were six councillors, three foremen, and 121 paper workers in Kyōto and Fushimi under the jurisdiction of these two influential Japanese families, all making the reclaimed paper, which was highly esteemed throughout Japan.

At the present time the Japanese manufacture a vast variety of papers by the traditional hand process and in the early centuries of the craft there was also this abundance of varieties. The names Danshi, Sugihara, Hanshi, Torinoko,* and scores of other appellations are as familiar today as they were centuries ago.[6]

The exact date of the origin of papermaking in Echizen, one of the great Japanese papermaking districts of the present day, is not known, but there is a fanciful local legend that purports to be ancient. A certain deity, so the legend goes, revealed himself by the side of the stream, and, disguised as a beautiful woman, he placed a part of his kimono upon a bamboo stick in imitation of a papermaking mould; this he then dipped into the stream and shook as if in the act of forming a sheet of paper. The villagers upon seeing the strange happening were much excited and astonished and implored to be told the significance of the unusual actions. The reply, according to the story, was: "The soil of this dukedom is poor and lacks fertility, but the water from the mountain streams is pure and clear. I shall therefore teach you papermaking so that all may live by this craft." The villagers asked who the stranger might be and received only the reply: "My name is

---

* The name Torinoko paper literally means "egg" paper, due, no doubt, to the paper having somewhat the tone and texture of eggshell. After the draft of the Versailles Peace Treaty, following the first World War, had been formulated and was ready for the final engrossing, there was considerable speculation as to what paper would be chosen by the authorities for inscribing this important document. Numerous makes of paper were examined and eliminated and finally the selection rested with just two papers: the famed Whatman handmade paper made in Kent, England, and the Torinoko handmade paper of Japan. For political reasons it was at last agreed to use the Japanese Torinoko paper, a choice that proved none too appropriate.[7]

FIG. 33   *The main building of the shrine at Okamoto, Japan, one of the most impressive sanctuaries in the world dedicated to the ancient craft of papermaking.*

Mizuha-Nome-no-Mikoto." The moment the answer was given, the apparition disappeared and was seen no more by the simple village people. Soon after this strange occurrence the art of papermaking was established in Echizen, and the people from the surrounding countryside built, near the village of Okamoto, a beautiful Shinto shrine and dedicated it to Mizuha-Nome-no-Mikoto, the mythical founder of Echizen papermaking. The lovely old grey group of wooden, tiled-roof buildings, some half dozen in number, is set on a quiet and lonely hillside amid giant evergreen trees through which penetrate thin streaks of light casting weird patterns upon the moss-covered roofs of the inspiring shrine — one of the most impressive sanctuaries in the world dedicated to the craft of papermaking (Figure 33).

While the first paper of China was probably fabricated from disintegrated cloth, it was not long before the bark of trees and other vegetation was employed as a material for the purpose. It is recorded that the mulberry, hemp, and China grass were used as papermaking materials previous to the third century of our era. The first paper introduced into Japan from Korea (about A.D. 610) was made from mulberry (*Broussonetia papyrifera*) bark (Fig-

Fig. 34 *Paper mul-*
berry (Broussonetia pa-
pyrifera), *the universal*
papermaking bark of
the Far East.

Fig. 35 *Gampi*
(Wikstrœmia ca-
nescens), *used in*
Japan in making
thin, tough paper.

Fig. 36 *Mitsu-*
mata (Edgeworthia
papyrifera), *from*
which the well-known
Imperial Japanese vel-
lum is made.

ure 34). Gampi (*Wikstrœmia canescens*) (Figure 35), a plant of
wild growth, has apparently been in use as a papermaking fibre
since the ninth century. Its use was probably discovered by the
Japanese. According to the Chinese scholar Su Tung-p'o, who
lived from 1036 to 1101, bamboo was just beginning to be employed in China for making paper. Rice straw as a paper material
dates from a later period, 1334–1521. The origin of mitsumata
(*Edgeworthia papyrifera*) (Figure 36) as a papermaking material
is uncertain, but there is a record stating that in the year 1597 a
papermaking family was granted the privilege of gathering mitsumata bark in a certain locality of Japan. This plant is of the
family *Thymelæaceæ* and is symbolized in Chinese by the character "lucky fragrance." The genus *Edgeworthia* denotes "yellow
lucky fragrance" (Figure 37).

The earliest specimens of Oriental papers in the Hunter Paper
Museum collection date from the fifth century onward and are
composed of hemp and mulberry fibres; the earliest of these papers are exceedingly well formed. Papermaking in China deteri-
orated from the seventh to the tenth century, when the paper became rather coarse and lumpy. The Japanese have made excellent

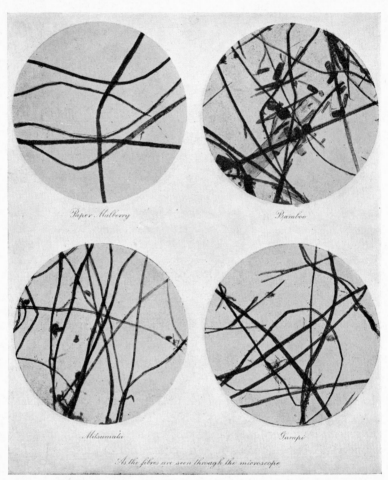

FIG. 37   *The four most important papermaking fibres of the Orient:*

Paper mulberry
(Broussonetia papyrifera, V*ent.*)

Bamboo
(Phyllostachys edulis, *Carr.*) *H. de Lehaie.*

Mitsumata
(Edgeworthia papyrifera, *Seib. and Zucc.*), (E. *chrysantha, Lindl.*), *of the family* Thymelæ-aceæ.

Gampi
(Wikstrœmia canescens, *Meisn.*), (Passerina gampi, S. *and Z.*), *of the same family as the mitsumata.*

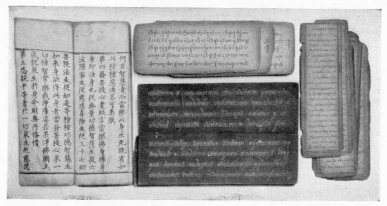

FIG. 38   *Old manuscripts written on the soft, absorbent paper of the Orient. The Chinese, Tibetan, and Mongolian manuscripts are on paper made from the inner bark of the mulberry* (Broussonetia papyrifera); *the black Siamese manuscript is on paper made from the bark of the khoi* (Streblus asper), *stained with a pigment made from the nuts of the betel palm* (Areca cathecu).

paper from the introduction of the craft in the seventh century. Practically all of the ancient Chinese and Japanese paper was formed on the flexible type of mould upon which all papermaking is founded.

The Chinese and Japanese people had a profound reverence for paper and for the craftsman who fabricated the thin, delicate sheets. This was only natural, as the earliest paper was used chiefly for inscribing the sayings of Kung Fu-tsŭ (Confucius) and for other writings deeply concerned with the religious life of the East. It would be just as difficult for an Occidental to understand the traditions of the ancient Chinese and Japanese classical writings as it would to comprehend the study, thought, and practice given by them to the technique of calligraphy, and the important part that paper and all manner of writing materials played in the lives of the great Asiatic scholars.

The history of Chinese calligraphy is believed to be as ancient as the civilization of China. It is difficult, however, for the Westerner to comprehend and appreciate the mysteries and perplexities of Chinese brush writing, even though he may have a knowledge of Chinese painting. Calligraphy is one of the highest forms of Chinese art, and every painting is accompanied by beautifully executed characters. To the Chinese scholar his calligraphy — and in turn his paper, ink, ink-stone, and brushes — are his very life. Unless an Occidental connoisseur has been reared in the artistic traditions of China it is difficult for him to grasp the æsthetic significance of Chinese writing and to visualize the time and thought given to the perfection of brush strokes with carbon ink upon thin absorbent paper (Figure 38).

From China paper found its way into central Asia and Persia by a route well known to the caravans which sought to open a road connecting the Pacific with the Mediterranean. This road was later mapped by Marco Polo in the thirteenth century, following the Gobi Desert, the Desert of Takla Makan, and the Tarim Valley, and finally arriving at Samarkand. Chinese paper made from bark and the fibres of rags and hemp may possibly have been imported and sold in Samarkand, but it is thought that paper was not actually made in Samarkand until after A.D. 751, the year a battle was fought by the Chinese in Turkestan on the banks of the Tharaz River. It is recorded that among the Chinese prisoners taken in this conflict there were a number of skilled papermakers, and their captors set these craftsmen to work fabricating paper. Up to this time the art of making paper had been a closely guarded secret in the country of its inception. The manufacture of paper was favoured in Samarkand by the abundant crops of flax and hemp, as well as by the numerous irrigation canals, as plenty of pure water was then, as now, a necessary requisite for paper-production.

From Samarkand the craft of making paper spread to Baghdad and Damascus and finally into Egypt and Morocco. It required almost five hundred years to find its way into Europe from Samarkand, as there was little communication between the East and the West. It is not known whether the craft was first introduced into Spain or Italy, each country having its own claimants. In any event, the first papermaking in Europe was accomplished in the twelfth or thirteenth century, or over a thousand years after its inception in China. The early paper of Europe was regarded with disfavour, as not only was it higher in price and more fragile than parchment, which had been used for bookmaking, but it was distrusted on account of its introduction by Jews and Arabs. A fanaticism drove the Christian world to condemn, and even destroy, everything that suggested the Moslem civilization, although the European scribes no doubt knew that the newly introduced substance, paper, would eventually take the place of their cherished parchment.[8]

Since papermaking in China, as well as in Europe, was an established art long before the advent of printing, it is only natural that paper vitally influenced the craft of printing. The nature of the paper dictated the methods employed in printing. In both the Orient and the Occident much of the first paper had been made especially for calligraphy, the inception of the art of writing having preceded the invention of papermaking and the later invention of printing by many hundreds of years. The first block printing of the Orient and the earliest impressions made from movable types in Europe were imprinted upon sheets of paper that had been made primarily for the purpose of writing. Chinese and Japanese paper has always been thin, soft, pliable, and absorbent, owing to the Asiatic vegetable fibres and their preparation as well as to the process of forming the sheets of paper upon flexible moulds made of bamboo. This paper lent itself readily to the steady, firm strokes of the brush used in the drawing of Chinese and Japanese characters. This particular style of calligraphy required an absorbent paper, and on account of the thin, transparent quality of the sheets, only one side of the paper was written upon. When the Empress Shōtoku of Japan had her million printed charms executed, A.D. 770,* and when the Diamond Sutra was printed in China by Wang Chieh, A.D. 868,[9] only paper that had primarily been made for writing was available and therefore the method of printing was adapted to the paper at hand — not the paper to the printing. The printing was naturally influenced, for with the soft, pliable paper it was possible to make an impression from a woodblock in the simplest and easiest manner. The process consisted in spreading the incised surface of the block with pigment, placing a sheet of paper upon the inked relief, and rubbing the upper side of the paper with a fibre or cloth ball by hand until a definite impression was made. (For a description of ink-making see page

---

* See Chapter iii.

75: note.) Following the practice of all Chinese and Japanese calligraphy, only one side of the sheet was used, and to this day in all Chinese wood-block book-printing, only one side of the paper is employed.

In the same way the first book-printers of Europe had to make their work conform to paper that had been made primarily for writing. When Johann Gutenberg established his printing office in Mainz, there were no European-made papers suited to the simplicity of the Chinese and Japanese methods of making an ink impression from wood-blocks. The paper of Europe was made from macerated linen and cotton cloth, each sheet being dipped in a solution of gelatine rendered from the hoofs, hides, and horns of animals. The linen and cotton rags and the animal glue formed a hard, opaque, and impervious surface well adapted to the European mode of writing with a quill pen, but entirely unsuited for printing in the non-laborious and unpretentious manner long before adopted by the Chinese and Japanese. There is no record that Gutenberg had paper made specially for his purpose, and as it was no doubt his desire to keep the newly invented process of typography and printing to himself, it is not likely that he would have exposed his secrets by venturing to the paper mills and demanding paper that would precisely suit his own special printing requirements. Therefore, in Europe, as in the Orient, paper that had been made primarily for writing was employed for the first book-printing. In China and Japan the thin, soft mulberry-bark paper was suited to the most simple and direct manner of reproduction from wood-blocks, while with the hard rag paper of Europe a method of printing that would give a much stronger impression had to be devised. It was this unyielding linen and cotton paper, made impervious to fluid writing ink by the application of animal gelatine, that made necessary the invention of the printing press.

Paper that had been fabricated purposely for writing not only determined the sizes or dimensions of the books printed by Gutenberg and the volumes that were to follow, but highly influenced the method of making an ink impression from type to paper. Unlike the thin, transparent papers of the Orient, only one side of which could be used for writing or printing, the paper of Europe, thick and opaque, lent itself readily to writing or printing on both sides of the sheets. The construction and form of Oriental and

Occidental books were therefore influenced by the paper available, and for this reason we have two distinct schools of book-printing — the Oriental with its delicate wood-block impressions on one side of the sheet, and the European on both sides of the paper with the comparatively heavy indentations made from metal types with the aid of the cumbersome hand press.

III

Empress Shōtoku and Her Million Printed Prayers

THE FIRST TEXT PRINTING UPON PAPER TO BE
EXECUTED IN THE WORLD

As outlined in the foregoing chapter, papermaking was introduced into Japan about A.D. 610. At this time Japan was experienc-
ing a more complete cultural change than at any previous period.
Japan was entirely under the influence of China, the most intellectual and most highly developed country in the entire world.
Numerous Buddhist missionaries found their way from China to
Japan, and in turn Japanese students in pursuit of education
visited China, returning to their native land after years of study,
inspired by the culture and refinement of the Celestial Empire.
The returning Japanese students introduced Chinese customs and
manners into their own country and it was acknowledged throughout Japan that the arts, crafts, literature, and religion of China
should be admired and adopted by Japan as highly desirable. The
Japanese were most eager to emulate every superior Chinese custom and there was universal approval when the government officials selected a Chinese scholar to direct the lately founded university in Nara, the new capital of Japan; the Japanese wished to
pattern their place of government as closely as possible after the
Chinese capital in Sian Fu, the old seat of the T'ang Dynasty.

In 716 a promising young Japanese, Kibi-no-mabi, much under
the spell of the elegant Chinese customs introduced into Japan
by Chinese travellers and returning Japanese students, set out
from his native land with a sincere desire and ambition for a long
course of study in cultured China. After almost twenty years of
tutoring under scholarly Chinese professors he returned to Japan,
one of the most learned men of his country. Kibi-no-mabi was wel-

comed home with loud acclaim and within a short time he was
requested to enter the service of the Nara government. In this
capacity he had the opportunity of introducing to a greater degree than ever before the customs and manners of the superior
Chinese. It is recorded, but often disputed, that this eminent
Chinese-trained Japanese scholar was the inventor of the *katakana*,* a Japanese form of writing derived from the ancient Chinese characters, but using only a section or portion of each character in the composition of the numerous symbols. The importance
and influence of Kibi-no-mabi does not rest upon the cultural refinements he introduced from China, nor upon the possibility of
the calligraphic invention, but upon the fact that he eventually
became the tutor of the Empress Shōtoku,† under whose guidance
and sponsorship the first block printing upon paper was accomplished.

In China and in Japan printing from wood-blocks was preceded
by the use of seals. In modern times such seals are cut in metal,
wood, jade, ivory, stone, and water-buffalo horn. The employment
of incised seals in making impressions with pigment upon paper
was, to a degree, a form of printing. Also, there are examples of
stamped, or printed, cloth and leather preserved in Japanese temples, dating from the first half of the eighth century.‡ True block
printing on paper of a definite nature, however, had its origin
some time between A.D. 767 and 770.

Nara was the capital of Japan from A.D. 710 to 784, and during
this period the seat of government was decidedly under Buddhistic influence. It was while under the leadership of the Empress
Shōtoku, who reigned with but few interruptions from 749 until
769, that the control of the Nara government by the Buddhist

---

* The Chinese characters in their entirety were the first symbols employed
by the Japanese in writing their native tongue. The first effort to replace these
characters gave rise to the *kana*, a contraction of *kani-na*, signifying borrowed
names. The *katakana*, or side letters, are the oldest and most simple form of
Japanese writing. According to J. C. Hepburn (*Chinese Written Language;*
Tōkyō, 1888), the system was invented by Kibi Daishi, who died A.D. 776.

† A.D. 749, accession of Empress Kōken on the abdication of Shōmu;
A.D. 758, accession of Empress Junnin on the abdication of Kōken; A.D. 765,
deposition and murder of Junnin by Empress Kōken, who resumed the throne
as Empress Shōtoku.

‡ "From the early period of Nara (A.D. 708–806) there was a method of
printing various patterns on cloth, known as *suri-goromo*." *Hōsho yoroku*, by
Yōshiro Wada (6 volumes; Tōkyō, 1918).

priests reached its height. In 735 an epidemic of smallpox visited Japan, and with this dreadful catastrophe in mind the Empress Shōtoku attached a hundred and sixteen special priests to her court for the express purpose of driving out the demons of disease and evil spirits thought to have been the cause of the epidemic. It might have been to either this smallpox scourge or a desire to make penance for the loss of life that occurred in the suppression of the rebellion of 764 * that the world owes the invention of text printing upon sheets of paper. The Empress sanctioned the printing of a million paper prayers, each prayer, or *dhāranī*, enshrined in its own individual three-storey wooden pagoda (*hyaku-man tō*).† About the year 770, after working for six years on the project, the printing of the prayers and the turning and fashioning of the wooden pagodas was finally completed. This event, important alike to the Orient and the Occident, is documented by early Japanese manuscripts; its authenticity is clearly set forth as a definite accomplishment in early Japanese history. The momentous event is described in the histories of the Imperial family of Japan and in many local records of the temples where the printed *dhāranī* and their pagoda receptacles were originally deposited at the command of the Empress. The official history, the *Shoku Nihongi*,‡ gives this account of the printed prayers, under

---

* The revolt of Emi Oshikatsu, in the 5th year of Tempei-Hoji. See *Ko kwatsu-zhi ban no ken-kyū*, by K. Kawase (2 volumes).

† The wooden pagodas in which the rolled paper *dhāranī* are housed and protected were made on a lathe, the wood surface originally covered with a white pigment, which has disintegrated through the centuries. The pagodas measure about eight inches in height and approximately four inches in diameter at the base. The top section, which is removable, allowing access to the small round scroll chamber, is termed in Japanese *kurin,* meaning "nine-ringed wheel." These nine-rimmed spires, or stoppers, are made of the wood of the *katsura* (*Cercidiphyllum japonicum*), a Japanese tree that reaches a height of ninety feet; the bases of the pagodas are turned from the *hinoki* (*Chamæcyparis obtusa*), a cypress tree that grows in Japan to about one hundred and twenty feet in height. The wooden pagodas are more common than the rolled printed papers, as numerous pagodas have been found empty, the papers having been removed or lost centuries ago. In rare instances colour has been applied to the outside surface of the pagodas, and several of the wooden receptacles have been discovered with signatures and dates on the under sides of the bases.

‡ *Shoku Nihongi,* compiled by Suge-no, Mami-chi, is a record of events in Japanese history for the years 704 to 791. The compilation was in charge of the compiler in the year 780. He died in 813, aged about seventy years. The description of the Empress Shōtoku printing will be found in Book XXX.

Fig. 39   *A wooden pagoda used as a receptacle for one of Empress Shōtoku's printed charms, the world's first printing upon paper.*

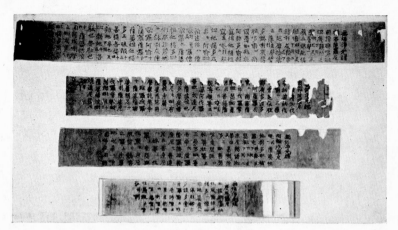

Fig. 40   *The four Empress Shōtoku dhāranī of* A.D. *770, the first text printing upon paper.*

No. 1. Kompon: length 22 inches, width 2⅜ inches, 40 lines
No. 2. Jīshin: "   16   "   "   2⅜   "   31   "
No. 3. Sōrin: "   16⅜   "   "   2¼   "   23   "
No. 4. Rokudo: "   12   "   "   2$\frac{1}{16}$ "   15   "

It will be noticed that the first column (reading from right to left in the Chinese manner) of five characters is the same in each dhāranī: *(wu kou ching kuang ching,* 無 垢 淨 光 經*). This first column is the title for the text that follows and may be literally translated as meaning "the purity of prayer." Among the public libraries and museums having well-preserved specimens of the* dhāranī *are the Chicago Art Institute, Chicago; Columbia University, New York; Congressional Library, Washington; Harvard University, Cambridge; Paper Museum, Cambridge; Peabody Museum, Salem; New York Times Library, New York; Yale University, New Haven; New York Public Library, New York; and several private collections.*

the date of the 25th day of the fourth month of the year 770 (May 24): " After the eight years of civil war had been brought to an end, the Empress proclaimed a vow and ordered one million three-storey pagodas made, four and a half inches high and three and a half inches in diameter at the base. Within each of the pagodas (Figure 39) was placed a single copy of one of the four * *dhāranī*:

---

* Thomas Francis Carter in his *The Invention of Printing in China* (New York, 1925) states (page 36): "there were six different charms." This is a mistake; Dr. Carter, usually so accurate, was confused in this instance. The

Kompon (or Nemoto), Jīshin (or Jīshinin), Sōrin, and Rokudo (Figure 40).* When this work was completed, the pagodas were distributed among various temples. One hundred and fifty-seven men, from officials to menials, who had participated in the work, were granted titles, each according to his station." The following account has been taken from an old temple record: "In the year 767 there were built two small halls for pagodas on the east and west sides of the temple . . . a million pagodas were made which were equally divided † among ten temples.‡ In each pagoda was preserved a charm (dhāranī) in block print."

These two contemporary manuscripts give authentic accounts of the printed prayers; also, what is more convincing, a number of these pagodas are preserved in the temples of Japan.§ A dozen or more genuine paper dhāranī and their pagodas have been taken from the Japanese temples and are now in Occidental museums. In the manuscript records describing this printing accomplishment the number of printed prayers was stated to be "a million," but this great number should perhaps not be taken too literally.

---

fourth dhāranī (Rokudo) literally means "six times," or the six cardinal virtues, or the passing to Nirvana: namely, charity, morality, patience, energy, contemplation, and wisdom. It was probably a wrong translation of the Rokudo that confused Dr. Carter into believing that there were six dhāranī; actually there were but four.

* The four dhāranī used by Empress Shōtoku were taken from the sūtra: Vimala suddha prabhāsa mahādhāranī (Japanese: Mu-ku zhō-kwō dai dhāranī kyō). The dhāranī are Sanskrit forms of prayer transliterated in Chinese characters. It is most difficult to restore the original Sanskrit, except that of the dhāranī in the sūtras whose original texts have been preserved. The scripture is said to be a story of a Brahman, Gobirasencha, who appealed to Buddha for help when he was told by a prophet, Zensō-shi, that he had only seven more days to live.

† 100,000 printed papers and their pagodas were said to have been allotted to each of the ten temples.

‡ The ten Buddhist temples were: Taian-ji, Genkō-ji, Kōfuku-ji, Yakushi-ji, Tōdai-ji, Saidai-ji, Hōryū-ji (in Yamato Province), Shitennō-ji (in Settsu Province), Sūfuku-ji (in Omi Province), and Kokubun-ji. Nine of these temples (ji) were burnt and no printed papers or pagodas confined in them remain; only examples in Hōryū temple, near Nara, have been preserved.

§ In 1908 Mr. S. Taira, a Japanese antiquarian, reported that only 43,930 pagodas had survived in Hōryū-ji and only 300 of these were in perfect condition. In the catalogue of national treasures (Tokken kokuhō mokuroku), edited by Katsumi Kuroita, and published in Tōkyō in 1908, there were listed as under state protection, as of January 1908: 102 wooden pagodas and the following printed dhāranī: 27 Nemoto (or Kompon), 39 Jīshin, 23 Sōrin, and 7 Rokudo. The Rokudo is more rare than the other three.

No doubt there was a desire to convey to the populace the impression that a vast number of the prayers had been made and the expression may have been used in a purely symbolic sense.

The making of the paper and the printing of these prayers was probably the first instance of mass production; certainly the project involved more extensive manufacture of paper for one specific purpose than had previously been attempted. While even today the separate printing of a million strips of paper would be a considerable undertaking, the actual making of the paper for these *dhāranī* did not represent such a tremendous task as might be imagined. In the Orient in the eighth century a papermaking mould capable of forming paper that measured 20 by 22 inches would not have been unusually large, and upon such a mould one worker could have easily formed 500 sheets a day. From each sheet of paper of these dimensions eight strips of paper the size of the individual prayers could have been cut. This would make possible every day the manufacture of sufficient paper for the printing of 4,000 prayers, one person working at the vat. To have formed the quantity of paper required for the million prayers only about 250 working days, or about forty weeks' time would have been needed. For the cultivation and gathering of the material, beating, drying, finishing, and cutting the paper additional craftsmen would have been necessary, but the whole undertaking, voluminous as it appears, would have required the labour of only eight or ten artisans working less than a year. The printing of the prayers and the turning of the wooden pagodas would have necessitated much more time and labour than the production of the paper.

More often than not the paper upon which the *dhāranī* are printed is found in a deplorable condition, having suffered through the ravages of the destructive "silver fish," * so prevalent in the Far East. The paper that I have examined is composed one hundred per cent of hemp (*Cannabis sativa*), and is of the "laid" type,† having a decided Korean quality testifying that papermak-

---

* A fish moth, insect of the genus *Lepisma*.

† In the specimens I have examined there are about 18 "laid" lines to the inch and the "chain" lines are unevenly spaced, running from ⅝ of an inch to 1⅛ inches apart. The paper averages .0005 in thickness, bulking about 2½ inches to the ream of 500 sheets. The paper is of a light tan colour, as would naturally be the case with unbleached hemp as the material. There is

ing had only lately been introduced into Japan from China, by the usual Korean route.

There is no contemporary documentary evidence setting forth the actual method used in the printing of these prayers and for years there has been a deal of controversy among historians and bibliographers on this point. Several of these *dhāranī* are in the Paper Museum and numerous photographs of the printed papers from other collections have been assembled. Two methods of printing have been advanced: (a) printing from movable type; (b) printing from some sort of block — wood, metal, or porcelain. It requires very little study to dismiss the movable-type theory, for after an examination of many of the prayers it will be seen conclusively that the characters were not cast individually — there are too many renderings of the same character. Aside from this, the even impression of the printing is against the theory of individual types, as in any form of primitive hand-casting there would necessarily be a discrepancy in the heights of the separate types. It may be stated emphatically that individual types were not used and therefore the method rests with some sort of block upon the surface of which the many characters stood in relief. These characters could have been cut directly into blocks of stone, wood, or metal; or porcelain or metal blocks may have been cast from some suitable material in which the characters had been incised. While the use of wood-blocks would appear to be the most practical and logical, there are certain elusive characteristics about this early printing, difficult to define, that do not suggest the use of a material as soft as wood.

Over a thousand years elapsed from the time of the original setting down in the *Shoku Nihongi* of this remarkable achievement before a Japanese scholar devoted any attention to the actual method used in printing the *dhāranī* of 770; it was not until 1797 [1] that a Japanese historian offered an opinion as to the method used in the accomplishment of the world's first text printing upon paper. This writer was Fujiwara Teikan (1722–89), who advanced the observation that copperplates had been employed by the Empress Shōtoku and her retinue in reproducing the million printed prayers. Other Japanese writers on antiquarian subjects of the

---

no sizing or loading of any kind and apparently the paper had no special finishing other than the ordinary pressing.

same opinion as Fujiwara Teikan in the theory that copperplates were the medium used are: Noritane Ninagawa,[2] (1835–82), Tokujō Ōya,[3] Osamu Ryō,[4] Minamoto Kiyomichi,[5] Takurei Hirai,[6] Yasuhiko Kimiya,[7] Yano Michiya, and Tsuji Zennosuke.[8] That wood-blocks were used in the production of this early printing is the belief of such well-known Japanese historians as Moroshige Kondō [9] (1757–1815), Yoshino Sakakibara [10] (1832–81), Yorisuke Numata,[11] Sho Nakayama,[12] Kamezo Asakura,[13] Mayori Kurokawa,[14] and Noritake Tsuda.[15] Only two noted Japanese antiquarians advance the theory that movable types were used: Kariya Ekisai [16] and Masazumi Eto.[17]

The attention given by Occidental writers to this earliest of all text printing has not been at all commensurate with the importance of the accomplishment in graphic-arts history. Very little has been written in French or German on this subject and in English the bibliography would be limited to several short articles [18] and to the six-page chapter in Dr. Carter's excellent treatise on printing in China.[19] Dr. Carter states: ". . . Whether the blocks used were of wood or metal is still uncertain, but they were probably of wood. . . . Slight variations among the impressions of the same charm (*dhāranī*) have led some to question the fact that the charms were actually printed from blocks at all. In answer to this, it has been correctly pointed out that such a large number of impressions would have required several blocks for each charm, as only about 10,000 impressions can be taken from a wooden block before it is worn down. . . . The spreading of the ink in some of the impressions has been thought by some to indicate that the plates were of metal. On the other hand the variation between impressions of the same charm would indicate wood. The latter would be more in keeping with the general history of block printing, as far as is known."

Dr. Carter states that only 10,000 impressions could be had from a single wood-block. In this case 100 separate blocks would have been required; the estimate given by Dr. Carter is much too low and is without foundation.* It is to be assumed that if wood

---

* In the report of the United States National Museum for 1892 (pages 221–44), T. Tokuno writes regarding the number of impressions that could be made per day from a wood-block: "The printer of *Yinaka genji*, Tsurusabrō, printed 3,000 sheets per day from the black block. . . ." According to

was employed in printing the million prayers it was side-grain as is customary in the Orient, and not end-grain as used in the Western world.

From the short article [20] by Dr. Cyrus H. Peake, director of the Chinese department, Columbia University, regarding the printing of the *dhāranī* of A.D. 770, the following may be quoted: ". . . The desire to print was to be found not only among the literati and officials of China, but also among the Buddhist priests. They desired to print in large quantity for sale and distribution among the devoted, paper prayer charms and pictures of the Buddha. It is not surprising, therefore, that the oldest extant examples of printing characters upon paper by means of wood-blocks * were for religious reasons. These were Buddhist prayer charms and were printed in Japan by order of the Empress Shōtoku in A.D. 770."

Dr. Shio Sakanishi, formerly of the division of Orientalia, Library of Congress, has given considerable study to the method used in printing the "million paper charms" and she has made numerous experiments in an endeavour to clarify the procedure employed. Dr. Sakanishi, under date of April 24, 1941, writes: ". . . we started experiments with soft clay and wrote characters on it with a blunt stylus and dried the clay in the sun. After about ten trials we made some successful ones. . . . The use of wood-blocks and movable types are discredited. It is suggested that characters were written with a stylus on some medium, probably clay, which was baked, and the plate made by pouring metal

---

Dr. Carter a block would be worn out after being used but three or four days! For lack of Oriental data concerning the number of impressions possible from a single block, we turn to the Occidental work on wood-engraving by Jean Baptiste Michel Papillon: *Traité historique et pratique de la gravure en bois* (Paris, 1766). In this book (page 423) the author tells of his grandfather, Jean Papillon, using nothing but the wood of the pear tree for his woodengraving. He describes a large block representing the Holy Virgin from which each year 5,000 to 6,000 impressions were taken over a period of ninety years, making about 500,000 impressions from a single block. Papillon mentions another wood-block having been used for about 1,000 impressions a year, with the total of 60,000 to 80,000 printings from the one block.

* Dr. Peake has evidently forsaken his idea of wood-blocks, for in a letter to me dated December 23, 1940 he makes the following comment: "Concerning the material from which the *dhāranī* were printed Dr. Tsunoda of our department tells me that Japanese scholars tend to favour the belief now that they were printed from porcelain blocks . . . a few scholars believe iron was used, but they are now in the minority. Apparently very few, if any, now believe they were printed from wood-blocks."

over it." It would be entirely feasible to produce an evenly faced casting, or stereotype, from a clay base. For this purpose it would be necessary to spread the clay thinly (the actual depth of the characters) over a smooth metal plate and then incise the characters through the clay to the plate. With this method the characters would be drawn in the ordinary manner, as the casting would reverse the letters for proper printing. This system would be much the same as the old "chalk-plate" process in use in America many years ago for producing crude illustrations for newspapers.

From the foregoing controversial opinions it will be seen that the historians and bibliographers, as well as those versed in the mechanics of the graphic arts, have not been able to determine definitely the precise method employed in the eighth century in producing the text printing of the Empress Shōtoku *dhāranī*.

It has been my privilege to devote considerable research in an investigation regarding the paper upon which the *dhāranī* were printed; also it has been my good fortune to be able to study the method employed in printing the prayers and in Japan, Europe, and America I have examined numerous specimens. I have my own theory relative to the method used in printing the *dhāranī* and I hope that it will not be considered presumptuous to advance this opinion, although my ideas differ from those set down by the Japanese scholars.

About fifteen years ago while travelling in northern Korea I discovered among a great store of old wood-blocks a single printing block of stone. This block, now in the Paper Museum, is incised in relief with a human figure and eleven Chinese characters, suited for printing in the ordinary Oriental manner. The size of this stone block is six by nine inches, one half inch in thickness. While the block is undated, I suggest that it was cut as early as the fifteenth, perhaps the fourteenth, century. This printing block is of steatite (magnesium hydrous orthosilicate), also known as pagodite or agalmatolite. This type of stone is not native to Japan or to Korea, but it is common in southern China. Even as early as the eighth century there was extensive commerce among the countries of Asia and it would not have been unusual for quantities of this stone to reach Korea or Japan. Any materials used by craftsmen were readily conveyed from one Oriental country to another and they were always procurable no matter what the distance or the hardship of transport. For example, we always think of China as the home of jade, but in reality there has never been a pound of jade unearthed in China. It is only through the beautiful carvings that China for centuries has been known as the country of jade — not through the actual production of the stone.

In my numerous experiments in an endeavour to determine the method used in printing the million paper *dhāranī* I have made impressions from old Chinese wood-blocks, from metal plates, and from the steatite block found in Korea. It is my conclusion that the impressions from the stone block more closely resemble the elusive characteristics of the original eighth-century printing than the impressions made from any other material. The similarity is not easily defined, but the nature of the impressions upon hemp paper from the stone, with their lightly inked * and non-absorbent

---

* The ink used in printing the *dhāranī* has offered no particular enigma, as it appears obvious that the impressions were made through the use of some sort of black pigment mixed with a liquid readily soluble in water. According to Liu Yu of the Yüan or Mongol Dynasty (A.D. 1280–1368), writing in the *Tz'u-yüan* encyclopædia, the inventor of ink suitable for both writing and printing was an ingenious Chinese by the name of Wei Tang who lived during the fourth or fifth century after Christ. The ink was made by placing several twisted cotton or hemp wicks in a bowl of oil that had been pressed from fir wood. Over the burning wicks was suspended a cone of metal, the interior of which was soon coated with lamp-black. The black powder was scraped from the cone and when mixed with liquid was ready for printing. For making impressions from blocks of wood, stone, or metal the ink was applied to the raised characters by means of a round brush fashioned of coir fibre (*Cocos nucifera*). After the ink had been spread fairly evenly, a sheet of soft, unsized paper was laid upon the inked surface of the block, and the uppermost side of the paper was then rubbed with a pliable flat tool also composed of coir fibre. This was the simplest and most direct manner of making an impression from a raised surface upon paper; no press whatever was required. In an examination of the text printing of the *dhāranī* of A.D. 770 it will be seen that the ink is readily soluble in water, as it is possible to brush clear water upon a single printed character, cover the wet character with a piece of absorbent paper and make a transfer of the character, in reverse, by slightly rubbing the paper. This could not be done had the black pigment been mixed with oil or lacquer. In making experimental impressions from the steatite block with lamp-black mixed with water upon paper made of hemp, the same general characteristics of the ancient Empress Shōtoku printing were the result. In an endeavour to discover the exact method used in the first printing the use of stone blocks should not be entirely overlooked.

quality, gives every indication that stone may have been employed in producing the world's earliest text printing upon paper.

Unless an original block actually used in the *dhāranī* printing — be it stone, wood, metal, or porcelain — is discovered in some hidden corner of Japan, China, or Korea, the production of the parent of all text printing must remain a mystery. Though this original printing is thought to have been executed in Japan, the whole masterful undertaking was made possible through the knowledge and skill of the Chinese, to whom the Japanese will always remain in debt.

IV

The Hand-Mould

THE PAPERMAKERS' MOST ESSENTIAL TOOL, UPON
WHICH REST THE TWO THOUSAND YEARS OF
PAPERMAKING HISTORY

IT is interesting to formulate an imaginary picture of those first
eventful days of papermaking carried on in the old walled city
of Lei-yang, Hunan Province, at the beginning of the second century after Christ and to speculate as to the procedure followed by
those ancient Chinese artisans.

As has been explained, the calligraphy of the archaic Chinese
was written upon woven cloth, and as the roll or scroll manuscripts
were trimmed to assure uniformity and neatness, small clippings
of the cloth fell to the floor as waste. These discarded cloth fragments probably suggested the possibility of remaking the material
into a substance that would also serve for writing. In experimenting with the waste cloth it was natural that the Chinese conceived
the idea of first wetting and then beating the material until it was
reduced to a fibre. This was accomplished by hand with mortar
and pestle, the most elementary form of maceration. The tangled
and matted appearance of the beaten cloth fibres at once suggested the possibility of forming the myriad filaments into thin
layers or sheets. The fibres were hastily thrown into a tub or vat
filled with clear water, and when the eunuch Ts'ai Lun, a member
of the Imperial Guard, the genius credited with the invention of
paper, saw the minute fibres floating on the crest of the water, as
windblown seeds from the milkweed and dandelion float upon
the surface of a pond or stream, they no doubt suggested the feasi-
bility of lifting up the matted and tangled film from the water's
surface and transferring the leaf or sheet intact so that it might dry
in the sun. The difficult task was to devise an implement capable

FIG. 41   *Pouring the macer-*
ated pulp upon the moulds, one
of the most ancient methods of
forming sheets of paper. China.

FIG. 42   *With the "pouring"*
type of mould it was necessary to
allow the newly formed sheets of
paper to dry upon the surface of
the moulds. China.

of picking up the matted fibres from the surface of the water and
at the same time suffer the water to escape, leaving the interwoven
stratum of fibres in an even, homogeneous sheet of paper. This
need brought forth the invention of the papermaking mould, the
implement that has remained throughout the centuries the most
essential tool in forming paper by hand, and upon the principle
of which the modern paper-machine is founded. To the papermaker the mould is as important as the loom is to the weaver.

THE "WOVE" MOULD

Inasmuch as no paper is in existence from the first forty-five or
fifty years after its invention, it is only possible to surmise the construction of the original moulds. It is likely that the first mould, as
conceived and used by Ts'ai Lun and his helpers, was nothing
more than a square of coarsely woven cloth held within a four-
sided bamboo frame. This type of mould could have been successfully used in making paper by two distinct methods: In the first
method the mould could have been dipped perpendicularly into
the water upon which the macerated fibres floated and brought
up horizontally *under* them, lifting the matted fibres as in a sieve,
allowing the water to drain through the meshes of the cloth. In
the second method the mould could have been held flat and the
fibres *poured* upon the woven material, the cloth, or in some instances rattan, retaining the fibres in a moist sheet and at the

Fig. 43   *After the moisture from the sheets had evaporated, the dry paper was easily stripped from the moulds. China.*

same time allowing the water to drain through the interstices of the woven material (Figure 41). In either case the mould with the thin deposit of matted and felted fibres adhering to its surface was placed in the sun for drying (Figure 42). After the moisture from the sheet had evaporated, the paper was easily stripped from the mould (Figure 43). The warp and woof of the mould left impressions in the paper, in the same way as watermarks are formed in handmade paper today.

With an implement of this type it was necessary to allow the moist sheet of paper to dry upon the mould's surface, and if much paper was to be made, many moulds would have been needed, as the drying of each individual sheet would have required about a half hour in the sun.

The entire development of papermaking is so closely connected with mould construction that it is only through a study of moulds that the long history of paper is revealed. Without a knowledge of mould-making throughout the centuries it would not be possible to arrive at definite conclusions regarding the formation of the ancient Oriental papers that have been discovered by archæological

Fig. 44   *Two fragments of paper of the Eastern Han period* (A.D. 25–220), *the most ancient paper known to exist in the world. British Museum.*

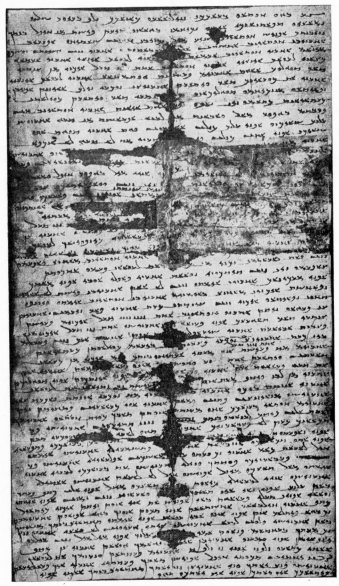

FIG. 45 *Manuscript on paper (24 by 41 cm.) found in 1907 by Sir Aurel Stein in the ruins of the Great Chinese Wall. Date about* A.D. *150. British Museum.*

Fig. 46   *The drying of paper in Fatshan, Kwangtung Province, China. In this province the "pouring" type of "wove" mould is still in use.*

expeditions in the Far East. While it has not been my privilege to examine *all* of the papers unearthed by Sir Aurel Stein and Dr. Sven Hedin,* I believe that these examples of early paper show distinctly the impressions of only bamboo moulds of the "laid" type (Figures 44, 45). While I am inclined to surmise that the original paper of China was formed on a fabric mould of the "wove" style, the discoveries of old Chinese papers do not bear out this supposition. There are no specimens of paper, however, from the earliest years of the craft which might prove this assumption. To my knowledge, no second-century paper of the "wove" type, showing the impressions of the woven fabric upon which it was formed, has ever been discovered in Asia. In my own numer-

---

* Sir Aurel Stein, an eminent authority on Asia, on one of his journeys through Chinese Turkestan discovered several parcels of folded paper which, upon ultimate examination under the microscope, proved to be formed partly of rag fibres. Authorities place the date of these sheets at about A.D. 150. Paper dating from A.D. 250–300 was also found by Dr. Stein in Niya in Turkestan. The earliest paper that is clearly dated was found by Dr. Sven Hedin at Loulan, the date being A.D. 264.

ous experiments in an endeavour to arrive at the methods employed by the actual inventor of paper, I have come to the conclusion that the "wove" mould must have been the earliest form used, and that the beaten fibres were poured upon the mould and the moist sheet left to dry upon it. This style of mould may have been used only a short time, but sufficiently long to convince the inventor that he had conceived a method of forming a highly useful material entirely suited for calligraphy — not only had a substance at last been developed that would eventually become a substitute for the various materials that had previously been used for writing, but a surface that was far better suited to the purpose than had ever been known.

In Kwangtung Province, China, at the present time, the "wove" style of mould, upon which the fibre is poured and allowed to dry, is in use (Figure 46). There is no record as to the number of years this type of mould, or the method employed, has been used, but it is interesting to note that the locality where these "wove" moulds are found is not more than two hundred miles from Lei-yang, near Henchow, Hunan Province, the seat of the invention of papermaking by Ts'ai Lun about A.D. 105.

The photograph of the present-day Kwangtung "wove" mould gives a clear conception of its construction. The mould pictured (Figure 47) is capable of forming sheets of paper measuring 14 by 18 inches. The two lateral bars of bamboo are 27 inches in length and about one inch in diameter, the "legs" protruding about three and a half inches beyond the point where the two cross-bars, also of bamboo, are placed. The two lateral bamboo strips are made of *ch'a kan chu* (*Arundinaria sp.*). The cross-bars, which are equal in length, plus the diameters of the two lateral bars into which they are mortised, are about three fourths of an inch in diameter and are made from split *mou chu* (*Phyllostachys pubescens* [Carr.] de Lehaie). The woven screen, upon which the fibrous pulp is poured to form a sheet of paper, is composed of *ch'u ma* (*Bœhmeria nivea*, Gaud) (ramie, rhea, or China grass), and is made to fit precisely the opening in the bamboo framework. The warp and woof strands of this material are about the thickness of common cotton string and are twisted to give strength. The woven ramie screen is fastened to the four bamboo bars by strips of slender bamboo run at intervals through the cloth and

FIG. 47   *The Fatshan type of mould, onto which the macerated stock is poured. It is my contention that this was the original type of "wove" mould, dating from the second century after Christ.*

around the bamboo bars. There are no supports, or ribs, under the woven ramie material.

THE "LAID" MOULDS OF CHINA

I will not venture a surmise as to when the "laid" type of mould was first used; the earliest paper discovered by Sir Aurel Stein and Dr. Sven Hedin shows clearly the impressions of moulds of this construction, but this paper does not date from the first half century of the craft. My contention that the "wove" mould was probably the first form used has no other foundation than that the conception of this type of mould, so simple to make and to use, would naturally have been the first to enter the mind of the originator of paper. It is my belief that the "laid" type of mould dipped *into* the vat of suspended fibres (Figures 48, 49, 50) was an after invention — perhaps following the "wove" mould by only a short time, but by a sufficient period to give the "wove" mould first place in the chronological development of this implement.

FIG. 48   *Papermaking in China. The vatman is in the act of dipping the mould into the vat, which is filled with macerated bamboo fibre. (From an original drawing from the year 1800 in the Victoria and Albert Museum, London.)*

FIG. 49   *Papermaking in China. Forming the sheets in the mould, couching the moist paper, and placing the sheets upon the wall to dry. (From* Arts, métiers et cultures de la Chine, Paris, 1814.)

FIG. 50   *A Chinese papermaker in the act of dipping a mould into the vat of macerated fibre; in the centre background another worker is couching a sheet of paper from the flexible mould-cover. Modern papermaking near Peking.*

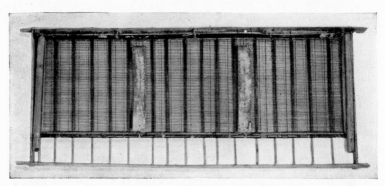

FIG. 51   *The original type of Chinese "laid" transfer mould. The invention of this type of mould was one of the great advancements in papermaking as from it the sheets could be removed immediately after forming.*

An ancient artisan of genius conceived the idea of a mould from which the wet sheet of paper could be removed while still moist (Figure 51). This constituted the first real advance in papermaking, as it enabled the artisan to form sheets continually upon the same mould. For this purpose the mould-covering (Figure 52) had to be constructed of a smooth and firm material from which the moist sheet would readily free itself. Such a mould-covering was made by placing thin strips of rounded bamboo side by side and stitching or lacing them together at regular intervals with silk, flax, camel-, yak-, or horse-hair. The bamboo strips, as well as the stitches, left impressions in every sheet of paper made upon the mould. The marks or indentations made by the pieces of bamboo are now known as "laid-lines," while the less noticeable impressions of the stitches are termed "chain-lines," as the hair lacing consisted of chain stitching over and under the strips of bamboo. In the paper of a Chinese block print attributed to the tenth century (T'ang Dynasty, A.D. 618–907), now before me, I find by holding the paper to the light that there were in the original mould twenty-three bamboo strips to every inch, as there are impressions of twenty-three "laid-lines" to every inch in the paper. The hair stitchings, or "chain-lines," of the mould that was used in forming the paper upon which this text was printed were spaced at intervals of approximately one and one-sixteenth inches.

FIG. 52   A Chinese worker holding a "laid" transfer type of paper-making mould, made of bamboo splints laced with horsehair. This mould would be capable of forming four sheets of paper at one dipping, each sheet measuring about 10 by 10 inches. The worker is holding the two deckle sticks in his left hand.

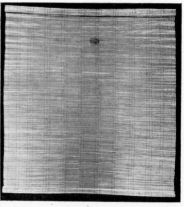

FIG. 53   A mould-frame. The "laid" mould-cover, made of grass or bamboo, lies upon the mould-frame during the dipping of the mould; the mould-frame, with its ribs, supporting the mould-cover, keeping it flat. The principle of all Oriental moulds is practically the same. This mould-frame was procured in the paper-village of Kagaziguda, near Secunderabad, Hyderabad, southern India.

FIG. 54   A mould-cover. The "laid" mould-cover rests upon the mould-frame (Figure 53) during the forming of a sheet of paper. The "laid-lines" (grass or bamboo) and the "chain-lines" (horsehair) cause slight indentations in every sheet of paper formed thereon. This was the original "laid" paper. This mould-cover was acquired in the village of Kalpi, central India.

The laced bamboo mould-cover resembled a piece of matting. When a sheet of paper was to be made, the covering was placed loosely on the shallow wooden framework (Figure 53), which supported it firmly; the entire mould, both frame and cover, was then dipped into the vat of macerated pulp and brought to the surface loaded with the wet, fibrous material. The thin paper stock was prevented from flowing beyond the top and bottom edges of the matting by bamboo rods laced to the mat at its extremities, parallel with the "laid" bamboo strips. The flow of pulp on the right and left sides was kept within boundaries by the workman, who dipped the mould, holding two wooden sticks, one in each hand, along the outer edges of the matting, parallel to the "chain" stitches (Figure 55). Thus the four outside edges were fenced in

Fig. 55   *A young Chinese worker holding a "laid" transfer mould of the divided type, capable of forming three separate sheets of paper at each dipping; the sheets measure about 10 inches square. Note the manner in which the loose deckle sticks are held. This type of mould is shown in Figure 51.*

such a manner that the wet paper stock or pulp was kept within bounds, forming a sheet of paper almost the size of the mould-covering (Figure 54). In *couching*,* or laying down, a sheet of paper, the matting was lifted free from the framework and the wet layer of paper deposited flat, one sheet upon another, the under-most sheet upon a board, the workman rolling up the matting, from the top edge to the bottom, leaving the moist, tender sheet firm and unwrinkled (Figures 56, 57, 58, 59).

While this type of mould construction seems complicated, it was the simplest and best method that could have been devised, and upon this early Oriental form of mould the manner of making paper in all ages has rested; even the most modern paper-machine employs precisely the same principles.

While these moulds may differ in the construction of the frame-

---

* From the verb *coucher*, to lay down; Old French *colcher*, *culcher*, from *colchier;* from Latin *collocare*, to place.

FIG. 56   *The worker at the extreme left is couching a sheet of newly formed paper from the mould-cover. The sheets are laid one upon another, without interleaving felts as is the European practice. This is the papermaking school in Seoul, Korea, where the Japanese have endeavoured to teach the methods of Japan with the hope of supplanting the more ancient technique of Korea.*

FIG. 57   *In the Orient the sheets of paper are couched one upon another and then subjected to pressure to expel the surplus water. Paper made from Asiatic fibre and properly treated can be readily separated after pressing. A "slab" of paper just as it came from the press is shown in the centre of the picture. This paper is ready for separating and drying. The two balls at the right are pulp prepared for the vat. South China.*

work and the manner of keeping the wet paper stock within bounds, the top covering, or matting, is usually of the same form of fabrication, and the principle of the whole operation of papermaking is almost identical.

These bamboo moulds of the "laid" pattern were used by the Chinese many centuries before the introduction of papermaking into Europe. To my knowledge, no watermark in the form of an object or design has ever been found in paper from the period of the first vegetable-filament moulds. Perhaps the ancients did not think of this means of marking their paper; or perhaps it may have occurred to them and, finding the bamboo strips so inflexible, the idea was not carried out. The "laid-" and "chain-lines" of the moulds caused indentations in the paper unintentionally, but the use of insignia or devices was not practised by the early Oriental workers in paper.

It is not possible to determine the date of the introduction of bamboo moulds, nor can it be stated at what time metal wire succeeded vegetable filaments as a material for mould-covering. The

FIG. 58   *The Japanese worker is lifting the flexible mould-cover after depositing a sheet of moist paper on the pile. In the Orient no felts are used; each sheet is couched one upon another.*

Moors established papermaking in Spain in the twelfth century, and it is thought that wire replaced the natural fibre moulds in Europe not long after that time. At whatever period wire took the place of bamboo, the metal was used in precisely the same manner as the rounded bamboo reeds, and the metal wires continued to impress the "laid-" and "chain-lines" in every sheet of paper formed upon them, reproducing almost in counterpart the lines left by the bamboo moulds. There is great variation in the distance between the "chain-lines" and also in the number of "laid-lines" to the inch, in sheets of paper made on either the ancient bamboo or the later metal-wire moulds.

The earliest Chinese print to depict a papermaking mould may be found in the treatise on papermaking entitled *T'ien kung k'ai wu*, by Sung Ying-hsing, issued in 1634 (Figure 60). The mould depicted in this wood-block illustration is without doubt of the "laid" type. In this seventeenth-century print the wooden framework of the mould is erroneously shown in the hands of the *coucher* apparently in the act of *couching*, or laying down, a sheet

Fɪɢ. 59   *Couching paper in Japan from a mould-cover such as that shown in Figure 71. The flexible bamboo mould-cover is lifted in a rolling motion, leaving the newly formed sheet of paper smooth and unwrinkled.*

of paper. This technical fault was probably a misconception of the artist, as the delineation of the vatman in a companion print (Figure 61) shows quite clearly that the framework is supporting the "laid" bamboo mould-cover and it would be from the flexible bamboo screen only that the paper would naturally be *couched*. One of the earliest Chinese "laid" moulds in the Paper Museum collection dates from about the year 1830, but from an examination of ancient Chinese paper it would be determined that practically the same type of mould was used as far back as the third century of our era. This particular Chinese mould from more than a hundred years ago is capable of making paper measuring about 22 by 35 inches, but of course the same style of "laid" mould was capable of forming sheets of paper much larger than these dimensions. The mould in question has a soft-wood frame with twenty square supporting ribs; the mould-cover of finely cut bamboo has twenty-one "laid-lines" to the inch, the "chain-lines" of horsehair being one and three-quarters inches apart. In all of the paper-

Fig. 60   *The first illustration depicting papermaking to appear in a Chinese book. From the work by Sung Ying-hsing entitled T'ien kung k'ai wu, first issued in 1634.*

Fig. 61   *The Chinese vatman is dipping the mould-cover supported by the mould-frame into the vat containing macerated bamboo fibre. (From T'ien kung k'ai wu, by Sung Ying-hsing, 1634.)*

making districts of China "laid" moulds of this style are in use. Some of these moulds are made with frames and supporting ribs cut from China fir (*Cunninghamia lanceolata,* Hook. f.), while other moulds have delicate ribs fashioned from arrow bamboo (*Arundinaria* or *Sasa sp.*). The "laid" bamboo mould-covers are usually laced with horsehair or ramie, but twisted cotton is not unknown as a material used in lacing the "chain-lines."

In the Paper Museum collection of Chinese "laid" moulds dating from the nineteenth century to the present day, there is such a variation of spacing in the bamboo "laid-lines" and in the widths between the rows of "chain" stitches that a classification would be a difficult undertaking. It can be said, however, that the original type of "laid" mould from the earliest years of Chinese papermaking served as a model for all the moulds that followed, and throughout the world there has been but slight change in their

FIG. 62   *A view of the papermaking village of Ompei, Korea, where is made the thin paper used in the windows and the thick paper used on the floors of native Korean houses. Sheets of paper are spread on the ground to dry.*

pattern. The principle of the invention remains practically unaltered.

THE MOULDS OF KOREA

The craft of papermaking was introduced into Korea from China, and while the exact time is unknown the inception dates from a very early period. Unfortunately I do not have any ancient Korean moulds, but in my assemblage of papermaking equipment from the Orient there are Korean moulds dating from the past fifty or sixty years. In visiting the small handmade-paper hamlets in Korea (Figure 62) I did not find a counterpart of the "wove" type of mould such as is used in Kwangtung Province, south China, nor do I believe that the "wove" mould ever played a prominent part in Korean papermaking. Korean papers have always had their own special characteristics, largely due to the moulds on which they were formed. Like the common "laid" mould of China, the Korean mould (Figure 63) consists of four

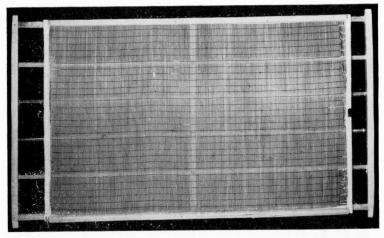

FIG. 63   A Korean papermaking mould from the paper-village of
Ompei, central Korea. This mould is capable of forming paper measuring about 28 by 46 inches.

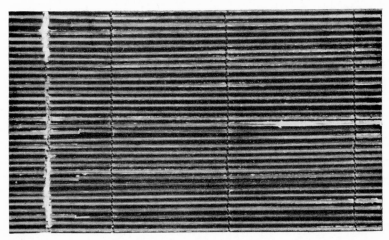

FIG. 64   A section of a mould-cover in exact size. This cover is composed of grass (Andropogon micranthus) laced at intervals with horsehair. From the papermaking village near Srinagar, Kashmir, north
India.

Fig. 65   *Two workers using the Korean mould as shown in Figure 63. Paper of this kind is used on the floors of Korean houses. Ompei, Korea.*

separate parts: the frame, the laid-cover, and the two deckle sticks. While bamboo is the most common material used in making Korean "laid" moulds, there have been instances where a tall Korean grass (*Miscanthus sp.*) has been found suitable for the purpose. In India grass has long formed a useful material for the making of "laid" mould-covers (Figure 64).

All Korean moulds, as well as the paper made on them, may be distinguished by several marked characteristics: the "laid-lines" run the narrow way and the "chain-lines," often narrowly spaced and irregular, run the length of the mould. In an examination of hundreds of sheets of Korean paper, dating from the sixteenth century onward, I have found that every sheet conforms to this formula. In all other Oriental (and Occidental) moulds the opposite of this arrangement may be expected. The Korean mould is of the regulation pattern and has been used in forming sheets of paper measuring 28½ by 46½ inches. This sort of paper, after a number of sheets have been beaten or pressed together and oiled, is used for the permanent covering of floors in native Korean houses, and

Fig. 66   A papermaking unit in the village of Ompei, Korea, near Seoul. The Korean moulds are operated by two workers. The heavy paper in the foreground is used on the floors of Korean houses.

in single thickness the paper is used in lieu of glass in the windows (Figures 65, 66).

THE MOULDS OF JAPAN

From China, by way of Korea, the Japanese received most of their arts, and papermaking was no exception. The craft of making paper was introduced from China into Korea and in turn the Koreans, during the seventh century, established papermaking in Japan (Figures 67, 68, 69, 70). Not only did the Japanese, with their innate skill, become expert papermakers, but the moulds fabricated by them display a highly developed technique not found in the papermaking moulds of any other country, either Oriental or Occidental. While the moulds of Japan are more complex than those of any other part of Asia, the manner of their construction and their ultimate use in forming sheets of paper are practically the same as in China and Korea. The Japanese in late years have given thought to such commercial necessities as more rapid pro-

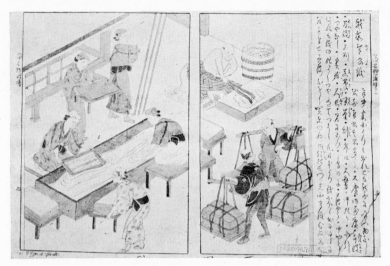

Fɪɢ. 67   *Japanese papermaking as shown in an eighteenth-century print — beating, forming the sheet, drying, and packing. From:* Sankai Meibutu-zue.

duction and the adaptability of certain styles of moulds for particular requirements.

The most common type of mould used in Japan (Figures 71, 72) is distinguishable from all others by the "deckle," or upper *sugeta*, being hinged to the lower *sugeta*, or frame (Figure 73). Moreover, this pattern of mould has two handles protruding from the hinged deckle and spaced conveniently for the worker to grasp. Moulds of this type are used in making the thinnest tissue paper, usually from the bark of the mulberry tree, called in Japan *kozo*. The uncut and untrimmed paper fashioned on the mould pictured (Figure 71) would measure about 22¾ by 62½ inches, but these exceedingly thin papers are usually trimmed and cut into convenient sizes to suit numerous commercial uses throughout the world. The mould-cover is made for forming "wove" paper of the finest texture, and every effort has been made to eliminate any markings or impressions that the mould-cover might leave in the paper. This has been accomplished by covering the usual "laid" bamboo cover with finely woven silk textile in which the warp and woof threads run about thirty-four to the inch, the silk being lacquered as a protection against the constant moisture to

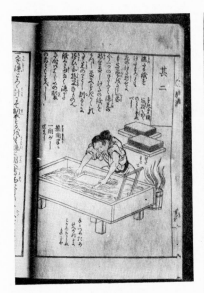 

FIG. 68   A Japanese paper-maker dipping the mould in the act of forming a sheet of paper. (From the eighteenth-century work Kamisuki Chôhôki, by Kuni-higashi of the province of Se-kishu.)

FIG. 69   Papermaking in Ja-pan. The woman worker is dip-ping the bamboo mould to form a sheet of paper. A pile of newly formed sheets is on the stool at the right. (From a coloured wood-block print by Gyokuransai Sada-hide, 1820–67.)

which it must be subjected. The supporting framework for this "wove" mould-covering is made of soft wood with thin copper hinges and catches, the complete frame weighing but five pounds, while the silk cover, with its flexible bamboo under-support, weighs only one and one-quarter pounds. From the photograph there may be seen the thirteen ribs, or cross-bars, that support the "wove" covering during the dipping of the mould. Each of these wooden ribs is surmounted by a copper-wire bridge which holds the "wove" cover above and away from the ribs, thus elim-inating any impressions or streaks in the finished paper which would be caused by the suction of the ribs if the covering were laid directly against the wooden rib supports. These slightly curved wire bridges are a recent innovation and were adopted

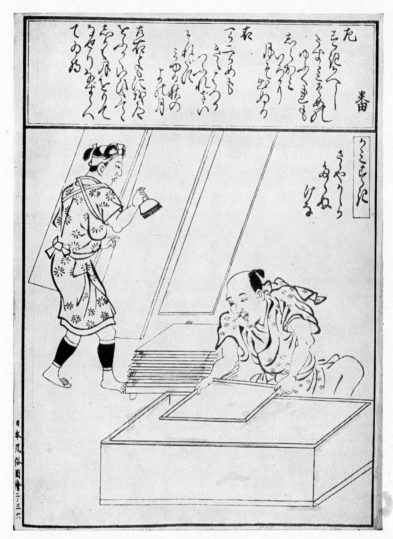

FIG. 70   *Papermaking in Japan, showing the vatman and the paper-drier. (From a wood-block print by Hishikawa Moronobu in the four-volume work:* Wakoku Shōshoku Edzukushi, *1681.)*

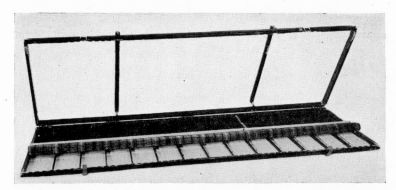

FIG. 71   *The most common type of Japanese papermaking mould.*
Most of the mulberry papers exported to America and Europe are
formed on moulds of this type. Paper measuring 22¾ by 62½ inches
can be formed. From Kōchi, Shikoku, Japan.

FIG. 72   *The same type of mould, but smaller, as shown in Figure*
71. This mould has a cover of the "laid" type, while the mould pictured
in Figure 71 is covered with woven silk and forms paper of the "wove"
style. Gifu Prefecture, Japan.

FIG. 73   *Forming and couching sheets of paper with the type of mould shown in Figures 71, 72. Japan.*

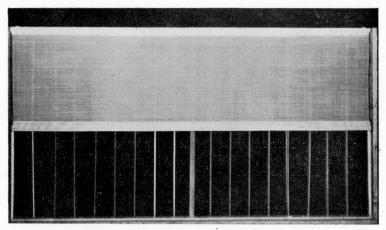

FIG. 74   *A mould for making shōji, a paper used in lieu of glass in old-time Japanese houses. Two women operate a mould of this size, forming paper that measures 29 by 67 inches. The mould-cover is rolled to show construction of the mould-frame. From Okayama, Japan.*

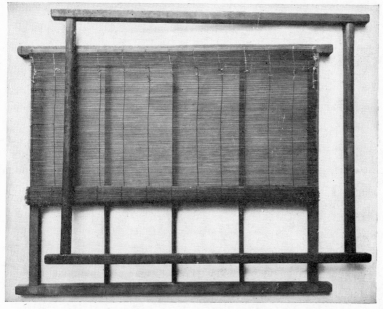

FIG. 75   *A small "laid" mould of Japan used in making many varieties of useful and artistic papers. This is a common type and may be found in all papermaking districts of Japan.*

solely to remedy the streaks, which were a slight annoyance to the foreign trade in using the paper for special purposes.

The large mould shown in Figure 74 was originally used in Okayama, Japan, in making *shōji* (window paper), the size being 29 by 67 inches. It requires two skilled women to form paper on a mould of this giant size. As stated before, so many varieties of moulds (cf. Figure 75) are used in Japan that only the important ones have been described.

THE MOULDS OF KASHMIR, BENGAL, AND OTHER PAPERMAKING LOCALITIES OF INDIA

The moulds of Kashmir, where papermaking is thought to have been first introduced into India, show the influence of their Persian origin, and to the moulds of Kashmir the design of all other moulds of India can be directly traced. The construction of Chi-

FIG. 76   *Papermaking mould of Kashmir, northern India. This mould is shown in use in Figures 77–80. The finely polished manuscript papers of Kashmir are formed on "laid" moulds made of grass (Andropogon micranthus) laced with horsehair. The size of the paper made in Kashmir approximates 32 by 36 inches.*

nese papermaking moulds was reflected in those of Persia, and the moulds of India were in turn modelled after those of Persia. It is only natural, therefore, that the present-day moulds of India follow, to a great extent, the pattern of the ancient moulds of China. The Kashmir moulds in the Paper Museum are representative of those in use in modern times, but it is reasonable to believe that these moulds have undergone few changes, if any, since the intro-

Fig. 77 *The vatman dipping the mould shown in Figure 76. Kashmir, northern India.*   Fig. 78 *After the paper has been formed on the mould shown in Figure 76. Kashmir, northern India.*

duction of papermaking into northern India. Certainly the construction of the present-day moulds of Kashmir would not suggest that there has been any alteration from the time of their introduction. While the modern tool, as in the past, is simply conceived and crudely made, its construction nevertheless shows considerable scientific knowledge.

The Kashmir mould (Figure 76) consists of two distinct parts: the mould-frame and the mould-cover, the frame acting as a sup-

Figs. 79, 80 *In couching, or laying down, a sheet of paper in Asiatic papermaking the matting is lifted free from the framework of the mould and the wet sheet of paper deposited flat, one sheet upon another, the workman rolling up the matting, or mould-cover, from the top edge to the bottom, leaving the moist, tender sheet firm and unwrinkled. Kashmir, India.*

Fig. 81   *A papermaking mould of India. The grass mould-cover is rolled to show the wooden mould-frame. From the old papermaking town of Sailkot, the Punjab, northern India.*

port for the cover. The mould-frame of Kashmir is composed of sixteen separate pieces of wood, with two extra deckle sticks used as side deckles, in the manner of the Chinese moulds. Four of the sixteen pieces represent the actual frame of the mould; the remaining twelve compose the ribs, or cross-bars, of the mould-frame. The four outer frame sections are usually cut from strips of deodar (*Cedrus deodara*). These four sections are mortised at the corners, making a square resembling a plain picture frame, the outside measurements being 32 by 36 inches. Between the top and bottom sections of this square are placed the twelve triangular-shaped

FIG. 82　*The Indian vatman in the process of dipping the mould to form a sheet of paper. Autsahai, Bengal, northern India.*

FIG. 83　*The Indian shown in Figure 82 couching the moist sheet of paper from the flexible mould-cover. The mould-frame remains on the vat. Autsahai, Bengal, northern India.*

FIG. 84　*A worker in the Mohandas K. Gandhi school of paper-making weaving a grass mould-cover on a primitive loom. Kalpi, central India.*

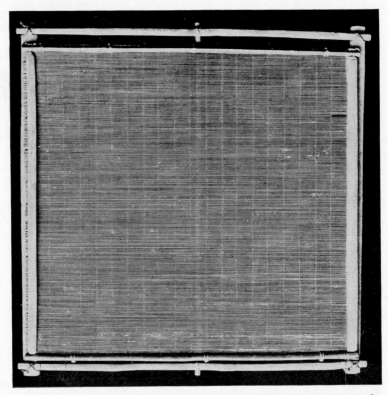

Fig. 85   *The mould of Bengal. This is the only province of India where bamboo is used for mould-covers, as in China. All other districts in India use grass for this purpose. From Autsahai, central Bengal, India.*

ribs, causing the four-sided frame to take on the appearance of a barred window. The triangular shape of the ribs forms a suction as the mould is lifted from the water (Figures 77, 78). In couching, or laying down, the newly formed sheet from the surface of the mould-cover, the method used in Kashmir, as well as in most other parts of India, differs little from that of China, Korea, and Japan, previously explained (Figures 79, 80).

The mould-cover of Kashmir, unlike the covers of China and Japan, is composed of many lengths of dried grass *laid* side by side and laced together at intervals with horsehair. The grass (*Andropogon micranthus*) grows abundantly in India and forms a practical papermaking surface, but not equal to the best "laid" bamboo moulds of China or Japan. The horsehair lacings ("chain-lines") are taken from the tail of the animal and are usually black or brown in colour. The weaving of the grass mould-covers requires considerable dexterity, but perhaps not so much ingenuity as that expended upon a "laid" bamboo mould-cover. A Kashmir mould-cover to be used on a 32-by-36-inch mould-frame would need to measure about 29 by 33 inches, but after the deckle edges have been cut away, the paper formed on a mould of these dimensions would measure only about 26 by 30 inches. There are no standard sizes for Kashmir paper and there are no set rules for the distance between "chain-lines" or the number of "laid-lines" to the inch.

The moulds of the Punjab (Figure 81), Central Provinces, United Provinces, Bombay Presidency, Madras, Hyderabad, and Bengal (Figures 82, 83) are all modelled, more or less, on the Kashmir pattern (Figure 84). With the exception of one province, all mould-covers of India are composed of grass (Figure 64); but in the papermaking sections of Bengal (Figure 85) bamboo is used in very much the same manner as in China, only perhaps not to the same degree of refinement as by the Chinese artisans.

THE MOULDS OF INDO–CHINA

The papers of Indo-China are formed on moulds that resemble those of China to a great degree, but in Indo-China we find no loose deckle sticks, the deckle being very much like the *sugeta* of Japan, only it is not hinged (Figure 86). The papermaking centre of Indo-China is in Tonkin, and the mould pictured was acquired in the connecting paper-villages of Lang-Buoi and Yên-Thai, lying along the muddy road not far from Hanoi. Here paper has been made for hundreds of years without interruption. The frame for the mould shown in the illustration is made of wood, and the "laid" cover is composed of unusually delicate bamboo splints laced with horsehair. The mould shown is capable of forming paper measuring 10 by 24 inches. The paper made by hand in Indo-China is consumed locally by the merchants for accounting and for use in religious ceremonies (Figure 87).

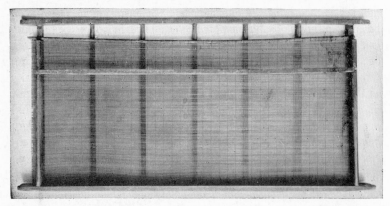

FIG. 86   *Papermaking mould from Tonkin, northern Indo-China.
This type of mould is used by women workers, and sheets of paper
measuring about 10 by 24 inches are made. From the paper-village
of Yên-Thai, where paper has been made continuously for more than
six hundred years.*

FIG. 87   *In Indo-China the mould is dipped into the vat with the
far side first, the opposite of the European custom. This mould is shown
in Figure 86. From the Paper Village of Yên-Thai, Tonkin, Indo-China.*

FIG. 88   *Making paper in Ti-bet in the most ancient Oriental manner. The macerated fibres are poured upon the mould. Gyantse, Tibet.*

FIG. 89   *The mould after the sheet has been formed upon its surface. Gyantse, Tibet.*

THE MOULDS OF SIAM, BURMA, NEPAL, BHUTAN, AND TIBET

In this category of moulds we find a somewhat different tech-nique in the actual papermaking. As previously outlined, paper was formed either by *dipping* the mould *into* the fibrous water or *pouring* the macerated fibres *upon* the mould's surface. It is im-possible to state which was the first method of making paper. In present-day papermaking in Siam, Burma, Nepal, Bhutan, and Tibet (Figures 88, 89, 90) the paper stock, or pulp, is *poured upon* the mould — the mould is *not dipped.* For this particular method of forming sheets of paper the mould is floated on a stream, or pool, of clear water, and the macerated bark fibres mixed with water in a bucket are thrown upon the cloth covering of the mould as it floats on the surface of the stream (Figures 91, 92, 93). Here we have perhaps the original method of making paper in using the "wove" type of mould and in the actual formation of the sheets.

The moulds of Siam, Burma, Nepal, Bhutan, and Tibet are all made in practically the same manner; it will suffice to describe the Siamese implement as representative. The moulds used in Siam are constructed so that the paper is long and narrow in shape, con-forming to the character of Siamese books. The most common width of paper is about 16 inches, but it is not usual to find Si-

FIG. 90   Tibetan workers forming their large sheets of paper by pouring the macerated pulp into the cloth moulds while floating on a pool of water. The pulp is whipped with sticks to assist in distributing the fibre over the entire mould in a fairly even sheet. From Gyantse, Tibet.

FIG. 91   In Siam the paper stock is poured upon the mould as it floats in a stream. The "floating" type of mould is also used in Tibet, Burma, and Nepal. From Bangsoom, south Siam.

FIG. 92   After the fibres have been intertwined upon the mould, it is lifted from the stream and the paper allowed to dry upon the mould.

Fig. 93   *Siamese papermaking moulds made of teak and woven cotton fabric. Moulds of this type are shown in use in Figures 91 and 92. Inasmuch as the paper remains on the moulds until dry, many moulds are necessary. From the now abandoned Tym and Piung Niltongkum mill, Bangsoom, Siam.*

amese, Burmese, and Tibetan manuscripts as wide as 27 inches.[*]
The length of Siamese moulds varies from 60 to 80 inches. The

---

[*] The papers made in the southern Shan States of Burma are usually fabricated from the inner bark of the paper mulberry. The heaviest paper made in Burma measures 32 by 66 inches; a lighter-weight paper, admired by Western artists for the printing of wood-blocks and etchings, measures 25 by 26½ inches. The coloured papers made in the Shan States in blue, red, yellow, green, and pink and used in the manufacture of umbrellas are made in a size approximating 22 by 29 inches.

In Nepal the bark of the Nepal paper plant (*Daphne cannabina* or *Daphne papyracea*) forms the material from which paper is made. The paper is said to be immune from the ravages of insects. The usual sizes of Nepal paper are 30½ by 62 and 28 by 64 inches. The paper of Bhutan is usually square, measuring about 23 by 24 inches.

In making paper in Tibet the inner bark is peeled from the stalk of the shrub by women, who boil the material for two days before it is finally beaten to a fibre by hand. The macerated fibre is next mixed with water in tea-churns, where it is thoroughly agitated. The stock, or watery pulp, is then poured upon "wove" cotton moulds in the Siamese and Burmese manner.

frames of the moulds are usually made of teak (*Tectona grandis,* Linn. f.) of the family *Verbenaceæ,* and are held together by teak pins and wedges. The four outside strips measure about three quarters of an inch in thickness and one and one-half inches in breadth. The cloth upon which the paper is actually formed is woven by hand, the material being pure cotton (*Gossypium herbaceum*). The woven cloth has from 12 to 22 threads to the inch, and the common width in which the cloth is woven is approximately 17 inches, a sufficient width for fully two thirds of the moulds used in Siam (Figure 93). As with all cloth moulds of this type, each sheet of paper must dry upon the mould, and therefore if much paper is to be formed, a good many moulds are required, as the process of drying a sheet of paper of this large size would require fully three quarters of an hour, even in the hot sun of the tropics.

EUROPEAN MOULDS

When papermaking was introduced into Spain about the year 1150, it is probable that the European workmen at first made use of the bamboo moulds that had been conceived in China a thousand years previously. It was not long, however, before the European artisans had substituted metal wires in place of the bamboo and horsehair, since bamboo was not a commodity readily obtainable in the Occident. Also, in place of the Oriental flexible "laid" mould-cover (Figure 54) which was removable from the mould-frame (Figure 53), the European papermakers adopted the rigid mould (Figures 94, 95) as more suited to the formation of rag fibres into sheets of paper. The Europeans used a fence, or "deckle," to keep the newly formed paper within bounds, just as had been the practice in the East. In transplanting the "laid" type of mould from Asia to Europe, as previously explained, the same

---

Each sheet is dried upon its individual mould as shown in the Tibetan photograph, Figure 151. The citizens of Shari Dzong, a great Tibetan papermaking centre, pay their taxes in paper and every year 12,000 sheets, each sheet measuring 12 square feet, are sent to Lhasa, where its ultimate sale constitutes a considerable source of revenue for the lama. In other papermaking centres of Tibet the sizes of the paper are: Tsöna, 23 by 25 inches; Nyemo paper, made near Toling Tsophuk, 27 by 55 inches; Kongbu, 27 by 42 inches; Takpo, 31 by 36 inches; Gyantse, 31 by 72 inches.

Fig. 94   *The rigid "laid" mould of the Occident. The Oriental design of "laid-" and "chain-lines" will be noted. France, mid nineteenth century.*

type of mould-cover was retained. But the papers of the West were impressed with the "laid-and-chain" marks of metal wires (Figures 96, 97), while the papers of the East had been impressed with the "laid-and-chain" pattern of the bamboo or grass reeds stitched together with animal hair, cotton, or silk. In both the Orient and the Occident there is a vast difference in the number of "laid-lines" to the inch; also there is no uniformity as to the distance between the "chain," or stitched, lines.

In the paper used in printing the Gutenberg Bible (1450–5), there are about 28 "laid-lines" to the inch, while some of the paper used by Gutenberg's successor, Peter Schöffer, has 24 lines to the inch. Moulds that had 32 wires to the inch were in use at the John Tate mill, the first to be established in England, in 1495.*

---

* In so far as is known, the first paper mill in England was set up by John Tate in Hertford near the close of the fifteenth century. Tate's paper was used by the well-known printer Wynkyn de Worde for his first English edition of *Bartholomæus: De proprietatibus rerum,* as appears from these three lines in the volume:

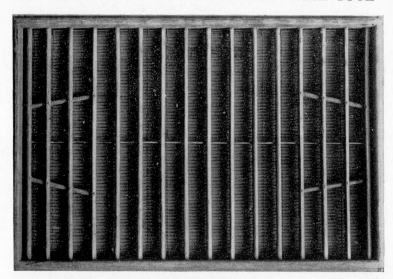

Fig. 95   *The back of the "laid" mould shown in Figure 94. It will
be noticed in this mould that the "chain-lines" do not follow along the
ribs, but this is unusual and probably due to the mould-frame being
re-covered.*

> And John Tate the yonger Ioye mote he broke
> Whiche late hathe in Englonde doo make this paper thynne
> That now in our englyssh this boke is prynted Inne

While this book is not dated, it may be assumed that it appeared in 1496. The
watermark of the Tate mill is an eight-pointed star within two circles, somewhat resembling a cart-wheel. Paper of the same type is also found in the
Golden Legend, printed by de Worde. This work is dated 1498.

John Tate was a mercer in London, the son of John Tate, who was Lord
Mayor in 1473. Tate the younger died in 1507, and his will contains several
references to the paper mill. In the first place he bequeathed to Thomas Bolls
of Hertford "as moche whit paper as shal extende to the summe of xxvi s.
viij d. . . . owte of my paper mill at Hertford." Then he directed his execu-
tors to dispose of the paper mill, "with all the goods, woods, pastures, medes,
with all the commodities concerning said myll to the moost advantage." Finally, in leaving to his eldest son, Robert, all the lands in Hertfordshire and
Essex, the paper mill was excluded: "My paper myll with the appurtenaunces
to be always excepted and to be sold." The John Tate paper mill was evidently shortlived, as there is no evidence of its existence before 1494 or after
1498. The paper fabricated in the Tate mill was remarkably fine, as is at-
tested by Thomas Dibdin, who has the following to say in his *Bibliotheca
Spenceriana:* "The *paper,* press-work and embellishments of the *Bartholomæus* are perhaps unrivalled by the efforts of any other artist in our country
within the period." The Tate mill was no doubt forced to cease operations
because of the strong competition of the papermakers from abroad.

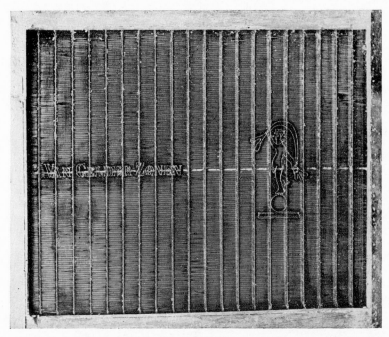

Fig. 96   *The metal "laid" mould of Europe. This type of mould came into use during the twelfth century and was directly patterned after the "laid" transfer mould of China as shown in Figures 51, 52, 55.*

The paper used by Erhart Ratdolt at Augsburg, in 1490–2, shows from 32 to 38 lines to the inch, while the paper printed on by Berthold Ruppel in Basel has but 20. The "chain-lines" or sewing-wires varied greatly also and are found spaced from half an inch to fully two inches apart. From this it will be seen that location or period has little bearing on the number of lines found in old papers, and that therefore there is no possible way of cataloguing or indexing these impressions in paper so that a particular time or place of origin may be determined. Ancient paper, both Oriental and Occidental, must be placed by its general characteristics and not by any list of rules that can be given as infallible.

Metal wire was originally made in Europe by beating the material into thin plates, and then cutting it into strips and rounding them with a hammer. The earliest Occidental moulds must have been made with wires fashioned in this manner, as the first water-

FIG. 97   *A back view of the Van Gelder Zonen mould shown in Figure 96. In this mould the "chain-lines" follow the ribs of the mould in the proper manner.*

mark, dating from about 1282, was no doubt formed of metal and not of bamboo. Wire-making by use of the draw-plate was probably known in Nürnberg early in the fourteenth century; the *History of Augsburg* (1351) and that of Nürnberg (1360) mention the "wiredrawers" (*Drahtzieher*). The draw-plate was imported into France by Richard Archal, and first made its appearance in England in 1565, having been taken to that country by a German workman named Schultz. An English patent by Brockedon, dated 1819, specifies the use of diamonds, rubies, sapphires, and other gems, drilled for draw-eyes and mounted in iron, to be used in the drawing of wire. The draw-plate, made of metal or of hard precious stones, like most other appliances thought to have had their origin in Europe, was without doubt first used in the Orient many centuries before it was conceived in the Occident.

In France a company or guild of wiredrawers existed previous to 1583, and in London there was an incorporated company under the title of "The Art and Mystery of Drawing and Flattening of Wire." [1] The motto of these artisans was *Love draws friendship,* and they had their workshops in Crooked Lane before the alterations in London Bridge. It is thought that iron wire was used first as a mould-covering at the introduction of papermaking into Spain, but the use of brass was centuries old at this time and brass soon took the place of iron as a more suitable metal for the purpose.

In European moulds the wires were permanently fastened to the wooden frames, and in this way differed from the Oriental method of using detached covers. The European moulds were rigid, so that the wet sheets of paper formed thereon were couched in a manner different from the Chinese or Persian fashion. This change constituted, in early centuries as at present, the greatest deviation between Oriental and Occidental methods of operation. In forming sheets of paper in the East the paper stock was kept from flowing over the mould by the use of loose sticks, while in the West the wet fibrous mass was kept within bounds by a fence joined permanently at the corners and placed on the mould when a sheet of paper was to be formed, and removed so that the sheet might be couched. This narrow rim or fence was called a "deckle" and it not only prevented the macerated fibre from flowing over the sides of the mould, but determined the size of the sheet of paper as well. The term "deckle" had its origin in either the German word *"Deckel"* or the old Dutch *"dekfel,"* meaning "cover." As the word was not used in England before the day of John Spilman,* the German who established a paper mill

---

* Of the old papermakers of England, John Spilman is today the best known, this being due to a poem compiled by Thomas Churchyard (1520?– 1604) in 1588, and also to the fact that it is thought Spilman's mill was referred to by Shakespeare in *II King Henry VI, IV,* vii. Spilman was a German, a native of the town of Lindau on Lake Constance, and after moving to England he became one of Queen Elizabeth's goldsmiths. He leased a mill on the Darent in the royal manor of Bicknores at Dartford, Kent, which he converted into a paper mill, known to have been making paper in 1588. Early in the year 1589 Spilman obtained a patent which gave him a monopoly of papermaking and the collecting of rags in the Kingdom. After holding the patent for eight years he surrendered it, and in its place another patent covering a period of fourteen years was given to his mill. This patent embraced the privilege of making white writing paper and paper to be used for other purposes as well. It appears that there were several infringements of Spilman's patent, but they were evidently settled peacefully, as the papermaker-goldsmith was knighted in 1605, upon a visit to the paper mill in Dartford by King James.

in Dartford, Kent, in 1588, he in all probability introduced the term into English paper mills.

Until the latter part of the eighteenth century the "chain" wires had been laced or sewed directly to the wooden ribs, or supports,

---

Shakespeare's reference to a paper mill occurs in a speech of Jack Cade to Lord Say: "Thou hast most traitorously corrupted the youth of the realm in erecting a grammar-school; and whereas, before, our forefathers had no other books but the score and the tally, thou hast caused printing to be used; and, contrary to the king, his crown and dignity, thou hast built a paper-mill." This play was first published in 1594, and it may be that Shakespeare had this mill and its monopoly in mind when he wrote the lines. Jack Cade's rebellion took place in 1450, and certainly Lord Say had nothing whatever to do with paper mills. His son, however, acquired by marriage a property at North Newton, Oxfordshire, and it is known that North Newton mill was at one time used for manufacturing paper; this has led some writers to advance Shakespeare's words as evidence establishing this North Newton mill as the first paper mill in England.

The poem by Thomas Churchyard relative to the John Spilman paper mill first appeared in 1588, under the title of: *A Discription and playne discourse of paper, and the whole benefits that Paper brings, with rehersall, and setting foorth in verse a Paper myll built nere Darthford, by a High Germaine, called Master Spilman, Ieweller to the Queenes Maiestie*. The complete poem consists of 353 lines printed in a quarto volume of fifteen pages, with bordered title-page. While these verses throw no light on the technical history of papermaking, they are, nevertheless, of interest as the first description of the craft to appear in English. The work was prefaced by a dedicatory epistle addressed: "To my honourable friend Sir Walter Raleigh," under the title: "A Sparke of Friendship and Warme Goodwill, etc." The composition is much too long to reprint in its entirety; a few salient verses that deal particularly with the subject of paper will suffice:

> I prayse the man, that first did Paper make,
> the onely thing that sets all vertues forth:
> It shoes new bookes, and keeps old workes awake,
> much more of price than all this world is worth;
> Though partchment duer, a greater time and space,
> yet can it not, put paper out of place:
> For paper still from man to man doth go,
> when partchment comes in few men's hands, you knowe.
>
> Then he that made, for us a Paper mill,
> is worthy well, of love and worldes good will,
> And though his name, be Spillman by degree,
> yet Help-man nowe, he shall be calde by mee.
> Six hundred men, are set a worke by him,
> that else might starve, or seeke abroad their bread,
> Who nowe lives well, and goes full brave and trim,
> and who may boast they are with paper fed.
>
> The hammers thump, and make as lowde a noyse,
> as Fuller doth, that beates his woolen cloth,

FIG. 99   A sheet of "laid" paper showing the "modern" pattern — the elimination of the dark streaks.

FIG. 98   A sheet of "laid" paper showing the "antique" pattern — the dark streaks at either side of the "laid" lines.

of the moulds, which caused the pulp to lie heavier along each side of every "chain-line" in the sheets of paper. European paper made before about 1800 may oftentimes be distinguished by this peculiarity. Paper of this kind is rightly called "antique laid" (Figure 98). Modern papermakers do not use this term correctly, but

In open shewe, then sundry secrete toyes,
makes rotten ragges, to yeelde a thicked froth:
Then is it stampt, and washt as white as snowe,
then flong on frame, and hang'd to dry I trow:
Thus paper streight, it is to write upon,
as it were rubde, and smoothde with slicking stone.

Sir John Spilman's tomb may be seen in the Dartford parish church, Dartford, Kent. The monument consists of two effigies in colour, one of Sir John, who died in November 1626, the other of his wife, Elizabeth, who died in May 1607. The tomb was restored and placed in its present situation in the church before 1876 by the Fraternity of Papermakers.

See "Papermaking in England, 1588–1680," by Rhys Jenkins in the *Library Association Record*, Vol. II, No. 11, November 1900, London; and *Dartford, Some Historical Notes*, by Sidney Kilworth Keyes (Dartford, England, 1933).

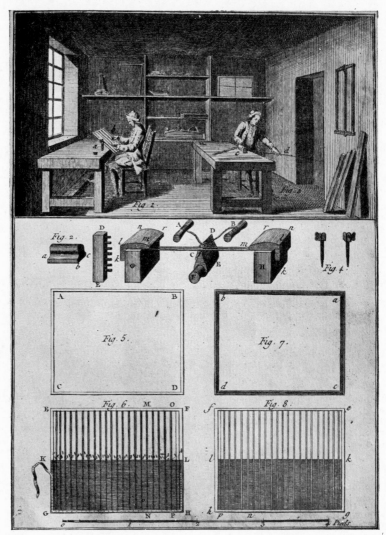

FIG. 100   A paper-mould-maker's shop, showing tools, moulds, and deckle in process of fabrication. (From the work on papermaking by Nicolas Desmarets, 1725–1815, published in Paris, 1744.)

apply it to any rough-surfaced "laid" paper. Old paper with pronounced irregularities in the "laid-lines" is known as "mediæval laid." The heaviness along the ribs or "chain-lines," noticeable in both antique and mediæval "laid" papers, was eliminated by holding the covering away from the ribs of the mould by the use of wires running parallel with, and under, the "laid" wires. This prevented the paper stock from settling at each side of the "chain-lines," a tendency caused by a peculiar suction of the wedge-shaped ribs as the mould was lifted from the vat (Figure 99). Slight variations are found in great varieties in old paper and give some clue as to period and locality. Very few Oriental moulds had rib supports under each "chain-line" and therefore the paper made upon them does not show the peculiar characteristics that are apparent in European "mediæval" or "antique laid" papers.

The mould-making (Figure 100) required great skill, as these implements were constantly in and out of warm water, and if the wooden frames had not been joined properly at the corners, they would soon have warped and become useless. When paper was being made, two moulds and one deckle were required at each vat, so it was essential that the deckle fit each mould perfectly.

The wood used for European mould-making was prepared by cutting the straight-grained, well-seasoned material into narrow boards, free from all knots and blemishes. These boards were boiled in water, again and again, and finally slowly dried. The process was repeated many times before the material was considered ready for use. The finest present-day moulds are composed of at least three varieties of wood, including maple and mahogany, while the old paper-moulds were usually made of but one species — for the most part oak.

When the art of papermaking was introduced into the American colonies in the late seventeenth century, there were no wire-drawers or wireworkers in this country, so that the few moulds required by the pioneer mill were imported from Europe, possibly from Holland. It was not many years, however, before moulds were being fashioned in their entirety in this country. The first American mould-maker, Isaac Langle, was a resident of Germantown, not far distant from the Rittenhouse paper mill. It is not known whether he learned the craft of drawing and weaving wire in Germany, or acquired the trade so that he might supply the Pennsylvania papermakers with the much-needed moulds. In any event, he was making moulds for the Ephrata mill in Lancaster County as early as 1740. Aside from this, little is known of this pioneer craftsman. After Langle's death, in 1744, there appeared an advertisement for the sale of a *Siebmachersweberstuhl mit einen dazu gehörigen eisern Schienen-zug und anders zugehör* (a wire-weaver's frame with an iron apparatus for wire-drawing and other belongings). These were the simple and unpretentious tools that had been used by this early paper-mould-maker in all of his work.

Nathan Sellers, who is usually given the credit of having been the pioneer worker in paper-moulds, did not commence his operations until about 1770. A few years later he abandoned his calling so that he could join the Continental Army, but his work was considered of such importance to the papermakers of the country that he was requested to return home and resume his trade. Sellers was an expert artisan and executed considerable work for the government, many of his moulds being used for forming sheets of paper at the Willcox mill in Pennsylvania, where much of the government paper was fabricated. Many of the tools that had been made and used by Sellers, comprising straightening-boards, wiredrawing blocks of lignum-vitæ wood, wire-plates, and pincers, were in the possession of one of his descendants until his removal to the West in 1841. One of the most important implements employed by wireworkers was a straightening-board. Sellers had fashioned one of these, after his own ideas and inclinations, which embodied the principles of the ones then used in France and England, but much improved; so much so as to have been reinvented and patented in France as late as 1800. The tool consisted of a series of stout wood or metal pins securely fixed in a board; the wire being drawn between this row of pegs was first bent in one direction and then the other, in a waving line, the bends gradually diminishing or shortening until the wire became perfectly straight.

Mark Willcox of Ivy Mills, Chester, Pennsylvania, was obliged to import some moulds from England, and the following bill for them is still preserved:

London, August 2d 1783

Captn Falconer Bot of Peter Wynne	£	s	d
1 Pair Double Fools Cap Paper Moulds	5	5	
1 Pair Double Post *Do*	5		
Box for *Do*		2	
2 fine Brass wire washers 24 Inch by 20			
is 6–8/at 5	1	13	
2 Pieces coarse *Do* for back wires 6.8 at 1.9		11	8
	£ 12	12	0

An original bill from Nathan Sellers for the making of moulds is also in existence, and reads:

Tench Francis Esq. to N^N & D^D Sellers Dr

June 18th 1791

for a fine paper mould for Bank paper with box	£ 4.	10.	0
for 88 watermark letter at 1.10½	8.	5.	0
for 14 *do* figures		15.	0
for 8 *do* private		8.	0

Recd Paymt Oct 5. 1791

N^n & D^d Sellers

The "wove" mould-covering (Figure 101) is thought to have been originated in Europe by John Baskerville (1706–75), and the date of his rediscovery is usually given as about 1750. John Baskerville has long held the honour of having invented and used for the first time in Europe paper of the "wove" type. In late years, however, this distinction tendered the great Birmingham printer has been disputed in favour of the Balston paper mill, Maidstone, Kent, an establishment originally purchased by James Whatman and a Mr. Brookes in the year 1731. In 1759, two years after the Baskerville *Virgil* was issued, the Whatman mill manufactured genuine "wove" paper for a book by Edward Capell entitled: *Prolusions; or Select Pieces of Ancient Poetry*. In this book the "W" of the Whatman watermark has been found; also, in the edition of Æsop printed by Baskerville in 1761 this same watermark appears. In a thorough examination of various copies of the Baskerville *Virgil* of 1757 it has not been possible to discover any watermark whatever, but the paper may have been made in the Whatman mill, as it is now generally accepted that

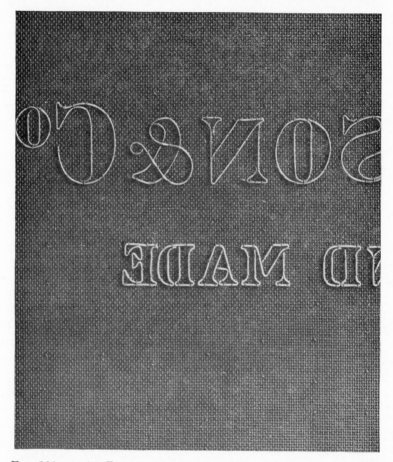

FIG. 101   *A full-size section of a "wove" mould, showing the woven brass wire and the manner in which the watermark letters are sewed to the mould.*

John Baskerville did not operate a paper mill of his own. It was probably Baskerville who suggested the use of woven wire moulds and the paper was actually fabricated in the Whatman mill. The histories of the Whatman mill lay no claim to the invention having taken place in that establishment, but employees of the mill have stated that the credit for the manufacture of the first European "wove" paper should go to the Turkey paper mill (What-

man-Balston), Maidstone, rather than to John Baskerville, the
famed typefounder and printer of Birmingham. Baskerville's effort was to produce paper for his book-printing which would afford a smoother surface than paper of the "laid" pattern, in use
in Europe ever since the introduction of the craft into Spain in
the twelfth century. The "wove" covering was made of fine brass
screening and received its name from being woven on a loom
in about the same manner as cloth. It left in the paper an in-
distinct impression resembling a fabric. Baskerville had been in the
japanning and metal-working trades before becoming a printer,
so that he was naturally familiar with this material, metal screening having been used in England for other purposes a number of
years before it was put to use as a material upon which to form
sheets of paper. While this printer of Birmingham was the first
European to adopt the "wove" type of mould, paper of this kind
had been fabricated in the Orient for many years, the Orientals
having used coarsely woven cloth as a means of retaining the macerated fibre, which, when dry, was paper. The first book to be
printed on European "wove" paper was Baskerville's magnificent
quarto edition of *Publii Virgilii Maronis Bucolica, Georgica, et
Æneis,* which was published in Birmingham in 1757. Another edition of Virgil was issued by the same printer in 1771, under the
earlier date of 1757. It is the first printing of the 1757 edition that
is of interest on account of the paper upon which it was printed.*
The 1757 edition of Virgil immediately created a furor in English
and Continental literary circles and Baskerville received no end
of praise and commendation for his work. The new style of smooth
paper was acclaimed universally. William Shenstone, the noted
English poet, wrote of this work in 1757: "My neighbour, Baskerville, at the close of this month (March, 1757) will publish his
fine edition of Virgil; it will for type and paper be a perfect curiosity." Baskerville's *Virgil* of 1757 was the first European book
in which "wove" paper was used, and as late as 1790 paper of this
kind was common in England. In the copy of *Virgil* before me
there are but 186 of the entire 432 pages on "wove" paper, the re-

---

* The first edition of this work may be distinguished by the fact that the
tenth and eleventh books of the *Æneid* are headed: *Liber Decimus. Æneidos,*
and *Liber Undecimus. Æneidos,* while in the 1771 printing they appear uniform with other titles: *Æneidos Liber Decimus, Æneidos Liber Undecimus.*

maining pages, 246, being on very fine antique "laid" paper. In the first "wove" or *papier vélin* sheets the ribs of the moulds appear distinct and pronounced when the paper is held to the light. This defect was caused by the woven wire mould covering having been sewed directly to the ribs, or supports, of the mould. Perhaps the "wove" cover that was used in making the paper for the *Virgil* had been stretched directly over a mould of the "laid" type. These imperfections appeared in paper until about 1800, when they were eliminated by placing a coarsely woven metal screen under the top "wove" covering. It is not known whether Baskerville made his own paper or had it fabricated in a neighbouring mill. In a letter to Horace Walpole, fourth Earl of Orford (1717–97), written in 1762, Baskerville wrote: "The ink, presses, chases, moulds for casting, and all apparatus for printing were made in my own shops," but he did not state that he possessed any papermaking appliances. From this it may be assumed that he did not operate a paper mill, and it is reasonable to believe that he was kept occupied with typefounding and printing without adding to his labours the making of paper.

In the preface to Baskerville's edition of *Paradise Lost* (1758) the printer expressed his gratification that the "improvement" in the paper which had been used in the *Virgil* in the preceding year had been recognized by the public. "I must own," he wrote, "it gives me great satisfaction to find that my edition of Virgil has been so favourably received. The improvement in the manufacture of the paper, the colour, and firmness of the ink were not overlooked." Although the "wove" paper was acclaimed by Baskerville and the literary public in general, it does not appear that he made exclusive use of paper of this type, for a number of editions appeared after 1757 imprinted upon paper of the old style; even the Baskerville folio Bible of 1769 is printed entirely upon antique "laid" paper.

It was "wove" paper of English fabrication that Benjamin Franklin exhibited in Paris about the year 1777. The novel paper made a favourable impression upon the papermakers and printers of France, and they desired to procure moulds for duplicating this type of paper which did not show any "laid-lines" and which had a smooth surface like a piece of woven silk. In 1779 M. Didot, the noted Parisian printer and publisher, having seen the *papier* *vélin* that Baskerville had used, addressed a letter to M. Johannot of Annonay, a skilled papermaker, asking him to endeavour to duplicate the smooth and even surface of this new paper.* Johannot was successful in his experiments, and for his work in this field he was in 1781 awarded a gold medal by Louis XVI. In 1782 M. Réveillon produced finely executed specimens of "wove" paper, a number of samples of which he presented to the Académie des Sciences, receiving considerable praise for his initial attempts.

The exact date of the introduction of "wove" moulds into America is not known. In a letter written by George Escol Sellers, a grandson of Nathan Sellers, previously referred to, the following is said regarding moulds of this type: "When in England in 1832, William Matthews, son-in-law and successor of Fausett, I think was the name, mentioned some entries of a shipment of both wire for 'laid' and 'woven' wire for vellum moulds, to John Sellers, the father of Nathan, as far back as 1773. They were the only weavers of brass vellum (wove) wire at the time, and the principal mould-makers in England. Their wire works were at Chepstone, on the River Wye."

The first book to be issued in America on "wove" paper in which the paper is mentioned was a small volume of poems, *Elegiac Sonnets and Other Poems* by Charlotte Smith. This volume was published by Isaiah Thomas, printed at Worcester, Massachusetts, in 1795. In a preface to this book dated October 1795, Thomas wrote: ". . . The making of the particular kind of paper on which these Sonnets are printed, is a new business in America; and but lately introduced into Great Britain; it is the first manufactured by the Editor." †

---

* The Johannot mill produced some of the finest "wove" paper of the later eighteenth century, and the portrait watermarks in "wove" paper made by this mill at the beginning of the nineteenth century were the most brilliant of the period. The outlines of the portraits were formed of single wires, but in some instances the "wove" covering was made in two thicknesses, giving a slight density to the background of the picture. As early as 1804 Johannot produced a simple line portrait of "Napoléon Empereur des Français, Roi d'Italie" in "wove" paper. The portraits and arms of "Louis XVIII Roi de France" (1814), and "Marie Caroline" (1817) would even today be considered beautiful examples of artistic watermarking. The original Johannot mill was established in Ambert about 1634, later moving to Annonay.

† This little book of 126 pages measures 5¾ by 3½ inches, and is specified as "the first Worcester edition, from the sixth London edition, with additions. Only the text is printed on *wove* paper which has approximately 30

It is thought that the term "wove" in connection with paper-making was first used in the patent granted to Henry Fourdrinier and dated July 24, 1806 (No. 2951). This specification reads in part: "The method of making a machine for manufacturing paper of an indefinite length, laid and *wove* with separate moulds . . . a number of moulds of the description called laid or *wove*, are hooked or fastened together to form one long mould." This term is again mentioned in the English patent of Léger Didot, dated June 2, 1812 (No. 3568), where the specification begins: "Certain other improvements upon the said machine for making both *wove* and laid paper, etc." The definition given in Rees's *Cyclopædia* (1819) is as follows: "By a modern improvement, these marks ['laid-' and 'chain-lines'] are avoided, and the paper has a smooth, even surface. For this purpose the wire is wove in a loom, exactly like cloth, and stretched over the frame of the mould. . . . The wove paper, as it is called when made on these moulds, is a very superior article to the old paper, particularly for books; but a prejudice still prevails in favour of the old paper with lines, which obliges manufacturers still to make it, though by no means so fine or good as wove."

John Baskerville was born in 1706, in Wolverley, Worcester-shire. In the year 1745 he entered the japanning trade, where a liking for things of a mechanical nature was developed. While still occupied at his first calling, he started in the printing trade and in this work became one of the most renowned craftsmen in the annals of English typography. He cut the punches for his type and did much to elevate type design in England. The books printed by him are known for their neatness, the brilliancy of the ink, and the smoothness of the paper. This he accomplished by placing each printed sheet as it came from the press, while the paper was still damp and the ink undried, between hot plates of polished copper and subjected them to a slight pressure. Baskerville died in 1775, and from his will, which he had written in 1773, it would appear that he had a mill of some kind on his estate in Birmingham, for it directs that his body is "to be buried in a conical building in my own premises heretofore used as a mill, which I have lately raised higher and painted, and in a

wires to the inch. The five engravings used to illustrate the poems are all printed on paper of the traditional *laid* type.

vault which I have prepared for it." It may be that Baskerville carried on the craft of papermaking, as several writers suggest, in the building mentioned in his will, but it is probable that this structure was not of sufficient size for this purpose. According to Thomas Hansard in his *Typographia* (1825), the mill mentioned in the Baskerville will was nothing more than a tomb of masonry in the shape of a cone, under a windmill. Baskerville's house was destroyed in the riots of 1791, but his remains continued undisturbed until 1821, when a canal was cut through the estate and his leaden coffin was exhumed and reburied in a spot that is now a question of debate.

I do not care for "wove" handmade paper for book-printing, unless it be of Oriental origin; the European type lacks character and possesses not nearly the quality and beauty of the original "laid" paper. It is hardly proper to use old-style type in printing a book upon "wove" paper, and it is perhaps an anachronism to mark machine-made paper with "laid-lines," for paper formed on a machine is naturally of the "wove" variety and any "laid-line" watermarking applied by use of a "dandy-roll" is an imitation.

In 1790 John Phipps, an Englishman, patented a method for teaching writing and drawing by means of watermarked lines in paper. The specification is dated August 21, 1790, and reads: "A method to facilitate the acquirement of several of the useful and polite arts by an easy, effectual, and expeditious manner of teaching writing and drawing, which is done by fabricating the moulds, wove or washing wires, or other wire on which sheets of paper are made, so that every sheet shall come out of or from them properly adapted for the purposes, when finished by the maker in the usual manner, by having the lines made and the copies set for writing, and the outlines and sketch for drawing, by what is called the watermark, for the learner to trace over." This absurd method for the teaching of writing and drawing was but little used, and the interest in the novel idea lies chiefly in the fact that this was the first English patent pertaining to moulds for papermaking. The earliest American patent relating to paper-moulds was granted on April 11, 1793 to John Carnes, Jr., of Delaware; the original patent was destroyed by fire in the Patent Office and no record of it is available. The first English patent to deal with the actual making of moulds followed the American patent by about three months, being dated June 27, 1793 and granted to Joseph Moseley Elliot. The abridged description reads: "A machine or engine for working and binding of wire, and making of moulds used by papermakers, and for the more correct and expeditious method of working and binding wire for sieves, screens, etc."

While there are no rules for distinguishing the paper of one century or country from another, it is possible by making a study of the texture and fibre of the paper and of the "laid-" and "chainlines" and the character of their impressions to arrive at the approximate date and determine in what country and under what conditions the paper was made. With European "wove" paper it is not easy to attach a date to the sheets, but paper of this type was usually watermarked with the year in which it was made, and as wire-wove paper of the Baskerville style has been in use only since about 1750, it has not sufficient age to excite much curiosity from a historical point of view. As the first paper made in the Orient was formed on crudely made moulds covered with loosely woven cloth, we must accept the "wove" as the original type of paper. The "laid" bamboo mould came into use a number of years later, and as it was the first style of mould from which a sheet of paper could be taken while wet, this invention must, as I have said, be considered the most important step in the development of Oriental papermaking. Long after the advent of the bamboo "laid" mould came the wire "laid" mould of Europe, first fashioned with iron wire and later with the more durable and non-rusting brass. In the middle of the eighteenth century the *vélin* type of mould was reinvented, but instead of using the woven fabric of the East, from which a moist sheet of paper could not be taken, a woven brass screen was employed which formed a firm and rigid surface. At the close of the eighteenth and the beginning of the nineteenth centuries came inventions for making paper by machine. These inventions used the original idea of the transfer, or Oriental, mould, except that in the machine the mould was continuous, and formed the paper, not in single sheets as by hand, but in any desired length. The great paper industry of today is built upon the original Oriental bamboo mould which came into being almost two thousand years ago.

F<small>IG</small>. 102   *Both of these moulds are of modern make, but the large one is constructed in imitation of an "antique laid" mould, while the small mould, without its deckle, shows the under wires and therefore is of the "modern laid" pattern.*

MODERN HANDMADE PAPER–MOULDS OF EUROPE

The ordinary moulds (Figure 102) in use in commercial handmade paper mills of today are usually made of mahogany, the material being about five twelfths of an inch in thickness and constructed like a very shallow rectangular box, without top or bottom. The corners are joined as shown in (*c*) and (*d*) of Figure

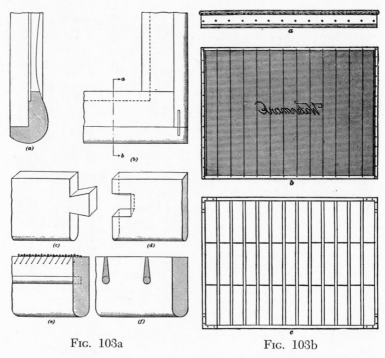

FIG. 103a   FIG. 103b

Construction of a modern papermaking mould and deckle of European type.

103a, the ends dovetailing into each other. The sides that make up the frame are rounded on the under edges, as indicated in (e) and (f) of Figure 103a. The frame is bound at the corners with brass strips screwed to the wood, as shown in Figure 103b (c). Running across this rectangular frame, from one long side to the other, are wooden ribs, the tops of which are flush with the top of the mould, and about one and one-eighth inches apart. The ribs have a wedge-shaped cross-section which causes a suction that acts on the top face of the mould when it is lifted from the vat. The ribs are fastened to the frame of the mould by small, round projections on their ends. These pegs fit into holes bored in the frame. Figure 103a (e) shows a side view of one of these ribs, and Figure 103a (f) shows an end view of two of them. The ribs stand so that their centre lines are perpendicular to the faces of the frame, the wide edge being down. This makes the opening between the ribs smaller at the bottom than at the top; and when the frame is raised vertically upward through the liquid stock, this construction causes more of the liquid to be lifted than flows immediately through the opening, the result being that a partial vacuum is left behind, which causes a slight suction. The ribs are braced by two heavy brass wires running through them lengthwise of the frame (from one short side to the other), as shown in Figure 103b (c).

After the wooden parts of the mould have been completed, with frame, ribs, and fastenings in place, the wire covering is added. This covering may be either "laid" or "wove," since the woodwork is the same in either case. For making a "laid" mould, the first covering added is a series of wires that act as a backing. These backing wires average about nine to the inch. The heavier wires of this backing run the long way of the mould (from left to right as the mould is held in the hands of the papermaker). However, before this backing is added to the wooden frame, it is stitched together with finer wires running in a direction at right angles to that of the heavier wires running lengthwise; and these finer wires are so spaced that each falls directly over one of the wooden ribs. After the backing wires are applied, the "laid" wires are added. These wires are woven in the same manner as the backing, but the "laid," or outside, wires are spaced closer together, averaging about twenty-two to the inch in an ordinary mould. The two coverings, the latter on top of the former, are stitched or sewed to the ribs with fine wire, the ribs being pierced for the purpose, as indicated in Figure 103a (e). The ends of these wires are fastened with small copper nails along the mahogany frame, the entire four edges being bound with a narrow strip of copper, thus securing all of the free ends of the wires. A finished mould is shown in Figure 103b (b). In comparing the European mould "laid" covering (Figures 94, 96, 102) with that of the Orient (Figures 51, 52, 54, 55, 72, 75), the similarity will be noted, as the "laid" brass wire mould of the Occident has been founded and patterned directly on the Oriental "laid" bamboo mould of ancient times.

In a European "wove" mould (Figure 101), the covering is finely woven brass wire, made in the same manner as window screening, only more compact, the average number of wires, both ways, being about fifty-two to the inch. The "wove" covering is applied to the wooden frame of the mould over a backing of coarser woven wire, and is stitched to the ribs of the mould so as to lie flat. It is then tacked and bound with strips of copper in the same manner as the "laid" covering. Along the four edges of the "wove" covering the wire gauze is pierced with holes to help drainage. These holes are about three eighths of an inch apart and placed so that they come under the deckle when it is placed on the mould.

Over the mould, whether it be "laid" or "wove," is fitted a deckle, shown on the larger mould in Figure 102. It is the deckle that determines the size of the sheet to be made on the mould, but it has little to do with the thickness of the sheet of paper. In commercial papermaking by hand there must be two moulds and one deckle for every size of sheet that is to be moulded. The deckle, or fence, must fit each mould equally well and should slip on and off easily. A sectional view of the deckle, taken on the line *ab*, is shown in Figure 103a (*a*). Figure 103a (*b*) shows a corner of the deckle as viewed from underneath; that is, when looking at the side which lies next to the mould.

The making of moulds and deckles for commercial handmade paper mills is extremely difficult work; it requires not only great skill, but also a good knowledge of materials. The wood must be seasoned with care, since it has to withstand the constant strain of being in and out of warm water, as I have said before. There are no firms in America making wood moulds for handmade paper, but in England there are several artisans engaged in work of this kind.

More than 240 different sizes of paper are manufactured at the present time. Handmade paper can be formed in any desired size, depending upon the dimensions of the moulds. The best-known sizes of European papers are the following:

> *Antiquarian,* 31 by 53 inches. The largest paper made by hand in Europe, manufactured only by the James Whatman mill, Maidstone, Kent, England. The paper is used for drawing and for printing large books, maps, etc.
>
> *Atlas,* 26 by 34. Drawing and printing paper originally made for

maps and atlases printed from engraved plates and coloured by hand.

Billet Note, 6 by 8. An old-style size of correspondence paper.

Colombier, 23½ by 34½. A writing and drawing paper originally watermarked with a dove, the emblem of the Holy Spirit. The dove watermark was common in American papermaking during the eighteenth and early nineteenth centuries. It was extensively used by the Pennsylvania papermakers.

Crown, 15 by 20. A standard size of printing paper watermarked with a regal crown. Papers are also known by Half Crown, Double Crown, Extra Double Crown, etc. C. M. Briquet in his four-volume work *Les Filigranes* (1907) depicts more than 275 different versions of the crown watermark in use previous to A.D. 1600.

Demy, 17½ by 22½ printing paper; 15½ by 20 writing paper and drawing paper. The term demy is from the French *demi,* half.

Elephant, 23 by 28. Also Double Elephant, a plate printing and drawing paper measuring 26¾ by 40 inches. This paper was originally watermarked with a crudely executed figure of an elephant.

Emperor, 48 by 72 inches. The largest paper ever to be made by hand in Europe. (See: *Antiquarian*) The Chinese have made paper in a hand-mould measuring 48 by 84 inches.

Foolscap, 13½ by 17 printing paper; 13¼ by 16½ writing paper. The name is taken from the ancient watermarked emblem of a court jester and dates from the middle of the fifteenth century. In England the foolscap watermark was replaced by the figure of Britannia.

Grand Eagle, 28¾ by 42. A standard size of drawing paper. The term was taken from an ancient watermark of the eagle dating as early as the beginning of the fourteenth century.

Hand, 16 by 22 Middle-hand; 20 by 25 Royal-hand. The ancient hand watermark has ceased to denote a special size, but was originally derived from the watermark of a hand or glove. Briquet pictures upward of one thousand different hand devices used by European papermakers previous to the year 1600.

Imperial, 22 by 30 writing and printing paper. Also Double Imperial, Large Imperial, Small Half Imperial, etc.

Post, 14¼ by 19 writing paper; 15½ by 19¼ printing paper. The watermark was derived from the ancient emblem of the post-horn. The horn watermark dates from the fourteenth century and was used by Pennsylvania papermakers in the eighteenth century.

Pott, 12½ by 15½ with slight variations. The name was originally derived from an emblem representing the Sangraal, a pot or chalice thought to have been divided into different compartments for holding food or drink. Briquet illustrates almost one thousand variations of the pott watermark previous to the year 1600, the earliest being from 1322.

Royal, 19 by 24 writing paper; 20 by 25 printing paper. Also Double Royal, Half Royal, Super Royal, Extra Royal, etc. Formerly watermarked with an ornamental shield surmounted by a fleur-de-lis.

V

The Maceration of Materials for
Papermaking

FROM THE PRIMITIVE MORTAR AND PESTLE OF
ANCIENT CHINA TO THE IMPROVED
HOLLANDER OF EUROPE

THE EARLIEST papermakers, the Chinese, may at first have used silk, both raw and woven, as material for their paper; in later years mulberry bark, hemp, bamboo, and other fibres were used. Certainly it is significant that the two prominent Chinese characters, of ancient origin, denoting "paper" embody the meanings of both silk and cloth. In the most common character for "paper" (紙, *chih*), we find radical 120 (糸), of six strokes, meaning "silk." The other, less common character for "paper" (帋) embodies the radical 50 (巾), of three strokes, meaning "napkin" or "cloth." The remaining parts of these two characters are made up of radical 83 (氏), of four strokes, meaning a surname.[1]

The original Chinese method of beating or macerating the cloth or bark to a pulp was by placing the material, with water, in stone mortars and pounding the mass to fibres by means of pestles, or mallets, operated by hand (Figure 104).

The Arabs learned the craft of papermaking, A.D. 751, from Chinese prisoners in Samarkand. In their own country the Chinese at this date used the bark of mulberry trees for their paper, but, this material not being readily available in Samarkand, the Arabs employed linen as a substitute.

The Arabs probably disintegrated linen rags by placing them in heaps, saturating them with water, and allowing a fermentation

FIG. 104   *The original Chinese method of beating the fragments of cloth or bark to a pulp was by placing the material, with water, in mortars and pounding the mass to fibre by means of pestles, or mallets, operated by hand. (Photograph by Springer Pictures, Inc. for the moving picture made for the Kenwood Felt Company)*

to take place, then boiling the mass in wood ashes. The boiled rags were then placed in cloth bags and suspended in a running stream, the action of which removed a great part of the alkaline residue and much of the dirt (Figure 105). The original method of beating the cleansed rags to a pulp was doubtless an imitation of the Chinese manner, but later in the development of papermaking by both the Chinese and the Arabs a trip-hammer was put into use. The workers treading upon the end of the horizontal tilt-bar of this implement caused the hammer to fall heavily upon the substance to be beaten (Figures 110, 111, 114). This required far less labour than the mortar and pestle of the ancient Chinese, yet for hundreds of years after the improved method of maceration had been invented by the Arabs and adopted in various parts of Asia, the hand beating of the bark for papermaking was em-

FIG. 105   *The macerated rags were placed in cloth bags and sus-*
pended in a running stream, the action of which removed the alkaline
residue and much of the dirt.

ployed in China and Japan. The cleansed bark was wetted, laid
on a heavy stone, and pounded with wooden clubs or mallets. To
this day many of the more remote handmade-paper mills in China,
Korea, Siam, and Japan (Figures 106, 107, 108, 109, 115, 116, 117)
employ this centuries-old method of reducing the barks to usable
fibre. In the paper-villages of Tonkin, Indo-China, some of the
workers in paper are using at the present time the old mortar
with pestle wielded by hand, the most ancient Chinese method
(Figure 112). The raw material of Indo-China is mulberry and
bamboo, which after being boiled in lime may be readily beaten
in this manner (Figure 113). The ancient Samarkand method of
beating is still in use in many of the modern handmade-paper
mills of India. The native papermakers of India use as their raw
materials jute, discarded gunny sacks, and old papers. These substances are cut to bits, and placed in stone or wooden troughs,
where the material is allowed to soak in lime for a period of sev-

FIG. 106   *The beating of bark for papermaking as depicted by Hokusai (1760–1849), the renowned Japanese wood-block artist. Three wooden boards with paper drying upon them are shown in the background of the print.*

eral days. After this mildly disintegrating process has been completed, the material is thrown into rough stone mortars sunk in the ground, where it is beaten by heavy pestles, like huge hammers, balanced on pivots. Men and boys stand on the long horizontal beams, letting the hammers fall upon the jute or other material over and over again until the substance is beaten to a pulp suitable for forming into sheets of paper (Figures 118, 119, 120).

Fɪɢ. 107   *The two wooden mallets in the centre of the photograph were used in Japan in the beating of bark for papermaking. The other objects include a small knife and wooden block used in separating the inner from the outer bark; a paper-trimming knife, and a brush used in applying the moist paper to the drying-boards. These tools are from the great papermaking centre of Gifu, Japan.*

This process is practically identical with that of Samarkand in use a thousand years ago. In several of the old papermaking villages in central Korea and southern India there remain remnants of a former method of beating by means of stone rolls that had been actuated by animal power. Owing to the scarcity of grass and food for the beasts, however, this method of macerating papermaking material in both Korea and India has long since given way to manual labour (Figures 121, 122, 123).

In the present-day handmade paper mills of Japan the beating is carried on in some of the larger establishments with modern equipment, but in many of the smaller mills this work is performed in a most primitive manner, by action of hand-wielded mallets. In the government mill, Tōkyō, where the superb "vellum" papers are made, the barks of the mitsumata, mulberry, and gampi undergo careful cleaning processes, all done by hand in the most painstaking manner (Figure 124); the barks are finally boiled in cauldrons that suggest the appliances of past generations (Fig-

FIG. 108   Mrs. Piung Niltongkum preparing the bark of the khoi
(Streblus asper) for the hand beating process. Since this photograph
was made, in Bangsoom, southern
Siam, the old lady has died and
the daughter (Figure 109) has
ceased making paper, a family
craft for many past generations.

FIG. 109   The beating of the
inner bark of the khoi tree of Siam
is done by pounding the material
with a wooden mallet as the moistened bark is spread upon a heavy
plank or stone. Several of the long,
narrow "wove" moulds may be
seen behind Luolin Niltongkum,
the young lady who is doing the
beating.

FIG. 110   Maceration of papermaking material in China, by
means of the trip-hammer actuated by foot power. (From Arts,
métiers et cultures de la Chine,
Paris, 1814.)

FIG. 111   The interior of a
Chinese paper mill, showing at
extreme right the huge hammer
employed in the maceration of
papermaking materials.

Fig. 112   *The most ancient method of beating paper stock, as prac-tised at the present time in the Paper Villages, near Hanoi, Tonkin, Indo-China.*

ure 125). In my visits to the Imperial paper mill I was amazed to see the dilapidated condition of the buildings and the muddy, unkempt surroundings of the premises. Few of the glass windows in the buildings remained intact and the entire structure gave the appearance of poverty and lassitude. To somewhat lesser degree the same could be said of the Imperial printing office, where the exquisitely watermarked paper from the Imperial mill is printed in the most elaborate and delicate engraving on American-built presses. The Japanese paper money is the most difficult to counter-feit of any currency issued in the world, owing more, perhaps, to the paper than to the fine engraving. In talking to a boastful di-rector of one of the large paper mills of Japan I was given to under-stand that Japanese artisans could duplicate the United States paper money with ease, but, much to my informant's delight, I was told that no government of the Western world could successfully imitate the Japanese money. This is not only due to the fine water-

FIG. 113   *Preparing the bark preliminary to beating in the pictur-esque papermaking centre near Hanoi, Tonkin, Indo-China. For more than five hundred years paper has been made along the muddy high-ways of Tonkin and Annam villages.*

marking, but to the fact that certain Oriental fibres are not gen-erally available in the Occident, at least not on a scale sufficiently abundant for papermaking.

Upon completion of my last journey in Japan, after I had in-spected several hundred handmade and machine paper mills, and I was leaving for Korea and Manchuria, my kind friends the Japa-nese papermakers arranged a banquet in my honour. I learned that my companions were considering the purchase of an elaborate gift that was to be presented to me on the night of the final dinner.

Fig. 114   *The "improved" stamper of Indo-China. The men operate the stamper by treading on the tilt-bar. Tonkin, northern Indo-China.*

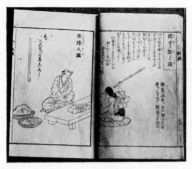

FIG. 115   Beating papermaking materials in Japan. From the eighteenth-century work by Kunihigashi.

FIG. 116   Beating bark by the ancient hand process. This method of maceration is fast dying in Japan and may be seen in only a few localities. Shigarami village, Japan.

FIG. 117   The beating of mulberry bark in Taikyū, Korea. The long wooden beaters differ from those of China, Indo-China, Siam, and Japan.

Fig. 118   *In India, as in China and Indo-China, the paper stock is reduced to pulp by means of a heavy hammer actuated by a man treading on the tilt-bar. Wardha, central India.*

I was naturally reluctant to accept anything that might be expensive and cause these good people any hardship, as even in 1935 they were complaining about inflation and the excessive cost of living. I suggested that they give me something readily procurable and inexpensive — for instance, some seeds of the mitsumata and gampi plants. This they cheerfully agreed to do. When the rather tiring banquet was at last over and the guests were about to depart, I was ceremoniously presented with a finely made box fitted with two compartments: one side held a number of ounces of the coveted mitsumata seeds and the opposite space was filled with the seeds of the gampi. In all innocence I accepted the token of friendship and told my hosts that I would plant the seeds in my own garden in America. Little did I suspect on that last evening of my visit in beautiful Japan that my kind and obliging Japanese friends had caused every seed that had been given to me to be boiled until all possibility of germination had been destroyed!

The more experienced papermakers of Japan were of the opinion

Fig. 119   *A scale model of a water-power stamping-mill in operation in northern Kashmir, India. The first paper mills of Europe employed stampers modelled after the mills of the Far East. Paper Museum of the Massachusetts Institute of Technology.*

that the fibres beaten by the hand mallets made better paper than those macerated in the "Hollander" type of beater. This is no doubt true as the hand beating draws out the fibres, leaving them long, strong, and tenacious. To emulate this hand beating the Japanese constructed mechanically operated stampers that very closely duplicate the hand action. In Figures 126 and 127 two types of such a machine are shown, and to a great extent the material reduced to fibre in this manner is superior to that produced in a regulation power beater. The Japanese were adverse to show these machines and I had no little difficulty in procuring the two photographs. For the most part, the large handmade paper mills of Japan are equipped with small beaters of the European style (Figures 128, 129).

When papermaking was first introduced into Europe, the meth-

FIG. 121 *An improvised Hollander for hand operation, modelled after a regulation beater of the Occidental type. This machine was constructed by the students in Mohandas Karamchand Gandhi's school of papermaking, Wardha, Central Provinces, India.*

FIG. 120 *The wooden undershot water-wheel of a pulp mill near Srinagar, Kashmir. Paper has been made for hundreds of years in this locality. This is the same type of water-wheel as shown in Figure 119.*

FIG. 122 *Stone roll and circular trough formerly used in Korea for the maceration of papermaking materials. The power was supplied by a pony, but owing to the lack of food for the beast this method of beating was abandoned a number of years ago. The paper-village of Ompei, north of Seoul, Korea.*

FIG. 123 *A stone roll, actuated by animal power, formerly used in southern India for the maceration of jute and hemp papermaking material. A number of these old stone rolls remain, but they are no longer used. This particular specimen is in the papermaking village of Kagaziguda, near Secunderbad, Hyderabad.*

FIG. 124   *Japanese girls picking the specks and foreign matter from the bark after boiling, preliminary to the beating process. In the Imperial paper mill, near Tō-kyō, Japan.*

FIG. 125   *The barks of the mulberry, mitsumata, and gampi must undergo a slight boiling, or cooking, before they are ready for beating. After the cooking process the bark is freed of specks as shown in Figure 124. This photograph was made in one of the largest handmade paper mills of Japan.*

FIG. 126   *A mechanical beating equipment used in Japan that emulates the old hand method of macerating the mulberry, mitsumata, and gampi barks. This machine is less efficient than the more modern set of stampers shown in Figure 127.*

FIG. 127   *In Japan the handmade papermakers have endeavoured to duplicate the superior qualities of hand beating by mechanical means. This mediæval-appearing contrivance, based on the ancient principle of stampers, is thorough and efficient.*

FIG. 128   *Small   Hollanders
such as used in the large and efficient handmade paper mills of
Japan. It is only in the "company"
mills that equipment of this modern kind is employed. In many of
the small "cottage" mills the material is beaten by hand.*

FIG. 129   *In Japan, the pulp,
or stock, does not flow to the vats,
but it is formed into balls and
placed in the vats by hand, each
ball representing a certain number
of sheets of paper. This is the
practice in even the largest mills
where paper is made by hand.*

ods of the East were no doubt used for the maceration of the pulp.
It did not take the Europeans long, however, to devise a better
method of beating, for about 1151 there was invented at Xátiva
(now Játiva or St. Felipe de Játiva), an ancient city of Valencia,
Spain, a stamping-mill operated by water-power. At that period
linen and cotton were used as material for making paper. For the
preliminary treatment well-worn cloth was wetted and pressed
into balls, which were left in piles for six weeks or two months,
being kept moist. This caused a fermentation, manifested by the
increased temperature of the mass, the rags assuming a peculiar
colour, not unlike that of the dregs of wine. This method of preparation was wasteful in the extreme, as fully one third of the
material was rotted beyond use; but the portion suited for paper
was tender and easily beaten, so that the action of the newly
invented stamping-mills had immediate effect upon the disintegrated rags.

During the first centuries of papermaking in Europe the demand for paper was slight, but after the advent of printing from
movable types in the middle of the fifteenth century the demand
became greater, and by the close of the century the art of papermaking on the Continent had assumed considerable proportions
and had spread to many places where the craft had not hitherto

been practised. During this period linen was used in wastefully large quantities, as there was considerable loss of the material during the fermenting process and also in the actual stamping of the rags into fibre. In the fifteenth century in Europe there was not of course the great variety of cloth that there is at present, so that the sorting of the rags was not a difficult problem as it is today. The linen and cotton fabrics of that period were naturally all woven by hand and, being free from chemicals and bleaching agents, were ideal materials from which to fabricate paper. Linen of the whitest kind was desired, but cotton was not rejected. When materials of different weights and substances were used, they were, in the best mills, pounded or stamped separately and mixed after beating, for without this precaution much of the fibre would have been lost, the finer particles escaping with the water during the lengthy process of reducing the tougher and coarser fabrics.

In the mills of less importance, where the rags were fewer, they were left to decompose for longer periods as the heaps, being smaller, did not heat so rapidly. The length of time for this process also depended upon the quality of the rags; the finest linen did not break down so quickly as the coarse, and linen that had been worn as clothing required more time than new material, because the internal humidity that disposed the fibres to fermentation was more considerable in new or coarse than in worn or fine linen. When slight traces of fungi appeared on the heaps or piles of rags it was considered that the process was well under way.* In some

---

* It is possible that the treatment of the rags has caused much of the "foxing" prevalent in books from the beginning of the sixteenth century on to about the middle of the nineteenth century. The descriptive term "foxing" was probably applied to the reddish-brown spots in paper on account of the resemblance to the rusty-brown coat of the fox. According to Iiams and Beckwith writing in the *Library Quarterly* under the title of "Notes on the Causes and Prevention of 'Foxing' in Books," (October 1935, Volume V, No. 4, pages 407–18): ". . . One seldom finds examples of 'foxing' in incunabula, or books printed before 1501. On the other hand, very often titles issued from the Baskerville press during the third quarter of the eighteenth century show signs of discoloration." The European papers of the fifteenth and previous centuries give evidence that the papermakers exercised extreme care in the preparation of the rags, but after this period, when printing became more general, the demand for paper increased tremendously and to speed the process the makers of paper were forced to hurry the treatment of the material. They did not use sufficient water or allow enough time for the proper cleansing of the fibres. There is opportunity for study of the cause and prevention of "foxing," so disfiguring in the papers of many valuable books.

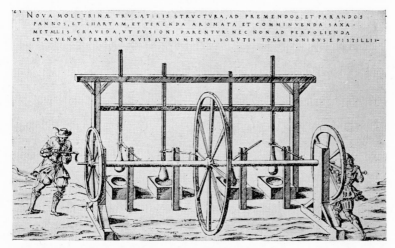

NOVA MOLETRINÆ TRVSATILIS STRVCTVRA, AD PREMENDOS ET PARANDOS
PANNOS, ET CHARTAM, ET TERENDA AROMATA ET COMMINVENDA SAXA
METALLIS GRAVIDA, VT FVSIONI PARENTVR NEC NON AD PERPOLIENDA
ET ACVENDA FERRI QVÆVIS INTRVMENTA, SOLVTIS TOLLENONIBVS E PISTILLIS

Fig. 130   *The earliest European delineation of macerating material
for making into paper.* (*From* Théâtre des instruments mathématiques
et mécaniques, by *Jacques Besson, Lyon, 1579.*)

mills lime was thrown upon the rags to assist in the disintegration,
but this was detrimental to the material, and paper made from material so treated was never so strong or lasting as that which had
been allowed to ferment naturally. In the eighteenth century the
use of lime was absolutely prohibited in France. After the fermentation process the rags were washed and rubbed by hand, for during the fermentation the material acquired a saddened yellow
tone which the workers endeavoured to eliminate. This step was
accomplished only with difficulty; in fact, most of the paper from
the early mills shows a pleasing creamy tint, to a great extent the
result of the fermenting process.

After the cloth had been reduced to a broken and flaccid state
by the mild form of disintegration and had been at least partially
cleansed by washing, it was ready to be triturated into pulp for
forming the actual sheets of paper. The stamping-mills that were
originated in Spain consisted of rows of great wooden hammers,
or mallets, which were caused to rise and fall by means of a series
of cams on a stout axis or axle (Figure 130). These hammers, or
pestles, operated up and down in troughs into which the rags were
thrown; the troughs or "vat-holes," as they were termed, were

Fig. 131   A section of an early European stamping-mill for the beating of papermaking material. The stampers are of wood, the vat of stone.

Fig. 132   In the old European stamping-mills the water was usually filtered through a series of large wooden reservoirs, each having an opening fitted with bars or screens which eliminated much of the foreign matter from the water. (From the Universal Magazine, London, May 1762.)

Fig. 133   A set of ancient stampers in an old paper mill in Annonay, Ardèche, France, no longer in operation. The heavy oak stampers are shod with metal and their action produces long, drawn-out fibre which makes strong and enduring paper.

Fig. 134   An old German mill showing the stampers. This equipment was originally in a paper mill in Haynsburg, founded 1700, and continued in operation until 1909. The appliances were then removed to the Deutsches Museum, München, but have now been destroyed.

fashioned from great blocks of stone or from logs of the oak tree, the wooden cavities being lined with iron or lead (Figures 131, 132, 133, 134). These early European mills were actuated by water-power, which differentiated them from many mills of the Orient, where the beating had for the most part been accomplished by the power of man. While European workmen received from the Oriental artisans the principles of papermaking, it was not long before they had put to use their own methods in the entire operation — the rigid, metal-covered mould was devised, a better and less laborious process of beating was adopted, and streams and rivers were put to work to turn their paper mills. Yet after these innovations were brought into use the craft experienced but few changes over a period of several hundred years; in the fifteenth and sixteenth centuries European paper was made very much as it had been in the twelfth.

Toward the seventeenth century the mills did show slight changes, but the principle of the *modus operandi* remained unaltered. At this period the stampers were constructed on a larger scale and were a little more developed in their capacity, the stamps being divided into three classes. The first set of stampers or pestles were shod with rough iron teeth or spikes, which frayed the cloth while a stream of pure water ran into each stone or wooden trough and cleansed the rags, the discarded dirty water flowing off through holes in the sides of the receptacles, over which was placed woven horsehair screening to prevent the escape of any material that had already been beaten to fine fibre. This procedure replaced the more laborious method of hand washing used at the inception of papermaking in Europe. When the rags were partially cleansed and somewhat mangled, they were bailed out of the first set of troughs and placed under the next set of stamps, which were less heavily shod. In the second operation the stream of pure water was continued to complete the washing process. The fresh water was supplied through a wooden leader to each trough or vat-hole, either by gravity from a mountain spring or from the stream that furnished the locomotion for the stampers. The water was usually filtered through a series of large wooden reservoirs, each having an opening covered with iron bars placed closely together, which eliminated the gravel and the larger particles of dirt and vegetable matter from the water (Figure 132). The final treatment of the partly beaten rags, or half-stuff, was given by the third and last set of stampers, which were usually made of plain wood, without iron or steel facing. At this stage running water was excluded, for by this time the rags had become so macerated that much of the fibre would have been lost through the strainers or washing screens.

Fig. 136   The   European
stampers as depicted in the work
by Georg Andreæ Böckler (Nürnberg, 1662).

Fig. 135   The original stampers of Europe, patterned after
those of Asia. (From the book on
machinery by Vittorio Zonca,
Padua, 1607.)

It is recorded that Ulman Stromer, who established a paper mill
in Nürnberg about 1390, "employed two rollers (axes) which set
eighteen stampers in motion." [2] In an illustration in the Italian
book on machinery by Vittorio Zonca,[3] printed in Padua in 1607,
the engraver depicts for the first time a set of these water-driven
stampers (Figure 135). In this engraving there are eight stampers
to one receptacle, while in the volume by Georg Andreæ Böckler,[4]
published in Germany and dated 1662, three stampers are shown
to each trough (Figure 136). According to the three-volume work
by Sung Ying-hsing,[5] this same type of power stamper (Figure
137) was in use in China for other purposes than papermaking as
early as 1634, when the book was issued. The Chinese probably
used the machine previous to this date; perhaps they were the first
artisans to employ this mode of beating and the Europeans de-

水碓

盖利
用茅

FIG. 137　　*A mill for stamping grain as shown in the Chinese book* T'ien kung k'ai wu, *by Sung Ying-hsing, published in 1634. This mill employs the same principle as used in the early paper mills of Europe.*

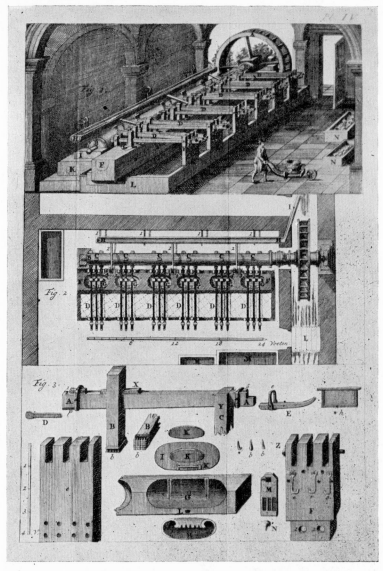

FIG. 138   *A French stamping-mill as pictured in the well-known work* Art de faire le papier, *compiled by Joseph Jérôme Le Français de Lalande (Paris, 1761).*

veloped the stampers for papermaking purposes from the Chinese machine. It is not possible to answer this question, but we do know that a water-power stamping-machine was first delineated in the Orient in 1634 and in the Occident in 1607. The Chinese stampers show four sets of cams and pounders. According to illustrations in the work by Leonhardt Christoph Sturm,[6] published in 1718, there were in Europe at that time five sets of stampers to each stone or wooden trough and four troughs at each side of one axis, the axis and its cams actuating forty separate stamps, and one water-wheel turning the entire apparatus. The stamping-mills were slowly developed from the crude and cumbersome machine such as Zonca pictured, until a good German mill had as many as twenty-five troughs with four individual stampers to each trough, while French machines had from three to five stampers to each receptacle (Figure 138).* These stamping-mills were used for the

---

* In England during the latter part of the seventeenth century four patents were issued pertaining to the maceration of papermaking materials:

A.D. 1682 to Nathaniell Bladen, of Inner Temple, London. "An Engine, Method, and Mill, whereby Hempe, Flax, Lynnen, Cotton, Cordage, Silke, Woolen, and all Sorts of Materiall whereof all manner Pasteboard and of Paper for Writing, Printing, and for all other Sorts of Uses, hath been or may be made, are Prepared and Wrought into Paper and Pasteboard much Speedier and Cheaper than by the Mills now used, being a New Invencon, never yett Practiced in any of our Kingdoms or Dominions, and of great Advantage to all our loveing Subjects."

A.D. 1684 to Christopher Jackson, of Rither, in our County of Kent. "A Mill or Engine, either for Wind or Water, which dissolueth, Whiteneth, and Grindeth Raggs, and Prepareth all other Materialls whereof Paper and Pasteboard hath been or may be made, in farr less Tyme than the Mills hitherto in use do."

A.D. 1691 to John Tizack, of Wapping, in our County of Middlesex. "A Way by an Engine to be worked by one or more Men for the well and more easy pounding and brusing of raggs fitt to make paper, which said engine has never been used in England before."

A.D. 1692 to Thomas Hutton. "A New Way of Makeing Paper in Great Quantities and with less Charge and Labour and more Advantage than ever hath been yett practiced in England or elsewhere, by a Mill or Engine to be Driven either by Winde, Sailes, or Water Wheeles, and to worke Eighty or more Stampers at once, different from all other Mills now used. . . ."

The specifications of these four patents are meagre, so that it is not possible to determine the type of "engine" designated, but it may be supposed the inventions did not embody any of the principles of the "Hollander."

In 1696 the beating of papermaking materials is mentioned in an English book for the first time: in a book on machinery by Venturi Mandey, published in London under the title *Mechanick Powers; or, the Mystery of Nature and*

maceration of rags by the early American papermakers, but their use was discontinued in this country a number of years before they were entirely abandoned in Europe. The Willcox mill of Pennsylvania was not established until 1729, but it is recorded that its first method of reducing rags to pulp was by the use of a stamping-mill.[7] This was the third paper mill set up in America. It is not known when the stampers were discarded in this country, but it is thought that they remained in use until about the year 1780. With the use of these old machines the fibres of the cloth were slowly drawn out, almost to full length, which is one of the reasons the papers of the stamping-mill period show such remarkable strength and endurance. By making a study of old paper it is possible to tell by the peculiarities of the fibres in what manner they were reduced to pulp. The stampers did not cut or lacerate the delicate fibres; the action of these machines was rather to rub and fray the material.

The papermakers of Holland with their windmills found it difficult to compete with the mills of Germany, where there was plenty of water-power. The ingenious Dutch therefore tried to devise a method of macerating rags that would require less power than the stamping-mills and at the same time be more productive than the ancient method. In the latter part of the seventeenth century a Dutchman, whose name has been lost to posterity, conceived the idea of the cylinder beater for reducing rags to fibres suitable for the making of paper. This machine is known to this day as the "Hollander," after the country of its invention. It consisted of an oblong wooden tub, rounded at both ends, in which revolved a solid wooden roll made from the trunk of a tree and fitted with about thirty iron knives. The linen and cotton rags circulated around the tub and were lacerated by the action of the metal bars of the roll revolving over a metal or stone bed-plate set in the bottom of the tub directly under the roll. The material was kept in constant motion by the impetus given by a backfall and by the rotation of the roll. With the invention of the Hollander the

---

Art Unvail'd. The paragraph (page 71) reads: "Also Engines to make Paper, in which a wooden Cylinder of sufficient magnitude standing out, furnisht with little troughs, takes up wooden Mallotts, which bruise and break whatever is laid under them to powder." No illustrations of stampers were given in any English books of the seventeenth century except the small, somewhat obscure woodcut in the *Visible World* (London, 1658).

putrefaction of the rags ceased in some mills, the cloth being washed and beaten without preliminary treatment.

The Hollander was naturally first used in the country of its origin, but it is known that the invention was in use in Germany as early as 1710.* In 1725 the papermaker Keferstein in Saxony wrote: "The Hollander in Freiburg furnishes in one day as much pulp as eight stamper-holes do in eight days." Even after the introduction of the Dutch beating-engine many mills in Germany and France, as well as in Italy, retained the old stampers for the breaking of rags, and employed the Hollanders to complete the beating. In 1716 one of the largest paper mills in Germany operated twenty-five sets of stampers, of four each, which supplied three dipping-vats with paper stock. This same mill in 1777 had thirteen sets of stampers and three Hollanders, which macerated sufficient stock for workmen to make paper from four dipping-vats. In 1829 this mill reduced the number of stampers to eight sets and increased the Hollanders to four. This equipment furnished the beaten stock to the same four vats. As early as 1760 one of the largest paper mills in France had discarded the stampers altogether, but operated twelve of the Dutch beaters, which supplied the beaten fibre for forming the sheets of paper from twenty vats. A mill of this magnitude would have had a capacity of about seventy-five reams of finished paper a day.

The first paper mill in central Massachusetts was established by Abijah Burbank in 1775 and was considered at the time one of the best-equipped mills in this country. This establishment operated two Hollanders, with rolls two feet in length and twenty-six inches in diameter, which produced the required amount of stock for two vats. A mill of this size would have had a capacity of from four to five thousand sheets of demy paper a day.

The earliest volume to mention the Dutch invention of the Hollander was a small book by Johann Joachim Becher,† a German

---

* According to Dr. Hans Bockwitz in *Zur Kulturgeschichte des Papiers* (1939), the earliest use of the Hollander, or beater, in Bavaria was in 1712. It is stated that one Hollander was capable of preparing the same amount of material in five or six hours as could have been macerated in the old-style stampers of five vat-holes in twenty-four hours.

† The date of the invention and the first use of the Hollander, or beater, was thought to have been about 1710 until the discovery of this small volume, published in Frankfurt in 1682 under the title: *Närrische Weissheit und Weise Narrheit: oder Ein Hundert so Politische als Physicalische, Mechani-*

writer on mechanics. This book was issued in 1682. Dr. Becher writes (page 66): "One does not know who conceived the art of papermaking, but it is a fine and wonderful invention. In the ordinary method the rags are beaten with many stampers and much rattling. I have seen, however, a new kind of paper mill, in Serndamm in Holland, which operates, not with the crude stampers, but by the use of a Roll, and within a short time and without difficulty the rags are macerated to a pulp."

The earliest engraving of the Dutch beating-engine (Figure 140) is shown in the book by Leonhardt Christoph Sturm * dealing with mill machinery which was printed in Augsburg in 1718, the title being *Vollständige Mühlen Baukunst*. In this volume one of the engravings shows the Hollanders placed in a circle, so that four or five of the machines could have been actuated by one huge wooden cog-wheel, which in turn was operated by a windmill or

---

sche und Mercantilische Concepten und Propositionen. The description given by Becher is definitely that of the newly invented beater, so it may be assumed that this machine was in use in Holland some time previous to Becher's visit. A second edition of this book appeared in 1706 and in this edition the same passage relative to the Serndamm machine may be found on page 69; another edition was issued in 1725.

Dr. Johann Joachim Becher was born in Speyer in 1635, the son of a Lutheran minister who died during Becher's infancy. Becher was a student of theology, mathematics, medicine, chemistry, philosophy, economics, and art. At twenty he began his writings, which embrace these subjects. Becher evidently visited Holland previous to 1680, for in that year he left Germany for England and it is recorded that owing to storms he was twenty-eight days in a sailing ship before he finally arrived in the British Isles. During this long voyage he compiled the little book that is of so much interest to the historian of papermaking. Evidently Dr. Becher returned to his native land for the publication of his book, since later that same year he went back to England, where he died in his forty-seventh year.

* Sturm's researches in Dutch paper mills, where he drew for the first time a picture of a beater, occurred almost forty years after the eventful visit of Dr. Becher and his original description of this important machine. Sturm had much the same background as Dr. Becher, and the two men recorded, one in writing, the other in illustration, the origin of a papermaking appliance that has undergone few changes to the present day. Sturm was born in Altdorf in 1669, the son of a professor of mathematics and physics in the Altdorf University. He received his first instruction from his father, and at fourteen he was entered in the university as a student of theology; at eighteen he received a Master of Arts degree. Finding theology distasteful, he relinquished this subject so that he might become a student of architecture. He eventually was chosen as building director for the Duke Ludwig Rudolf at Blankenburg in Braunschweig. Sturm died in 1719, the year following the publication of his important work on the subject of mill machinery.

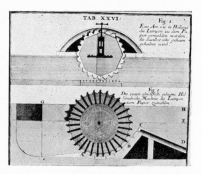

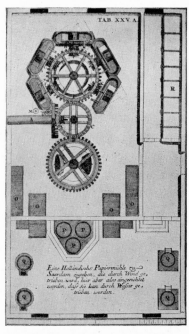

FIG. 140   The first delineation
of the Hollander as pictured in
the volume on machinery by Leonhardt Christoph Sturm (Augsburg, 1718).

FIG. 139   Five Hollanders for the maceration of rags for papermaking and two millstones for the grinding of flour, all operated by one
water-wheel. (From Sturm's Vollständige Mühlen Baukunst, Augsburg,
1718.)

water-wheel — in Holland by the power of the wind, and in Germany and France by the weight and force of water. In another of
the prints in Sturm's book there are illustrated five Dutch beaters
in combination with two millstones (Figure 139), the stones grinding flour at the same time the beaters reduced rags to a fibrous
pulp for papermaking. This combination of making flour and paper in the same mill was not usually practised, and some writers
have advanced the thought that the placing of the millstones in
the engraving was nothing more than a fancy of the author, who
produced the book after a journey through Holland, where he had
visited mills used for various industries. It is recorded that Nicholas Hasselbaugh, who was operating the former De Wees mill in
Pennsylvania in the late eighteenth century, had a pair of stones
in connection with the paper mill and carried on an extensive

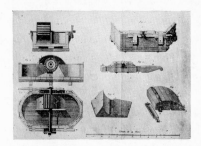

Fig. 141   *Various elevations of the Hollander, showing the roll, backfall, etc. From an eighteenth-century print.*

Fig. 142   *The earliest engraving of the Hollander to appear in the country of its invention; published in Amsterdam, 1734.*

Fig. 143   *The operation of Hollanders by the power of the wind. From the engraving in the rare pamphlet of 1801 by Johann Christoph Ludwig.*

business in both flour and paper. Hendrick Onderdonk, who set up an early paper mill in New York at Roslyn, Long Island, in 1773, also ground grist and made paper in the same mill. Thirty years ago I visited a handmade-paper mill in the south of England and saw in operation a large wooden water-wheel that furnished the power for operating two Hollanders and two sets of millstones, both papermaking and the milling of grain being carried on under the same roof. This mill was later demolished, and as I was present at the time, much of the old papermaking equipment was acquired and brought to America, where it was ultimately used in the revival of the handmade-paper industry in Lime Rock, Connecticut.

In the Hollanders of the mid eighteenth century (Figure 141) the washing and cleansing of the linen and cotton were accomplished by the use of two screens, called "chesses," which extended through the hood, or "chapiter," just in front of the revolving roll. The screen nearest the roll was fashioned of coarsely woven metal wire, and the other of fine cloth made of horsehair. At the base of these two screens a hole-scupper or "dalot" was placed, which carried away the unclean water as it was thrown through both of the screens by the velocity of the revolving roll. Fresh water was supplied continually to the beater tub during the washing process, and the mission of the two screens was to prevent the escape and waste of any fibrous material. An engraving in *Groot Volkomen Moolenboek,* published in Amsterdam in 1734, depicting this form of washer, was the first illustration of the Hollander to appear in the country of its invention (Figure 142).

The German papermakers were slow to take advantage of the newly devised Dutch machine, no doubt thinking, and rightly too, that the old method of macerating cloth by means of stamping-mills made the best paper. Both Frederick the Great and Maria Theresa encouraged the master papermakers to install the improved Dutch beaters and discard the old-time stampers. By the year 1800 there was but one paper mill in all England where the stampers remained in use. The French were the last to adopt Hollanders exclusively, and until 1861 the French Government insisted that all pulp that was to be used for making paper for the Stamp Office be beaten by the primitive stamping-mills, thus assuring long-fibred stock and therefore stronger and more durable paper. In 1801 Johann Christoph Ludwig recommended that

Fig. 144　A modern Hollander of comparatively small size. The beater roll is housed under the rounded hood, the pulp travelling around the beater tub between the revolving roll and the stationary bed-plate, which lies under the roll. The worker is adding dye to colour the macerated stock. (Courtesy, Hammermill Paper Company)

the German papermakers adopt the Dutch windmills as a means of driving the beating-engines, and he compiled a small pamphlet regarding his observations (Figure 143).[8] As late as 1920 there was a set of the old stampers in operation in the south of the Tyrol, and several Italian and German mills still retain them in their buildings as curiosities. In 1925 I was offered a set of these ancient stampers by the last member of one of the old German paper-making families, the troughs of stone worn by use and the wooden parts almost falling into decay.

In the Hollanders of the present day (Figures 144, 145) a few improvements have been made, but in principle of conception and general construction they are almost identical with the old machine of Dutch invention shown in Sturm's book of machinery of 1718.

F𝕚𝕘. 145   *A Hollander of modern type. The insert gives a clear conception of the revolving roll and stationary bed-plate. Note the similarity of this present-day machine with the beater of 1718 as depicted in Figure 140.* (Courtesy, Hammermill Paper Company)

VI

Early Papermaking Processes and Methods

THE METHODS that were used in the making of paper during the early centuries of the craft are naturally vague after a lapse of almost two thousand years. No records indicate to us the manner in which the Chinese first made paper; but as with the ancient arts of the weaver and the potter, the method of hand fabrication in this craft must have changed but little from its inception to the present day. Almost two thousand years ago sheets of paper were made from disintegrated fibre upon flat moulds, and in this fashion paper is still formed, the only difference being in the treatment of the fibre and in the construction of the moulds; in principle the process remains unchanged. The original papermakers of China probably poured the fibrous pulp upon the cloth-covered frames, or moulds, but it was not long before the craftsmen practised the more expeditious method of dipping the moulds directly into the macerated liquid material. This change of method was one of the important steps in papermaking technique, as it enabled the artisans not only to form better sheets of paper, but to produce them in greater quantity. There is no way of arriving at the exact period when moulds were first dipped, but it probably did not take the ingenious Chinese a great while to discover the new and more efficient method. The pouring of the fibrous stock upon the moulds is still practised in Tibet, Burma, Nepal, Bhutan, Siam,[1] and some parts of China. (See Figures 41, 90, 91.)

Whatever the methods employed in the Orient at the inception of papermaking, the method used when the craft was introduced into Spain during the twelfth century was to dip the mould into a vat filled with macerated liquid pulp and bring it to the surface laden with the matted and felted fibre, which, after drying, was paper. In the four centuries following there was little development in papermaking. Before the invention of printing in Europe the use of paper was limited, but with the ushering in of this art the craft of the papermaker had its real impetus. It was during the fifteenth century that the fabrication of paper developed into a notable industry, and present-day interest in old papermaking dates from the infancy of printing rather than from more remote periods.

The precise methods used by papermakers in the days of Gutenberg, Jenson, and Caxton are no more clear to us than are the exact processes employed by the early printers in their type-making. The oldest print in either the Orient or the Occident representing an interior view of a paper mill (Figure 146) is that of Jost Amman,* from the year 1568, but this woodcut throws no more light on the details of papermaking than does the print of the old typefoundry, in the same volume and by the same artist, show us how type was made at that time. It is only by piecing together material from many and varied sources that we are able to arrive at the methods used by the early craftsmen. The art of papermaking was jealously guarded by the old workers, and, there being little intercourse between the different mills, it was natural that the papermakers in each locality should have had their own methods. Even today there is a secrecy among the makers of handmade paper in both the Orient and the Occident, and the various mills show a pronounced variation in equipment and methods of operation.

In an examination of old Asiatic and European paper it may be readily perceived that the sheets were formed upon flat moulds, and from the impressions left in the paper by the material of which these moulds were made, it is not difficult to determine how the moulds were constructed. The moulds differed slightly in work-

---

* The print may be found in a book of trades issued in Frankfurt am Main under the title: *Eygentliche Beschreibung aller Stände auff Erden, hoher und nidriger, geistlicher und weltlicher, aller Künsten, Handwercken und Händeln* (1568). In this little book 115 trades or callings are pictured by Jost Amman (1539–91); under each woodcut there is a verse about the particular craft compiled by Hans Sachs (1494–1576), the cobbler-poet of Nürnberg. The woodcut of the papermaker is the eighteenth in the book and follows the illustration depicting the woodcutter at work. A translation of the verse by Hans Sachs reads:

> Rags are brought unto my mill
> Where much water turns the wheel,
> They are cut and torn and shredded,
> To the pulp is water added;
> Then the sheets 'twixt felts must lie
> While I wring them in my press.
> Lastly, hang them up to dry
> Snow-white in glossy loveliness.

Fig. 146   *The earliest picture of papermaking. The woodcut is by Jost Amman, the poem by Hans Sachs.*

manship in the various countries and localities, and therefore we have inherited in documents, manuscripts, and books innumerable varieties of paper, defying classification; yet it is clear that the fundamental principles of both mould construction and the actual making of the paper have undergone few changes since the original invention by the Chinese.

In all old European paper mills, aside from the appliances that were used in the preparation of the pulp or paper stock (described in Chapter v), there were four essential utensils used: the vat, the moulds, the felts, and the press. In every antique engraving produced in Europe depicting the papermakers' art these four necessary appliances will be seen. In the fifteenth century the vat for holding the fibrous liquid was simply a round or oblong wooden tub, about five feet in breadth, reaching in height to the worker's waist, and bound with stout hoops. The old vats were probably made from huge wine casks or tuns cut through the centre, as it is not likely that there were special shops where papermaking equipment was manufactured. Doubtless the mills designed and constructed their own appliances to suit their individual needs (Figure 147). The earliest engraving representing papermaking shows no appurtenances to the vats, but during the seventeenth century several inventions were made which greatly facilitated the work. The most important of these was the introduction of the charcoal heater, which was annexed to the back of the vat to warm the stock. By the more rapid evaporation that resulted the workers were enabled to make a greater number of sheets in a day. In France this heater was known as a "pistolet," and it was the practice to place the vat against an outside wall so that the smoke from the heater or grate would not permeate the vat-house and soil the paper during the moulding process.*

In pioneer papermaking in America the vat was heated in much the same manner. The only contemporary description of this old

---

* The earliest British patent pertaining to the heating of vats for papermaking was issued to William Scott and George Gregory on August 16, 1793. The specification reads: "Their invention is for heating water and other stuff in vats for making paper by introducing steam. . . . The common and ordinary method now used for heating water and other stuff in vats for making paper is by introducing fuel into a pan placed within the vat, which not only consumes a large quantity of coal, but is likewise uncertain and irregular in the heat . . . the new method causes the paper to be free from a great part of the dust and nastiness which unavoidably mix with it from heating the vats by fuel." The specification is accompanied by a plate which shows the steam introduced into the vats by means of coils of pipe protruding directly into the dipping-vats. This is the same method of heating the paper stock as is employed at the present time in the commercial handmade-paper mills of Europe.

Fig. 147   *Papermaking in Europe in the seventeenth century. The vatman, coucher, and layman are performing their respective duties. The "pistolet," or heating device, may be seen at the extreme left of the illustration.*

method of warming the stock in the vat is that given in the manuscript diary of Ebenezer Hiram Stedman, who was born in Dorchester, Massachusetts, November 11, 1808. In 1816 young Stedman and his father, a Massachusetts papermaker, migrated to Kentucky to work in a paper mill in Lexington. The account of young Stedman's trials with the "pistolet" is taken from this exceedingly interesting old diary. Stedman wrote: "From January till May I would have to get up in the mornings at 2 o'clock, the first thing was to make a fire to warm the water in the vat, where they dipt up the pulp to form the sheets of paper. I had to go into a hole on my hands and knees, ten feet long, by three feet square, to make a fire in what was called a pot. The smoke came out of the hole I went in and this was on the outside of the mill. Exposed to the weather in winter no one will ever realize how much I suffered with cold, snow, rain, and smoke. Many times I have had to hold my breath while making the fire and dodge in for a chance to put in a stick of wood, then back out for the place was too small to turn around. After making the fire then I would have to wake up the vatman and the coucher and the other workmen in the paper mill."

Another improvement in the equipment was a platform or bridge which extended from one side of the vat to the other. This bridge, as shown in the old engravings, supported the "horn," against which the mould with its newly formed sheet was placed to drain. The bridge does not appear in the woodcut of 1568 by Jost Amman, nor in the illustration of 1662 by Georg Andreæ Böckler (Figures 136 and 146), but in as much as a bridge is partially discernible in a very crude woodcut of 1658,[2] it may have been in use as early as Böckler's time in some parts of Europe.

During the process of moulding the sheets of paper it was essential that the fibrous material be kept from settling to the bottom of the dipping-vat. Originally this was accomplished by the action of a pole in the hands of a workman, a means of agitation still used in most Oriental mills. A slight improvement was later made by placing on the end of the pole a wooden disk pierced with holes, which increased the effectiveness of the stirring. Suggestions for more efficient work came slowly in the early mills, and each step, which now seems trivial, was no doubt welcomed as an ingenious invention by the old craftsmen. It was not until the latter part of the eighteenth century that a mechanical agitator was

Fig. 148   *The vatman stands before the vat holding the mould by its two narrow edges; the coucher stands at the back of the vat. This interesting photograph was made in an old paper mill in Auvergne, France, by Georges Degaast.*

devised, and even this went through various changes before the paddle-wheel, called a "hog," was finally adopted and used almost universally.*

---

* The various prints depicting papermaking appliances before the year 1800 do not show the mechanical agitator, so it may be assumed that this means of preventing the paper stock from settling in the vat was not employed on the Continent previous to this date. The earliest mention of this form of agitation that can be located appears in an article entitled "*Sur les papeteries et fabrication de papier-paille en Angleterre*" in *Annales des arts et manufactures, ou Mémoires technologiques,* October–November 1803. The article relates to a visit of a French papermaker to the Matthias Koops paper mills, Mill Bank, Westminster, England. The description reads: "The vats in nearly all the English paper mills are fitted with agitators placed near the bottom, to which is given a slow motion. This agitator, or paddle-wheel, which the English have given the name 'hog,' keeps the macerated stock in the vat in constant movement and prevents it from settling to the bottom of the vat."

The first European method of supplying the vat was by transferring the macerated stock from the storage chest by means of hand buckets, a most tedious procedure.* It was not until the seventeenth century that a supply by gravity was devised. I once visited a paper mill in Europe that had been equipped in the late eighteenth century, where the fibrous liquid had been conveyed to the vat from a large stone cistern by means of a long winding wooden trough; the stock or pulp had been lifted and thrown into this trough by a huge wooden wheel fitted with copper buckets.

After the vat had been filled to within a few inches of its brim with the diluted linen and cotton fibres that had been macerated under the stamping-mills, the fibrous material was ready to be formed into sheets of paper. A workman (Figures 148, 149), called a vatman, stood on a platform in front of the vat, holding a mould firmly by the two narrow sides; around this mould was a removable deckle or frame, which acted in the manner of a shallow fence around its edges. (Moulds and deckles are described in detail in Chapter iv.) The vatman plunged the mould, at an almost perpendicular angle, into the fibrous liquid substance, and when the mould was well submerged he turned it face upwards and lifted it horizontally from the vat. By this action the mould was evenly covered with the macerated linen and cotton, and the stock not needed for the particular weight or thickness of paper being moulded was allowed to run over the far edge of the mould into the vat, to be used again. The vatman then shook the newly formed sheet on the surface of the mould, first from right to left, then from back to front. These motions crossed and matted the fibres, making the sheets of paper almost equally strong in both directions, and at the same time expelling considerable water from the sheet. The wires of the mould retained the fibres, but allowed the water to drain through as in a sieve. The vatman then removed

---

It is due to a great extent to this invention that the English paper possesses a uniform blueness from the smalt colouring as without the agitator the colour (dye) would have a tendency to settle. The 'hog' holds the colouring in suspension in the liquid fibre and assures the high quality of the English blue paper."

* This method of supplying the vats with stock is practised in the Orient; even in the most efficient handmade-paper mills of Japan the pulp is placed in the vats without the help of mechanical means.

FIG. 149   *In India the vat-man sits at his work, and while the mould and vat are different from those of the Occident, the principle of the papermaking process remains the same. Photograph made in the small mill of Mamudeen Khagjee, Sailkot, Punjab, India.*

FIG. 150   *The coucher, at the left, is in the act of laying a newly formed sheet of paper upon the felt; the vatman has just formed a sheet upon the mould. Photograph made in the seventeenth-century mill at Arnhem, Gelderland Province, Netherlands. Previous to the war this mill was made into a museum, but its present fate is unknown.*

the wooden deckle, which left the moist sheet of paper, cut sharply along its four edges, upon the mould. The next operation of the vatman was to pass the mould along the bridge to the second artisan, known as the "coucher," and proceed to form another sheet with a second mould, using the same deckle. The coucher placed the mould, with its thin moist sheet, against the inclined drainage-horn, or "asp," which allowed the surplus water to drain back into the vat. When the wet sheet of paper had solidified upon the mould to the proper extent — a stage determined by a distinctive lustre over its surface — the coucher turned the mould completely over and deposited the wet sheet of paper upon a piece of felting (Figure 150). The couching was done with a quick, deft motion, rocking the mould from one long edge to the other, leaving the sheet, flat and unwrinkled, upon the woollen cloth. These processes were repeated over and over, the vatman and coucher working together, until a pile of 144 sheets of paper had been formed and couched, each sheet of wet paper separated from the next by a piece of felt somewhat larger than the size of the paper. The pile of six quires was termed a "post," and the next operation was to place the post in a press to expel the excess water.[3] *

In the earliest form of Chinese papermaking the sheets were dried directly upon the woven textile moulds upon which they had been formed, so that couching, or removing the paper from the mould while wet, was not required (Figure 151; see also Figures 42–46). After the introduction in China of the "laid" bamboo mould, when dipping was used, it was the practice to couch each sheet as it was formed, one upon another without interleaving cloths. This method is in use at the present time in many parts of Asia, including China, Japan, Korea, Indo-China, and India.[4]

At the introduction of papermaking into Europe, felt of some kind was in all probability used as a material for the couching of paper. It is not likely that the old craftsmen employed woven wool cloth such as the makers of handmade paper use at present, but a more compact, matted substance of hair or wool. The woven material that is used by modern papermakers is called felt, but the name is a misnomer, as felt is a compressed mass and does not necessarily consist of warp and weft. Years ago in Catholic countries the feltmakers celebrated the 23rd of November, St. Clement's Day, with a great festival. It is stated that this saint, when on a pilgrimage, placed carded wool between his feet and the soles

---

* The term "post" was used for any pile of wet sheets interleaved by felts; the origin of the word is obscure. While the usual number of newly moulded sheets in a post was six quires, the amount would vary according to the size of the paper being made; with paper of large dimensions the post would be made up of as many sheets as could be handled and pressed conveniently. The term "post" may have been introduced into England by German or Italian workers as the word probably came originally from the German *Posten* or Italian *posto*, which in turn were derived from the Latin *positum*.

The term "quire" (Middle English *quaer, quair;* Old French *quayer, quaer, cayer, caier;* French *cahier;* Low Latin *quaternus, quaternum,* from the Latin *quaterni*) denotes four sheets of paper or parchment folded together into eight leaves; hence any set of folded sheets fitting one within another, as the sheets of a book. The modern use of the term quire is usually applied to twenty-four sheets of paper, either folded or unfolded. A "ream" of paper is made up of twenty quires, or 480 sheets. This term comes from the Arabic word *rizmah,* meaning a bundle, especially of paper. The term was probably introduced into Spain along with the craft of papermaking in the twelfth century, where the word became *rezma* or *resma*. The Middle English term was *reme;* Old French *rayme;* French *rame*. According to Webster, a regulation ream is 480 sheets, but sometimes 472 of drawing or handmade paper, 500 sheets of news or book paper, and a printer's "perfect ream" 516 sheets.

FIG. 151   *Tibetan women drying paper, which adheres to the moulds upon which it has been formed. This is the most ancient method. Gyantse, Tibet.*

of his sandals, and at the end of his journey found that the wool had been converted into felt. However, the invention of felt by St. Clement is to be questioned, as this material was in use long before his time. The Greeks manufactured true felt as early as 900 B.C., long before the art of papermaking.[5] Papyrus was made before this period, it is true, but this is a laminated substance, not made from macerated and disintegrated fibre as is true paper. Both the Greeks and the Romans made use of matted felt for caps, blankets, and the lining of helmets. Since the material was thicker than common cloth, it presented a more effectual obstacle to missile weapons; hence when the soldiers under Julius Cæsar were annoyed by Pompey's archers, they made shirts of heavy felt and wore them for defence. The Scythians, who from the most remote time roamed the lands of northern Asia, as did the Tatars, their successors, used felt for both clothing and material for making tents. It is therefore quite evident that had the early papermakers, even the original Chinese, desired felt for the couching of their paper, it could have been readily procured.

It is not known when felt came into use as a material for receiving the wet sheets of paper as they were couched from the moulds, nor is it known when woven wool cloth was substituted for matted felting for the couching of paper, but it is probable that some sort of woven material was in use for the purpose as early as the thirteenth century. No special wool cloths were fabricated for papermaking until the eighteenth century, although there was an incorporated company of feltmakers in England as early as 1604. These artisans made felt for hats, but it is not recorded that they attempted any woven or matted material especially for papermakers. The material used for the making of felt was not only wool, but the hair of the seal, rabbit, monkey, goat, and camel.

The best description of woven cloth such as was used in the eighteenth century by the makers of paper is furnished by Nicolas Desmarets in *Traité de l'art de fabriquer le papier*, published in Paris in 1788:

The felts have two surfaces furnished with different naps. That side which has the longest nap is applied to the couched sheets, and on the side with the shortest the fresh leaves are laid. If this arrangement of the felting was changed, and the sheets laid upon the surface with a long nap, not only would they not apply themselves accurately to the felt, but the long stiff hairs would pierce the paper or cause depressions, which would injure the texture. On the contrary, the leaves fit themselves evenly to the side with a short nap, which absorbs the surplus water and gives a sufficient consistency for the coucher. It is also from this side that the layman detaches the sheets after the post has passed through the press so that the different character of these surfaces is an assistance to the layman as well as to the coucher. The material of which the felting is made requires great care on the part of the papermakers, and much attention and knowledge of the art of papermaking on the part of the manufacturer who prepares them. They should be firm enough to spread evenly upon the leaves without wrinkling or needing to be displaced. Also, they should be supple enough to adapt themselves to the work of the coucher, who applies the mould successively from one edge of the felt to the other upon every intermediate point. As the felts have to resist the reiterated efforts of the coucher and the press, it is necessary that the warp of these cloths should be very strong and therefore made of combed and well-twisted wool. And as they should be clean and quickly absorb and give up again a certain

Fig. 152   *An ancient screw press used in pressing the "posts," to extract the excess water, known as the "wet" press. It was this type of press that the European papermakers used before the invention of the hydraulic press. In an old paper mill in Auvergne, France; photograph by Georges Degaast.*

Fig. 153   *An eighteenth century "dry" press. After the paper had been exchanged and dried in the loft, it was placed in a press of this type. This photograph was made in 1928 in an old paper-mill building in Haslock on Main, Germany.*

amount of water, their weft should be of carded wool quite loosely spun and woven in about the same manner as light cloth. It results from this that the weft abundantly fills the stuff and covers the warp in such a way that the texture is not marked upon the paper, which would injure its grain by the irregular impression of an uncovered warp and weft, as is often observed in establishments where felts not woven upon these principles are used, which does not denote a great deal of talent upon the part of the papermaker. If the material were too closely woven, like ordinary cloths, or even the finest kinds, it would not absorb the water enough to enable the sheets to adhere and assume a certain consistency. It is for this reason that Carcassonne cloths are very well adapted to this purpose, and that those of Louviers, of which the texture is very close, would not take the leaves of paper couched upon them in experiments several times repeated, because the water could not sufficiently

FIG. 154   *In the Orient the papermakers use the ancient lever press,*
adding stones as more pressure is desired. Kōchi, Japan. The Oriental
papermakers do not use felting between each sheet of newly formed
paper as is the practice in the Occident.

penetrate them. It is very essential that the warp of the stuff intended
to be made into felts should be strong and tough, so that they may be
of good service and wear well.

For pressing the water from the piles of paper and felts a
wooden screw press such as was portrayed by Jost Amman in 1568
and Georg Andreæ Böckler in 1662 was employed in the old mills
(Figures 136, 146, 152, 153, 154, 155). As these presses had to yield
an immense pressure, they were massive and cumbersome, and
constituted one of the most expensive appliances of the old paper
mills. After the post had been placed under the platen of the press,
all of the workers in the various parts of the mill were summoned
together by the ringing of a bell to exert their strength in turning
down the screw of the press by means of a long wooden lever.*

---

* In the Ebenezer Hiram Stedman diary the following account of the
method used in pressing the posts in an early nineteenth-century paper mill
in Kentucky is given, and it will be noted that the procedure is not unlike
that practised in Europe. Stedman wrote: "It was my duty when Layboy to

FIG. 155   *In Indo-China the paper is pressed by means of a lever hung with stones, the same method as employed by the Japanese at the present time. From the Paper Village near Hanoi, French Indo-China.*

FIG. 156   *The "Sampson" used in procuring additional pressure in the press. After a half-dozen men had tightened the press as much as possible in the ordinary manner, a rope was attached to the pole, or lever, and by means of the windlass considerable more water was pressed from the "post" of paper. From the same seventeenth-century Auvergne, France, mill as the press shown in Figure 152. Photograph by Georges Degaast.*

blow a horn and notify all the men in the mill to come to help press the post. The man that tended the rag engine was the first one to come and help pull the post under the press, on top of this post was placed a plank like the one the post laid on, and the space between the post of paper and the screw-press was filled up with press-blocks, ten inches square and three feet long. The screw was then placed upon it and screwed down with a short lever as tight as four men could press. Then a lever, or pole, sixteen to twenty feet long and six inches in diameter, as much as two men could lift, with this six men pressed the post till all the water that was in the post was pressed out. The post of paper was then drawn from the press, then commenced my work as Layboy, to separate the sheets of paper from the felts. To my left hand the lay-stool to place the paper on; on my right was the post of paper and felts. To separate the sheets of paper was a particular kind of work, the sheets being wet, hardly dry enough to bare their own weight, so easy to tear. To separate them I had to stand half-bent, all day, and when the day's work was done my back would ache so that many a night I could not sleep."

Stedman's diary is the most complete account of early American papermaking and it is especially interesting in its relation to Kentucky, where the first paper mill west of the Susquehanna River was established in 1793, only sixty-five years after the original paper mill in New England was set in operation.

As the platen of the press closed downward upon the felts and newly formed paper, an abundance of water was forced from the mass, the post being reduced from about two feet in thickness to barely six inches. In later years a device called a "Samson" or "sampson" was brought into use in the larger mills (Figure 156). This device acted as a windlass, and with the power of six men the pressing was more efficient than had been previously possible, giving the paper a more compact texture. To ensure a uniform pressure on the pile of paper and felting the workmen placed thin bevelled boards around the top of the post, for without this precaution the centre would have received more pressure than the edges. The results of these apparently simple innovations are reflected in the old papers, and without a knowledge of the different methods of working it is not possible to determine the age or origin of antique papers.

After pressing, the weight of the paper and felts from the loss of the water had been reduced tenfold, and the fibres of the sheets of paper had been so matted and felted together by the great pressure that the sheets were lifted from the woollen cloths without tearing, each sheet being a homogeneous piece of paper, although far from being entirely dry. The third workman in the process of old papermaking was known as the "layman," and it was his duty to free each sheet of paper from the interleaving felts and to place the sheets in a neat and even pile, one upon another, on an inclined stool or bench (Figures 157, 158, 159). The felts were returned to the coucher to be used in making the following post. These pure wool cloths were expensive, and the old mills had but one set for each size of paper that they made. By long hours and diligent work it was possible for the three workmen to make twenty posts, or about five and one half reams of paper, a day. Had but a single mould been used, one man acting as both vatman and coucher, scarcely one fourth of this amount would have been made.

After the sheets had been placed directly one upon another by the layman, the pile was again subjected to pressure. This procedure, although the pressure was light, brought out a little more water, which formed in drops upon the edges of the sheets. After this second pressing the sheets of paper were separated, again built into a pile, but in a different rotation, and subjected to a little

Fig. 157   *The workers are taking the semi-dry paper from the felts after the initial pressing. The paper will be stacked in a neat pile, ready for the second pressing in the "dry" press, as shown in Figure 153.*

Fig. 158   *These two companion photographs were made in 1936 in one of the remaining seventeenth-century paper mills of Auvergne, an old province of France. Both photographs were made by Georges Degaast, French bibliographer.*

heavier pressure than could have been given before, owing to the tendency of the sheets to stick together. This rearrangement of the sheets was repeated until the paper acquired the desired smoothness of finish. The roughness of much of this paper previous to the sixteenth century would indicate that before that time this exchanging or parting was not in practice in some localities, the paper evidently having received no finishing after removal from the woollen felts. In an examination of old paper, especially Italian and Dutch, it will be noticed that many of the sheets retain the impressions left by the material upon which they were couched. The early American papermakers did not devote much time or labour to the exchanging, although this procedure was, and still is, the secret of giving to handmade paper a beautiful finish and texture.

The next process was the drying of the paper, which was one of the most particular operations of the mill. The paper was taken from the pile, after the last pressing, in "spurs" of four or five sheets, as in this moist state they adhered together. Had the sheets been dried separately they would have wrinkled, but when taken in spurs the paper dried smoothly and without excessive curling. The drying-lofts of the old paper mills were situated in the top storeys of the buildings, where the air was reasonably free from

Fig. 159   *Removing the pressed paper from the felts. The paint-*
ing, by François Angeli, was made in Ambert in the ancient Auvergne
papermaking centre. The "Sampson" may be seen at the right of the
picture.

particles of dirt and soot. The walls of these lofts were fitted with sliding wooden shutters which could be shifted to let in or exclude the air. The spurs of paper were hung over ropes that had been woven from cow- or horse-hair, coated with beeswax. These heavy ropes, supported by horizontal wooden frames called "tribbles" or "trebles," * were stretched throughout the loft, and the entrance of the air was arranged so that it came in contact with the full breadth of the sheets and not against the edges of the paper. Ropes are still used in European mills for drying handmade paper, but the paper mills of America in the days of loft drying employed round or half-round wooden poles for this purpose.

In the fifteenth- and sixteenth-century mills the drying was carried on in the most primitive manner, and it is not unusual in paper from this period to find stains through the middle of the sheets caused by the hair ropes upon which they had been hung to dry (Figures 160, 161). During the development of papermaking in America some of the mills transported their paper to the printers before it had dried thoroughly, as the makers were not able to supply the demand with sufficient rapidity. In many folio volumes, particularly from the seventeenth century, the pages bulged in the centres, causing the leaves to lie in ridges, somewhat in the shape of a diamond. While this defect is more noticeable in folios, it may be found in smaller books also. It was caused by the paper not having been exchanged or pressed sufficiently. During the drying the weight of the paper stretched the sheets, causing them to bulge in the centres. The Oriental papers were dried in various ways: upon the moulds on which they had been formed (Figures 42, 43, 46, 172); or spread flat against boards (Figures 162, 163, 164, 166, 177); or brushed against smooth masonry walls in the sun (Figures 167, 168, 170); also, upon ropes or poles (Figures 169, 178), and spread upon the ground (as shown in Figures 165 and 171). In drying paper against plaster walls the sheets were held rigid and flat, so that many of the Oriental papers are unusually smooth, especially on one side.

---

* The wooden "trebles" were pierced with holes at evenly spaced intervals for the support of the hair ropes, which were known as "treble-lines." The word "treble" may have come originally from the ropes having been formed of three strands, but this is uncertain; the precise origin of the word remains obscure.

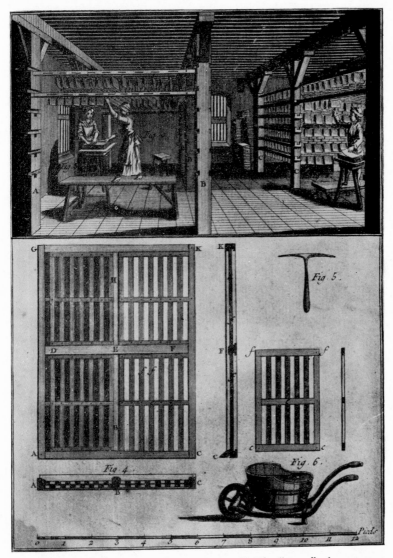

Fig. 160   *The drying-loft of a paper mill. The "spurs" of paper are being hung upon ropes by means of the "T," shown in Fig. 5 in the plate. This same method of drying paper is in use in Europe at the present time. From the engraving in the work (1774) by Nicolas Desmarets.*

Fig. 161   *The drying-loft of a seventeenth-century French paper mill. The paper was hung upon hair ropes; the shutters for the entrance or exclusion of air appear at the right of the picture. Photograph by Georges Degaast.*

Fig. 162   *The Japanese paper-makers brush their paper upon smooth wooden boards for drying. A coir-fibre brush used in "pasting" the paper to the boards is shown in Figure 107. Photograph made in 1933 in Ogawa-Machi, Saitama Prefecture, Japan.*

Fig. 163   *In Japan the moist sheets of paper are "pasted" against boards for drying.*

Fig. 164   *In southern Korea the paper is dried upon wooden boards, in the same manner as in Japan. This method originated in China and was introduced into Japan from Korea.*

Fig. 165   *Drying paper in the village of Ompei, central Korea. This paper would eventually be laminated and used on the floors of native Korean houses. The boy would think nothing of carrying his burden to Seoul, a distance of eight or ten miles.*

Fig. 166   *Drying paper in India. The individual sheets of newly made paper are "pasted" against a smooth metal plate. This is an improvement on the old method of placing the sheets against plaster walls. Autsahai, Bengal, India.*

Fig. 167   *In India the moist sheets of newly made paper are spread with a brush against plaster walls for drying. Photograph made near the ancient paper centre of Sailkot, Punjab, northern India.*

Fɪɢ. 168   *Drying paper in China in the seventeenth century by
placing the newly formed, moist sheets against a heated wall. This
same method is in use in both China and Indo-China at the present
time. (From* Tʻien kung kʻai wu, *by Sung Ying-hsing, 1634.)*

FIG. 169   Drying paper over cow-hair ropes. Sailkot, Punjab, India.

FIG. 170   After the moist sheets of paper have dried they fall to the ground from the smooth plaster walls. In India the paper is spread against the walls by the use of brushes, shown in Figure 176. Photograph made in 1937 in the papermaking district of Sailkot, Punjab, India.

FIG. 171   Drying paper in China. In the papermaking districts it is not unusual to see whole hillsides literally covered with drying paper.

FIG. 172   In Siam the paper is dried upon the moulds on which it was formed, in the manner used in China in the second century. The long, narrow moulds form paper that is suitable in shape for the folding books of Siam. The elderly papermaker is Tym Niltongkum, now deceased, Bangsoom, Siam.

The drying completed, the old European papermakers dipped their paper into an animal size that had been made from the parings of hides, which they procured from the parchment-makers. It was necessary to size the paper so that it would be impervious to ink, but sizing was more needed in writing than in printing papers. Many books of the fifteenth century were printed upon paper that had not been sized, this extra treatment not being essential for a type impression. The sizing was accomplished by a worker holding a number of sheets with the aid of two wooden sticks and dipping the paper into the warm glutinous liquid. The sheets were then pressed to extract the superfluous gelatine. This crude method of sizing the paper was extremely wasteful, as many sheets were torn and bruised beyond use. The sizing room of the early Occidental paper mills was for this reason known as the "slaughter house." One of the earliest Oriental methods of sizing paper consisted in covering the surface of the sheets with a thin coating of gypsum. The next improvement was to render the body of the paper, as well as the surface, impermeable to ink by the use of lichen, starch, or rice flour (Figure 173). The Chinese used starch as a size for paper as early as A.D. 768.

In an examination of more than a hundred different volumes of incunabula (books printed in Europe before 1501) I have found that the papermakers of the fifteenth century followed no definite formula as to the sizing of their papers; many of the sheets are heavily sized, others contain a limited amount of sizing, and a small number no sizing at all. Most of the modern European handmade papers, like some papers used in the early centuries of printing, are sized too densely and give the printer who employs the old traditional hand press no end of difficulty in his work. The earliest European book to mention the actual sizing of paper is the small volume entitled *Papyrus sive Ars conficiendæ Papyri*, compiled by J. Imberdis, Claromonti, and issued in 1693. This was the first treatise on the art of papermaking to be published in France. Father Imberdis was a Jesuit, and being a native of Ambert in Auvergne, he was familiar with the paper mills of that district, a very old seat of French papermaking; some historians contend that the first paper mills of France were set up in Auvergne. Judging from his detailed account of papermaking, Father Imberdis must have possessed a most observant and inquisi-

FIG. 173   *The Asiatic papermakers cover their papers with a thin coating of rice or wheat paste, which acts as a size, rendering the paper impervious to ink. In European papermaking the size was rendered from the hides of animals. Kashmir, India.*

tive mind. The entire treatise is in the nature of a descriptive poem giving a semi-technical version of papermaking as it was then practised in France. He states, with keen insight and knowledge uncommon in the layman, that the sheets of paper are far from perfect when they leave the mould, for even after being formed thereon the paper must pass through numerous hands and be subjected to a thousand manipulations before it is ready to leave the mill. No one but a maker of handmade paper can truly appreciate the significance of this statement. The author of the poem gives two methods of testing paper for its writing qualities. The first is to crumple the paper in the hands; if the sound resembles that of parchment under the same treatment the paper should prove satisfactory, as this shows it is well sized with animal glue. The second test is to wet the paper with the tongue; if the saliva penetrates through the sheet, showing that there is little or no sizing, the paper is unfit for the application of fluid writing ink. In men-

Fig. 174   *In India the finish-*
ing of paper is accomplished by
rubbing the sheets with a smooth
stone. This process gives the
paper a highly polished surface
well adapted to calligraphy.

Fig. 175   *In India the paper*
is polished by means of a smooth
stone laboriously rubbed by hand.
The papers so treated are used
for manuscripts. Sailkot, Punjab,
India.

tioning the many difficulties and hardships of the papermakers'
craft Father Imberdis has this to say: "Heaven does not permit
such a divine art to be made easy for mortals here below."

After the sizing operation was completed, the paper was again
dried and taken to a room called the "saul" or "salle." In England
the finishing room of a paper mill has been known by this name
for several hundred years. The term may have come originally
from the German word *Saal*, and it is reasonable to surmise that
it was first used in England by John Spilman, the German who established a mill in Kent in 1588. The "salle" was that part of the
mill where the paper was surfaced and packed for transportation.
The earliest method of producing a smooth surface on the paper
was to burnish each sheet by hand by the use of an agate or other
glossy stone (Figures 174, 175, 176). The Orientals gave their
paper a glass-like surface by this procedure. One side of the sheet
only was burnished, but as the reverse side was laid against a
smooth slab of wood it also took on a certain amount of finish.
Even when the Asiatic scribes made use of European paper, they
subjected it to a polishing with an agate or stone burnisher, which
gave the paper an Oriental appearance. This action also closed the
pores of the sheets and rendered them more suited for writing
upon with ink. A mechanical method of imparting a surface to
paper was brought into use in Europe in the early seventeenth

FIG. 176   *Papermaking tools of Kashmir, India. The brushes are used in applying paper to the walls for drying (Figures 167, 170); the tool shown in the centre is used in sizing the paper (Figure 173); and for rendering a smooth surface to the sheets the paper is laboriously rubbed (Figures 174, 175) with polished stones set in clay or wooden handles, as shown at the right of the photograph.*

century. This consisted of a pressing-hammer of huge construction, operated by water-power (Figure 179). The idea for the apparatus was borrowed by the papermakers from the bookbinders, as these craftsmen had employed this mechanism for polishing the backs of books for many years before the papermakers adopted it. This machine gave the paper a more uniform surface than had been possible by the hand rubbing method. The results achieved by the use of the glazing-hammer were soon spread to the different mills by travelling workers, and it was not long before this machine was used universally. The hand burnishers looked upon the introduction of the hammer none too kindly, for when it came into use they had to seek other employment. In Germany the intro-

FIG. 177   Paper drying on
boards in one of the large "company" handmade paper mills of
Japan. In Figure 163 the process
of drying may be seen in one of
the hundreds of "cottage" mills.

FIG. 178   The inspection and
inside drying-room of one of Japan's large "company" handmade
paper mills. The photograph was
made in 1933 in Kōchi, Shikoku
Island, Japan.

FIG. 179   An eighteenth-century French paper mill, showing the
vatman, coucher, press, and at the extreme left the old method of glaz-
ing the paper by means of a huge hammer actuated by water-power.

duction of the glazing-hammer about the year 1540 caused a division among the makers of paper. The mills that continued the
use of the old hand burnishers would not allow, under severe
punishment, any artisan to work for them who had been employed
in a mill where the new mechanical device was used. The con-

troversy became so heated that the government threatened to confiscate the tools used in hand burnishing, and recommended that the mills adopt the new pressing- or glazing-hammers. In spite of this ruling, however, the mill-owners continued to polish or finish their paper in the manner they desired. Polishing by hand always gave the paper a streaked and uneven appearance owing to the narrowness of the glazing-stone, while the huge hammers imparted an almost uniform surface over the entire sheet. In old Oriental and Occidental papers these slight variations are traceable and afford somewhat of a clue as to the origin of the paper. About 1720 the pressing-hammers gave way to wooden glazing-rolls for giving the paper a smooth surface. These were a Dutch invention and consisted of two large rollers,* cut from the solid trunk of a tree, between which the paper was pressed. The finish which this machine imparted was as superior to that of the pressing-hammer as that had been to the original hand burnishing by stone.

After the paper was finished it was packed for transportation by wrapping in heavy coarse paper of a brown or grey colour; this wrapping paper was made from the dregs of the vat, which could not have been used for moulding book or writing paper. While there are no paper-package labels from the fifteenth century extant, there have been a good many preserved from later centuries (Figures 180, 181, 182, 183).

The methods used at present in making handmade paper differ but little from those described. Several improvements in the construction of the vats have been made, the chief of which was the "knotter," which eliminated foreign substances and knotted fibres from the paper stock before it ran into the vat. This appliance, an American invention,† came into general use about 1819; before

---

* The earliest United States patent in the Paper Museum covering the glazing-roll, or plater, is dated February 27, 1827, and was issued to Ira White and Leonard Gale of Newbury, Orange County, Vermont. The patent describes a machine "for the useful improvement in the art of finishing paper, to render its surface smooth without injuring its strength . . . and to improve it in durability and firmness." The original patent, on parchment, is signed by J. Q. Adams, President.

† The earliest United States patent in the Paper Museum covering the knotter is dated March 12, 1831, and was issued to Solomon Stimpson of Newbury, Orange County, Vermont. The patent describes "a new and useful improvement in the art of papermaking for separating the knots, knobs,

FIG. 180   *The ream label of a Braunschweig papermaker, "Andreas Bernhart, Papiermacher auff der Ocker." A figure of a horse was also used by this German papermaker as a watermark. The label dates from about 1550.*

FIG. 181   *An eighteenth-century Dutch ream label. Engraved pictorial labels were used by nearly all European papermakers; in America they were in use until the introduction of the paper-machine.*

its introduction it was necessary to scrape out from the sheets the knots made by twisted fibres or by bits of broken buttons, pieces of stone, wood, metal, or earthy matter. These could not be removed without considerable injury to the paper, often causing holes in it. The knotter or strainer was greatly improved in 1832 by a Kentish papermaker, and it is this form of the appliance that is still in use in handmade-paper mills. Another improvement was the use of a steam pipe for the heating of the stock in the vat in place of the old pistolet, while the primitive stirring-pole was su-

etc., from the pulp before the sheet is formed, and also for graduating the quality of pulp necessary to form the sheet, etc." The original patent, on parchment, is signed by Andrew Jackson, President. The first English patent covering a knotter for the cleansing of paper pulp before it entered the vat was granted to Richard Ibotson on July 29, 1830. Previous to 1830–5 much of the paper was embedded with knotted and unbeaten fibres. In the best mills these imperfections were removed with knives before the paper was sold.

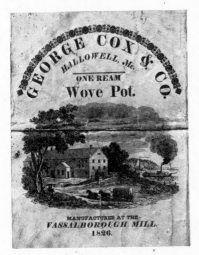

Fig. 182   An American ream label of 1826, from the handmade paper mill of George Cox and Company, Vassalborough mill, Hallowell, Maine.

Fig. 183   Lottery tickets of a Milton, Massachusetts, paper mill. Money was often raised in this manner for the establishment of mills. This example is dated May 6, 1782.

perseded by an agitator that revolved in the bottom of the vat, keeping the liquid material in constant motion. The heavy wooden screw press may still be seen in several of the older handmade-paper mills in Europe, but the hydrostatic press is now used by all well-equipped vat mills. This was invented in 1790, but was not adopted until long after that date, although Joseph Bramah, the originator, recommended it for use in paper mills.*

---

* The first use of the hydraulic press in paper manufacture was probably in the Matthias Koops mill, Mill Bank, Westminster. This mill, established in 1801, was originally equipped with old-fashioned screw presses, but from a French account of this mill we learn that at least one hydraulic press was in use. Under the title of *"Sur les papeteries et fabrication de papier-paille en Angleterre"* in *Annales des arts et manufactures, ou Mémoires technologiques,* October–November 1803, we read: "It is there that we saw for the first time the use of the hydraulic press, which pressed the water from the paper and felts from five vats. This new press has the advantage of not shaking the buildings when it is used; also, the pressure is considerably greater than that of

The method of drying handmade paper (Figure 161) remains today very much as it was in the fifteenth century, but the old sizing tub has been replaced by a machine composed of a trough and rollers, each separate sheet of paper being led through the warm size in the trough upon an endless felt. A century or more ago the heavy wooden rolls of the Dutch glazing-machine gave way to iron, but the principle of the apparatus remained about the same as in the early eighteenth-century original. Every appliance of a modern handmade paper mill can be traced to its Oriental origin, the steps of development being separated by centuries. To be able to determine the locality and period of old papers it is necessary to make a minute study of the ancient papermaking appliances, as the succession of innovations, occurring in different countries at various periods, caused changes in the character of paper throughout the ages. To the casual observer these changes are insignificant, but to the student of papermaking they are clues that, followed, lead to secrets of the craft he loves.

---

the old screw press and one can limit the pressure as desired by simply turning a tap; the press is disengaged in an instant. We have been astonished by the different applications of the hydraulic press we have seen in England. . . . We have remarked that the low cost of machinery in England makes it possible for the establishment of all kinds of mechanism at a reasonable figure."

VII

Paper: a Sacred Material

THE USE OF PAPER IN THE ORIENT FOR CEREMONIES
AND PURPOSES UNKNOWN IN THE WESTERN WORLD

WHILE my interest in paper in the Far East has been primarily in its actual manufacture, I have not been unmindful of the uses of paper in the Orient. In investigating handmade paper fabrication in China the wayfarer will at once be interested in the use of paper in religious rites and sacrifices, as well as for many of the practical purposes for which it is employed. Also, in Japan and Korea great quantities of paper are used in ways totally unknown in the Occident. In this chapter, therefore, an account of the development and use of Chinese ceremonial paper, and an outline of the present-day uses of paper in Japan and Korea for utilitarian purposes, will be undertaken.

Before the advent of paper, or as early as the period of the Western or Former Han Dynasty (206 B.C.–A.D. 25), wealthy Chinese placed silver and copper coins in the tombs and coffins of their deceased relatives, so that the departed might have an abundance of money for various purposes in the spirit world. The authenticity of this statement rests upon the assertion in the *Chronicles of the Former Han* [1] that during the reign of Emperor Wu Ti (140–86 B.C.) vandals entered the vault of one of his ancestors, Wên Ti, (179–156 B.C.) and made away with the silver coins therein. After the invention of paper by Ts'ai Lun, while Emperor Ho Ti (A.D. 89–106) ruled the country, we are informed by the *Chronicles of the Later Han* [2] that paper was placed in the tombs as a substitute for the metal coins of earlier years. During the dynasties of Wei and Chin, from the beginning of the Three Kingdoms (A.D. 221–420), it is recorded that "cunning knaves" cut paper into forms and offered it to the spirits in lieu of genuine silver and copper coins.

According to the numismatical work entitled *Ch'üan-pu t'ung-chih*,[3] published in China in 1833, the first paper notes issued in the Celestial Empire made their appearance during the reign of Emperor Kao Tsung (A.D. 650–683), of the T'ang Dynasty.

By the fourteenth century paper money was fairly common in China. Most of the notes of the Ming Dynasty are dark grey in colour,* owing to the use of both the dark outer bark and the white inner bark of the mulberry tree in their making. Legend has it that Emperor Wu (A.D. 1368–98) tried to procure a suitable paper for the printing of money and to this end consulted with the wise men of his realm for advice. One of the learned group suggested that counterfeiting could only be prevented by mixing the macerated hearts of great literary men with the mulberry-bark pulp. The Emperor is said to have taken this suggestion under advisement, but at length he decided it would be a grave mistake to destroy the literary men of China simply for the purpose of using their hearts as ingredients for paper. In talking over the problem with the Empress she suggested that the same result could be achieved without interfering with the lives of their scholarly subjects. The Empress brought forth the thought that the heart of any true literary man was actually in his writings. Therefore, the wise Empress asked the Emperor to have collected the papers upon which the great Chinese authors and poets had set down their writings. The manuscripts were duly macerated and added to the mulberry bark and it was thought that the dark grey

---

* Many of the early Chinese papers have a slightly yellow tone, due, no doubt, to direct dyeing rather than to the natural colour of the papermaking fibre. The colouring matter was probably used more as an insecticide than from any desire to beautify the paper by changing its tone. This slightly poisonous matter, known in China as *huang-neih* or *huang-po* (黃蘗), was taken from the seeds of the *Phellodendron amurense*, commonly known as the Amoor cork tree. As early as A.D. 674 a Chinese edict specified that all papers to be used for certain types of documents and religious records must be treated in this manner. There are numerous references in Chinese literature to the use of this yellow substance as a dye for paper and it has been found that manuscripts so treated have a toxic effect and would repel the ravages of insects. The colouring matter was probably added to the paper, by either dipping or brushing, after the paper had been finished. It is thought that dyeing the pulp in the vat before it was formed into paper was a later development, perhaps conceived by the Koreans at least several hundred years after the Chinese edict of the seventh century.

tone of the money papers was due to the black ink used in the calligraphy upon the paper.

After the issuance of the first paper money it no doubt became the custom to make imitations, but not counterfeits, of these notes for burial with the dead. During the period of K'ai Yüan (A.D. 713–739), T'ang Yüan Tsung, a most superstitious person, established Wang Yü as High Master of Ceremonies. This minister began the burning of mock paper money at the Imperial sacrifices, and he himself had great faith in the practice. According to the *Chronicles of the T'ang Dynasty*,[4] however, the custom was condemned by numerous Chinese scholars, who were apprehensive that the rite might become popular with the rank and file of the people; but in spite of the severe condemnation of the learned gentlemen the custom soon became prevalent among all classes and in all parts of the vast country. To the present day the rite is practised in every city and hamlet of China, as well as in all Asiatic countries where the Chinese have immigrated. There was, indeed, sound argument in favour of the imitation paper money. The practice of burying the actual silver and copper coins with the dead not only made the tombs a prey for robbers, but removed an immense amount of money from circulation, a serious matter in a land where metals were scarce. For these two reasons, no doubt, the use of genuine coins was abandoned, and in their place pieces of paper made to resemble somewhat the newly introduced paper notes were substituted. The tomb papers (Figures 184, 185) were not in any way a direct copy of the real paper money, as such an imitation would have been punishable by decapitation.

The disillusioned scholars who condemned the rite were too few to prevail against the hundreds of thousands who sanctioned and approved the ghostly practice, but their unceasing protests, and the protests of others who followed them, are recorded in old Chinese histories. Among the men who thus protested was an official named Wang Ssŭ Tsung, who lived during the reign of Chên Tsung (A.D. 998–1023), of the Sung Dynasty. This gentleman, who occupied the position of Prefect of the Second Order, forbade all unorthodox sacrifices and caused many of the temples of the false gods to be destroyed. On his deathbed Wang Ssŭ Tsung was distressed when his family burned offerings to procure his content-

Fig. 185   A wood-block for printing mantras, or charms, called wang shêng ch'ien, denoting money for the hereafter. The paper used for these prints is usually of bamboo fibre.

Fig. 184   A wood-block for the printing of "spirit-money" to be burnt at Chinese funerals. The characters read: "Ten thousand cash for all time; treasure, gold, silver."

ment in the next world, and, according to the ancient records, "raised his feeble voice and cried: 'If the spirits are intelligent, how can they accept bribes?'" In the reign of Hui Tsung (A.D. 1101–26), of the Sung Dynasty, there were two ministers, Kao Fêng and Liao Yung Chung, who presented a petition to abolish the burning of ceremonial papers. The petition read: "The custom of burning perforated paper made to resemble money, so as to assure happiness in the spirit world, is an absurd delusion; if the spirits have intelligence the practice is an insult to them." It is likely that the sheets of perforated paper, made in the shape of round coins pierced with square holes for stringing, was the original "spirit-money," inasmuch as metal coins preceded paper notes by many centuries. With all the apparent disbelief in the rite by the scholarly gentry, the funeral of Emperor Kao Tsung (A.D. 1127–63) was a most elaborate show of the burning of ceremonial papers and mock money and of all manner of paper images set afire before his remains. The heir-apparent, Hsiao Tsung (A.D. 1163–1290), however, was contemptuous of the practice and rebuked the officials at the ceremony by saying: "The burning of spirit-money is a Buddhist practice to deliver the soul from Hades; my holy sire needs no such things."

These few instances of approval and disapproval will serve to show that in early times, as at present, there was much agitation relative to the use of paper for sacrificial offerings, and that all through the centuries there has been a never ceasing controversy as to whether or not the old rite should be continued.

Marco Polo (1254–1323), during his researches in China, was amazed at the use of great quantities of paper in native ceremonies and in his writings we find many references to this dominating practice, a use for paper entirely unknown in Europe. (It is of interest to note that the Chinese were the first to use toilet paper, for in a book published in France in 1718 it is recorded that Arabs travelling in China in the ninth century were confronted with such paper. The book giving this information is Eusebius Renaudot's *Anciennes Relations des Indes et de la Chine de deux voyageurs Mohametans.*[5] The passage relating to toilet paper appears on page 17 and reads as follows: *"Ils ne sont pas soigneux de la propreté et ils ne se lavent pas avec de l'eau, quand ils ont esté à leurs necessitez; mais ils s'essuyent seulement avec du papier."*)

The use of ornamental paper cut to represent various objects and burned at Chinese funerals long antedates the time of Marco Polo and has continued through the centuries to this day; every year thousands of reams of paper are consumed by fire in ceremonial offerings. Objects of all kinds are constructed of paper and burned at the bier of the deceased so the departing spirit may have an abundance of the things represented by the frail paper effigies. Along certain streets in all the great cities of China, as well as in all large communities of Asia where Chinese people dwell, there may be seen open shops, usually clustered three or four together, where these ghost-like paper replicas are fashioned — highly ornate cardboard chests with shiny gold and silver paper locks, flowing robes of paper painted with golden dragons and complicated patterns, shoes, hats, and all manner of wearing apparel made of paper (Figure 186). For the relatives of the wealthy the craftsmen in paper also construct full-sized carts, horses, and even automobiles, the thought being that when these fragile representations

FIG. 186   *A Mandarin coat made entirely of paper and decorated by hand in a most elaborate manner. Paper clothing of this kind is burnt at Chinese funerals to enable the deceased to have fine garments in the nether world. Procured from a Chinese funeral shop in Bangkok, Siam.*

go up in smoke they will eventually assume reality in heaven and the deceased will have horses and vehicles at his disposal. I have often marvelled at the skill and patience of these artisans who fashion the paper objects, as they work in their open-fronted shops along the narrow, dirty streets and courts. The façade of each shop is usually decorated with a number of gaily painted mirrors, and the interior takes on the appearance of a veritable paper museum, all kinds of funeral paraphernalia made of paper hanging from the rafters, and shelves, drawers, and cases literally overflowing with every conceivable variety of decorated and coloured paper used in the making of these weird reproductions. Quality and workmanship vary to suit both the rich and the lowly, but all alike are destined to be burned at funerals. In Bangkok, where the population is largely Chinese, I recall standing before one of these shops for hours watching the construction of the effigy of a huge dog, the frame made of thin strips of bamboo, all covered with many thicknesses of paper and finally realistically painted with water colours. Upon asking the Chinese worker for what purpose the paper dog was intended, I was told that a wealthy Chinese merchant had just died and that this was a representation of his mastiff; the imitation animal had been ordered by the dead man's relatives and would be burned at his funeral to assure his master of having his favourite dog with him when he reached the spirit world.

Everywhere such paper animals, paper clothing, and vehicles go up in smoke at Chinese funeral ceremonies, yet the number of these objects is insignificant compared with the quantities of mock money burned every year in China and all over Asia where Chinese have made their homes. It is probably reasoned by many Chinese that if sufficient "money" is burned the deceased relative or friend will be able to purchase elaborate clothing, fine horses, and other necessities and luxuries after reaching the spirit world, making it unnecessary to burn paper images made in imitation of these things for the departed to enjoy them.

In many Chinese homes the paper is burned before the coffin of the deceased, consumed upon a stone hearth in the living-quarters. It goes without saying that numerous disastrous fires have been caused by over-zealous indulgence in burning paper images and imitation paper money. The following dispatch to American newspapers from Taiyuan, China, dated June 17, 1936, is significant: "The performance of an ancient Chinese ritual of mourning today cost the life of the widow and son of a general one week after he had been assassinated. Buddhist monks were burning in effigy the household utensils and money of General Li Sheng-ta in front of his coffin. The flames were carried by a draught to other paper images that were near the casket in honour of the dead. A roaring fire developed in a few seconds. The widow and son rushed in to save the corpse from the burning paper replicas and both were fatally burned."

Among the numerous Chinese death ceremonies at which I have been present I especially recall the occasion when I was invited to attend the funeral of a relative of an old scholarly gentleman who asked me to meet him at a certain road-crossing so that he might guide me to the house of death. He appeared promptly at the hour agreed upon, dressed in long silk robes and padded slippers, and mounted in state upon a nickel-plated bicycle, the handle-bars of which were laden with mock money and paper images — an anachronism that afforded me much secret amusement.

In the large centres the ordinary ceremonial papers, put up in compact packages, are usually sold in special shops dealing in joss paper, candles, incense sticks, and other items used in sacrificial offerings. In the villages and outlying country districts the more common funeral papers may be had in almost any shop where groceries are sold, the bundles of paper being invariably stored on the upper shelves of the orderly stores, pungent with the aroma of spices, roots, ginger, nuts, and herbs. I have procured these sacrificial papers in the great cities of China, as well as in muddy country hamlets; in the moist, mouldy shops of Indo-China, in the stores of the Chinese section of old Manila, in the small sidewalk shops of the villages of Java and Sumatra, in the queer Chinese markets of Kuala Lumpur, Penang, Singapore, and other settlements of Malaysia, and in the paper-shops of Bangkok's crooked lanes and winding canals (Figure 187). In the Chinese quarter of New York I have gone from store to store and from shopkeeper to shopkeeper seeking the small bales of "spirit-paper," but I have found that most of the Chinese living in America know nothing of its use. In one cramped establishment, kept by a parchment-faced Chinese, I found a small assortment of the less pretentious ceremonial papers, along with the bamboo paper trays in which they

Fig. 187   *Eleven examples of the common varieties of Chinese spirit-paper, burnt at funerals and in front of the family portraits. These papers are made of bamboo and straw and are usually decorated with tinfoil and printed with wood-blocks, such as in Figures 184 and 185.*

are sometimes placed, fan-like, for burning. I was informed that the custom of consigning imitation money to the flames is seldom preserved by the Chinese after leaving Asia, and that paper is burned only by the transplanted Celestials of the older generation who insist upon following the ancient traditional rites of the homeland (Figure 188).

China is a vast country, the topography of which makes intercourse between districts exceedingly difficult. It is therefore a land of many dialects and of many provinces, the comparative isolation of which tends to preserve ancient local customs and ceremonies. It has been my experience that even the educated Chinese of North China are entirely unfamiliar with the customs and practices of their countrymen living in the south; also that the people

Fig. 188   *A small Chinese country temple with bundles of bamboo and straw spirit-paper neatly piled in front of the building ready for burning and sacrificial offerings.*

from the coastal provinces know very little regarding the ceremonial customs of inner China. The religious ceremonies of various isolated districts do not arise entirely from Confucianism, nor are they wholly Buddhistic or Taoistic; they are largely of local origin and exhibit different practices even in adjacent provinces. The one thing common to all Chinese ceremonies, especially funerals, is the desire of the relatives of the deceased to outdistance in display anything that has been attempted previously in their particular neighbourhood. This is attended by complications, the rivalry often leading ambitious families to bankruptcy, since they think little of spending five or even ten times as much money for a funeral as they actually possess. The Chinese people are noted for their love of gambling, but their desire for elaborate and costly funerals occupies almost as large a place in their hearts as their various games of chance.

It is evident that paper plays a prominent part in myriad Chinese ceremonies.[6] The fibrous substance called paper is regarded in a vastly different light in the Orient from what it is in the Occident, for in the Far East it has a spiritual significance that overshadows its practical use, while in the Western world the purposes

FIG. 189   *A furnace for burning sacred paper. This furnace was dedicated to Emperor Ch'êng Tsu (1403–25), of the Ming Dynasty. These ornamental incinerators were usually built in the temple court- yards at the left of the main building. On sacrificial days imitation paper money and other ceremonial papers are carried to the temples, where they are reverentially consigned to flames in the furnaces.*

FIG. 191 *Rice straw has long been used as a material for making paper in China. In the foreground is a potching bed of stone; the piled straw has been treated with lime.*

FIG. 190 *Chinese workers cutting and preparing the bamboo for the makers of spirit-paper. According to the scholar Su-Tung-p'o, the fibre of the bamboo has been used as a papermaking material since the eleventh century.*

for which paper is intended are purely practical and utilitarian. In dealing with the use of ceremonial paper in China, therefore, it is essential to realize the respect and reverence that this substance commands in the Celestial Empire and to endeavour, if possible, to attain an appreciation of the Chinese viewpoint relative to paper — a viewpoint that has been inherited by the Chinese through hundreds of years of paper symbolism and paper worship (Figure 189).

A large portion of the paper used in China for ceremonial purposes is manufactured by hand in Chekiang. In the statistics compiled in 1935 by the Minister of Industry, Nanking,[7] the number of individual handmade-paper mills in Chekiang Province in 1933 was 24,437. These small, family mills, termed *tsao hu*, are found principally in Fuyang, Yühang, and Yungchia, with Ch'ühsien, T'unglu, Chuchi, Hsinteng, and Hsiaoshan of lesser importance. The capital involved in the handmade-paper industry of Chekiang Province in 1933 amounted to about five million Shanghai dollars, half of this money being invested in Fuyang. The establishments where the finished paper is sold are known as *chih hong* or *chih po chuang*, the most important centre for selling the sacrificial papers being the city of Hangchow. In Chekiang there are almost 127,000 workers engaged in making handmade paper, the artisans

Fig. 192   *A Chinese workman removing the partially disintegrated bamboo from the pit, after it had been in a lime and water solution for several months. It is next cleansed in clear water to remove the lime, then beaten for the papermakers. North Kwangtung Province, China.*

varying in number in each small cottage mill according to the kind of paper fabricated. Where bamboo is used as raw material the number of workers varies from four to six for each mill, while in making *pi* paper from the bark of trees, or *ts'ao* paper from rice-straw, only three men are needed (Figures 190, 191). In Fuyang alone there are over 40,000 papermakers at work in some ten thousand individual mills. The annual production of handmade paper in Chekiang Province in 1933 was valued at more than twenty million dollars. The paper made from bamboo represents about three fourths of the total production, the bamboos used being classified as *ch'ing kao, pai liao,* and *huang liao.*

In making paper from bamboo, straw, and the bark of trees it is necessary to use a different method of preparation for each material, but the actual process of forming the fibre into sheets of paper is practically identical. In using bamboo the canes are stripped of their leaves and shoots, tied into bundles, and steeped in a pond until the green outer skin, or bark, can be removed. After splitting, the bamboos are placed in layers in a sunken pit lined with stones, layers of canes alternating with layers of lime (Figure 192). The pit is then filled with water and the bamboo allowed to soak thoroughly for several months. After this intense treatment in the lime solution the bamboo is taken from the pit and placed in clear water to free the material from any trace of the caustic. After a vigorous cleansing the semi-disintegrated bamboo is beaten by hand, or by water- or buffalo-power. This final process renders the fibre suitable for forming into sheets of paper by the use of the hand-mould.

In preparing the bark for making the superior *pi* paper, the branches of the trees are cut during the winter months, tied into bundles, and finally given a steaming in an iron cauldron for two or three hours. After this preliminary treatment the branches are removed from the cauldron and the outer bark stripped from the stalks; the bark is then dried in the sun. A second boiling in lime reduces the bark to a semi-macerated condition, after which it is bleached — a process that requires from seven to eleven weeks. The bleached bark is finally placed upon a stone slab and beaten with hand mallets until it becomes a fibrous pulp. Before this pulp can be moulded into paper a mucilaginous gum made from the leaves of deciduous trees is added to the substance.

The Chinese paper termed *ts'ao* is of a yellow colour and is made from rice-straw. The process of reducing this material to a pulp is much simpler than that used for either bamboo or tree barks. The straw first receives a preliminary pounding and then after saturation in a lime solution is buried in a trench. When properly disintegrated, the straw is removed and placed in porous cloth bags, which in turn are suspended in a running stream so that the fibres may be cleansed of all particles of lime. The straw fibre, being of a tender nature, requires far less beating than either bamboo or bark. The forming of the sheets of paper upon moulds is practically the same with each of the three distinct types of fibres.

From this account of the use of paper in China for ceremonial purposes it must not be surmised that the Chinese make no other use of paper. Aside from the usual requirements of native book-printing, the papers of China are used extensively in the lining of clothing and in the making of sandals and slippers; also in the fabrication of toys, firecrackers, and fireworks, so much in evidence in all parts of China at festival time. Throughout China paper is always in evidence for many unusual purposes, and for the most part it is manufactured by hand from bamboo, straw, or mulberry bark or a mixture of these fibres.

JAPAN

In travelling through the more remote papermaking districts of Japan on the narrow, rough, and often dangerous roads, passing endless processions of carts, jinrikishas, and pedestrians along almost continuous lanes of low-built villages, the Occidental traveller cannot but observe two dominant features — the absence of chimneys on the houses and shops, and the use of great quantities of handmade paper for everyday purposes.

The rooms of Japanese houses are heated by large, heavy earthenware bowls, known as *hibachi,* in each of which several pieces of charcoal burn with a red glow within a nest of sand or asbestos, the charcoal being dextrously put in place by the use of ornamental brass chopsticks. To the visitor from the Occident, accustomed to central heating supplemented by roaring wood fires within huge chimneys, the Japanese method of heating seems cheerless and inadequate, but in the elimination of complicated heating devices and chimneys the Nipponese have dispensed with one of the most expensive features of house construction. It is doubtful, however, if the native people of Japan, huddled about the small charcoal fires, are ever wholly warm during the cold, damp winter months, as they are constantly rubbing their hands above the *hibachi* in an effort to absorb what little heat may arise. The living-quarters of Japanese houses are fairly large, and usually one or two outside walls of each room are fitted with small oblong frames of frail wood over which paper is pasted, allowing the entrance of some light but preventing all vision from either the inside or the outside (Figure 193). Even in the north country the Japanese houses and inns have only these thin paper windows to separate the meagre indoor comfort afforded by their charcoal heaters from the drifted snowbanks and cold winds from the mountains.*

---

* From a scientific standpoint it has lately been proved that the use of paper in windows is more healthful than the use of glass. The paper permits the beneficial ultraviolet rays of the sun to penetrate into the room, while glass excludes these rays. Also, paper is a warm substance, as is evidenced in the use of paper in keeping the body warm; glass is extremely cold.

While Oriental houses with their fragile, although fairly practical, paper windows would not be adequate in material comfort for us, we of the Occident could doubtless learn much in economy from the Chinese and Japanese of the use of paper in ways unknown in the Western world. For instance, the burden of window-washing is eliminated with the use of paper windows, as each spring the old soiled paper is removed and fresh paper pasted to the wooden window frames. Oriental artisans have developed a wide variety of papers and adapted them to almost every conceivable use. This development in Japan is largely due to the growth of certain trees and shrubs, the bark of which, when unadulterated with European wood pulps, forms excellent paper-making fibre. With the Japanese innate ability to execute hand work and through the use of the mulberry (*Broussonetia papyrifera*), mitsumata (*Edgeworthia papyrifera*), and gampi (*Wikstrœmia canescens*) fibres as raw materials, the handmade papers of Japan fabricated previous to the modern tendency to haste and cheapening were admirably adapted to many Occidental æsthetic and industrial uses. In late years, however, the Japanese have lessened the quality, and thereby the desirability, of their papers by the admixture of inferior foreign wood pulps. Also, they have reduced the quality of their handmade papers by the employment of mechanical drying devices and supplementing honest hand work with the introduction of power-driven beaters and other appliances for the acceleration of the process.

In Europe and America, as well as in the Orient, there are fast-running machines producing paper in continuous rolls of hundreds of feet each minute, but these short-fibred, easily torn, mechanically-made papers would not endure the ordeal to which the old Japanese handmade papers were subjected in the making of windows, lanterns, partition screens, umbrellas, rain-cloaks, bags, and tarpaulins, and for all sorts of other requirements where glass, metal, leather, rubber, and cloth are employed in the Occident. The general impression existing among Western people is that Japan has a mild climate, and therefore more delicate and fragile objects can survive. But this is not the case; both summer and winter in Japan are most severe and are trying even to an American accustomed to rigorous winters and to summers that are damp and warm. In preindustrialized Japan it was only through the use of superior and unique papermaking materials and genuine ability in the craft of paper fabrication that the Japanese were able to make papers that gave faithful service through long periods, being used over and over again. In former times it was not uncommon to see paper umbrellas that had been in use many years, and any traveller knows that Japan could never be called a rainless country. The observant wayfarer who has sojourned in the mountainous little islands during the spring months is cognizant of the hardships the paper umbrellas had to endure, for in Japan it often rains for several days without interruption; yet no matter how wet and dank it may have been, the peasants were always to be seen walking through the rain-soaked rice fields with their stilted wooden sandals and their charmingly coloured umbrellas.

Along the country roads of Japan it was always interesting to watch the great variety of man- and beast-drawn carts laden with every kind of native commodity, each cart with its paper tarpaulin. Every little vehicle had this oiled-paper protection, impervious to water and lighter in weight and cheaper than cloth, which during sunny weather was folded and packed away in the cart. These seemingly frail paper coverings endured the trying conditions to which they were subjected from one year to another and finally wore out only through constant use, like any other supposedly more durable material. The jinrikisha men in the towns and villages during the periodical rains wore mantles of oiled paper, for this covering not only was effective in keeping them dry, but could be purchased in large pieces for a few sen. The workers in the fields, the men labouring on the roads, and the watchmen at the railway crossings depended upon coverings of paper to keep them dry.

The oiled paper of Japan could formerly be purchased in the smallest of shops, and every peasant cottage had a stock of sheets of divers sizes, which were used again and again for many household requirements. In the tea-growing districts stout oiled-paper bags were used for holding the newly picked leaves and it was not unusual to see paper sacks that had given service for half a dozen years literally covered with patches of paper where they had been repaired from time to time. Paper bags for the storing of grain were also common, for paper that had been oiled or tanned with the fermented juice of green persimmons, the method used to render the material durable, was not easily destroyed by insects. The Occidental traveller never ceased wondering at the almost unlimited use of paper by the Japanese for utilitarian purposes.

The Japanese have been making handmade paper for more than thirteen centuries, and through the ages its myriad applications to local needs have been almost without limit. The most unusual and fantastic use of the paper, however, occurred during the late war when the Japanese military undertook to dispatch bomb-laden paper balloons to the shores of the United States with the hope of inflicting death and destruction and causing untold consternation. The paper used in making these balloons, of remarkable tensile strength, was made of long, drawn-out mulberry fibre, and to render the material impervious to water it was treated in the manner long used by the Japanese in waterproofing their paper umbrellas, bags, tarpaulins, and many other useful commodities used outdoors. Specimens of the balloon paper show many small paper patches, resembling the repaired paper bags that are used from one year to another by the tea-growers of Shizuoka. It is probable that the paper used in constructing the balloons was made in a number of different isolated mills, an assumption that is evidenced by the various colours of the paper and the technique employed in its formation. In the state of Montana balloons of a brown-yellow colour as well as of an almost pure white tone were found, while in Oregon paper balloons of a pleasing light-blue shade were discovered. The paper balloons were responsible for the deaths of several persons and perhaps they were instrumental in causing a few small forest fires, but considering the magnitude of the effort the military results obtained by the Japanese were infinitesimal.

After the Japanese surrender the Staff Officers Technical Section, Japanese Headquarters, Tōkyō, revealed that they worked for two years in an attempt to perfect the paper balloons and 9,000,000 yen (more than $2,000,000) was expended on the project. Each balloon was about forty feet in diameter and all together, according to the Japanese, nine thousand of the bomb-laden balloons were launched from three different sites near Tōkyō. Japanese scientists had the course of the sky-weapons computed in detail: each balloon would spiral upward more than ten thousand yards, they estimated, then eastward winds would speed them across the Pacific at 125 to 190 miles an hour in a straight course for the United States. Timing devices were set to explode the bombs from forty to fifty hours after the balloons had been launched. While an undetermined number of the balloons did land in the United States, one as far east as Michigan, details of the outcome of the dubious experiment were kept secret in this country so the Japanese were uncertain and bewildered as to the effect the sinister paper balloons were having on their Occidental enemy. Before the close of the war the Japanese came to the conclusion that most of the balloons were going down in the Pacific Ocean, and by April 20, 1945 the entire project, which had employed thousands of women papermakers, was abandoned as a complete failure.

KOREA

While Korea for years has been dominated by Japan, this peninsula country has not been modernized to the same extent as Japan; Korea still retains many of its age-old customs and traditions. In Korean houses paper plays a part that is unique, for in place of the regularly shaped grass mats used on the floors of Japanese houses, the Koreans use thick oiled paper, a thoroughly practical material when their method of heating is considered. In Korea the rooms are kept warm, not by the picturesque but impractical *hibachi* of Japan, but by an oven under the floor. The smoke is emitted by way of a tile chimney running underground and finally rising within a brick wall at a considerable distance from the house; though in lowly homes the smoke escapes directly from the house foundation without the expense or bother of a tile chimney. For actual comfort the Korean house is preferable to the old-time Japanese house. In both countries the people live close to the floor, and in Korea the floors are delightfully warm; while in Japan, even though covered with the thick straw mats, the floors are usually cold and uncomfortable. In Korea, as in Japan and in some parts of China, paper is used for windows (Figure 194).

A census of the handmade paper industry of Japan would show between twelve and fifteen hundred individual mills, each operating from one to forty vats. In China and Japan papermaking by

FIG. 193   *The interior of a Japanese tea-room in Kyoto, showing the paper windows. The paper, called* shōji, *is usually made from mulberry-bark fibre; the paper is replaced once each year, so there is no window-washing. The custom, of course, came originally from China.*

FIG. 194   *In Korea, as in some parts of China, the window frames are covered with thin, stout paper made from the white inner bark of the mulberry. This photograph was taken in the home of a well-to-do merchant, Seoul.*

hand is by no means an obsolete industry, and new uses for paper are constantly being developed. It is possible that the fabrication of paper by hand will continue for all time in the Orient, as labour costs are comparatively low and there is considerable natural papermaking material. Coupled with these two important conditions is the fact that many of the utilitarian handmade papers of the East have desirable qualities that cannot be duplicated successfully by the papermaking machine. In Japan in the year 1932 (the latest figures available) the value of paper made by hand was 14,000,000 yen, while that manufactured by machinery was 43,-000,000 yen — surely a comparison that is favourable to the ancient hand process when compared with conditions in Occidental countries. In three great papermaking districts of Japan — Gifu, Fukui, Kōchi — there were in 1934 almost six thousand families who gained their support through the fabrication of handmade paper. The Japanese, however, have not been slow in adopting the papermaking machine, but there are many varieties of paper made in Japan that can be formed successfully only by the use of a hand-mould in the hands of a skilled and patient craftsman.

The papers of China, Japan, and Korea, used in the myriad ways that have been described, are for the most part made by the traditional hand methods. The chief fibres used for making Oriental papers, as previously outlined, are bamboo, rice-straw, mulberry, mitsumata, and gampi barks. These materials grow and are used in China, Japan, and Indo-China. The material used in most of the handmade papers of Siam is the native *khoi* bark (*Streblus asper*); in India jute (*Corchorus olitorius*) and hemp (*Crotalaria juncea*) and discarded papers (*naddi*) are largely used for papermaking. In Nepal the *Daphne cannabina* is the bark used in making the large sheets of paper used in this northern country, while in Burma and Tibet a species of the mulberry tree yields the papermaking fibre.

In Europe and America handmade paper is regarded as a luxury, something to be used only for the printing of expensive books, for etchings and elaborate stationery. Indeed, the greater part of the people of the Occident live their entire lives without ever even seeing any paper that has been formed by the hand method. In the more traditional Orient this condition does not exist. Every person, from peasant to plutocrat, comes in daily contact with common, useful things that have been made of handmade paper — things fabricated by artisans who regard their craftsmanship as edified through its use by workaday people for humble purposes. The makers of handmade paper in the Orient, unlike those of the Occident, do not feel that their handiwork should be restricted only to the libraries and drawing-rooms of those who have the means to indulge in finely printed books and expensive engravings. Their art is not exclusive, but inclusive, an ideal which is the result of an ancient civilization where handmade paper has always been used for making lowly objects, and where traditions and training have been handed down through countless generations of papermaking families.

VIII

The Paper and the Papermakers of Europe and America during the Early Years of Printing

THE PAPER fabricated in the fifteenth- and sixteenth-century mills did not vary in size to the same extent as paper made in later years, owing to the limited demand for sheets of diverse dimensions and to the expense of production. For every size of paper two moulds and one deckle * were required, appliances fashioned only with difficulty and considerable outlay of money. In the early years of printing, the paper was seldom cut, the sheets being printed upon in the original sizes formed in the moulds, although in many cases the deckle edges were trimmed away. In all old paper, as well as in the handmade papers of the present day, there is a considerable variation in the thickness and finish, and in single books the leaves vary noticeably in weight.

The tone of the old paper was never entirely uniform, and owing to the absence of chemicals in the manufacture, the grades of paper differed strikingly in colour. The best paper was of a creamy tint, while the poorer grades, made from old and discoloured materials, were a light coffee tone, and at times even a dark grey. The bleaching of linen and cotton rags for papermaking was not in general use until the early nineteenth century, and all paper made before that time assumed the tone of the material from which it was made; the water used in the early mills also had considerable influence upon the shade or tint of the paper. In the wintertime, especially, it was difficult to clarify the water for use in the paper

---

* The use of two moulds and one deckle applies only to the making of paper in the European manner where the vatman forms the sheets and the coucher lays them down. In all Asiatic papermaking based on the Oriental principle only one mould is required for each size of paper as the same worker acts as both vatman and coucher.

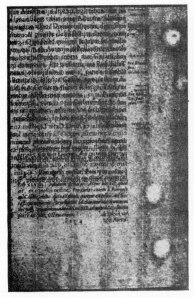

FIG. 195   *These round, semi-transparent spots, found in much old paper, were caused by drops of water falling on the newly formed sheets. This specimen is of Dutch origin, the printing from 1668.*

FIG. 196   *Ruffled or blurred "chain-lines" are common in handmade paper of European origin. This imperfection is usually caused by the coucher.*

mills. This muddy appearance is noticeable in many of the early American-made papers. It is interesting to note that in England very little paper except that of a coarse quality and greyish tone was produced until the late seventeenth century, about the time papermaking was introduced into the American colonies. In France blueing was often added to the paper stock to counteract the discoloration caused by muddy water.

In holding old paper to the light it is not uncommon to notice in the sheets round semi-transparent spots, somewhat smaller than a dime (Figure 195). These spots have a thinner surface than the rest of the sheet, resembling a watermark to some extent, and may be found in modern handmade paper as well as in the old. They were caused by drops of water falling from the workers' hands upon the moist sheet just after it had been dipped; the water

Fig. 197   *Before the invention of the knotter, tangled fibres and foreign matter of all kinds found their way into the sheets of paper. This example is of German origin, printed by Anton Koberger, Nürnberg, 1478.*

spreading the wet fibres formed almost perfectly round indentations in the finished paper, discernible only when the sheet is held to the light. When these drops do appear in paper there are usually several of them, of various sizes, as a rule near the corners of the sheets. There are also in some of the old papers ruffled or blurred "chain-lines," a slight imperfection not entirely absent in hand-made papers of the present day (Figure 196). This blurring of either the "chain" or "laid" wire impressions was caused by the coucher having allowed the mould to slip, with its thin deposit of pulp, just as he was in the act of couching the sheet upon the felting. Another defect, encountered only in old paper, is a peppered appearance throughout the sheet, due to the knotting of certain of the fibres (Figure 197). It would hardly be possible to examine thoroughly any fifteenth- or sixteenth-century book without finding all of these imperfections represented in the paper. It is not unusual to discover embedded in old papers hairs loosened from the felt in the pressing process; or human hairs fallen from the head of the vatman or coucher. In the Paper Museum there is a piece of paper in which has been embedded a fifteenth-century mosquito, visible only when the sheet is held to the light. To pre-

FIG. 198   *The rough edges on Occidental handmade paper are caused by the deckle, or cover, that fits around the four sides of the mould, shown in Figures 94–96 and 102. In (a) is shown an early American paper with extremely irregular edges, produced by a badly fitting deckle. In (b) a modern handmade paper is pictured with intentional rough edges, caused by slightly raising the wooden deckle from the mould. The papers (c) and (d) are also handmade, the deckles being fitted properly to the moulds upon which they were formed. A handmade filter-paper deckle edge is shown in (e), while (f) and (g) show deckle edges made on a mould-machine as described in Chapter xii. The deckle edge formed by the deckle-straps of the Fourdrinier machine is shown in (h).*

vent the intermingling of foreign substances with the paper pulp was a trying problem for the old papermakers. Even at the present time artisans have no end of trouble with stray particles which enter the beater, and, broken there into hundreds of minute pieces, find their way into the vat and cause unsightly specks in the sheets of paper.

In examining early printed books it will be noticed that in many instances the deckle or rough edges (Figure 198) have been cut away. In some cases this trimming was done before the paper was printed upon, as many of the old typographers no doubt regarded the deckle edges simply as necessary imperfections in the making of the paper. When the deckle edges were left undisturbed by the printer they often suffered at the hands of the binder, so it is more usual to find early volumes with cut edges than with the original deckles. The weapon with which the binder dealt the most deadly blows was the "plough," with which he cut away the margins, placing the printing in a false position on the page of the book, and often denuding the volumes of a portion of the very text. In binding, books were often trimmed to such an extent that a folio became a quarto, or a quarto an octavo, in size. Modern bibliographers usually catalogue these old volumes by measurement instead of by the paper. If a book was printed on a once-folded sheet, it would always be a folio, no matter how much a ruthless or ignorant binder may have cut it down. In the early printed books this trimming was possible as the margins were purposely left wide for the notes of the readers, so that a folio could have been reduced several inches without interfering with the text. The only way to arrive at the original size of an old volume is to examine the paper on which it was printed. In the paper-moulds the "chain-lines" invariably ran the short way of the sheet, and the "laid-lines" the long way, or from right to left as the mould was held in the hands of the vatman. In binding a folio volume the sheets were folded in the centre, the "chain-lines" running up and down, parallel with the fold. No matter if the margins have been trimmed off, it is always possible by this means to see that the volume was originally a folio. In a quarto the paper was again folded, so that the "chain-lines" ran across the page, from left to right. With an octavo the "chain-lines" ran up and down as in a folio.

Before me is a book from the Aldine Press, dated 1522, which was catalogued as an octavo, for its actual measurements (12 by 20 cm.) would indicate this size. Originally, however, the volume was a quarto, as the "chain-lines" in the paper run across the pages. On the other hand, the edition of *Artemus de Bello Gallico* printed by Nicholas Jenson in Venice in 1471 is usually, because of its large size, set down by the cataloguers as a folio, but in this book the "chain-lines" run across the pages, so it must be a quarto. This test holds good for a great many books, between octavo and folio. It can be relied upon because it is a natural test and is applicable to all books of Occidental origin.

The size of the largest paper used by William Caxton [1] was 15¾ by 22 inches. This paper was used for two books only: the first and second editions of the *Golden Legend* (first edition finished at Westminster the 20th of November 1483; the second edition appearing soon after, but without date; printed in double columns, containing 464 folios). This size was probably found too large for convenient printing, as for all of the other Caxton books smaller paper was used, varying in size from 11 by 16 to 13 by 18½ inches. The average size of moulds used for making paper in Europe during the fifteenth century was about 14 by 19 inches; the largest sheets measured about 18½ by 26½ inches. These were convenient sizes for the mould-makers to fabricate and also for the papermakers to form sheets upon; the larger the moulds, the more difficult they were to handle, as their weight when laden with the wet pulp, or stock, was far greater than would be imagined.

In Great Britain even as late as 1818 it was ordained by law that no newspaper should exceed in dimensions 22 by 32 inches. "So desirous were the publishers of newspapers at that time for a larger surface," wrote Charles Cowan [2] in his reminiscences of his early days in a handmade-paper mill at St. Mary Cray, Kent, "that an order for a large quantity of paper reached us, the size to be 22½ by 32½ inches, and the stationer stated that he would assume all risk of passing it through the Stamp Office." This would have given a surface of 731 square inches to each sheet instead of the statutory maximum of 704 square inches. About the largest surface of the fifteenth-century papers was 470 square inches, while a surface of approximately 235 square inches was the most common. The largest size of handmade paper that is fabricated at present is made in the James Whatman, Springfield mill at Maidstone, Kent, the sheet being termed "antiquarian" and measuring 31 by 53 inches, a surface of 1,643 square inches.[3] For making sheets of this giant size the mould is hung on a mechanical lifting device and six or eight men are required in the dipping and couching processes. It was at this renowned mill that the size of handmade paper known as "medium" (17½ by 22 inches) was first made two sheets on a

FIG. 199   The divided mould thought to have been first used in Europe in 1826 in the James Whatman mill, Maidstone, Kent. Aside from being divided by a wooden section in the centre, removable with the deckle, this mould is also divided into sheets of letter-paper size by "tearing-wires." The paper stock lies thinner along these wires and therefore may be torn with an edge resembling a genuine deckle. Each sheet of the eight formed at one dipping of the mould would have two genuine and two false deckle edges. The Chinese used divided moulds centuries before their use in Europe. See Figures 51, 52, 55.

FIG. 200   Through the action of the "tearing-wire" laced to the "laid" wires, this mould is capable of forming two sheets of letter paper at each dipping. Every sheet would have three genuine deckle edges and one false deckle edge. This manner of economizing labour is used largely in the making of stationery.

FIG. 201 *The engraving of the city of Nürnberg from Schedel's* Liber Chronicarum *of 1493. The group of five buildings at the right of the woodcut, outside the wall, was Ulman Stromer's paper mill, the first in Germany.*

mould,* a deckle running through the mould dividing it into two equal parts so that two sheets could be dipped and couched with practically the same effort as had been previously expended in making one sheet (Figures 199, 200). This was in 1826, and the innovation caused a split among the makers belonging to "the Original Society" which lasted several years. The section of artisans who were adverse to making two sheets of medium paper simultaneously on a mould called themselves the "Deckles," while those agreeing to make the paper in the new and novel manner were known as the "Stars." After a reconciliation of the two factions Mr. Balston, the owner of the Whatman mill, summoned William Grigsby, one of his workers and the leader of the Stars, who always wore on his jacket a ten-pointed star, denoting the number of vats in the mill, and gave him a sovereign for each point, bidding the vatman and couchers spend the money in jollification.

The first organized union of papermakers in England was

---

* See Figures 51, 52, 55 for the use of the divided mould in China.

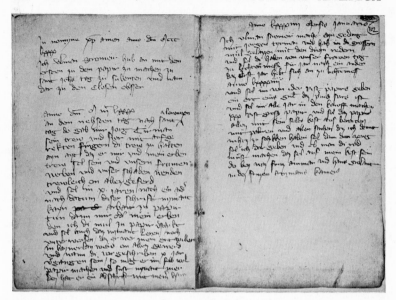

FIG. 202　*Two pages from the fourteenth-century diary of Ulman Stromer, the first paper-mill owner in Germany. The original manuscript diary is in the National Museum, Nürnberg; it is the earliest European document concerning the craft of papermaking.*

founded in 1800, but as early as 1784 there was a strike among the workers in this craft. The earliest recorded labour dispute in a paper mill antedated the founding of the union in England by more than four hundred years. This strike occurred in the Ulman Stromer mill, the earliest papermaking establishment in Germany (Figure 201). In the Germanic National Museum, Nürnberg, there is a manuscript diary entitled: *Püchl von meim geslecht und von abentewr* (Figure 202). This manuscript, begun by Ulman Stromer about the year 1390, not only is the first document in Europe relating to papermaking technique, but sets down an account of the earliest controversy between capital and labour in the paper industry. Ulman Stromer was a member of the senate that governed Nürnberg, and his mill was located just outside the western wall of the city, at the point where the Pegnitz River emerges into the fields. Previous to his papermaking venture Stromer had been a merchant, and on his journeys of trade to

Italy, where paper had been made since 1276, he had seen the craft practised. He was convinced that he would be successful with an establishment of the same kind in his native Germany, especially if he could secure a monopoly in this work. No one in Nürnberg was versed in making paper, so it was necessary that the erstwhile trader procure his artisans elsewhere. He set out to find several foreigners who were skilled in the craft of paper-making, and after considerable deliberation succeeded in inducing a number of artisans to leave their positions in Lombardy.

Ulman Stromer was at this time sixty-two years of age, and his experience in trading had made him keen and of a cautious disposition. After procuring the workers he forced them to swear to be loyal to him and to guard carefully the secrets of their craft so that there would be no likelihood of other mills springing up in Germany. Accordingly, Ulman Stromer wrote in his diary that Closen Obsser, the German he had engaged as foreman, "promised to be faithful unto me and declared on his oath that he would be true to me and my heirs, that he would be my overseer at the mill, keep me from harm, and that as long as he lived he would make paper for no one else save me and for my heirs and would not teach any man to make paper in any way at all. This took place on the Sunday next before St. Lawrence's Day, in my room at the time of evening prayer in the year 1390 when my son Jörg was present." Thus having his foreman's faithfulness assured, Stromer proceeded to have his other German workers take the same oath. He recorded in his chronicle that, "it was on the day after St. Lawrence when Jörg Tyrmann swore on oath to the saints that he would help my progress materially and that for ten years he would make paper only for me and my heirs and would not instruct anyone except by my sanction. But when the ten years are past he may make paper for himself, but for no one else, and he may then teach those who make paper for him, but for no one else, as long as he lives."

These men, like himself, were Germans, but with the skilled Italian workers Stromer felt there was need for extra precaution, so he took them before a procurator named Conradus, and Stromer's sons, brother, and brother-in-law acted as witnesses to the affidavits. The contract with the Italian workmen read: "In the year 1390, Franciscus de Marchia, and Marcus, his brother, and his manservant Bartholomeus pledged their loyalty to me and swore on oath of the holy saints that they would for ever be faithful and would not divulge the secrets of papermaking to anyone in all the German lands this side of the mountains of Normandy."

The precautions taken by Stromer to guard his own interests excited the suspicions of the Italians; they concluded that if their labours were so indispensable to the success of the paper mill, it would be more to their advantage to control the mill themselves than to permit Stromer to be their master. With this thought in view the Lombards tried to hamper the progress of the mill in every possible manner, hoping that Stromer would become weary and discouraged with the whole venture and eventually lease the mill to them so that they might operate it as they pleased. Continuing with his diary, Ulman Stromer wrote: "the Italians were most troublesome the first year and caused me many difficulties, not suffering the third water-wheel to turn at all. My first two wheels operated eighteen stampers and even these were idle a great part of the time as the foreign workers wished to produce as little paper as possible so as to force me to allow them to have the mill for a rent of 200 gulden a year. This I would not agree to do and they then offered to give me an amount of paper. From this I understood that they wished to ruin me and deprive me of my paper mill."

In mediæval times the master had great authority over his workers. Stromer recorded in this diary: "In the year 1391, on the twentieth of August, I took Franz and his brother Marcus and shut them in the tower." On the fourth day of their imprisonment the unruly Italians sent for Stromer's brother-in-law, thinking that he would be more lenient with them than Stromer himself. A reconciliation was effected and the two men were liberated on the fourth day, but not until they had sworn that they would cause no further trouble and would do their full share of work at the paper mill.

The confinement in the tower had the desired result upon the scheming Italians and they worked more in harmony thereafter. Encouraged by the improved discipline, Ulman Stromer engaged additional papermakers, who were duly sworn like the others. A carpenter was required to repair the stampers and vats, for in

1392 Stromer recorded: "In my back room Erhart Zymerman has been engaged to be my servant for one year. He is to do the carpentry work at the mill or he will polish paper, and his wife will sort rags, or hang paper on lines to dry, or count the paper. Wages will be paid them, a good house in which to live and fire-wood withal." Ulman Stromer operated the paper mill from 1390 to 1394, when he leased the property to Jörg Tyrmann for a period of four years. Stromer died in the year 1407 at the age of seventy-nine. This manuscript diary is the most valuable docu-ment in the entire annals of papermaking.

On June 20, 1788 Benjamin Franklin (1706–90) read before the members of the American Philosophical Society of Philadel-phia a treatise on papermaking,* which was later published in

---

* Benjamin Franklin's discussion of papermaking technique constitutes the only strictly American contribution to the bibliography of papermaking that appeared in the eighteenth century. Dr. Franklin was eighty-two years of age when the following was communicated to the society: "In Europe to have a large surface of paper connected together and smooth on one side, the following operations are performed. 1. A number of small sheets are to be made separately. 2. These are to be couched, one by one, between blankets. 3. When a heap is formed it must be put under a strong press, to force out the water. 4. Then the blankets are to be taken away, one by one, and the sheets hung up to dry. 5. When dry they are to be again pressed, or if to be sized, they must be dipped into size made of warm water, in which glue and alum are dissolved. 6. They must be pressed again to force out the super-fluous size. 7. They must be hung up a second time to dry, which if the air happens to be damp requires some days. 8. They must then be taken down, laid together, and again pressed. 9. They must be pasted together at their edges. 10. The whole must be glazed by labour, with a flint.

"In China if they would make sheets, suppose of four and an half ells long and one and an half ells wide, they have two large vats, each five ells long and two ells wide, made of brick, lined with a plaster that holds water. In these the stuff is mixed ready to work.

"Between these vats is built a kiln or stove, with two inclining sides; each side somewhat larger than the sheet of paper; they are covered with a fine stucco that takes a polish, and are so contrived as to be well heated by a small fire circulating in the walls.

"The mould is made with thin but deep sides, that it may be both light and stiff: It is suspended at each end with cords that pass over pullies fas-tened to the ceiling, their ends connected with a counterpoise nearly equal to the weight of the mould.

"Two men at each end of the mould, lifting it out of the water by the help of the counterpoise, turn it and apply it with the stuff for the sheet, to the smooth surface of the stove, against which they press it, to force out great part of the water through the wires. The heat of the wall soon evapo-rates the rest, and a boy takes off the dried sheet by rolling it up. The side next the stove receives the even polish of the stucco, and is thereby better

Fig. 203   The Chinese method of forming large sheets of paper as described in an address read by Benjamin Franklin before the members of the American Philosophical Society, Philadelphia, June 20, 1788. Franklin suggested that the same principle be adopted in America, as the need for larger sheets of paper than was possible with the Occidental mould was keenly felt. (From Arts, métiers et cultures de la Chine, Paris, 1814.)

Fig. 204   The Chinese method of drying sheets of paper against a heated oven as described by Benjamin Franklin in his address read before the members of the American Philosophical Society, Philadelphia, June 20, 1788. This engraving is from the same source as Figure 203.

the *Transactions* of this society.[4] Dr. Franklin describes in his essay the laborious method used in Europe for forming large sheets of paper, and then relates the simple manner employed by the Chinese papermakers in solving the difficulty (Figure 203). The European method consisted in pasting small sheets together at the edges and burnishing the joints with an agate or flint held in a wooden handle. In China a large mould was used, operated by two workmen. The large sheets were dried upon the flat in-

fitted to receive the impressions of fine prints. If a degree of sizing is required, a decoction of rice is mixed with the stuff in the vat.

"Thus the great sheet is obtained, smooth and sized, and a number of the European operations saved.

"As the stove has two polished sides, and there are two vats, the same operation is at the same time performed by two men at the other vat; and one fire serves."

Although Dr. Franklin's observations are none too accurate, they do lead us to believe that he had far more than the layman's conception of Chinese papermaking. In mentioning "wires" Franklin, of course, means the bamboos of the mould.

FIG. 205   *Chinese workers forming and drying large sheets of paper as described by Benjamin Franklin in 1788. Dr. Franklin suggested that American papermakers adopt this method. From an original water-colour painting of the latter eighteenth century.*

clining sides of a heated oven or kiln, which gave one side of each sheet a remarkably smooth surface (Figures 204, 205). Franklin states that by this method the Chinese workmen could make paper "four and an half ells long by one and an half ells wide." (The largest Chinese paper in the Paper Museum collection is from the Ming period and measures 48 by 84 inches.)

Benjamin Franklin's interest in papermaking led him to have his own watermark, which may be seen in some of the paper upon which he printed, including copies of *Poor Richard's Almanac.* The watermark consists of a fleur-de-lis within a shield, surmounted by a crown, with the initials B F in single-line lettering underneath. As further evidence of Franklin's  concern with paper there is a doggerel poem attributed to him in which different types of men are compared with various kinds of paper. Inasmuch as the verses mention ten varieties of paper in use in Franklin's time and have seldom been printed, the poetic effort of the good doctor is given in full. The following version has been taken from a little calf-bound book entitled: *The Columbian Orator: containing a Variety of Original and Selected Pieces . . . calculated to improve Youth and Others in the Ornamental and Useful Art of Eloquence.* Boston, Manning and Loring, Feb. 1807: *

> Some wit of old; such wits of old there were,
> Whose hints show'd meaning, whose allusions, care,
> By one brave stroke, to mark all human kind,
> Call'd clear *blank paper* every infant mind;
> When still, as op'ning sense her dictates wrote,
> Fair virtue put a seal, or vice a blot.
>
> The thought was happy, pertinent, and true,
> Methinks a genius might the plan pursue.
> I, (can you pardon my presumption?) I,
> No wit, no genius, yet for once will try.

---

* The original printing of this amusing poem appeared in the *American Museum* (Philadelphia, October 1787) when Franklin was in his eighty-first year. In this publication the poem is headed: "On paper. — Ascribed to dr. Franklin." The poem was included without comment in the *Works of the Late Dr. Benjamin Franklin,* printed by G. G. J. and J. Robinson, London, 1793. It was similarly printed in the 1802 London edition, but in the 1806 London edition of Franklin's complete works the editor made the following comment: "We have been told that this poem is not Franklin's and the name of some other person was at the time mentioned to us as the author; but as we have forgotten both the name and the authority, and as the poem has been ascribed to Dr. Franklin in the *American Museum,* we think it not right to omit it." In Jared Sparks's edition of the works of Benjamin Franklin (Boston, 1840) the poem is reprinted on pages 161–3.

Various the papers, various wants produce,
The wants of fashion, elegance, and use.
Men are as various: and, if right I scan,
Each sort of *paper* represents some *man.*

Pray note the fop; half powder and half lace;
Nice, as a band-box were, his dwelling-place;
He's the *gilt paper,* which apart you store,
And lock from vulgar hands in the scrutoire.

Mechanics, servants, farmers, and so forth,
Are *copy paper* of inferior worth;
Less priz'd, more useful, for your desk decreed,
Free to all pens, and prompt at ev'ry need.

The wretch, whom av'rice bids to pinch and spare,
Starve, cheat, and pilfer, to enrich an heir,
Is coarse *brown paper,* such as pedlars choose
To wrap up wares, which better men will use.

Take next the miser's contrast, who destroys
Health, fame, and fortune, in a round of joys.
Will any paper match him? Yes, throughout,
He's a true *sinking paper,** past all doubt.

The retail politician's anxious thought
Deems this side always right, and that stark naught;
He foams with censure; with applause he raves,
A dupe to rumours, and a tool of knaves;
He'll want no type his weakness to proclaim,
While such a thing as *fools-cap* has a name.

The hasty gentleman, whose blood runs high,
Who picks a quarrel if you step awry,
Who can't a jest, or hint, or look endure:
What's he? What? *Touch-paper* † to be sure.

What are our poets, take them as they fall,
Good, bad, rich, poor, much read, not read at all?
Them and their works in the same class you'll find;
They are the mere *waste-paper* of mankind.

---

* An old name for blotting paper.

† A kind of paper used in making fireworks; also used by prestidigitators
when a quick-burning paper is desired.

Observe the maiden, innocently sweet,
She's fair *white-paper,* an unsullied sheet;
On which the happy man, whom fate ordains,
May write his name, and take her for his pains.

One instance more, and only one I'll bring;
'Tis the great man who scorns a little thing;
Whose thoughts, whose deeds, whose maxims are his own,
Form'd on the feelings of his heart alone:
True genuine *royal paper* is his breast;
Of all the kinds most precious, purest, best.

The Oriental papermakers have never had any standard sizes for paper, and throughout China, Japan, Korea, India, Tibet, and Indo-China the dimensions of the moulds vary greatly. The largest Japanese mould (see Figure 74) would be capable of producing sheets of paper 29 by 67 inches (1,943 square inches), the bamboo laid strips or reeds running lengthwise of the mould, as in European metal wire-covered moulds. This exceptionally large mould was procured near Okayama, a town in southwestern Japan, and had been used for making a paper called *shōji,* used in lieu of glass in the windows of old-time Japanese houses (Figure 193). In Japan, as well as in China, sheets of paper have always been fabricated in almost every conceivable size, but in late years, owing to the exportation of paper from these countries, the paper has been to a great extent standardized. All through India, however, the sizes and methods remain much as they were hundreds of years ago. As no paper is exported from India, there is little need for uniformity, the various small cottage mills producing the paper for local markets only. In the southern Shan States of Burma the largest-size moulds measure 32 by 66 inches and are of the "wove" type, being covered with woven cloth. This large size of paper is produced east of Taunggyi at Mong Kung, and the paper is termed *kalats.* These large sheets, like the Japanese *shōji,* are cut to suit the various purposes of the native population. The Shan paper is made from paper-mulberry bark (*Broussonetia papyrifera*). In Kashmir the sheets of paper measure about 26 by 30 inches, a surface of 780 square inches. During the sixteenth and seventeenth centuries beautiful paper for manuscripts was made in Kashmir from rag stock. A village near Srinagar has long been the papermaking centre of Kashmir, and paper is still made in this region with clear and abundant water. In the Indian province of Bengal the paper usually measures about 21½ by 22½ inches in the uncut sheets, while in Tonkin, French Indo-China, where paper-making has been carried on undisturbed for hundreds of years, the moulds are smaller, averaging about 10 by 24 inches. The sizes of the Oriental papers have been cited for comparison with the old European sheets; the Oriental papers have not changed in size through the centuries to the same extent as the European handmade papers.

An idea of the cost of European paper in the fifteenth century may be gleaned from the prices that were paid by the directors of the Ripoli Press at Florence between 1474 and 1483. An orig-inal cost-book of this establishment is preserved in the Biblioteca Nazionale in Florence. This book shows that the nine sizes or qualities of paper would have varied in price from about two dollars a ream for the lesser size or quality to about six dollars a ream for the Bologna paper in common folio. The oldest bill that is recorded showing the price of paper is dated 1352 and reads: "To George Cosyn, for one quartern of royal paper, to make paint-ers' patters, 10d." According to this, a quire of royal paper in 1352 sold for about one third less than in the year 1483. In the contract between William Rittenhouse and William Bradford, dated 1697, the prices of paper were given, "ye writing paper at 20 shillings [the ream] and ye brown paper at 6 shillings pr. ream." The weekly wage of a papermaker in England during the latter part of the fif-teenth century was from two to three shillings. When the prices paid for paper at this time are considered, the wage of a workman seems low, but at that time labour did not hold the same important place that it did in later years. During the eighteenth and nine-teenth centuries the selling price of a ream of finished paper would have offset the weekly wage of one papermaker. In England dur-ing the early part of the eighteenth century a vatman earned from fifteen to eighteen shillings a week; in America at that time the wage was a little higher than in the papermaking districts of southern England. Eighteen shillings a week was a high wage compared with that of other trades; a bookbinder at that time re-ceived but twelve shillings a week and was required to work from six in the morning until nine at night, three hours longer than a papermaker's day. The following interesting account which appeared in a little book of trades in 1747 gives some idea of the requirements at that time of both the master and the worker: "Papermaking requires much water and a great deal of room, and therefore is altogether carried on at water-mills in the country, which undertakings are not numerous. It goes through various operations and divers hands before it is completed, and the moulding part, which is the principal, requires a nice hand and good eye. They take with an apprentice 5 to 10 pounds who work from six to six, and he ought not to be a very tender lad; they pay a journeyman moulder [vatman] 15 to 18 shillings a week; and a mill with the proper utensils (besides which there must be a reserve of at least 200 pounds, cash for a stock of rags, etc.) will stand one, minded to be a master, in 100 pounds, of which some have two or three. It is a very curious art taken as a whole, and so useful a manufacture, that it ought to be encouraged at home more than it is." From this account it will be seen that the life of a worker in an eighteenth-century paper mill was anything but indolent. He was required to be at the mill by six in the morning ready for work, and did not leave for his home until six in the evening. The noonday lunch was usually consumed while the men were working, but the more lenient masters allowed fifteen or twenty minutes for the repast. From the English book of trades of 1747 it would appear that papermakers at that time were looked upon with some degree of favour, but a hundred years earlier such was evidently not the case according to a petition dated 1636 to the Privy Council from the people of Buckinghamshire and Middlesex. These people living near the paper mills alleged that by converting corn mills into mills for the making of paper rents were advanced greatly and that the papermakers brought many poor and indigent to the parish whom they had to maintain. Also they complained that the papermakers were too highly paid and were able to save more from their wages than was possible with workers in other trades. The people further alleged that the papermakers brought plague into the country from their rags, that they killed the fish by their double water-wheels and by penning up the water flooded the countryside. They also petitioned that the paper was poorly made and would bear ink only on one side and was sold much dearer than formerly.

Many of the old German and French mills were provided with kitchens and sleeping-rooms which were used by some of the papermakers, others living in small cottages near their work. The papermaking centres were little communities in themselves, and many of the old artisans lived for one generation after another in the same spot, working at the same vat and with the same moulds that had been in use over long periods of time. In Holland it was the custom for some of the workers to live with the master of the mill where they were working, all having their meals at the same table.[5] From time immemorial it had been considered proper for papermakers to cease eating when the master of the house, by laying down his spoon, gave evidence that he had finished. There is a tradition that many of the early Dutch masters were anything but liberal, and that in order to prevent their workmen from consuming too much food, the dishes were served steaming hot, and before they had had time to cool sufficiently to be eaten, the master would lay down his spoon and the poor papermakers would be forced to leave their master's table before their lusty appetites had been satisfied. To this day in the old papermaking districts of Holland whenever children are noticed to be gulping their food they are chided by their parents' asking them if they have been reared by the papermakers. In the summertime the old Dutch artisans began their work in the mills at three thirty in the morning and ended their tasks at ten, the remainder of the day being spent in the fields and gardens, where they continued the constant stooping that was essential in the making of paper. The old workers, especially the vatmen and couchers, had to have strong and robust constitutions, but the constant stooping posture, combined with the heat of the paper stock in the vat, caused them to grow old prematurely, and at fifty many of these hard-working craftsmen appeared to have reached the allotted threescore years and ten. During the eighteenth century a great deal of paper was produced in Holland, it being recorded that in the year 1726 there were sold at Amsterdam a hundred thousand reams in a single day. William Rittenhouse, the first papermaker in the province of Pennsylvania, had worked in Amsterdam as early as 1678, when he was thirty-four years of age, but he had learned the craft of papermaking in his native city, Mülheim on the Ruhr. Rittenhouse was forty-four when he came to Pennsylvania in 1688 and it is interesting to surmise just how he had been influenced by the Dutch papermakers and to what extent he introduced the old Dutch customs into the pioneer paper mill of the New World.

In contrast to the custom of the old Dutch mill-owners in endeavouring to prevent the workers from satisfying their appetites at their master's table, we have an account showing the abundance of food supplied by a master papermaker in early nineteenth-century America. In the amusing manuscript diary of Ebenezer Hiram Stedman, quoted from previously, there is an intimate description of paper-mill life in pioneer Kentucky and Ohio. Some time before the year 1820 Stedman left the mill in Kentucky and ventured across the river into Ohio, where he readily found work in the erstwhile Christian Waldschmidt mill, the second papermaking establishment to be set up in the state, about 1810. An extract from the Stedman diary relative to mill life among the German immigrant papermakers reads: ". . . When Matthias Kugler came to the place he was an ignorant German, could not read or write; he worked for eight dollars a month for the man (Waldschmidt) who was later to be his father-in-law. One day young Kugler was sent by his master to the barn to flail out grain and he and his master's daughter got mixed up amongst the grain and Kugler had to marry her, that is the way it commenced. Matthias Kugler was now the master of the mill and Mrs. Kugler was head of everything. The first meal I had in the mill-house was supper and Kugler had a practice of initiating every new journeyman papermaker who came to his house by telling them that all the food on the table was cooked for the papermakers and the family and each worker was entitled to consume as much as he desired, but everything taken on the plates must be eaten as there was to be no waste; nothing was cooked to be thrown to the dogs or hogs." This short quotation from Stedman's interesting diary gives a little conception of the proprieties of the life of a papermaker in the "western country" during pioneer days when the craft of making paper by hand was practised in the Miami Valley, now an important paper-producing centre.

The old European papermakers, as well as the early American workers at this craft, were much too fond of their drink and could be found almost any night at the public houses which were located near the mills. The vatman and the coucher, who interchanged

FABRIANO.
Lieu de l'Etat de L'EGLISE il est
Dans la Marche d'Ancone

Se rend
A AMSTERDAM
Chez PIERRE MORTIER
Avec Privilege

J. BLAEU Excud.

Fig. 206   *The interior of a Fabriano (Italy) paper mill, showing the stampers, vat, couching, and press. (From* Novum Italiæ Theatrum, *1724.)*

their work, could readily have been distinguished by their red, muscular arms and hands and by their stooping backs. This condition was brought about by their having their arms in and out of warm water constantly, and continually bending over the dipping-vat and coucher's stool. The old mills were inadequately heated, and the vat-houses, where the moulding of the paper took place, were usually located where the light was poor, the atmosphere damp and gloomy, and the whole environment unhealthful (Figures 206, 207, 208). All through the history of papermaking by hand there was a scarcity of workers, due no doubt to the unwillingness of apprentices to learn a trade so disagreeable and arduous; only those with exceptional physical endurance could have remained long at the craft. The greatest strain was required of the vatman, owing to the four-way motion that he had to give to the mould in forming each separate sheet of paper. After work-

FIG. 207   *A French paper mill of the eighteenth century. (From the original painting in the Musée Lorrain.)*

ing years at the vat the craftsmen sometimes lost this "stroke" and were never again able to form a sheet of paper. Sometimes this paralysis has been known to attack workmen for different periods, during which time they were unable to work at the moulding of paper; then the ability to give the "stroke" or "shake" returned. Yet with all the disagreeable features of their craft, the old paper-makers were a happy and contented guild of workmen. As in other callings, there were those who disliked the monotony of living and working in one place, and these men journeyed from one mill to another, obtaining work wherever they might go. The paper-makers were extremely proud of their craft, for the apprenticeship was long, the work demanded dexterity and skill, and to become a proficient moulder and coucher of fine paper required no little ability of head and hand.

Nothing remains today of the old handmade-paper industry in America, since here, though not in the Old World, the advent of the papermaking machine soon swept aside the ancient, tedious

FIG. 208   *The interior of an old paper mill near Arnhem, Gelderland Province, Netherlands. A century or more ago the mill was in operation, but previous to the war it formed a section of an industrial museum.*

method of forming each sheet of paper separately. Just at the close of the Civil War all papermaking by hand had ceased on the North American continent. Most of the buildings that housed this important early industry have gone into decay, and not a vestige of any of the old equipment, except a few scattered moulds, remains. The original Rittenhouse mill,[6] the first to be established in America, in 1690, near Germantown, Pennsylvania, was swept away by high water in 1700, but Rittenhouse and his son Claus built another mill, a short distance below the site of the first, which was in operation in 1702. There is no authoritative picture of the original mill or of the second structure. According to the letters of William McCulloch [7] to Isaiah Thomas written between 1812 and 1815, the original Rittenhouse mill was of logs, the building extending over an undershot water-wheel, there being no dam or race. This Philadelphia antiquarian also states in his letters: "The Rittenhouses, one or more of them, have continued papermakers to this day. The first stone mill is still attached to the present mill and covers a large press with a screw, made of cherry, about eighteen inches diameter in the eye. This press verily appears to be an ancient affair. The mill is not at present employed by a Rittenhouse. It is rented as a paper mill; and the present papermaker Nicholas Rittenhouse employs another mill in the vicinity. . . . Jacob Rittenhouse made the large wooden screw, which was about the year 1755 for his uncle William. Jacob, the millwright, also invented, about the year 1760, the slanting plates for grinding rags; as straight ones only, with much delay of grinding, were in use before this discovery. . . . Jacob is still living, he is now 86 years of age, is blind, but retains an excellent memory unimpaired."

The buildings usually pictured as the Rittenhouse paper mill are two stone houses that are still standing. The larger of these was built in 1707 and was originally the home of William Rittenhouse and his son Claus, there being carved in the stone above one of the windows the inscription $C \begin{smallmatrix} W \\ \\ 1707 \end{smallmatrix} R$. This picturesque old stone house, with its steep, narrow, winding stairway and small cheerful rooms, is often pictured as the Rittenhouse paper mill, but was used only as a residence, never as a mill. To the public at large this old two-storey structure is better known today as the birthplace of David Rittenhouse (1732–96), the astronomer, than as the home of William Rittenhouse, the pioneer papermaker. It may be said without hesitation that nothing remains of the actual Rittenhouse mill, either the building or the equipment. Indeed, even the spot where this mill stood is unknown, nor will it ever be possible to trace the exact location with certainty. A like fate has overtaken the William De Wees mill, the second paper mill to be set up in the colonies. Of the buildings that housed it nothing remains. This mill, built in 1710, was a direct outgrowth of the Rittenhouse establishment, erected near the pioneer mill, on the west side of the Wissahickon Creek in that part of Germantown known at that period as Crefield.

The earliest reference in any publication to the Rittenhouse mill or to papermaking in America appeared in Philadelphia (printed by William Bradford) in 1692 and was written by Richard Frame, the title of the book being: *A Short Description of Pennsylvania, or, A Relation of What Things are Known, Enjoyed, and Like to be Discovered in the Said Province. Presented as a Token of Good Will to the People of England.* The verses are printed in full:

> The German-Town, of which I spoke before,
> Which is, at least in length one Mile or more,
> Where lives High-German People, and Low-Dutch,
> Whose Trade in weaving Linen Cloth is much.
> There grows the Flax, as also you may know,
> That from the same they do divide the Tow;
> Their trade fits well within this Habitation,
> We find Convenience for their Occasion.
> One trade brings in employment for another,
> So that we may suppose each Trade a Brother;
> From Linen Rags good Paper doth derive,
> The first Trade keeps the second Trade alive;
> Without the first, the second cannot be,
> Therefore since these two can so well agree,
> Convenience doth appear to place them nigh,
> One in German-Town, t'other hard by.
> A Paper-Mill near German-Town doth stand.
> So that the Flax, which first springs from the Land,
> First Flax, then Yarn, and then they must begin
> To weave the same, which they took pains to spin.
> Also, when on our backs it is well worn,
> Some of the same remains Ragged and Torn;
> Then of the Rags our Paper it is made,
> Which in process of time dost waste and fade;
> So, what comes from the Earth, appeareth plain,
> The same in Time, returns to Earth again.

The following verse was written by John Holme in 1696 under the title of *A True Relation of the Flourishing State of Pennsylvania,*[8] and is considered to have been the earliest metrical composition composed in Pennsylvania, but it was not published until 1847. The verse relates to William Bradford and the Rittenhouse paper mill:

> Here dwelt a printer and I find
> That he can both print books and bind;
> He wants not paper, ink, nor skill
> He's owner of a paper mill.

The paper mill is here hard by
And makes good paper frequently,
But the printer, as I do here tell,
Is gone into New York to dwell.
No doubt but he will lay up bags
If he can get good store of rags.
Kind friend, when thy old shift is rent
Let it to th' paper mill be sent.

Another work dealing in a minor degree with Pennsylvania papermaking appeared two years after John Holme's verse, in 1698, with the title: *An Historical and Geographical Account of the Province and Country of Pennsylvania*. This was published in London, and the reference to paper is: "All sorts of very good paper are made in German-Town, as also very fine German linen such as no person of quality need be asham'd to wear."

The third mill, also in the province of Pennsylvania,[9] was established by Thomas Willcox, about 1729, on the west branch of Chester Creek in that part of Chester County which in later years became Delaware County. It is recorded that as late as 1884 some of the buildings of this mill were standing, but whether or not these were part of the original structure it is not possible to say. When I visited the site of this old mill a number of years ago, nothing remained but the stone foundation, which stood in soggy ground almost covered with rank vegetation. A remnant of the old ivy vine, the original slip of which was brought to this country by Thomas Willcox from Devonshire in 1725, still clung to the ruined walls. It was on account of the abundant growth of this vine that the mill in its prosperous days was known as "Ivy Mills," and carried the device of an ivy leaf as its watermark. At the base of one of the crumbling masonry walls, deeply embedded in the marshy ground, lay a rusty and broken screw press fallen upon its side. It had been one of the indispensable implements of the old mill, and between its platens ream after ream of paper had been pressed — paper that had been made for ante-bellum banks, for the counting houses of some of America's oldest firms, and for the banks of the South American republics as well as those of Greece. It was not until March 1866 that the mill abandoned the manufacture of handmade paper. On the hill above the mill stands the old Willcox home, occupied by a direct descendant of this noted papermaking family. The old Willcox family burying-ground, enclosed within an iron fence, lies up the hill behind the house, and here rest this illustrious family of papermakers. Within the enclosure, but to one side, a small gravestone with the one word CAESAR marks the tomb of an old Negro slave whom Thomas Willcox had purchased from the captain of a slave-trading ship that had anchored in Delaware Bay. Caesar had been a faithful and intelligent papermaker in the Willcox mill, and at his death he was privileged to share the resting-place of his masters.

About 1736 a paper mill was established on the banks of the Cocalico Creek, near Ephrata, Lancaster County, Pennsylvania, by a branch of the Pietists of Germany, who came to this country in the early eighteenth century. This was the fourth paper mill in Pennsylvania.[10] When the site of this mill was visited more than a quarter century ago, there was nothing of the old buildings remaining; not even the foundations could be traced, for a woollen factory had been built upon the spot where the mill once stood. The building usually pictured in histories as the original *Papier-mühle* of this German religious colony was never a mill of any sort, but the home of one of the leaders of the cult. Not the oldest citizens of Ephrata could remember seeing the paper mill; it had been demolished many years before and no authentic picture exists.

Another locality visited, with the hope of finding at least a remnant of an early American paper mill, was the site of an early papermaking establishment in New York, which was set up in 1773 on what is now Silver Lake, a peaceful body of water that flows into the head of Hempstead Harbour, at Roslyn, Long Island. This enterprise was founded by Hendrick Onderdonk and two associates encouraged thereto by Hugh Gaine, a bookseller and printer of New York. The mill was prosperous and Onderdonk became a wealthy and influential man, living in a correspondingly handsome style. Whenever a noted personage came to the village, the master of the paper mill was invariably called upon to entertain him, as Onderdonk was the leader in the small community. On the morning of April 24, 1790 word came suddenly to the village, and to the Onderdonk household in particular, that the President of the United States was on his way through the island, and that he would stop with the papermill owner for breakfast.[11] The Onderdonk family was around the table eating roasted clams when the message was received, and a great commotion arose among the women to get things in readiness for the honoured guest. They sprang from their benches, and in haste swept into their aprons the clam shells and cups and saucers, soon having the table cleared for a more formal repast for General Washington. After breakfast the President and Hendrick Onderdonk strolled to the hill west of the pond, and the General remarked that the locality would make an excellent place for a fort. They then visited the paper mill, Washington seeming much interested in the process of forming sheets of paper and asking many questions in regard to the methods employed. He was much absorbed in watching the men dip and couch the thin sheets, one at a time, and the vatman summoned sufficient courage politely to request that the President try his hand at the work. This Washington did, dipping the "laid" mould into the vat and bringing it to the surface laden with the snowy-white fibrous liquid. He then couched the sheet, the workman taking care to slip a small bit of paper between the felts that covered the sheet the noted visitor had made. Perhaps this means of identification was later found unnecessary, as the paper formed by a novice is generally distinguishable by its own characteristics. It is said that this sheet was a cherished possession of the mill for many years, but no trace of it can now be found. To be sure, there is no authentic record to support the story that George Washington actually made a sheet of paper when he visited the Onderdonk mill, but the situation is sufficiently picturesque for one at least to wish that it might have been true. One historian of Long Island has advanced the opinion that such a performance never took place, the only reason given being that it would have been beneath the dignity of the Father of our Country to stoop to such a workaday task; but, it would seem, Washington could have made just one sheet of paper without losing his rank as a gentleman! There have been several authentic instances of European nobility visiting paper mills and trying their skill in forming paper upon a mould. Charles Cowan in his *Reminiscences* relates that the Duke of Bordeaux, better known as Count de Chambord (1820–83), once visited the Valley-field mill and with his own royal hands made several sheets of paper upon a small mould. After the sheets had dried they were forwarded to His Royal Highness at Holyrood Palace and were graciously acknowledged. Surely if it were not beneath the dignity of a nobleman in imperialistic Europe to stand at a vat and make a few sheets of paper, our own George Washington could have performed the same task in democratic America without the loss of too much prestige.

General Washington was evidently much impressed by his visit to the Onderdonk mill, for in his diary under the date of his sojourn he had this to say: "I left Mr. Young's, Oyster Bay, before 6 o'clock on Saturday morning and passing through Mosquito Cove, breakfasted at a Mr. Onderdonk's at the head of a little bay where we were kindly received and well entertained. This gentleman works a grist and two paper mills, the last of which he seems to carry on with spirit and profit." George Washington was the possessor of his own watermarked correspondence paper and at least a few of his letters are inscribed in his own hand upon this form of stationery. The watermark is in the form of a circle with the lettering GEORGE WASHINGTON in outline running within the frame, the circle surmounted by a griffin or eagle. In the centre of the watermark a figure of Liberty sits somewhat uncomfortably upon a plough. It is not known where the paper was made, but it is likely that an American mill kept the General supplied as a favour.

The old stone foundations of the Onderdonk mill are all that now remain of Long Island's first paper mill. Within the low foundation a great tree grows which clearly shows how long ago the wooden mill had fallen into ruin.

Of the old American paper mills, the best-preserved structure is one that was erected in the late eighteenth century. It stands in Burnside, Connecticut, on the outskirts of Hartford, appearing most dignified and substantial amid its shabby modern surroundings. Originally it stood in the country, beside a stream, but houses and factories have pressed closer and closer until now the fine old structure must be demolished. The impressive building is about 30 by 40 feet, two storeys in height, and built of red sandstone, each block beautifully squared, and all laid together faultlessly in massive walls. By contrast the neigh-

FIG. 209   A scale model of the original Zenas Crane paper mill, founded 1801. From left to right are shown the press, the layman, the coucher, the vatman at the vat, and the stuff-chest. The model, at Dalton, Massachusetts, was built by the late George Moore and Dard Hunter.

bouring present-day buildings look mean and poor. The first floor of this old stone mill is divided into two rooms; one served as the vat-house, the other for the beating of rags. The second floor was used for drying and finishing; the original sliding shutters that had been used to introduce or exclude the air for the drying of paper are still intact and in fairly good working order. By going over this small building it is possible to picture every phase of the old hand process and to determine just how the artisans operated. The limitations of light and space and the crude appliances did not seem to deter the early workers, and not only did the paper they fabricated serve its purpose at the time, but much of it has lasted throughout the years and given to us the records of the past.

It has not been intended to give here complete historical accounts of these few early American mills, since this has been ably done in other volumes, but to set down brief descriptions of them as they now exist, so that a student of the history of papermaking in this country will know what to expect when he visits the

Fig. 210   *The Lessebo paper mill, Sweden. This fine type of permanent mill construction is found in all handmade paper mills of Europe. For the most part the modern European handmade paper mills are not the decayed remnants of the pre-machine industry, but these establishments are housed in substantial buildings with well-made, efficient equipment.*

sites of these pioneer paper mills. Papermaking in America grew early into a flourishing industry. At the close of the eighteenth century there were numerous small paper mills, and by the year 1810 there were no fewer than one hundred and eighty-five establishments where paper was made (Figure 209).

Previous to the first World War England had six mills devoted to this craft. Of the 1,043 vats that existed in Germany in 1846, only two or three remained in 1938; while in Holland, a great papermaking country, there were at this same period only three or four vats in operation. In 1938 Italy had a number of handmade-paper mills, and in France at this time two small establishments were still making paper by the old hand methods. In Sweden there was one lone mill (Figure 210).

In Asia the number of small cottage mills where paper is formed by hand is amazing, but these establishments would not be comparable to those of Europe. Between thirteen and fourteen hun-

FIG. 211   One of the larger of
hundreds of "cottage" mills of Japan where handmade paper is
produced. A mill such as this
would employ several dozen workers. In Ogawa-Machi, where this
mill is located, there are about
fifty such establishments.

FIG. 212   This mill is representative of the dozen or more
"company" mills of Japan where
paper is made by hand. A mill of
this proportion would employ several hundred workers, and in ordinary times the paper would be
exported.

FIG. 213   A fairly large handmade paper mill of Anhwei, China.
The bamboo, straw, or bark would
be boiled in the wooden receptacle at the left; a lime tub is seen
in the background. There are hundreds of mills like this in China.

FIG. 214   One of the thousands of "cottage" paper mills of
China. The primitive stone vat
equipment is found in the Fu Yang
district, where very good paper is
made from bamboo fibre. The
handmade paper mills shown in
Figures 211, 213, and 214 are typi-
cal of the industry in Japan and
China, carried on by the peasants
who cultivate the ground and
make paper.

dred individual handmade-paper mills existed in Japan in 1934, many of them operated within the small homes of the owners as cottage industries (Figure 211). There were a number of large handmade-paper mills in Japan, however, several of them employing hundreds of workers, both men and women (Figure 212). According to the bulletin issued by the Bureau of Trade of the province of Chekiang, China, in 1935, it was estimated that in this one province alone 24,437 individual households were engaged in making paper by hand, employing 126,852 workers.[12] Most of this paper finds use in religious rites and ceremonies. In the whole of China before the Japanese aggression, there were at least 40,000 cottages where paper was made in the traditional manner (Figures 213, 214). In Indo-China perhaps fifty small mills were in daily operation. In Siam only two or three hand mills remained, and in India a census might list two or three hundred individual owners of establishments making paper by hand, each employing from three to a dozen artisans. The paper made in the Netherlands East Indies is of the beaten type and cannot be classed as true paper, made from disintegrated fibre.

IX

Ancient Watermarks

SIX AND A HALF CENTURIES OF MYSTIC SYMBOLS

THE STUDY of watermarks attracted little attention until the early eighteenth century, when several writers on typographical subjects became sufficiently interested in the history of paper to devote a little of their research to papermaking archæology. During the nineteenth and twentieth centuries a number of works in French, German, Italian, Russian, Dutch, Spanish, and English were compiled dealing with the historical importance of old watermarks, and the past twenty years have seen an increasing interest in their lore. Several French and German antiquaries devoted their lives to the subject of watermarking, but so difficult is the study that no writer has satisfactorily fathomed the mysteries and complexities of these ancient devices. Almost every scholar who has written on the subject has advanced a different theory of their origin, utility, and meaning. Their symbolic aspect has been dealt with thoroughly, and numerous antiquarians have reproduced and indexed literally thousands of old watermarks from the thirteenth century onward, but without a definite theory of their inception and use.

It has been suggested that these archaic devices may have been used solely as marks of identification for sizes of moulds and the paper formed thereon, or as trade-marks of the papermakers who fashioned them. Others have advanced the theory that they may have been employed in a purely symbolic sense, as Harold Bayley [1] sets forth in his interesting books dealing with the semeiotic significance of the old papermakers' and printers' marks and emblems. According to Mr. Bayley, the watermarks of the Middle Ages were employed by heretical papermakers as symbols of religious propaganda. Europe at that time was overrun with mystic and puritanical sects, and the art of papermaking was one of the most developed trades of these religious bodies. Mr. Bayley says: ". . . The early papermaking districts were precisely those that were strongholds of the heretical sects known as the Albigenses. The word 'Albigenses' is a term applied loosely to the various pre-Reformation reformers whose strongholds stretched from Northern Spain across the southern provinces of France to Lombardy and Tuscany. In Spain and France they were known as Albigenses from Albi, the name of one of the prominent towns. In the Alpine provinces they were called Waldenses, from Peter Waldo, one of their most conspicuous members. In Italy, history alludes to them under the terms Cathari or Patarini." Mr. Bayley attaches symbolic importance to each of the watermarks used by these mystic people and believes that the papermarks carried with them signals of hidden meaning. This seems really more probable than to try to account for the multitude of watermarked designs as marks of identification for paper sizes or as trade-marks of the makers.

It is not entirely out of the way to suggest that the old watermarks were perhaps nothing more than a mere fancy with the papermakers, who may have formed the designs or emblems to satisfy their own artistic natures. In the entire craft of papermaking there is no part more interesting or fascinating than to couch a sheet of paper upon the felting and watch the impressed mark become clear and distinct as the water slowly evaporates. Another supposition regarding the use of the early papermarks is that since many of the workmen could not read, it was necessary to appeal to them by means of pictures. Simply to have marked a mould with letters or figures would have meant little to the artisans of the fourteenth and fifteenth centuries; it was essential to convey the meaning to them by the aid of illustrations. For the same reason the old signboards of inns and shops were always of a pictorial nature; the mere name of the tavern lettered upon the swinging sign, or of the commodity sold by the tradesmen, would not have been sufficient.

At the present time watermarks are trade-marks of the papermakers, pure and simple, but their ancient significance must remain more or less obscure. It is possible, however, to determine almost exactly the date at which watermarks were first introduced into sheets of paper.

In ancient Oriental papers no watermarks of symbols or devices

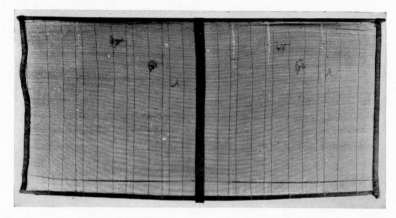

FIG. 215   A "laid" mould-cover made of bamboo and horsehair, from near Peking, China. Two sheets of paper would be formed at each dipping of the mould, each sheet measuring about 16 by 17 inches. Every sheet made on this mould would be watermarked with the three Chinese characters, Ting Jui T'ai.

are found. The earliest moulds upon which sheets of paper were formed were constructed of bamboo, a material that did not lend itself readily to forming applied designs which would watermark the paper. This fact may be sufficient to account for the absence of such marks in early Oriental papers. In the Paper Museum collection of Chinese papermaking moulds dating from fifty to a hundred years ago there is a mould-cover bearing a watermark (Figure 215). The three characters (Ting Jui T'ai) represent the name of the papermakers and are made of ramie (China grass). The lines of these characters are sufficiently flexible to assume any contour taken by the mould-cover during the couching process. In Europe it is likely that iron wires were used in making the first Occidental mould-covers when the art of papermaking was introduced into Spain about the year 1151, yet papermarks did not make their appearance until more than a century later.

The first use of watermarks occurred in Italy about the year 1282, and while they were lacking in complication of design, the forms of the emblems lead us to believe that they may have been employed as signals or symbols for conveying meanings among the workers who made them, or among those who used the paper in which the simple outline designs were impressed. The use of papermarks soon became general and hundreds of different devices were employed in every papermaking country throughout Europe. Watermarks multiplied in number through the centuries, until there were literally thousands upon thousands of different designs depicting almost every phase of nature and every human endeavour. About 1450, when printing from movable types was introduced into Europe, the art of watermarking paper was an accomplishment almost two centuries old. But when we consider nature's use of printing and watermarking from the beginning of time, it is indeed strange that man was so backward in his adoption of the arts of impression. Did not animals, no matter how remote, leave impressions or stamps of their feet in the sands, and vegetation impress itself in the earth and clay? These natural impressions, or indentations, are closely akin to the arts of watermarking and printing.

In examining old books a great profusion of watermarks may be noted in the paper of an individual volume, some fifteenth-century works containing a dozen or more different papermarks in a single book. To account for this variety some writers contend that it was necessary for the early printers to purchase their paper from scattered mills to enable them to procure sufficient material for their use, claiming that the mills were small and could not manufacture paper in sufficient quantities, uniform in size, thickness, and watermark. It is possible that such a course might have been essential in the fifteenth century, but it would not have seemed expedient in the sixteenth; for by the sixteenth century paper manufacture had become an important industry of vigorous growth in most European countries. It is recorded in Thomas Churchyard's poem * that John Spilman, who operated a paper mill in England in 1588, employed as many as six hundred workers, and England was not at that time a great paper-making country. This statement is probably erroneous, for in the half dozen mills of England today there are hardly this number of workers employed in making handmade paper; the methods of work do not differ greatly from those of several centuries ago. In the sixteenth century it is certain that supplies of book

---

* See page 120.

paper were abundant, yet in individual books printed in this century various papermarks are found.

It has been suggested that the different watermarks denoted various sizes of paper. This does not seem reasonable; with every size of paper a special pair of moulds would have been needed and the labour and expense of fashioning these moulds were too great to permit of such a vast variety of dimensions. In later years, to be sure, such marks as foolscap, hand, post, pott, etc., did denote sizes of paper, but these appellations were not used as size names until many years after the establishment of these particular emblems as watermarks; moreover, there were many mills using the same designs on different sizes of sheets. The foolscap mark traces back to 1479, but in England was later replaced by the figure of Britannia, the mark for this size of paper. Watermarks of pots or jugs are seldom found after the seventeenth century, being replaced by the Netherlands or English arms. Watermarks of hands were used extensively by the old papermakers in Germany and the Netherlands, and at times this mark resembled an iron gauntlet or glove, the initials or name of the maker often appearing on the wrist. According to several writers, the post-horn watermark first appeared in the year 1670, at the time the General Post Office was established in England. This is doubtless a mistake, as marks of this type have been found in documents upon paper bearing dates as early as the latter part of the fourteenth century.

The art of forming the actual wire watermark emblems that were applied to the moulds has been modified but little since their origin in the late thirteenth century. In Europe before the eighteenth century all paper was made on "laid" moulds, and the sheets so moulded retained the impressions of the "laid" and "chain" wires used in the construction of the moulds. Any wirework, in the form of objects, added to the top surface of this "laid" and "chain" wire covering (Figure 216) also made impressions in the paper. Why these indentations were called watermarks is not known, as the mark or device in paper is not caused by the use of water to any greater extent than is the sheet itself. In the German language the design impressed in the paper is called *Wasserzeichen*, which, like the English term "watermark," is confusing. In the French language the appellation is *filigrane*, and in

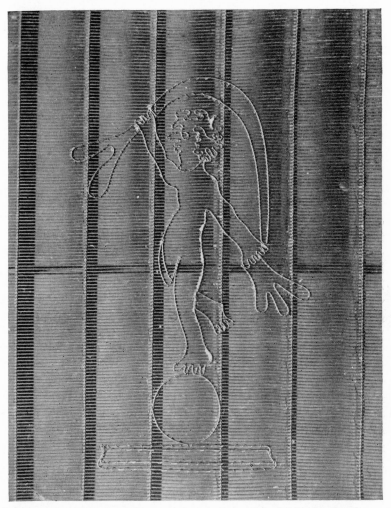

Fig. 216   *The actual wires of a watermark laced to the "laid" surface of a mould. The wires in the form of designs cause indentations
in the paper. The entire mould on which this watermark appears is
shown in Figure 96.*

Dutch *papiermerken*. These two names are more suitable. The first use of the term "watermark" in English appeared at the beginning of the eighteenth century, and as the name *Wasserzeichen* was apparently not used by German writers until the first part of the nineteenth century, we are led to believe that the name "watermark," faulty in its meaning as it is, had its origin in the English language.

The twisted forms used in producing the watermarks, or papermarks, were for centuries held in place on the surface of the moulds by means of thread-like wires * stitched back and forth, binding the mark to the "laid" and "chain" wires. In much of the old paper it is possible to detect the sewing-on wires around the watermarks when the sheets are held to a bright light. In many of the early papermarks the sewing-on wires are pronounced, owing to wire having been used that was almost as heavy as the wire of the mark itself. At least one writer has stated that the wire designs were fastened to the mould surfaces by the use of soft solder, but this appears to be a mistake, as this method of securing the watermarking wires in place was apparently not used until the first part of the nineteenth century. In watermarks from the thirteenth century the simplicity is striking, as at that time the devices were made of clumsy wire that would not admit of much twisting into complicated shapes. During the fourteenth and fifteenth centuries the wires gradually became finer and the designs more detailed.

The value of watermarks as a means of determining the dates of paper, books, and prints or the locality where the paper was made is to be questioned. Few of the early watermarks bear dates, and even when they do, the date of the mark must not be accepted as the time of the printing on the paper. The sheets might have been dated in the watermark and then remained in the mill a considerable time before the paper was sold, and after being sold the paper might have been held for years in the warehouse of the printer before being used. Paper made from fine material by careful and conscientious workmen should improve with age, seasoning adding to its printing quality. The early printers were doubt-

---

* In modern practice the watermark designs in wire are sewed to the hand-moulds by means of fine steel wire that has been plated with a non-rusting metal.

less aware of this characteristic. Also a dated mould might have been used for many years with the same date, the papermaker not troubling to change the figures. An example of such a discrepancy in dates in modern times is seen in a letter to me from the late Joseph Willcox, a direct descendant of the founder of Ivy Mills, the third paper mill to be established in Pennsylvania. Joseph Willcox took over the management of the mill in Chester in 1859, and there made the last handmade bank-note paper that was produced in the United States. His letter reads in part: "We had an order for an unusual size of paper and the only moulds we had of the particular size were dated 1810 in the watermarks. I did not like to take off that old date so I made a lot of paper with the mark 1810 in every sheet." This made a difference of almost fifty years from the date in the paper and the time when the paper was actually made.

It would also be unwise to rely upon a watermark as proof of where the paper was made or at what particular mill. Suppose that an early papermaker established a reputation for a superior quality of paper; there was nothing to prevent a newly set-up mill from using the watermark of the older and more prosperous concern. A striking illustration of this deception in our own time is the imitation of the watermark of the highly esteemed Whatman mill, established by James Whatman in Maidstone, England, in 1731. Certain unscrupulous Continental papermakers have duplicated the Whatman watermark and sold their papers without hesitation, the sheets often being accepted as genuine Whatman papers. It is not unlikely that in the early days of papermaking, moulds were sold by one mill to another without troubling to remove the wire watermarks; or the old worn moulds of a large mill may have fallen into the hands of a less prosperous maker who fabricated an inferior quality of paper. In this way one watermark design could have been used by numerous mills, over periods of many years, for papermaking moulds have always been well and strongly made and they do not easily wear beyond use if treated with any degree of care. From an archæological and artistic standpoint watermarks are of great interest, but for tracing *definitely* the dates of paper, or the exact localities of certain mills, the marks should not be relied upon implicitly.

Almost all writers touching upon the subject of ancient paper and watermarks attach importance to small changes that often appear in papermarks depicting the same subject. This seems to be unwarranted, for the slight variations may be due to very simple causes. The wire forms may have become detached from the moulds and have been replaced by a worker unskilled in wireworking — possibly the vatman or coucher. Every time a wire mark came loose from a mould, it had to be attached again, and in so doing some detail naturally was slightly changed from the original outline. This alone would account for the large number of marks, similar in subject, and supposedly from the same mill, but varying to a slight degree. Another simple cause for variance may be suggested: In the first volume of the Mazarin Bible, attributed to Johann Gutenberg, and printed between 1450 and 1455, there may be seen two papermarks of the bull or ox. In these two papermarks there is a striking resemblance; no doubt one was a copy of the other, and the two were supposed to be identical. It is probable that so late as the fifteenth century two moulds were used, as at present, in moulding paper at the vat. Each mould had a wire watermark of a bull, the two possibly formed by different workers, each one trying to rival the other in design, but keeping the two emblems within the same limits of space and general contour.*

The paper that was used in the forty-two-line Bible is of the finest quality and in many ways its excellence has never been surpassed. The watermark of the bunch of grapes (Figure 217) which is found in much of the Gutenberg Bible paper is unusual in its

---

* In the history of papermaking in our own country this variation of papermarks of the same subject is not unusual. For the past several years I have been making a study of early papermaking in western Pennsylvania, Kentucky, and Ohio, and many of the late eighteenth- and early nineteenth-century watermarks used in these states have been measured and photographed. In practically all of the papers made in the pioneer mills in the "western country" a marked variation in the watermarks is detectable. To cite but one instance: In Ohio the first papermaking establishment was set up in 1807. The watermark was a spread eagle with the word OHIO underneath in outline letters. All of the watermarks from this mill were intended to be identical, but apparently no standard pattern or template was employed in forming or twisting the wires. It is possible, therefore, to determine upon what particular mould a certain sheet of paper was formed. Through an examination of many sheets of paper in early account-books, documents, letters, etc., we have been able to arrive at the actual number of moulds each mill possessed.

Fig. 217   The bunch-of-grapes watermark in a page of the 42-line Bible, printed in 1450–5 and attributed to Johann Gutenberg. The original wires forming this watermark were twisted into form in the same manner as shown in Figures 216, 218, and 219.

brilliance and clearness, although the paper is long-fibred, which, as a rule, does not produce sharp and distinct watermarks. The strength of the paper is usually sacrificed if a well-defined and sharp watermark is desired. While the bunch of grapes as a papermark may be of Swiss origin, it is possible that the paper used in the first printed Bible was fabricated in Gutenberg's native land. No matter in what locality it was made, or in what particular mill, this paper shows technical skill and workmanship that is seldom encountered in modern times; the texture, strength, and tone have remained unchanged over almost five hundred years. Through the employment of bleach and chemicals, much of the machine-made paper and some of the handmade paper of our own time, even with the nearly five-hundred-year handicap, will no doubt suffer by comparison with that of the Gutenberg Bible in another such period, or about the year 2446.

After watermarking became general, during the fifteenth century, it was seldom that a sheet of paper was made without a distinguishing device of some nature. These emblems were sometimes placed in the centre of the sheets, or where the paper was folded in folio book-printing, but it is more usual to find two symbols or designs each appearing in the middle of the half-sheet of paper. Watermarks, from their origin until the latter part of the eighteenth century, when they began to lose their simplicity, may be consistently divided into four classes: The first of these would embrace the earliest known watermarks, which appeared in the form of crosses, ovals, circles, knots, triangles, three-hill symbols, and devices of the simplest kind that could have been readily twisted in wire. At this period a great many pommée crosses were also used as emblems for watermarking paper. This was a Greek cross with balls or circles placed at each end of the cross-bars. Another similar mark which is found in fourteenth-century Italian paper is a circle surmounted by a patriarchal or papal cross. The papermarks of this first group were in use from the origin of the art, about the year 1282, until the first quarter of the fifteenth century.

The second division of papermarks would include man and the works of man, and in the latter class of this particular group we find the greatest number of subjects, extending into thousands upon thousands of designs. The male figure is met with only in limited numbers and the female figure is rarely found except in mermaid form, usually holding a mirror. The human head, feet, and hands were also used separately as watermarks by the early workers. The mark of the hand was used by the papermakers of various countries for hundreds of years and was symbolic of both Fidelity and Labour. At times the hand shows two fingers bent downward, a sign of benediction. The hand watermark is also found surmounted by a cross, a star, a rose of bliss, or some like ornament, each of which had its symbolic significance. The size of paper known in later years as "hand" derived its name from the emblem. The watermark of the human foot is exceptional and has been encountered in only a few instances. The works of man would embrace agricultural implements, and small tools such as shears, spades, bellows, swords, scythes, hammers, pruning-hooks, and axes; with the works of man would also be included such watermarked objects as ships, anchors, anvils, bagpipes, keys, horns, scales, bishops' and cardinals' hats and staffs, curry-combs, weapons of all kinds, hawks' bells, as well as architectural ornaments, lettering, and escutcheons.

The earliest watermark of the human head was a portrait of Jesus Christ, and was of French origin, from about the year 1339. This device represents the Vera Icon, or True Image. The legend runs that the Saviour on the way to Calvary was encountered by the woman Berenice. Filled with compassion she wiped His face with her handkerchief, which miraculously retained an imprint of the divine features, whereupon Berenice was sainted and rechristened Veronica, an anagram of Vera Icon. It is no doubt the kerchief with the impress of this head that is reproduced in the late fourteenth-century watermark.

Watermarks of Jesus in profile appeared in limited numbers during the fourteenth, fifteenth, and sixteenth centuries. In these marks the head is usually represented with three locks or strands of hair, evidently meant to symbolize Christ's oneness with the Trinity. In most of these marks the mouth is open, intended to denote Jesus teaching. Another profile watermark used in the fifteenth century was that of a Negro slave. In some instances this head appears with a bandage raised from the eyes, symbolizing freedom.

Most of the early watermarks portraying the human figure and head were ecclesiastical in nature, as was natural since the church penetrated the workshops of the ancient craftsmen in a manner that cannot be conceived today. Nothing really artistic in the watermarking of portraits was accomplished until the middle of the eighteenth century, when we find the French and German papermakers making simple outline portraits of prominent personages.

In arranging papermarks in classes according to their subjects, the third group or division would embrace such marks as flowers, trees, leaves, vegetables, grain, plants, and fruits. In a number of the old emblems there are also combinations of vegetation and the works of man, such as a bunch of grapes with a bell or crown, or a pot or jug holding flowers or leaves.

The fourth and probably the most interesting group of watermarks would include wild, domesticated, and legendary animals, as well as snakes, fish, snails, turtles, crabs, scorpions, and all varieties of insects. It was the forms of animals that required most dexterity to twist in wire and gave the early artisans the greatest outlet for their skill. The bull's head, one of the earliest animal papermarks, made its appearance in 1310 and was a favourite emblem with papermakers for over two hundred years. The head of the bull was sometimes used without appurtenances, but more often it is found surmounted by a Latin cross, rose of bliss, half-moon, crown, flails, or like symbols. We find also a curled snake on the staff of a cross projecting from the bull's-head device, resembling a caduceus. Watermarks of the head of the bull, surmounted by both a snake and cross and the rose of bliss are found in some of the sheets of paper that were used in Miles Coverdale's translation of the Bible in 1536 — the first Bible printed in English. The bull's-head mark (Figure 218) in various forms also appears in paper that was used by William Caxton, Colard Mansion, Gerhard Leeu, and other noted printers who procured their paper from the Low Countries. The full figure of the bull is not so common a watermark as the head alone, but when it does appear it is interesting to note that the tail is usually divided into three strands. The bull as a symbol was handed down to the papermakers by the ancients, for chief among the multitude of idols and symbols was the god Apis, represented by the bull. The ox was emblematic of patience and strength, and in the writings of some of the early church Fathers it is accepted as a symbol of Christ the true sacrifice, also of prophets, apostles, and saints slain for

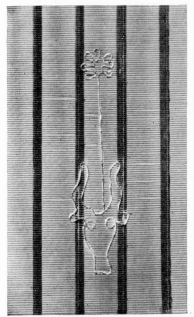

FIG. 218   *The bull's-head watermark in various forms appears in the paper used by William Caxton, Colard Mansion, Gerhard Leeu, and other noted printers who procured their paper from the Low Countries. This illustration shows the actual wires on the surface of the mould (sixteenth century).*

FIG. 219   *This camel watermark was constructed with two wires and laced to the mould with smaller sewing-wires. This camel mark is French, dating from about 1379.*

the sake of Christ, and of all who patiently bear the yoke and labour in silence for the good of others.

The unicorn, like the bull, is found as a watermark in the paper used by Caxton, and holds a prominent place in papermarks from the fifteenth to the seventeenth century. M. Briquet has recorded over eleven hundred different renderings of this animal used as a device for marking paper. The unicorn was symbolic of purity and innocence, and it was believed that the horn of this mythical animal was a panacea for all illness and an antidote for poisons.

The ancients believed the horn of the unicorn so sensitive that if a cup of poison was brought near it, a thick moisture would be expelled from the surface of the liquid, and if a piece of horn was thrown into the poison, the poison would bubble and in time boil over. It was also thought by the ancients that the horn was removable at will, like a kind of sword. Both the whole body and the head of the unicorn were used as watermarks by the old papermakers. They are seldom found as papermarks with any other symbol incorporated with them, but in a few instances a sword or cross protruding from the animals' back has been noted.

Another favourite animal watermark was the form of the dog, and numerous specimens are found extending over a period of about two hundred years. Like the bull and the unicorn, the dog device was used as a symbolic emblem by the ancients, and centuries later, along with other symbols, was adopted by papermakers for watermarking. Certain species of the canine were considered sacred by the ancient Egyptians and there are instances where sacred dogs were mummified by them. Early watermarks of the dog usually represent the greyhound, and a great many of them are drawn with considerable motion and vigour, a merit not often found in old papermarks.

The camel is prominent in the watermarks of the fifteenth century and is usually of crude workmanship and seen in a rather grotesque attitude. The camel mark here illustrated (Figure 219) shows the actual wire form on the surface of the mould. It was constructed of two wires, one starting at the ears and continuing around, shaping the tail and legs and terminating at the neck; the other wire completed the head, the eye being shaped by a crook in the second wire. This camel papermark is French, from about 1379.

Elephants, leopards, goats, lambs, dragons, cats, horses, and deer are found in abundance in watermarks from the middle of the fourteenth century onward. The cock is not a common mark in old paper, but a variety of specimens, mostly of French origin, have been discovered in the pages of antique books and manuscripts. Many of the chanticleer marks display ability in design as well as fashioning in wire. It is noticeable that the cock was generally formed with open bill, which, according to the authorities on symbolism, denotes the dawn of light. Birds of many kinds and

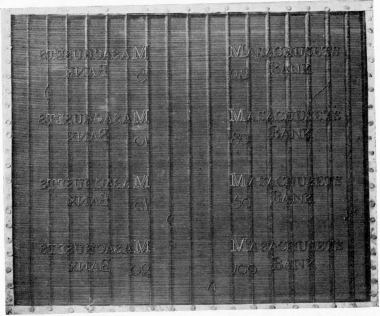

FIG. 220   An American-made papermaking mould used in a Massachusetts mill during the latter part of the eighteenth century. The watermarks read "MASACHUSETS BANK" in eight places, with the numbers 5, 10, 15, 20, etc. The short, irregularly twisted wires throughout the mould were placed there to detect counterfeiting of the paper.

sizes furnished a multitude of devices for the old papermakers in the marking of their papers. We find also in unlimited numbers representations of fish, as well as many examples of crustacean life of the sea.

During the first fifty years of papermaking in the American colonies there still existed among craftsmen a love for symbolic design, which was manifest in the watermarks of the period. But by the middle of the eighteenth century superstition and symbolism began to lose hold upon the artisans, and from that time, in the colonies as in Europe, symbolic watermarks and printers' marks began to fall into disuse. Watermarks with an emblematic significance were not uncommon in the early papermaking history of Pennsylvania, and the pioneer workers of this region were responsible for the most unusual specimens. New England, which contributed so much to the history of the applied arts in other fields, added little of an artistic or interesting nature to the watermark annals of America. The few marks that are recorded from this locality consist chiefly of names and initials of the papermakers, which have no special appeal to the imagination (Figure 220).

The first paper mill in the colonies, as has been said, was established in Pennsylvania by William Rittenhouse, a native of Germany, who was assisted in his undertaking by William Bradford, the first printer in Pennsylvania and New York, and two other worthy gentlemen. In all probability the papermaking moulds used by this mill had been brought from the chief founder's native land and were no doubt plain moulds, without watermarks. The first watermark used in Rittenhouse paper was the single word "Company," designating the original partnership. Judging from its crudity, it was fashioned by untrained and unskilled hands, probably by one of the mill workmen unaccustomed to forming objects in wire. This mark was used from about 1690, when the mill was established, until some time during the year 1704, when Bradford was induced to part with his share in the paper mill. In 1706 the property was in the full possession of Rittenhouse. The second papermark to be adopted by this pioneer mill was the monogram WR, the initials of the principal founder, on one half of the sheet of paper, while on the other half appeared a clover leaf inside a shield surmounted by a crown. Underneath the shield, in outline letters, was the word "Pensilvania." The

shield-and-crown device displays a great deal of Dutch and French influence, as watermarks of this style had been used by early papermakers in Holland, adopted by them from France, where the device had been used as a papermark as early as 1460. This emblem was an evolution of the bull's-head watermark. The crown and shield with three fleurs-de-lis constituted the arms of France, and this device was frequently used as a watermark by the papermakers of the Low Countries, probably in reference to the direct descent of the House of Burgundy from the kings of France. Papermarks of this character may be found in the paper used by William Caxton, the first printer in England, whose paper was procured from the Low Countries. No paper was produced in

England until the establishment of the John Tate mill in Hertford about 1496. The clover leaf, trefoil, or "klee-blatt," which Rittenhouse substituted for the fleur-de-lis, was adapted from the townmark or seal of the village of Germantown, a settlement not far distant from the location of the paper mill. This seal or emblem had been in use by the community only a short time before Rittenhouse put it to use as a watermark.

The next papermark to be adopted by this mill consisted simply of the letters KR, the initials of Claus Rittenhouse, the son of the founder, the name in Dutch being Klaas. With the use of this initial mark on the left half, the clover leaf was sometimes introduced on the right half of the paper. The only other watermark known to have been used by this family of papermakers was the letters IR, the initials of Jacob Rittenhouse, a great-grandson of the founder of the mill.

In 1710 William De Wees established the second paper mill in the colonies. This mill was really an outgrowth of the original Rittenhouse establishment. Apparently the De Wees owners did not make use of watermarks. It is recorded, however, that this mill manufactured "an imitation of asses-skin paper which was well executed."

In the year 1729 Thomas Willcox set up the third paper mill in the colony of Pennsylvania. This establishment used as a standard watermark a dove and olive-branch design with the initials of the papermaker — first TMW for the founder, and in later years MW, the initials of Mark Willcox, the son, who was operating the mill in 1767. In 1827 an ivy leaf was adopted as a watermark, the mill being known as Ivy Mills on account of the English ivy that covered the stone buildings. The original vine was brought from England by Thomas Willcox to Pennsylvania in 1725, from near the Old Ivy Bridge in Devonshire. This mill also used the familiar post-horn device as a watermark previous to 1787. The many bank-note papers executed at Ivy Mills were mostly watermarked with the names and marks of states and banks. One of the earliest of these papermarks was made for Pennsylvania in the year 1777. A letter of Revolutionary interest (dated March 11, 1778) concerning this watermark was written to Colonel Andrew Boyd, Sub-Lieutenant of Chester County, Pennsylvania, where the Willcox paper mill was located. This letter reads in part: "Mr. Willcox has in his possession a mould for making paper belonging to this state, which you are requested to bring away, it is marked with the word 'Pennsylvania' in twenty-four places, he did promise if the enemy came that way he would throw it into the mill dam."

The Gilpin mill, also in Pennsylvania, used the dove and branch watermark certainly as early as 1789, possibly from the establishment of this mill two years earlier. This mill in 1793 was using the word "Brandywine" as a watermark, as the Gilpin mill was situated on the Brandywine River. The dove and branch were a favourite watermark with American papermakers, for we find it used again in 1805 by Thomas Amies, the third mill to adopt this design as a trademark. The dove sometimes lacks the branch and is at times quite poorly drawn, but the identifying name is usually present, variously given as AMIES, AMIES PHILADA, etc. Amies was at one time superintendent of the Willcox mill at Chester, and after setting up his own establishment he adopted the dove and branch of Willcox origin as a watermark. A direct descendant of Thomas Willcox living in the old family home near Chester in 1925 had in his possession a pair of moulds that had been used in the old Ivy Mills, which bore the dove and branch watermarks. In the "western country" the dove and branch watermark was used by Jackson and Sharpless as early as 1809. This mill was located on Redstone Creek, Fayette County, Pennsylvania, and was the earliest papermaking establishment in western Pennsylvania.

The watermarks used by the New England paper mills during their pioneer history have never been systematically recorded and it is doubtful if the emblems employed by these early establishments could be gathered together with any degree of accuracy. The several watermarks used by the William Parks paper mill established at Williamsburg, Virginia, in the eighteenth century have been well described and pictured in a pamphlet issued by the corporation.

The fourth paper mill in Pennsylvania, established forty-six years after the original Rittenhouse project, was *Die Papier Mühle der Brüderschaft zu Ephrata,* already mentioned. Ephrata was a

communistic settlement made by a branch of the Pietists of Germany who emigrated to Pennsylvania in the early eighteenth century. The members of the community lived in a cloister or convent under monastic rules of celibacy and austerity. The community was self-sustaining, not only fabricating its own paper, but engaging in printing and bookbinding, as well as in a number of less pretentious crafts. Several of the buildings of the old cloisters are still standing and form one of the most interesting groups of early eighteenth-century construction in this country. The paper mill of the community at Ephrata was under the direction of the Funk Brothers, Samuel and Jacob, both experienced in the art of paper-making, having acquired the trade in Germany. The principal product of the mill was a coarse brown paper that they called "macalatur." This paper was never watermarked, but the finer grades of printing and writing papers bore marks of identification. One of the Ephrata papermarks was a large figure four, the perfect number, below which were the initials RF, a private mark of the Funk family. The letters FB for Funk Brüder
also appear, without the figure four, in some of the Ephrata publications. This mark may be studied in the paper used in the edition of
Theosophische Lectionen, printed in 1745. The most emblematic watermark of this idealistic community appears in the paper used in mystic books that they printed. This highly symbolic device consists of a Latin cross surmounted by a scroll with the word "ZION," two keys forming triangles with the uprights and arms of a cross, which rested upon a narrow panel bearing the name "EFRATA." The keys had reference to the
Clavicula Salomonis, or *Keys of Solomon,* a mystic book of the seventeenth century which was highly regarded by the brotherhood. The entire emblem was capped by a filagree, not unlike the upper part of the second Rittenhouse watermark. The cross-and-keys device may be found in books printed at Ephrata before 1745.

Several other watermarks that were used by this mill were the crown, the post-horn, and perhaps a three-circle device which again shows the perfect figure four, so much favoured by the Brotherhood. In going through one of the dilapidated buildings at Ephrata many years ago, I found an old chest that had been hidden under a heap of discarded lumber. When this chest was opened, it was found to contain about seventy sheets of paper, each sheet having eight pages of German text printed upon it; the paper was unfolded, just as it had come from the press in the eighteenth century. It is believed that this paper is of European make, but it is possible that it was made at the Ephrata mill upon moulds brought from Germany. In this paper the three-circle and figure-four device appears, but it is not possible to identify it definitely as an Ephrata watermark. The printing, however, is authen-

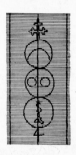

tically American. In the paper upon which early American books and newspapers were printed we find numerous watermarks, but it is an almost hopeless task to classify the marks and state precisely what mills produced them. Papermaking moulds were brought to this country from all parts of Europe and it is probable that many of them had watermarking wires already attached. In this way foreign marks were introduced into American-made sheets of paper.

As an example of the prejudice of the American public in the early nineteenth century regarding American-made paper the following amusing article is taken from Niles' *Weekly Register*, February 22, 1812: "About seven years ago I witnessed a circumstance which afforded me a high gratification. I was in a book-store when a person came in and asked for a ream of letter paper. The bookseller shewed some of an excellent quality, with which the customer was fully satisfied, — but asking the price, was led to suppose, from its *cheapness*, that it was *American*, and demanded if it was so? On receiving an answer in the affirmative, he said it would not do — he wanted '*English*.' 'I have *other* paper,' said the bookseller, 'for which I must have such and such a price, will you look at it, sir?' The price being *high* enough, the gentleman after much *examination* and *comparison* made his purchase, paid his money cheerfully, and carried his paper away. The two reams exhibited came from the *same mill*, and were taken out of the *same bundle!* Large quantities of paper are made in the United States with British watermarks, and, if not openly offered as British, at least *insinuated* to be so and sold as such. I can see no harm in it, — the quality is as good, and if the people *will* have preju-

dices, let them pay for them! We may laugh at this story and think
the purchaser was a fool — but, verily, many of us, though not
so silly as to paper, are as great dunces in other things. It is not
long since that certain manufacturers of dry goods to the East-
ward were compelled to pack their commodities in *British* cases
to insure their sale!" This sarcastic disquisition was in all probability written by that crusty old American journalist himself,
Hezekiah Niles (1777–1839), as he enjoyed nothing better than
to indulge in raillery and ridicule at the expense of others, especially those in high positions. In the issue of his *Register*, published at Baltimore, for August 5, 1820, he takes Congress to task
for supplying its members with writing paper watermarked with
the royal crown of England; he chides the members by writing:
". . . the paper is of a very fine quality, better, perhaps, than
four-fifths of the members of Congress ever used, perhaps ever
saw, before their arrival in Washington." He continues in the
same vein and suggests that the watermarks in Congressional paper convey more of the American spirit: "Let Congress use paper
that is watermarked with a codfish, a hoe-cake, a yoke of oxen, or
a race horse, — anything but the royal crown of England."

Each of the watermarks — whether the simple devices of the
thirteenth century, the human figure and head, man's works, vegetation, animals, or the devices of the early American papermakers — appears to have had its place in the world of symbolism, but
whether or not they meant anything, other than as marks of identification, is conjecture. It is reasonable to believe that they bore
some significance and held some vital place in the lives of the
craftsmen who fashioned them. For students of paper and papermaking it is unfortunate that the early artisans did not employ as
watermarks some object or utensil of their own calling. How interesting it would be to find a mould, a vat, or a paper press pictured as a watermark in a book page from the press of Gutenberg
or Caxton! But the old workers were accustomed to seeing and
handling their own implements and probably regarded the tools
of other crafts and walks of life as more curious and ingenious.
Whatever the origin or use of the papermarks, the many thousands of devices that we have inherited from the early papermakers are so varied that they form almost an encyclopædia of
design, and illustrate a multitude of mediæval objects and uten-

sils that otherwise might not have been recorded. Present-day workers in the paper industry may well be proud of the history and traditions of their trade, for no other craft of Europe can display such an endless array of designs extending over a period of almost seven hundred years.

X

Latter-Day Watermarks

THE NINETEENTH–CENTURY DEVELOPMENT OF WATERMARKS INTO AN ARTISTIC AND TECHNICAL ACHIEVEMENT

THE BANK OF ENGLAND was established in 1694, but it was not until sixty-four years later, in 1758, that its bank-notes were first forged. This original attempt at deception was in no way a skilled achievement where the perpetrator was versed in papermaking, watermarking, and engraving, but was the crude attempt of a Stafford linen draper, Richard William Vaughan, to change the figures of a note to a higher denomination. Vaughan was found guilty of the crime and was executed at Tyburn on the 11th of May 1758.

There were few who wished to emulate Vaughan, so for the following twenty years the counterfeiting of bank-notes was exceedingly rare. The next case of counterfeiting bank paper in England occurred in 1778 when John Mathieson, a native of Scotland, tried to manufacture spurious money duplicating that used by the Darlington Bank. Mathieson's methods were far more skilful and ingenious than the rough and cumbersome attempts of Vaughan. Mathieson was versed in engraving, and while he did not actually make his own paper, he devised imitation watermarks in plain paper which went undetected for a considerable time, as this mode of issuing fraudulent bank-notes was entirely new to the authorities and they could not conceive how their notes could possibly be imitated. In Mathieson's clever work the engraving was finely executed and the watermark, which the bankers had considered an infallible criterion, tallied so precisely with the original that no discrepancies could be detected. Several papermakers were of the opinion that the devices were genuine watermarks and had been placed in the paper in the usual manner during the process of forming the sheets, but Mathieson declared that this was not the case and claimed the marks were the result of a particular process known only to himself. After his apprehension he offered to explain the secret of his discovery provided the corporation would spare his life, but his proposal was rejected and his "secret" died with him.[1]

A watermark may be imitated by copying the design with a pointed stick dipped in the following preparations: spermaceti and linseed oil, equal parts, melted together in a water bath and then stirred until cold; or equal quantities of turpentine and Canada balsam, well shaken together until dissolved; or the megilp used by artists.[2] If the required designs or symbols be well drawn they will have some resemblance to a genuine watermark, as the liquids, when dry, render the paper somewhat transparent. It is needless to say, of course, that all these manœuvres are very easy to detect, since a false mark produced in this manner will fade completely when the paper is dipped in water, while an actual watermark when wet will become more brilliant and more discernible. Mathieson, the forger, no doubt resorted to an elementary process of this kind in his work and it is surprising that this simple method of creating artificial watermarks baffled the officials.

In 1773 an act was passed making the penalty death for copying the watermark in English bank-note paper; and to prevent imitation, it was enacted that no person should prepare any engraved bill or promissory note containing the words "Bank of England," or "Bank post bill," or expressing any sum in white letters on black ground in resemblance of "Bank paper," under the penalty of imprisonment for six months.[3]

Notwithstanding all the precautions taken and the penalties enacted by the British Government after their first experiences with counterfeiters, there was much deceit practised.

The next forger in the annals of the Bank of England was a man of rare skill as a designer, engraver, papermaker, and printer, and while his work was eventually detected, he evaded the authorities on every side. Charles Price, or "Old Patch" as he was called on account of a black cloth over one eye which he wore as a disguise, was one of those men whose whole abilities were employed in defrauding. His first efforts in counterfeiting were practised about the year 1780 and his false bank-notes were so skilfully engraved and the watermarks so perfectly executed that the Bank of England accepted his bank-notes without question, and they were discovered to be forgeries only after they had reached a particular department. Price carried on his unlawful work in Titchfield Street, London, and there had set up a small paper mill where he formed the sheets of paper with the forged watermarks. He was finally taken into custody, and his end was worthy of his life: he employed his son to procure the necessary implements of destruction and was found hanging in his cell in Bridewell Prison.[4]

In September 1801 the following advertisement appeared: "All the one and two pound notes issued by the Bank of England, on and after the first of August will, to prevent forgeries, be printed on a peculiar and purposely constructed paper; consequently those dated 31st July, or any subsequent day, will be impressed upon paper manufactured with waved or curved lines."

In the twenty years prior to 1817 there were no fewer than 870 prosecutions connected with bank-note forgery in Britain, three hundred persons being executed. In the Bank of England alone there were seventy clerks employed in detecting forged notes. The year 1818 was the culminating point of the crimes; in the first three months of that year there were 128 prosecutions by the bank, and by the end of the year thirty-two individuals had been hanged for note forgery. From January 1, 1812 to April 10, 1818 there were circulated 131,331 pieces of forged bank paper.[5]

By 1818 there was great consternation among the Bank of England officials, as well as among merchants and tradesmen, at the extent to which forgers had carried their skill. The engraving and printing did not hinder the efforts of a man who wished to turn his ingenuity to such a purpose; neither did the complications of papermaking and watermarking. The leading typographers and engravers of the day were engaged in trying to produce bank-notes that would not easily lend themselves to being imitated, and interest was aroused to such an extent that the Society of Arts attempted to supply remedies to counteract the spread of counterfeiting and published a report in 1819.[6]

No artisan laboured more diligently or more conscientiously than Sir William Congreve to arrive at some peculiar or technical complication in engraving or papermaking that would be a stumbling-block to even the most talented of forgers. While his plans were never adopted by the bank in their entirety, they were, nevertheless, of great importance and it was through his knowledge, patience, and skill that coloured watermarks were invented and brought into existence at so early a date, for at the beginning of the nineteenth century watermarking in England had not reached any great degree of perfection.

Sir William Congreve was born in Staffordshire in 1772. He was a General of artillery in the English Army and was attached to the Royal Laboratory at Woolwich. Sir William was a man of remarkable inventive genius and is now best known for his development of the rocket as a military weapon and for his writings relative to warfare. He died in France in 1828.

Congreve's first method of making coloured watermarks consisted in couching a thin layer of white paper and then laying another tinted sheet in the form of a design on the first wet sheet; then another white sheet was couched over this, which made a triple sheet. After pressing and drying, these layers became a homogeneous piece of paper, and the middle coloured layer could only be perceived when the sheet was held to the light. The lettering or device in the second, or coloured, sheet was made by the use of a stencil placed over the mould, cut in the form of the required design. As many colours as desired were inserted between the two outside layers of moist paper, each colour being formed separately (Figures 221, 222, 223, 224).

In 1818, the year in which counterfeiting had reached its height, Sir William endeavoured to have his triple paper adopted by the bank of England for their bank-notes. All of the experimental sheets of paper which he made to show the directors of the Bank, as well as his appeal to that institution to adopt his plan, were set down in a folio volume, the manuscript being in his own hand. This unique book * has been in my possession for a number of

---

* The volume measures 8¼ by 13 inches and contains 62 pages with 12 solid pages of manuscript in Sir William Congreve's hand. Thirty-six specimens of watermarked bank-note paper made for or by Congreve are tipped in the book, each example having a description by the inventor. The paper used throughout the book for text pages is watermarked 1818 and bears the name J. Rump. There is, of course, only the one copy of this volume and it forms a unique document in the evolution of papermaking and watermarking.

FIG. 221   A coloured watermarked paper produced in 1818 by Sir William Congreve.

FIG. 222   A watermarked bank-note made in colour by the use of a stencil. This is an example of the "triple paper" invented by Sir William Congreve, about 1818.

FIG. 223   *The first coloured watermark ever attempted. This sheet of paper was fabricated by Sir William Congreve and is composed of red, blue, yellow, and white cotton and linen pulp. This was the earliest experiment with the "triple paper."*

FIG. 224   *A two-colour watermarked sheet of paper made as an experiment for the Bank of England by Sir William Congreve. The four edges, or margins, of the paper are white, the background red made of macerated Adrianople (Turkey) red cloth. Period, 1818.*

years, and owing to its interesting nature the text is here reproduced verbatim:

Account of the Origin and Experiments of the Triple Paper invented
by Sir William Congreve and proposed for the new Bank-Note.

The first suggestion of this paper was given by me to the Commission in a Memoir read to them on the 30th October 1818. In a subsequent memoir dated the 11th December I stated some further particulars respecting this Paper and proposed extracting the colour partially
in the interior layer of the Paper by means of acids. Experiments to this
effect will be found in the annexed collection. On the 29th December I
procured a quantity of Adrianople red cloth, which I was induced to
consider the best colour for reasons that will be found to be stated at
full length in the following Memoir addressed to the Bank and sent this
cloth to Mr. Harman with directions to Mr. Brewer. Mr. Brewer proceeded immediately to Freefolk and made his first report to me on the
7th February 1819, after which a series of letters passed between us
containing directions from me to him from time to time, and his observations on sending me back the results as per copies dated February 8th,
10th, 12th, 15th, 16th, 19th, and March 19th.

With this cloth Mr. Brewer went through a regular series of experiments under my direction. Specimens of which are here annexed with
proper explanations. These experiments were at first all carried on by
making the triple Paper of three separate layers and three couchings.
On the 12th of February I desired to have some with two layers only
to be sent up that they might be printed on the interior layer and returned for another white layer, so that the printing would be in the
heart of every sheet of paper.

On the 19th of February it occurred to me that a good effect might
be produced by leaving part of the interior bare so as to produce a coloured border round the edge. This border helps to complete the genuineness of the triple Paper with the colour in the interior as is seen
in the Memoir to the Bank. In these experiments with the red pulp a
very curious effect was accidentally discovered by which the interior
coloured layer is mottled.

In the middle of April Mr. Portal endeavoured to produce an imitation of the triple Paper made on a small scale. A specimen is annexed
and it will be seen how unsuccessful an attempt it was. He did not pre-
tend that he was not obliged to go through all the process used by us
in making regular triple Paper, or that it did not require Papermakers
to fabricate it, for in fact he employed the same men that had carried
on my experiments, the only difference was that it was done in smaller
quantities and in truth that the effect in making it in smaller quantities

is visible enough in the specimen of his imitation. (Messrs. Portal have manufactured the bank-note paper for the Bank of England since 1725.)

This imitation, however, became the subject of discussion at the Commission whose faith in the security derivable from the triple Paper except by the regular process of Papermaking, was rather confirmed than shaken by this attempt of Mr. Portal, and it was subsequent to this that they recommended the adoption of this triple Paper to the Bank.

But to proceed in detailing the course of the experiments, — all the specimens hitherto produced were either without watermark, or with common wire watermark. I now conceived that a very superior water-mark might be produced by a filigree pattern cut out in metal, and accordingly on this principle an oval watermark in silver was prepared by Mr. Branston. The great security of this description of watermark is that the lines of the pattern may cross in the most complicated scroll or cheque work which involves a difficulty in the imitation either by varnish or by cutting out the middle leaf.

The next improvement which I suggested by letter to Mr. Portal of the 15th June was to attempt to make the triple Paper by three dippings and only one couching which I conceived would not only improve the brilliancy of the watermark, but would also save labour and expense in making the Paper by saving the operation of *two* couchings out of *three* in each sheet, and I accordingly prepared another watermark for the experiment. The result of this experiment fully justified my suppo-sition and some specimens are attached in which I think the art of Papermaking for Bank-Notes is brought to the highest state of per-fection.

I caused another watermark also to be made which was used quite on a different principle to any hitherto adopted, it was not attached to the mould, but to the deckle and lifted off with it, so as to carry away with it all the pulp where the watermark is intended to appear.

There are thirty-six specimens of paper affixed in the back of Congreve's manuscript volume. The first twenty-four examples were fabricated by the original method of three dippings and three couchings. These are the identical sheets which were fash-ioned by Mr. Brewer for Sir William, and were made, as Congreve states in his explanation, "with common dye; the paper thick and clumsy." Other specimens shown were produced "with the in-terior pulp made from Adrianople red cloth and the paper much finer." There are also sheets of two colour combinations, made with white and yellow, and white and red pulp. Congreve shows one sheet in four colours, red, yellow, blue, and white. This particular sheet of bank-note paper was the most complex ever attempted up to that time, and although Sir William stated that "it is crude and rough," the specimen has many good qualities; and when it is considered that this sheet of paper was made in the infancy of coloured watermarking, it must be regarded as a remarkable specimen. Congreve also gives specimens of paper with printing on the interior of the sheet, giving the appearance of a watermark in black. This was accomplished by printing with common printers' ink upon one leaf and then couching another leaf over the printed one. He also extracted the colour from the ink, leaving the lettering in white, resembling a genuine watermark made with wire. Of the attempt by Mr. Portal to imitate the Congreve triple paper, the inventor has this to say: "Mr. Portal's imitation of the Adrianople red triple paper, the badness of which imitation will be evident by comparing it with one of the genuine Adrianople notes below it." While Sir William's specimen is a little more brilliant in colour than that of Mr. Portal, it would be unfair to suggest that the "imitation" was nearly so bad as Sir William would lead us to believe.

In advocating the use of his triple paper in the making of bank-notes, Sir William Congreve directed this letter to the officials of the Bank of England:

TO THE GOVERNOR AND DIRECTORS OF THE BANK OF ENGLAND: — As the triple Paper which I have had the honour to propose and superintend for the new Bank-note seems now to be brought very nearly to perfection, I think it is desirable that I should give as concise and summary a view as I can of the principal points of security which I have had in view, in proposing this plan, and as all the points now left for decision rest entirely with the Governor and Directors of the Bank, I have thought it right to address this paper in particular to them.

First then, as to the security arising from the mode of fabricating this paper. I feel confident that no imitation of this paper with the layer of coloured pulp thrown into the interior, can be made without going through the process of papermaking, and indeed this has never been denied. The imitations that were attempted were made as paper and by papermakers, and no man has ever been bold enough to say he can produce the effects here produced by any process subsequent to the original formation of the paper.

This fact alone therefore, amounts to no ordinary security for most assuredly the forger cannot as at present by various simple means take a piece of common paper and produce the appearance of a watermark upon it. He must, as I have already observed, absolutely go through the process of papermaking, and moreover to produce the extraordinary clear watermark thus given he must discover and pursue a process quite new and little likely to be suspected even by an expert papermaker, of dipping the three layers of pulp, one upon the other, without couching, and still further of making the coloured layer in clear water. I say, therefore, that as this new and extraordinary system of manipulation has been found essential to the production of the new watermark so peculiarly clear and transparent, there is no probability, for the present at all events, of its being imitated even by a papermaker.

In the second place, as to the security arising from the introduction of colour. It is evident that the tint in the interior of the paper gives a brilliancy to the watermark which cannot be obliterated by the wearing of the note, or by its being soiled, whereas in the present white note, after being considerably rubbed and soiled, it is extremely difficult to distinguish the watermark. Another very important advantage in the introduction of colour in the interior of the note is that it is a much greater security than the thinness of the present paper against attempting any alteration in the value of a note, such as the making a ten pound out of a one or two pound note by erasure. This is a mode of forgery that has been practiced with the present paper, but with the coloured paper any erasure which would not show on colourless paper would produce a greater strength of colour by laying bare the interior.

With regard to the particular colour, the pale blue as far as appearance goes seems to be the most preferred, there are, however, reasons which induce me to prefer the pink produced by the Adrianople red dye, and which I shall here state as this is a point resting with the Bank, and one which I think well worthy their mature consideration as independent of the general security attached to the introduction of colour, much of the security depends upon the use of this particular dye. The fact is that the pink pulp with which the first specimens were produced was of a very peculiar and remarkable tint that can only be obtained from the Adrianople red and is moreover a colour that cannot by any possibility be applied to the pulp after it is made, but must actually have been given to the cloth previous to its being made into pulp. The least quantity of pulp that can be made at one time is one hundred weight.

As therefore to obtain pulp of this colour so large a quantity must be made at once, it is evident that the true Adrianople pink pulp, which can always be distinguished from any other tint, can only be made in a regular paper mill on the largest scale. The Adrianople red cloth from which this pulp must be obtained is not produced in more than two or three principal manufactories in this country, as the process of dyeing it is a most laborious, troublesome, and uncertain operation consisting of nine or ten different manipulations. By adding this dye, therefore, the security arising from the paper appears to be completed, for the forger would not only then be obliged to make the paper, but to make it in large quantities. I must confess therefore, that I am of opinion that although there seems a predilection for the blue tint, that this is a point which should be reconsidered and especially as the tint may be given in as light a shade as the blue, and as little detrimental to the effect of the printing.

Test of the genuineness of this Paper: — The most simple rule may be laid down for the test of the genuineness of the triple paper, namely that when held up to the light and looked through the colours will look much stronger than when looked at. Now, if the colour were not in the interior, which we have seen is a process too difficult for the ordinary forger to attempt in his paper, the very reverse would be the effect, that is, if the colour were stained on the surface which seems to be the only mode of imitation open to the forger, then would the colour look paler when looked through than when looked at, instead of looking stronger as in the genuine note. And to prove this difference to the Public on the note itself, a narrow border of the interior coloured pulp is left bare all round the note, in this border, therefore, the colour is superficial and accordingly when the note is held up to the light the border where the colour is superficial and which is the strongest tint when looked at, appears the palest when looked through, and vice versa, the remainder of the note, where the colour is in the interior and which appears the palest when looked at, is much the strongest tint when looked through. Thus the truth and value of this simple test are at once established on a first inspection.

Of the expense: — Mr. Brewer has informed me that it has been ascertained by experiments in the presence of Mr. Portal, that one man could on the last new plan of three dippings with only one couching make eight sheets of this new paper in ten minutes without any succession of moulds. The following is the calculation he founds upon this fact: 8 sheets in 10 minutes by one man; 48 sheets in one hour; 480 sheets in one day of ten hours. If there be eight notes on a sheet, 3840 notes may be made in one day by one man and if 20 men are employed they would make 76,800 notes in a day, which is, I believe, considerably more than required.

The Governor and Directors seriously considered the use of Sir William Congreve's invention for their bank-notes and conducted a number of experiments regarding its probable use. It appears that Mr. Portal, whose firm had long since made all of the Bank of England paper, did not take kindly to Sir William's new triple paper and dissuaded the bank officials from its adoption. Producing the triple paper would have involved great difficulties, and had the bank authorities and Mr. Portal seen fit to decide upon the new paper, its fabrication on so large a scale would have been a perplexing task for even the most adept of papermakers.

Sir William Congreve was naturally disappointed when the bank officials finally refused to make use of his paper for bank-notes, and in a communication addressed to the commission, dated September 11, 1819, he writes:

The main points as to the fabric of triple paper having been successfully accomplished, that is to say the cleanness and brilliancy of the watermark and the fitness of its texture for a bank-note having been brought to perfection, its adoption for that purpose having also been decided upon by the Commission, it was natural to suppose that time would have been given to realize the necessary arrangements for making it in sufficient quantity for the supply of the Bank. No preparations, therefore, or experiments were made for this object which was considered as the minor point until about a fortnight since, nor indeed was any opposition anticipated on this ground since the first objections stated were that the paper was too easily made, and not that it was too difficult. The event, however, has proved there was a want of due precaution and foresight in this want of preparation, for seeing the determined opposition that is made to it in every stage, arrangements for producing the supply ought certainly to have been made and proceeded hand in hand with the main operation of perfecting the paper.

As the matter now stands this paper has only been produced in a perfect state with the two note moulds. This much, however, has been ascertained from the experiments that have been tried with the eight note mould, that it is the breadth of these moulds and not their length that prevents the man from throwing off the water as well from an eight note, as from a two note mould. Now, if the notes of the eight note mould were put crossways instead of lengthways, the eight note mould might be made a very little broader than the two note mould, and might therefore be used equally well in the production of the triple paper.

I am, therefore, still convinced that the necessary quantity may thus be made with very little increase of means at Freefolk. I have no wish, however, to press the matter further on the Bank and Mr. Portal in defiance of such determined opposition on his part, if the Commission think fit to rescind their decision for its adoption. I have only to say that if such be the result I shall find other means of ascertaining for my own satisfaction after having taken so much trouble how far the fabrication of this paper can be realized on the great scale and at what expense.

[Signed] WILLIAM CONGREVE

As Mr. John Portal figured so prominently in the controversy between the Bank of England officials and Sir William Congreve regarding the triple paper, it may be interesting to trace the history of his family and his record and experience as a papermaker.

The Portals were a Huguenot family of Albigensian descent, their house, both ancient and noble, having long been associated with Toulouse. During the trouble under Louis XIV, Louis de Portal, then head of the family, attempted to escape, but he and his wife and one child were killed, and only the four other children managed to flee to Holland. One of these, Henri, attached himself to the court of William of Orange, and when the latter came over to England to supplant James II, he followed after a lapse of several years. Henri landed in Southampton in 1706 and found employment in the paper mill at South Stoneham, which belonged to the Governor and Company of White Papermakers in England. Here Henri de Portal mastered the many branches of papermaking. In 1711, when he attained his majority, Henri de Portal was naturalized and became Henry Portal. When he started out for himself, Henry first had the Bare mill, near Whitechurch, but in 1718 he took over the neighbouring Laverstoke mill, which the family has held ever since. The original tenure was a ninety-nine-year lease at five pounds and "one Reame of Fools-cap paper, neatly cut," per annum. Under the lease he was required to rebuild the mill, which he did in 1719. In 1725 Henry Portal secured the monopoly for making bank-note paper for the Bank of England.

The bank-notes that were manufactured in England previous to

Henry Portal's contract were of plain paper, without watermarking. Those from the Laverstoke mill had a watermark border of a loop pattern running around the edges of the sheets, and ever since 1725 the Bank of England notes have been watermarked.

Henry Portal died at Freefolk Pryors, adjoining Laverstoke mill, in 1747. He was succeeded by his son, Joseph Portal, who operated the mill until his death in 1793. His son John Portal, continued the fabrication of the Bank of England notes for a period of fifty-three years, until his death in 1848. The paper mill is still continued by the Portals — a record of over two hundred years in the same family.[7] It will be seen that John Portal, Sir William Congreve's adversary, had come from a family of papermakers and that his own long experience qualified him to advise the Bank of England authorities regarding the adoption of Congreve's triple paper.

Sir William Congreve was forty-six years of age when he discovered that three separate sheets of paper could be formed and couched as one sheet, thus introducing colour into the interior of the paper. There is no record of his having made any other triple paper than that shown to the Governor and Directors of the Bank of England in 1818, all of which is in the Paper Museum of the Massachusetts Institute of Technology. Congreve patented his invention on December 4, 1819.

There was but little accomplished in the art of coloured watermarking from the time of Congreve until about 1885 when Mr. Lee of Wookey Hole, near Wells, Somerset, England, undertook to revive and improve the art. Clayton Beadle in his article on watermarking [8] gives Lee the credit of being the pioneer in England in the making of coloured watermarks, but this is obviously a mistake. Mr. Beadle also states that Lee patented his invention in 1886, but a search through the British Patent Office records does not reveal a coloured-watermark patent under his name.

As late as 1900 W. Fairweather and A. and G. B. Fornari were granted a patent in England which reads in part: "A sheet of white or coloured pulp, having any design suitable for a watermark, is inserted between two plain sheets of pulp, and the three layers are pressed together to form a single sheet of paper. The mould consists of a base over which is stretched the sieve, the latter being covered with a plain plate having the required de-

FIG. 225   A portrait watermark of Louis XVIII, made in
1814 in the Johannot paper mill,
Annonay, Ardèche, France. The
finest watermarking of the nineteenth century was accomplished
at this mill.

FIG. 226   Marie Caroline in
watermarked paper as executed by
the Johannot firm. In this mark
and the one shown in Figure 225
the portraits are formed in drawn
wire with the backgrounds sunk in
the woven wire of the mould's surface. This is not light-and-shade
watermarking as invented in England about 1850.

sign cut in it. The watermark can only be seen by transmitted
light."

From the advent of papermaking in the thirteenth century until Congreve's invention there was practically no change in the
method of impressing designs in paper during the process of fabrication. After the experiments undertaken by Congreve it became apparent to European papermakers that the art of watermarking need not be limited to line lettering and simple devices
and emblems twisted in wire and applied to the surface of the
moulds. Contemporary with Congreve working in England was
Johannot carrying on the art of watermarking in France. This
French papermaking firm did excellent work and today specimens
of their papers are accepted as superior watermarking. With the
Johannot watermarks the woven wire was pressed so the stock, or
pulp, was held in two degrees of density or thickness, which
formed backgrounds for the outline single wire portraits or emblems. This was the first instance of simple light-and-shade watermarking; the Johannot mill was executing work of this kind as
early as 1812. Figures 225 and 226 are representative of early
nineteenth-century watermarks from the Johannot establishment,
whose origin dates at Ambert from the first part of the seven-

FIG. 228   *By an act of Congress, approved March 31, 1848, the President was authorized to borrow a sum not exceeding $16,000,000. The eagle-watermarked paper, made by hand in the Willcox mill, was used for the issuing of these bonds. This eagle mark was as elaborate as anything that had been made in America up to this time.*

FIG. 227   *A wire watermarked paper made for United States Treasury notes in 1843 by the Willcox mill, Pennsylvania. Only 35,000 sheets of paper were manufactured, all formed on hand moulds. This is the simplest form of watermarking.*

teenth century, and whose plant was later moved to Annonay. Portrait watermarks were also made in Germany during the late eighteenth and early nineteenth centuries, but the work is not comparable to that of Johannot. During the middle of the nineteenth century the art of watermarking was receiving considerable attention in America, especially at the Willcox mill in Pennsylvania. In Figure 227 is shown a watermarked treasury note paper made by this mill in 1843; in Figure 228 may be seen a fairly elaborate mark produced by Willcox in 1848 for the United States Government; and in Figure 229 may be studied what is perhaps the first bank-note paper ever made in the United States for a foreign government. This watermarked paper was made by the Willcox mill for the Bank of Greece in 1859. These three specimens from the Pennsylvania mill are superior to most of the watermarking done in America at this period.

Fig. 229   *A sheet of watermarked bank-note paper made for the Bank of Greece by the Willcox mill in 1859. This was probably the earliest bank paper to be made in this country for a foreign government.*

A decided change in the method of marking paper appeared during the mid nineteenth century when William Henry Smith, an Englishman, conceived the plan for complicated light-and-shade watermarking. This departure from the old manner of using single wires and simple impressed backgrounds was received with acclaim as a genuine artistic development. The expense of manufacturing the moulds, however, was considerable from a commercial standpoint. With the Smith method of watermarking any degree of density or lightness could be made into the paper so when the sheet was held to the light the paper would reveal, through its various thicknesses, any object or form, no matter how intricate the shading. Watermarked reproductions of the paintings of the old masters, as well as portraits of celebrities, were undertaken with surprisingly accurate and reasonably artistic results.

In making a light-and-shade watermark by use of the Smith plan, the portrait or object is modelled with small cutting and gouging tools in a sheet of wax, against the light, the wax finally assuming the desired picture. Whatever appears in the wax will eventually take form as watermarks in the finished sheets of paper. The initial step in the making of a light-and-shade watermark is to procure a sheet of common window glass somewhat larger on all sides than the watermark to be modelled. A square-cut frame, or fence, is made around the edges of the glass with clay; the melted wax is then poured upon the glass to a depth of about a quarter inch. A satisfactory composition for the wax can be made

FIG. 230   *The original of a portrait watermark. The portrait has been cut into a sheet of wax, about 3/16 of an inch in thickness. The degrees of density of the wax eventually determine the variations in the thickness of the macerated fibres on the mould.*

FIG. 231   *The electrotype made from the wax original shown in Figure 230. The wax must be coated with powdered graphite to render a metallic surface for electrotyping. The copper electrotype is backed with about a quarter of an inch of lead.*

from a mixture of pure beeswax and common paraffin, about half and half. After the wax has hardened, the clay frame is removed, leaving the wax cut squarely around the edges upon the glass. The glass and its wax coating are now placed in a wooden frame holder, against the light, either natural or artificial, but with all light blocked out except directly behind the wax. With small gouging tools, which the modeller himself must make, the process of cutting the portrait or other object commences. It is only natural that the deeper the incisions in the wax, the more light will penetrate. The various degrees of density cut in the wax will eventually hold the macerated papermaking fibres in these same thicknesses, thus causing any scale of light and shade. The cutting of a portrait in the wax cannot be done hurriedly; it requires the same skill that would be needed in the modelling of any sculpture. In making a watermark, however, there must be no under-

Fig. 232   *The woven brass wire screen after having been impressed over the electrotype shown in Figure 231. The embossed wire is applied to the frame of a papermaking mould, shown in Figures 234, 236, and 237. The deeper the cuts made in the original wax, the higher will be the surface of the woven wire, causing the paper stock to lie thin; the more dense the wax, the thicker will lie the macerated pulp on the mould.*

Fig. 233   *A completed sheet of paper after having been formed upon the embossed wire shown in Figure 232. In making clear and distinct watermarks it is essential that the fibres be beaten extremely short, thereby sacrificing the strength of the paper. The portrait of Lord Byron was modelled from a drawing made by the late Jules Maurice Gaspard.*

cuts or sharp or abrupt edges, as these would interfere with the final pressing of the woven wire cloth. Only through practice will even an adept modeller be able to incise a wax satisfactorily for watermarking. In Europe, previous to the war, there were not over five or six workers who had perfected watermark modelling.

After the wax has been incised (Figure 230), the surface of the wax is given a thorough coating of powdered graphite, or plumbago, which imparts a metallic surface to the wax. The graphite should be well rubbed into the crevices so that the wax re-

FIG. 234   *A light-and-shade mould for producing watermarked paper in all degrees of density and lightness. The process was invented by W. H. Smith, an Englishman, during the mid nineteenth century.*

ceives a complete surfacing. The next step is to make an electrotype of the wax (Figure 231). The electrotype should be about one thirty-second of an inch in thickness, and to hold it rigid it is usually backed with about a quarter inch of lead, cut squarely on the four edges. The next procedure is to impart the contours of the electrotype to the woven brass wire gauze that will later form the face or surface of the papermaking mould. The woven wire should be of fine quality with from 48 to 60 wires to the inch. Where the portrait or design is to be impressed, the wire should be annealled. The wire screen may be impressed into the electrotyped object by the use of burnishing tools; or if several moulds are to be made, a second electrotype should be made from the first, forming cameo and intaglio, more commonly known as male and female, dies. When two electrotypes have been made, the woven wire screen is pressed between them; with this method any number of mould-covers can be made exactly alike in every detail

Fig. 235   *A sheet of light-and-shade watermarked paper as produced on the mould pictured in Figure 234.*

(Figures 232, 233). In Figures 234, 236, and 237 are shown the actual moulds upon which many reams of paper have been formed. In Figure 238 may be seen the watermark used by Elbert Hubbard from forty to fifty years ago, the first genuine light-and-shade portrait watermark to be made for an American. This watermark was made from an etching of Mr. Hubbard by Otto J. Schneider, and the mould and paper were made in Italy by the well-known Fabriano firm of Pietro Miliani. In this instance four sheets were formed at each dipping of the mould, the sheets being divided by tearing wires, giving two genuine and two false deckles on every sheet of letter paper. In Figure 239 may be studied an elaborate English watermark made in 1874 to commemorate the four hundredth anniversary of the first printing in England, by William Caxton. This watermarked sheet of paper combines the single wire lines and the light-and-shade; the paper is of a light-yellow colour and measures about 20 by 22 inches; it was made by T. H. Saunders & Company, London. The King Edward watermark (Figure 240) was also made in England, while the splendid portrait watermark of King Albert (Figure 241) was

Fig. 236   *An elaborately watermarked mould used in making hand-made stationery. The oval design in the centre is the light-and-shade type, surrounded by simple wire lettering. The watermark of the star, or wheel, shown at the right of the mould is that of John Tate, who in 1495 founded the first paper mill in England; the first printer to use Tate paper was Wynkyn de Worde. At the left appears the watermark of William Rittenhouse, who established the first paper mill in America in 1690; the first printer to use this paper was William Bradford.*

FIG. 237   A light-and-shade mould for producing letter paper
measuring approximately seven by eight inches.

of Italian make; both watermarks measure approximately 13 by
16 inches. The watermarks of the Popes and St. Peter's Cathedral
were produced by the Fabriano firm, and the Cologne Cathedral
is of German make (Figures 242). Perhaps the masterpiece of
modern watermarking is the exquisite rendering of Raphael's
Madonna of the Chair, which was modelled in Italy, the paper
made by the handmade-paper mill of Pietro Miliani, Fabriano
(Figure 243), the size of the sheet about 15 by 17½ inches.

As previously mentioned, the expense of light-and-shade portrait watermarks places them beyond the possibility of commercial exploitation. The mould for making a special portrait
will cost from five hundred to over a thousand dollars, depending upon the size of the mould and the excellence of the modelling. After the moulds have been constructed, the cost of making
paper upon them is not great, about thirty dollars the ream. A
great many reams can be made upon a mould before it begins

FIG. 239　A　watermarked sheet of paper in which were used both single-line wires and the light-and-shade process. This sheet of paper measures 20 by 22 inches and was made in 1874 to commemorate the four hundredth anniversary of William Caxton's first printing in England.

FIG. 238　Letter paper used for private correspondence by the late Elbert Hubbard. The paper was made about 1900 in the Pietro Miliani mill, Fabriano, Italy. The light-and-shade watermark was modelled after an etching by Otto J. Schneider. A divided mould was used, enabling the vatman to form four sheets at each dipping; the colour of the paper is goldenrod.

to break down through the couching process, but with the original dies any number of mould-covers may be impressed (Figure 244).

In the United States the making of light-and-shade watermarks has not been highly developed, but in Europe and Japan watermarks made by the foregoing process have long played a prominent part in the prevention of counterfeiting. Light-and-shade watermarks may be successfully made on a hand-mould or on a cylinder-mould paper-machine, explained in a later section of this book; but with the use of a "dandy-roll" the result is usually somewhat dull and lacking in contrast and brilliance. The paper for the

FIG. 240   A watermarked portrait of King Edward VII. The
paper measures 13 by 16 inches
and was made in England about
forty years ago.

FIG. 241   A light-and-shade
portrait of Albert, King of the Bel-
gians. This watermark was made
in Italy and measures about the
same size as that of King Edward.

currency of Japan is made in the Imperial mill, Tōkyō, and is
beautifully watermarked in the manner described. In the Western
Hemisphere light-and-shade watermarks are used in the bank-note
paper of Argentina, Chile, and Uruguay, all made in Europe. The
following countries use bank-notes that bear light-and-shade watermarked portraits or other shaded emblems or devices: Algeria,
Australia, Ceylon, Fiji, France, Germany, Great Britain, India,
Indo-China, Iraq, Ireland, Italy, New Caledonia, New Zealand,
Persia, Portugal, Russia, South Africa, Straits Settlements, Turkey,
and Yugoslavia. The paper for these bank-notes was made for the
various governments in the mills of England, France, Germany,
Italy, and Russia.

During a recent visit in America, Dr. Leopoldo Marzano, technical director of the Banco d'Italia, Rome, called upon me and gave
me interesting information relative to the use of watermarks in
the paper money of the Italian Government. According to Dr.
Marzano, it is much more difficult to counterfeit light-and-shade
watermarks than for a forger to duplicate the engraving of a bank-

FIG. 242   *Vatican papers made by the Cartiere Pietro Miliani, Fabriano, Italy. The watermark of the Cologne Cathedral was made by the J. W. Zanders mill, Bergisch-Gladbach, Rhineland, Germany.*

note. If this assertion is correct, the counterfeiting of most European paper money would be a more highly skilled procedure than making spurious United States paper currency, which relies chiefly upon the intricate engraving to prevent falsification. In the entire history of counterfeiting there have been but few instances of actual papermaking; practically all counterfeiting of United States money is done upon paper readily procurable in any stationery store. In regard to the use of fine watermarks or delicate engravings as a precaution against forgery, it must be taken into consideration that brilliantly watermarked paper, with its necessarily short fibre, does not possess the wearing quality

FIG. 243   A *beautifully executed watermark depicting Raphael's*
Madonna of the Chair. *This watermark was produced in Italy by the*
renowned Pietro Miliani firm. Watermarking of this degree of perfec-
tion is the quintessence of the papermaking craft.

of long-fibred paper that is not dependent upon watermarking.
Strength and durability in paper must always be sacrificed to
achieve clear-cut and distinct watermarks.

FIG. 244   *Watermarked letter paper made in 1925 for the late Harry Worcester Smith, American inventor of textile machinery. The expense involved in the actual making of the mould was about one thousand dollars; the paper formed on the mould was furnished at thirty-five dollars the ream. It is possible to write with ink on watermarked paper without difficulty as the different thicknesses are not noticeable to the pen.*

XI

Papermaking Materials

WITH THE EIGHTEENTH–CENTURY DEVELOPMENT
OF PRINTING, OCCIDENTAL PAPERMAKERS
WERE FORCED TO BEGIN THEIR SEARCH
FOR VEGETABLE FIBRES NEVER BEFORE
USED

UNTIL the latter part of the eighteenth century practically all paper of Occidental origin had been made from linen or cotton rags or a mixture of these fibres. In using this superior material the papers made in Europe and America before about 1775 were, for the most part, of lasting and durable quality. (Cotton has a cellulose content of about 91 per cent; linen, hemp, jute, etc., vary from about 60 to 90 per cent pure cellulose.) During the first half of the eighteenth century there began an increased consumption of paper and it became more and more difficult for the papermakers to procure sufficient rags to cope with this comparatively fast-growing demand. Books were being issued for more general circulation, newspapers were established, and even popular magazines were beginning to make their weekly and monthly appearance. The sharp rise in the use of paper was unprecedented and in almost every periodical of the time, in both Europe and America, we find advertisements imploring the populace to "Save Your Rags." One of the Massachusetts paper mills operating in 1799 considered the rag shortage so acute that it produced quantities of writing paper which bore the significant watermark: "SAVE RAGS." Such paper was commonly sold and used in Boston during the end of the eighteenth and the beginning of the nineteenth centuries. In an issue of the *Boston News Letter*, 1769, there appeared an advertisement that "the bell cart will go through Boston about the end of each month to collect rags," and added:

Rags are as beauties which concealed lie,
But when in paper, how it charms the eye!
Pray save your rags, new beauties to discover,
For of paper, truly, every one's a lover;
By the pen and press such knowledge is displayed
As wouldn't exist if paper was not made.
Wisdom of things, mysterious, divine,
Illustriously doth on paper shine.

The Massachusetts General Court in 1776 required the Committee of Safety in each locality to appoint a suitable person to receive rags, and appealed to the inhabitants to save even the most insignificant quantity. The *Courier* of Norwich, Connecticut, insisted that every man should say to his wife: "Molly, make a rag-bag and hang it under the shelf where the big Bible lies"; and the Boston *Gazette*, 1798, urged that every child should be taught its "rag lesson." The postmaster in Troy, New York, in 1801, requested that the ladies of his state imitate the patriotism and frugality of the women of Massachusetts and Connecticut, who "display an elegant work-bag as part of the furniture of their parlours, in which every scrap of rag is carefully preserved for the papermakers."

Another advertisement showing the scarcity of rags during the latter part of the eighteenth century appears in the November 14, 1777 issue of the *North Carolina Gazette,* which in facetious mood reads: ". . . when the young ladies are assured, that by sending to the paper mill an old handkerchief, no longer fit to cover their snowy breasts, there is a possibility of its returning to them again in the more pleasing form of a *billet doux* from their lovers, the proprietors flatter themselves with great success." Perhaps the most instructive of the old "save rags" advertisements is found in the *Cheshire Advertiser,* Keene, New Hampshire, March 22, 1792. This advertisement reads: "Moses Johnson, informs all little misses, and others his customers, that he receives all kinds of cotton or linen rags, and flatters himself they will be encouraged to save them when they are informed 1½ pounds of rags will buy a primer or a story book, or one yard of ribbon, two thimbles, two rings, twelve good needles, two strings of beads, one penknife, nine rows of pins — 4 pounds of rags will buy a pair of handsome buckles, or the famous 'History of Robinson Crusoe,' who lived 28 years on an uninhabited island. . . ."

In connection with the scarcity and use of paper in America an interesting story is told of two incidents that purport to have taken place during the Revolution. When the Continental Army entered Philadelphia, after the evacuation of the British, the soldiers encountered a scarcity of paper for wrapping their black powder and lead balls to be used as ammunition in their muskets. The soldiers made a search of the town for paper and fell upon a great store of the much-needed material in the attic of a house formerly occupied as a printing shop by Benjamin Franklin. The loot consisted of about 2,500 copies of a sermon compiled by the Reverend Gilbert Tenant which had been printed in Franklin's establishment. The sermon, strangely enough, expounded the subject of *Defensive War*. The paper upon which the good minister's sermons had been printed was at once converted into cartridges and put to use in the Battle of Monmouth. Another instance where paper was needed in the making of ammunition was in 1777 during the Battle of Brandywine, when Continental soldiers procured the necessary paper by the acquisition of a two-horse wagonload of an unbound edition of Foxe's *Book of Martyrs,* which had just gone to the bindery in Ephrata, Pennsylvania.

To encourage the use of wool and at the same time save linen and cotton for the papermakers, the English Parliament in 1666 decreed that only wool could be used in burying the dead. In one year approximately 200,000 pounds of linen and cotton were saved for the papermakers by this edict. In both England and Germany at this period it was contrary to good citizenship to make use of linen or cotton clothing for burial. All garments used for this purpose had to be made of wool, a material unsuited for papermaking. Linen and cotton have always been and will always remain the finest material for Occidental papermaking, but by the beginning of the nineteenth century the need for other more plentiful materials was keenly felt and the search had begun in earnest. This quest for new fibres for papermaking was not brought about by a desire to discover more suitable or better materials for the purpose, but to find substances that were cheaper, more abundant, and more easily converted into paper — the demand was for speed and low cost; quality at this time was superseded by the necessity for quantity.

The earliest suggestion of a papermaking material that might have been substituted for linen and cotton occurred in 1684, when Edward Lloyd brought forth his impracticable plan of making paper from asbestos. Lloyd's suggestion may be found in *Philosophical Transactions*, November and June, 1684–85, pages 823–24. The experiment as communicated to the learned society by Mr. Lloyd reads:

An account of a sort of Paper made of *Linum asbestinum* found in Wales in a letter to the Publisher, from Edward Lloyd of Jesus Coll. Oxon.

In obedience to your commands I have here sent you all the account I am able to give at present of the *Lapis amianthus* or *Linum fossile asbestinum* which you were inform'd (and that truly) was to be found in the Isle of Anglesey: wherein I shall choose to refer it to your own judgment to determine whether this be the same kind with the *asbestos* of the ancients, or in some respects different from it. . . . It is found in no small quantity in the Parish of LLan-Fair yng Hornwy in the northern part of Anglesey; where it runs in veins through a rock of stone in hardness and colour not unlike *flint*. . . . It is composed of a *lanuginous* matter exactly resembling that of pappous plants. . . . Having pounded it and cleansed it, I brought it to the Paper-mil; and putting it in water in a vessel just capacious enough to make Paper with such a quantity; I stirred it pretty much, and desired the workmen to proceed with it in their usual method of making Paper, with their writing-paper mould: onely to stir it about ever before they put their mould in; considering it as a far more ponderous substance than what they used; and that consequently if not immediately taken up after it was agitated, it would subside. Paper made of it proved but very course and to apt to tear, whereof I have sent you a sheet. But this being the first tryal, I have some reasons to believe it may be much improved; nor did the workmen doubt but in case it were pounded in one of their mortars for 20 hours space it would make good writing-paper; which, when I shall receive sufficient quantity of it, I design to try. In the mean while be pleased to accept of this superficial account of it, in token of gratitude from, your most oblig'd servant E. Lloyd.

The papermakers of Europe had been satisfied to make use of linen and cotton fibres for more than five and a half centuries, for it was not until 1716 that there appeared in England the first treatise on the use of a practical material other than linen and cotton for papermaking. This little volume, apparently the forerunner of a magazine, was entitled: *Essays, for the Month of December 1716,*

FIG. 245   *The preparation of raw hemp as a papermaking material,*
as depicted by the Society of Gentlemen, London, December 1716. The
earliest treatise to be published in England regarding a substitute for
linen and cotton as substances for making into paper.

to be continued Monthly, by a Society of Gentlemen. For the ben-
efit of the People of England. The work was printed in London
and the part regarding papermaking may be found in Essay VI.
"The Society of Gentlemen" advanced the idea of using raw hemp
without spinning or weaving as a material from which to fabricate
paper, and a detailed description is given regarding its preparation for the purpose. The "Gentlemen" suggest also that paper
mills be set up on barges or flat-bottomed boats on the Thames
and the other navigable rivers of England, as they are on the Elbe
and the Danube, the power to be furnished by the flux and reflux
of the tide. There is an engraving in these *Essays* of 1716 depicting the manner in which hemp may be washed, boiled, pressed,
and dried so that it can be put to use as a substitute for linen and
cotton; it is suggested that the paper-mill owners plant hemp in
their mill yards and gardens and produce their own supply of
papermaking material (Figure 245).

The use of wood as a material from which to make paper was
first suggested in the Occident by René Antoine Ferchault de
Réaumur (1683–1757), a celebrated naturalist and physicist re-
siding in France. Réaumur had observed the habits of the wasp
(*Hymenopterous* of the family *Vespidæ*) and concluded that the

Fig. 246   *The wasp was the first papermaker. After examining the nests of this insect the French scientist Réaumur concluded that paper could be made from wood fibre.*

wood filaments that were used by these insects to construct their nests so resembling paper could also be used in the actual process of papermaking (Figure 246). Réaumur's observations regarding the habits of the wasp were laid before the French Royal Academy in a treatise dated November 15, 1719. Réaumur wrote: "The American wasps form very fine paper, like ours; they extract the fibres of common wood of the countries where they live. They teach us that paper can be made from the fibres of plants without the use of rags and linen, and seem to invite us to try whether we cannot make fine and good paper from the use of certain woods. If we had woods similar to those used by the American wasps for their paper, we could make the whitest paper, for this material is very white. By a further beating and breaking of the fibres that the wasps make and using the thin paste that comes from them, a very fine paper may be composed. This study should not be neglected, for it is, I dare say, important. The rags from which we make our paper are not an economical material and every papermaker knows that this substance is becoming rare. While the consumption of paper increases every day, the production of linen remains about the same. In addition to this the foreign mills draw upon us for material. The wasp seems to teach us a means of overcoming these difficulties." Réaumur further continued his observations regarding a heavier wasp-made paper: "But all of the wasps of the Kingdom that I know make nothing as singular as a species of wasp that lives in Canada. . . . At first glance, and even after examining the surface for a considerable time, one would accept the nest as the work of the hand of man. Its covering resembles our paper to such an extent that it is hard to detect a difference. It has the same gloss, and the colour is that of an old piece of manufactured paper which had formerly been white. It is fine paper and as heavy as that of ordinary portfolios."

Réaumur's most important observations relating to natural history may be found in *Mémoires pour servir à l'histoire des insectes*, published in Amsterdam, six volumes, 1737–48. The original intention of the author was to publish twelve volumes of this work, but he died during the process of compiling the seventh volume. Though there is no record of Réaumur's ever having actually made paper from wood, he was, no doubt, the first scientist to suggest or recommend its use for this purpose. Human invention in the making of paper had been anticipated by the wasp, which insect may be considered as a professional papermaker, devoting most of her time and energies to the fabrication of this material, which she uses in the construction of nests. For this purpose the wasp seeks dry wood — fence-rails and weather-beaten boards are a favourite source of supply. This substance she saws or rasps by mastication, mixes the macerated material with a natural size which is exuded for the purpose, and, working the whole into a paste, spreads the paper substance in a manner truly remarkable. The nest is usually a prolonged irregular spheroid, exceptionally light in weight, of a dark grey colour, and bound with repeated bands of paper to the bough from which it is suspended. The nest is water-resistant to a high degree, partly from the rounded top, but more from the fact that the paper strips of which it is composed overlap, like the shingles of a house, and from the fact that a semi-waterproof size is used in the composition. The community of papermaking wasps may amount to thirty thousand in a single season, according to Réaumur. It is interesting to note Réaumur's condemnation of himself for having neglected to attempt any experiments on his own account in making paper from wood. In 1742 his comment was: "I am ashamed that I have not yet tried this experiment, it is more than twenty years since I first realized its importance and made an announcement of it. But I had hoped

that someone would have been interested in making it his occupation."

The investigations of Réaumur, while not in actual papermaking, gave the hint to European scientists that paper might be made
from other substances than rags. In 1727–30 Franz Ernst Brückmann (1697–1753) compiled a book on geology,[1] a few copies of
which were printed on paper made of asbestos, the first use of asbestos for this purpose. Albert Seba (1665–1736), a Flemish writer
on natural history, compiled a set of books [2] issued in 1734–65, in
which he has the following to say regarding material from which
paper could possibly be made: "My country does not seem to lack
trees suitable for making paper, if people would give themselves
the necessary expense and trouble. 'Algæ marina' (seaweed), for
example, which is composed of long, strong viscous filaments,
might it not be proper for this purpose, as well as the mats of Mus-
covy, if they were prepared as the Japanese make their timber?"

In 1741 Jean Étienne Guettard (1715–86), of the Royal Academy of Sciences, and Physician to his Highness the Duke of Or-
léans, made his first observations regarding substitutes for rags
in making paper and wrote several articles [3] advocating the use of
conferva (swamp moss) as a papermaking material. One of the
articles was accompanied by actual specimens of papers made
from the bark, leaves, and woods of various trees, plants, and
shrubs. Guettard's observations were translated into English and
published in London in 1754.[4] In this volume, on miscellaneous
subjects, Guettard recommended the use of various forms of vegetation for papermaking. He had not, however, at this time carried
his ideas to any conclusion, for in his essay he says: "Such exam-
inations have always constituted my desires, since I thought of
making experiments upon paper. I have been unable, hitherto, to
accomplish my scheme; but, nevertheless, I have reason to hope
I shall one day see it accomplished." Guettard also suggested the
use of the cods of the common caterpillar as a suitable material
for making into paper and there were contemporary experiments
with this unwieldy substance, but from all accounts no paper of
usable quality was produced. In 1777 there was published in Philadelphia a small octavo volume [5] which contained the treatise by
Guettard that had appeared in France in 1741 and in England in

1754. This book is interesting as the first publication to be issued in America treating of papermaking materials.

John Strange (1732–99), an English diplomatist and traveller, wrote a pamphlet [6] in 1764, which was issued in Italy, relating to materials for making into paper. This treatise was compiled while the author was travelling in Italy and he tells about the paper of Cortona, a town of Tuscany, and gives a summary of the use of broom, a fabaceous shrub, and other plants for papermaking. While Strange recommended conferva (swamp moss) for various other uses, he did not deem it a suitable material from which to make paper.

In the chronological order of scientists who advanced their ideas as to new papermaking fibres to take the place of linen and cotton, we have the highly interesting and unusual work [7] of Jacob Christian Schäffer (1718–90), who did more than any of his predecessors in the quest for materials for papermaking. In 1765 he started a treatise on the subject which was issued in six volumes, the last appearing in 1771.[8] This is one of the rarest works on the subject of paper that have been published, only eight or ten copies being known in America. Schäffer was born in Querfurt, near Merseburg in Saxony, in the year 1718, but his family early removed to Regensburg, or Ratisbon, the capital of the Bavarian province of Oberpfalz, about one hundred and fifty miles south of his birthplace. Schäffer studied for the ministry and became a well-known clergyman in Regensburg, but it seems that he derived his greatest pleasure outside the church, as he devoted most of his time to the study of botany and natural history. His work on the fungi of Bavaria is still regarded as a standard authority. Schäffer's interest in the flora of Bavaria directed his attention to the possibility of new materials for papermaking, and it is with his researches in this direction that we are concerned. In his six-volume treatise Dr. Schäffer has left a permanent record of his experiments in the search for new papermaking materials, and the actual specimens of his paper establish the fact that he was the pioneer in the use of many vegetable fibres for the fabrication of paper. It was not Schäffer's desire, as he explains, to make well-finished paper; he simply wished to show the vast variety of vegetation available for the purpose. As his experiments were carried on previous to the discovery of bleach,* his examples of paper have the tint of the original materials from which they were made. In most of the samples about one fifth part cotton rags were added to the pulp to help bind the fibres together. A number of the specimens are sized, and nearly all have been printed upon, showing from what plant or fibre they had been made.

It is curious to note that one of the first specimens shown in Schäffer's books was made from wasps' nests — for was not the wasp, as Réaumur pointed out, the first papermaker? (Figure 247). Dr. Schäffer's researches extended over a period of more than eight years, and all of the materials with which he worked were gathered in his own garden or neighbouring fields. The mode of making the various samples of paper is given in detail. The materials, according to their nature, were first chopped by hand, the different kinds of wood having been reduced by a toothed plane. Most of the experiments were carried on in Dr. Schäffer's own

---

* The process of bleaching was invented in 1774 by Karl Wilhelm Scheele (1742–86). Dr. Scheele discovered a gas now known as chlorine, which, in combination with lime, came to be used in bleaching materials for the making of paper. Dr. Scheele was born in Stralsund, Pomerania, which at that period was part of Sweden. He studied chemistry in Gothenburg while serving an eight-year apprenticeship to an apothecary. Scheele next established himself in Uppsala and at the age of thirty-three he was elected to the Stockholm Academy of Sciences. Scheele later moved to Köping, where he became the proprietor of a pharmacy, and it was here that many of his experiments in chemistry were carried on. These researches embraced manganese dioxide, arsenic acid, quartz, clay, and alum. Dr. Scheele discovered chlorine, baryta (monoxide of barium), tungstic acid, glycerine, and arsine, the last one of the most poisonous of all substances. He wrote but one book, *Air and Fire*, published in 1777; his accumulated papers appeared in book form after his death. Sweden honoured Karl Wilhelm Scheele in 1942, the second centenary of his birth, by issuing two commemorative postage stamps.

The earliest English patent covering a bleaching agent was granted Clement and George Taylor, April 25, 1792. After receiving their patent the Messrs. Taylor, papermakers, were under the impression that their privilege gave them exclusive rights to bleach paper. Apparently other papermakers regarded the patent in a different light, for in 1792 there was issued in Edinburgh, Scotland, a 43-page booklet under the following title: *Memorial relative to the Invention of a New Method of Bleaching, Showing the Absurdity of Any Pretensions to an Exclusive Privilege for Using It in the Paper Manufacture.* The first technical work issued in English on the subject of bleaching paper was a translation by William Nicholson, Newman Street, London, of the French work by Pajot des Charmes. The English version of this book, published in London in 1799, gives short articles on the method of "bleaching written or printed papers and rags, whether unbleached, dyed or coloured"; also of the "bleaching of old written papers, to be worked up again."

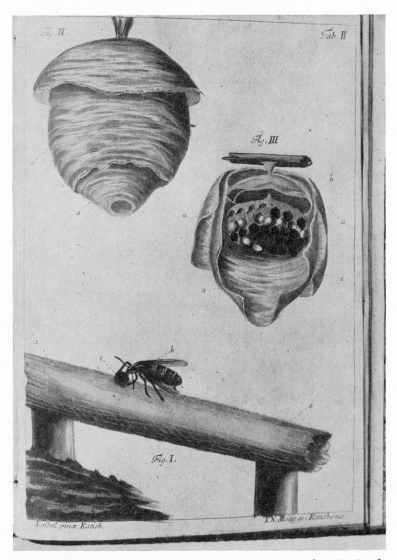

FIG. 247   *The wasp, the first papermaker, as pictured in Dr. Jacob Christian Schäffer's six-volume work on the subject of papermaking materials, 1765–71.*

home, and for the purpose of macerating the materials he employed a miniature set of stampers operated by hand (Figure 248). In most cases the vegetable matter was subjected to the stampers without preliminary treatment, but with a few of the materials milk of lime was used. With some of the more stubborn fibres the doctor used a stiff lime paste and suffered the material to remain in it for various lengths of time, and he noted that this treatment reduced the beating process and gave a brown tint to the wood.

There are not many copies of this work extant and the specimens in the various sets are not always identical. The compilation is more often found bound complete in one volume than in the six original pamphlets as Dr. Schäffer issued his work. The six volumes are designated on the title-pages as volumes one, two, one, two, three, and four. The first volume of this valuable work was completed January 30, 1765, and the book contains fifty-five pages of text, five plates, and fifteen specimens of paper. The examples include papers that were made from wasps' nests, and from various kinds of wood, moss, and vines. In volume two, dated April 3, 1765, there are twenty-eight pages of text and one plate. The specimens embrace papers fabricated from hemp, bark, straw, and cabbage stalks. The third volume (in the order of their appearance), dated November 3, 1765, has thirty-two text pages, and the specimens include papers made from asbestos, cattail and burdock stalks, thistles, and turf. Volume four was completed January 1, 1766, with twenty-four pages of text and eleven samples, including papers from seed, mallow, St.-John's-wort, and Indian corn husks. The fifth volume is dated April 15, 1767, and the sixth and last is dated 1771. These two books give specimens of paper made from genista, pine-cones, potatoes, old shingles, reeds; and bean, horse-chestnut, walnut, tulip, and linden leaves; also paper made from yellow- and brazil-wood.

Inasmuch as Dr. Schäffer's work is one of the most important works that deal with paper, and because the text is unusually interesting, it will not be out of the way to quote at length from the book:

It is generally known that the paper which, according to all evidence, has been used in Europe since the twelfth century is made of rags and worn-out linen. And the dearth of this material is now complained of

FIG. 248   *The frontispiece in one of the volumes of Dr. Schäffer's treatise on papermaking. This fanciful print depicts a set of stampers similar to the machine used by Dr. Schäffer in his experiments.*

everywhere. The most curious thing is that not only a certain kind of paper is wanting; statements of merchants reveal that in regard to wrapping paper, cardboard, etc., the want is even keener.

This general lack of paper, and the harm done thereby to administration, science, and commerce, brought a few years ago to my memory what various scholars — like Seba, Réaumur, Guettard, and others — had in mind and proposed in regard to papermaking. They believed, and with probability proved, that one is not exclusively bound in papermaking to linen, but can make paper just as well of a great many other things. It is generally known that rags originally were made of lint and hemp, which are plants themselves; thus these scholars came to the conclusion that every material which — like hemp and lint — consists of such soft, elastic, easily separated fibres as through the action of water turn to pulp and by drying attain a certain stiffness and firmness must be fit for papermaking.

Few objections can be reasonably raised against the statements of these scholars — and the more certain it is that besides hemp and lint there are many plants having the same necessary qualities, the more difficult it is to comprehend why these ideas have not been used for the public benefit, and why such experiments have not been longer, oftener, and in a more satisfactory way pursued. This regrettable neglect induced me three years ago to get to work with all possible energy. It seemed to me as if nature itself wished to encourage me in my task. Taking a walk outside of our city, chance led me to a place where one side of the field, from abundance of pappus of the poplar, and the other from "wool-blade," looked wholly white. At this sight the thought flashed through my mind: Could not paper be made from these plants?

Without losing time, I started at once to experiment. I gathered the pappus as well as the wool-blade, then talked the matter over with the papermaker of the town, Herr Meckenhäuser. How happy I was when — after examining the pappus — this good-natured man declared that, though the wool-blade did not seem to him fit for papermaking, the poplar-downs must by all means be tried out. But my joy was gone when I learned that the papermaker wanted five to twenty pounds of pappus. It was impossible to get such a quantity, and it cost me a great deal of talk before I could persuade him to make the experiment with the poplar-downs in a mortar. A few days later I received a few samples of the new paper. It was, at any rate, paper; one could print or even write on it. Only it was too ragged, and did not possess the necessary firmness, and besides it was full of little brown knots, the residue of the pounded kernels. Yet these first and imperfect samples provided the most convincing proof that the pappus of poplar is fit for papermaking, and the papermaker assured me that if a satisfactory quantity of pappus had been pounded in his regular beater instead of in the mortar, and if it had been further duly treated and finished, we could have obtained a reliable and usable paper.

Other occupations prevented me continuing my experiments in the following two years. Yet being urged from several sources, especially the Academy, I resumed the experiments. I gathered again a basketful of poplar pappus and wool-blade and gave it to the same papermaker. After a while I obtained paper from both species. The wool-blade paper came out unusually poor. It was extremely brittle, and all expense and labour seemed to be spent in vain. Nevertheless I wondered whether there could not be made better paper of wool-blade. It was evident that the wool lay too long in the lime, and its excessive brittleness and rigidity were caused by the lime and not by the nature of the material. I was anxious to know whether the next experiment supported my supposition. The paper made of pappus of poplar was incomparably better. It was a perfectly good writing paper, lacking nothing but a little more white to be accepted by everybody as rag paper. I noticed too that the sheets differed in colour. I now selected three different kinds. The first was dirty-white, the second grey, and the third yellowish. Could this difference be caused by the pappus itself? This seemed unlikely to me. I thought rather that the cause must be sought in the process of making. And I was not mistaken. For, to my questions, the papermaker avowed that he worked at three different times on the paper, and consequently one portion lay longer in the lime than the other. Could I not conclude from this that the grey and yellow colours had accidentally developed and that with better care a better quality could be produced?

I honoured myself by submitting three new and good samples to the Bavarian Academy, and without delay I made preparations for experiments with all of the materials which I thought might be fit for papermaking. And since my former experience convinced me that my aim would be very slowly and with double expense — if at all — reached if I depended on the papermaker alone, I decided myself to make all the experiments, from beginning to end, in my own home.

After Dr. Schäffer decided to become his own papermaker he employed a local artisan to explain to him the principles of the craft, instructed his servants, and after procuring several moulds he was ready to make his own experiments. The clergyman-papermaker had a small stamping-mill constructed, which was operated by hand, and in this machine, which he pictures in his book, most of the beating was accomplished for producing the samples of

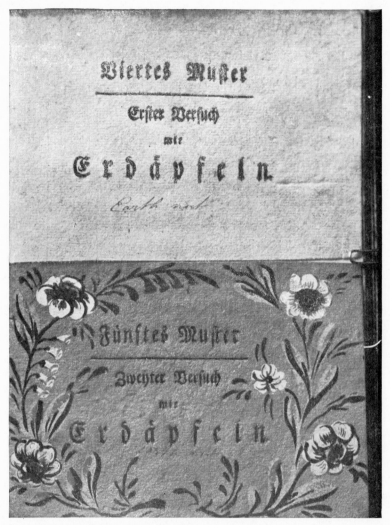

Fig. 249   *The two specimens in Dr. Schäffer's book showing the use of potatoes as papermaking fibre.*

papers shown in the six volumes. "And I started again to make paper," concludes the story of the ingenious Schäffer, "from poplar-downs, and shavings, and sawdust, and so forth. And what sweet satisfaction did I feel when I saw that everything came out better than I had imagined! In a short time I was able to produce a reliable new sort of paper. After such success, how could I forbear to make new and again new experiments? — especially when the cost of the tools and the studying of the process had already been met. I decided, therefore, to make these experiments my regular winter occupation. I could do so the more readily since the paper made hitherto found the warmest acknowledgment and I was urged to continue my experiments."

In making the specimens for his books Dr. Schäffer frequently found that the same plant, collected at different times, gave different results, as is evident in an examination of the specimens. Experiments were made in the use of potatoes for papermaking and it was found that sheets of paper could be fabricated from both the skins and the insides of this tuber (Figure 249). However, when the good doctor was carrying out his researches in the use of potatoes he could not that year (1767) procure enough of these vegetables for his work. In fact, potatoes were so little known in his country at that time that Schäffer felt that he needed to explain their use and wrote the following regarding them: "The earth-apple (potato) is a kind of plant known principally in Voigtland, France, Austria, and since some years also in Bavaria and the Pfalz, on whose fibrous roots there are produced, in the earth, uneven various-sized knotty and apple-like growths, which are known as earth-apples. These earth-apples are an uncommonly useful vegetable for the kitchen and for all housekeeping, particularly where there is a scarcity of bread. Poor people in many places not only really eat these earth-apples, but the appetite is satisfied by them as well as by bread."

The three sets of Schäffer's works in the Paper Museum collection are bound, each volume separately, in the original full calf with gold-tooled backs. In a complete set there should be 176 pages of text with ninety-five specimens of paper, two examples of lace, four samples of cloth, and fifteen engravings, a few of which have been coloured by hand (Figure 250).

The researches of Jacob Christian Schäffer were evidently con-

FIG. 250   *An example of paper in Dr. Schäffer's treatise which was painted upon by the doctor's daughter to show the adaptability of the paper for this purpose.*

sidered of importance at the time, for in 1770, or even before Schäffer's work was completed, there appeared in Amsterdam a book regarding his experiments. This book,[9] almost rarer than the Regensburg edition, comprises 32 pages of text, and one hand-coloured engraving of various forms of vegetation, including cat-tails, earthmoss, and "wilde wyngaard." There are eighteen speci-mens of paper, which embrace sheets made from nettles, straw, earthmoss, cattails, and aloe leaves.

In the eighteenth century, as may be seen from the foregoing works, there was considerable research and interest in finding new material, other than rags, from which to make paper. While there were numerous specimens of papers that had been made from newly discovered materials, the books of the scientists who had made the discoveries were printed upon paper fabricated from linen and cotton rags. The first complete book to be printed in Eu-rope on paper made from material other than linen and cotton was a small book of poems issued in France in 1784.[10] The paper used in this volume was made from a mixture of grass, lime-tree bark, and other plant fibres. It was not until 1786 that a book [11] was printed upon paper in which one of the new materials was used throughout. This was a small book of 156 pages, printed in London, comprising the works of Charles Michel de Villette (1736–93), and all of the text pages in one edition were printed upon paper made from the bark of the lime tree, while in another printing paper made from the marshmallow was used. At the back of the books there are single-sheet specimens of papers that had been made from nettles, hops, moss, reed grasses, three specimens of conferva, dandelion roots, prickwood or spindle-tree bark with its pellicle and crust, hazelnut, wood of the elm, bark of the lime or linden tree, leaves of the burdock, oak, and thistle; poplar, oak, and osier bark (Figure 251). The paper for this book, as well as the specimens, was made by Léorier Delisle, director of the Lan-glée paper mills, and in a prefatory note he writes: "To Monsieur le Marquis Ducrest: If my efforts, more than my success, in the art of papermaking have earned for me a recognition on your part, and if my long travels and experiences can permit me to as-pire to the protection of the august Prince whom you represent, I owe it to your clear impartiality, which characterizes your judg-ment. I have submitted to the paper-manufacturer all of the plants, the barks, and the common vegetables, and the papers that are at the back of this volume are the results of my experiences. I wish to prove that these materials may be substituted for the usual paper-making materials, which become rarer each day. You have been

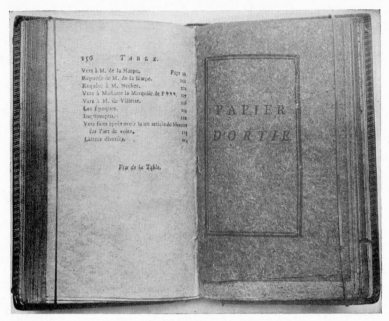

FIG. 251   A book of poems printed in 1786 on paper made from
the marshmallow. At the end of the volume there are specimens of
paper made from various materials, by Léorier Delisle.

the first, Monsieur, to appreciate the advantage of this discovery
and I emplore you to permit me to show the public the results of
my knowledge." Delisle had been preceded by Dr. Schäffer in the
use of materials to replace rags for papermaking, but the specimens made by Schäffer were fabricated with an admixture of linen
and cotton. Delisle, however, used nothing but the fibres of the
plants in the making of his paper and he therefore claimed greater
accomplishments than his predecessor. The question was carried
before the Académie des Sciences and a report relating to the work
of the two scientists was presented on November 18, 1786. This
report, signed by Berthollet, Lavoisier, and Sage, stated that the
papers of Delisle contained almost no linen or cotton while those
of Dr. Schäffer contained considerable rag fibre.

The work carried on by Dr. Schäffer in Germany apparently had
wide influence, for in 1787 in England we find the following ref-

erence to his experiments in the use of vegetable fibres in paper-making: "Several years since, the Society for the Encouragement of Arts, Manufacturers, and Commerce received from one of their corresponding members, Doctor Jacob Christian Schäffer of Regensburg, two volumes, containing a great variety of specimens of Paper, manufactured from RAW VEGETABLES: As several of these Papers seemed of good quality, it appeared to be well deserving the attention of the Society, to have a fair trial made of some of the refuse vegetable matters, that have hitherto been considered as of very little value, in order to know, whether they could or could not, be advantageously introduced into the manufacture of Paper; an article, of which the consumption, and consequently the price, is every day increasing. On this account, in the year 1787, a premium of TEN GUINEAS was offered to the person who should make the greatest quantity, not less than ten reams, of the best, and most useful Paper from vegetable substances not previously made into Cloth."

In the eighteenth century it was not unusual for manufacturers to comply with suggestions set forth by learned societies, and after Mr. Thomas Greaves, papermaker, of Mill Bank, near Warrington, had been informed of the proffered prize by Mr. More, a member of the Society, we find the following letter under date of August 10, 1787, addressed to Mr. More by Thomas Greaves, papermaker: "Sir, You will remember that when you was here with Mr. Wilkinson, you was desirous that I should attempt making of Paper from the Bark of Withins [? Salix alba or Salix nigra]. In consequence whereof I have made the trial, and now send you by Mr. Widder's waggon from Warrington, one ream of such Paper, which is made rather stouter than I wished, but that I could not readily avoid, from the tenderness of the material, when ground in the Engine. I send herewith, samples of the material, and how it was prepared. In the lower part of the bundle, you will find 24 half quires. In the upper part of the bundle, are 8 quires something finer, made from the Bark only, prepared and broke down in the state you will find it, wrapt up in another part of the bundle. I shall be glad to hear how you approve this article, which has been attended with a good deal of trouble, lots of time and expense; and indeed more than I expected, but that generally happens in any new undertaking. I presume you will receive the parcel in about ten days; And am, Sir, Your most obedient Servant, Thomas Greaves."

Although Mr. Greaves did not entirely comply with the conditions of the Society in the quantity of paper submitted, the members nevertheless evidently deemed the paper worthy of at least limited recognition, for the Society voted to grant their Silver Medal to the Warrington papermaker. The experiments undertaken by Mr. Greaves in his quest for a new papermaking fibre to take the place of linen and cotton rags did not terminate with the first lot of paper submitted to the Society, for in 1788 he was again awarded a prize by the members of the Society, this time not in the form of a medal, but the original substantial sum of ten guineas. In the development of papermaking in England the experiments carried on by Mr. Greaves are of especial interest. Apparently the work accomplished by him in the use of within bark as a usable fibre was a pioneer attempt in the British Isles, but his labour in this field has gone totally unheralded.

Ten years after the experiments of Thomas Greaves, in 1797, there appeared in London a pamphlet that set forth the use of jute as a suitable material from which paper could be fabricated. The pamphlet was printed upon paper made from this substance. The sixteen-page leaflet is entitled: *An Advantageous Hint: To the East India Company, Captains, Officers, Supercargoes, Importers of Rice and India Bale Goods. Also Grocers, Drapers, Gunpowder Makers, and Paper Makers in general.* The pamphlet has the following to say relating to jute as a papermaking material: "The paper on which this is printed is manufactured from an East India article, called Paut or Jute (*Crotalaria Juncea*, or *Paut*), there is a small quantity of bleached coloured rags mixed with it. . . . The first idea was communicated to J. Sewell, of Cornhill, by an ingenious Literary Gentleman, long resident in India, on account of an advertisement which appeared on the covers of the 'European Magazine' (Addressed to Ladies, not to destroy their linen rags), by J. Sewell, No. 32, Cornhill; who takes this method of recommending to Papermakers in general the manufacturing a useful paper (demy, crown, or cartridge), for use of Grocers, Chemists, &c. which will greatly decrease the consumption of rags, and of course the price of paper."

The next writer on the subject of papermaking materials as substitutes for linen and cotton rags was G. A. Senger, who compiled
what is now an exceedingly rare pamphlet.[12] The essay is printed
on paper that was made from conferva, a water plant, called by
Senger "water wool." He states that this water wool, or river paper, was the oldest form of papermaking in nature. This material
he termed a coralline product, being the web of water insects, seed
capsules, or insects' eggs. Senger discussed the probability of sufficient conferva being found to act as a substitute for rags as a
papermaking material. As Réaumur was the first writer to give account of the wasp as a fabricator of paper, Senger was the earliest
scientist to dwell at length upon conferva as a form of paper, also
a product of nature. Senger relates:

In my walks on the border of a small brook, I found both shores on
the side of the hedges covered with a slimy substance, which the over-
flowed brook had deposited. The surface of the water was covered with
a yellowish-green vegetation, and in the windings of the stream there
lay quantities of this fine vegetable product piled in heaps, which gave
additional beauty to the blooming shores of the flowing brook. The appearance of this beauty and the thought of a useful application of this
material awakened my interest, for I could not persuade myself that
thrifty Nature would have brought forth so much beauty and such a
great quantity of the fleecy substance without its having a useful purpose. This covering extending over the surface of the water was not only
a resting-place for insects of various sorts, and a well-secured storehouse
for their broods, but as Nature intends everywhere to give many advantages, I soon experienced that it contained a proper stuff for the
making of paper, and what is more surprising, a paper prepared by
Nature alone, without the assistance of imitating processes.

This peculiar web contains innumerable fleecy parts of vegetation,
which are generated, in the first part of the spring, on ponds and other
standing waters; they detach themselves from the bottom, and rise on
the surface, where they appear as a handsome green and yellow covering. After these fleecy particles have remained for some time on the
watery mirror, by the heat of the sun, and by the changing degrees
of cold and warmth of the water, they become more united and felted
together, bleached, and at last turned into a tough paper-like covering.
Or, if this fleecy substance is mixed together, and carried away by sudden inundations, occasioned by heavy rains, and deposited on the
shores, it then appears like a thin jelly or slime which, after it has
undergone several changes naturally produced by the contents of air

and water, turns into a kind of paper, which resembles the common paper; or where it has been produced upon clear water, it is not unlike a superior paper, of which some may be gathered nearly as white as writing paper.

The conferva paper used in Senger's book is of a green-grey colour, but even after one hundred and thirty years the paper is stout and is apparently in as good condition as when it was made; there was, however, no chemical bleaching used in its preparation. Senger's pamphlet consists of ninety-six pages with a paper cover.

In the search for new papermaking materials the work of Matthias Koops towers above all of his predecessors, for Koops is responsible for the growth of the paper industry as it is today. The experimental work of Réaumur, Guettard, Schäffer, Delisle, and Greaves, always of a limited nature, is important, and to these scientists should go the credit of the discovery in Europe of many papermaking fibres other than linen and cotton. It was Koops, however, who first made use of various vegetable fibres on a large commercial scale and within three years found himself in bankruptcy as a result of his pioneer efforts.

Matthias Koops has always been an enigma to the historians of papermaking, for while his work dates from only about a century and a half ago, little is known of the man or his life. In 1912 I undertook a diligent search in the British Museum and Great Seal Patent Office libraries in an endeavour to ascertain something regarding this elusive character, but nothing could be found; the contemporary files of the London *Times* revealed no information; no portrait exists. In 1800 Matthias Koops compiled an interesting book,[13] printed on paper made from fibres he himself had advocated as substitutes for the ever decreasing supply of linen and cotton rags. The first edition of this work "was printed on the first useful paper manufactured solely from straw." There is an appendix of seven pages "printed on paper made from wood alone, the product of this country, without any intermixture of rags, waste paper stock, bark, straw, or any other vegetable substance, from which paper might be, or has hitherto been manufactured." The paper used in the first edition is of the "laid" type and bears the watermark of the British arms and "G R." The second edition of the work by Koops, issued in London in 1801, was printed upon "paper re-made from old printed and written paper," with a sixteen-page appendix on paper made from wood. The paper used in this edition is of the "wove" style and bears no watermarks. Another printing of this book, the rarest of the three, and unlike the regular second edition, was printed on paper made from straw. Only a limited number of the third printing was issued. An engraving (12 by 14 inches), entitled *Noon*, by Austin, after J. Ruysdael, appeared at the beginning of the nineteenth century with the caption: "On paper made from straw alone, by Mr. Koops, 1800."

In 1800 and 1801 the Great Seal Patent Office, London, granted three patents * to Matthias Koops (Figure 252). The first was for the extraction of printing and writing ink from paper before repulping. The second and third patents covered the manufacture of paper from straw, hay, thistles, waste and refuse of hemp and flax and different kinds of wood and bark. As before mentioned, practically nothing has been recorded concerning Koops's commercial undertaking in the manufacture of paper from straw. In 1941, however, more than ninety documents covering the activities of this mill were discovered in an old English manor house. This bundle of faded papers, embracing letters, contracts, agreements, inventories, wage and labour disputes, lists of stockholders, etc., is now in the Paper Museum of the Massachusetts Institute of Technology and from this material may be gleaned the hopes, aspirations, successes, and final failure of "The Straw Paper Manufactory at Mill Bank underneath the Bridge at Westminster." † It

---

* "A.D. 1800, April 28th — No. 2392. Matthias Koops of Queen Street, Ranelagh, in the county of Middlesex, gentleman, for a mode of extracting printing and writing ink from printed and written paper, and converting the paper from which the ink is extracted into pulp, and making thereof paper fit for writing, printing, and other purposes."

"A.D. 1800, August 2nd — No. 2433. Matthias Koops of Queen Street, Ranelagh, in the county of Middlesex, gentleman, for a method of manufacturing paper from straw, hay, thistles, waste, and refuse of hemp and flax, and different kinds of wood and bark."

"A.D. 1801, February 17th — No. 2481. Matthias Koops of James Street, Westminster, gentleman, for a method of manufacturing paper from straw, hay, thistles, waste, and refuse of hemp and flax, and different kinds of wood and bark, fit for printing and other useful purposes."

† In the earliest papers of the concern the address is given in this manner. In the advertisement for the sale of the property, however, dated September 22, 1804, the location of the mill is given: "Neat Houses, Thames Bank, Westminster, and about one mile distant from Westminster Bridge." In 1912

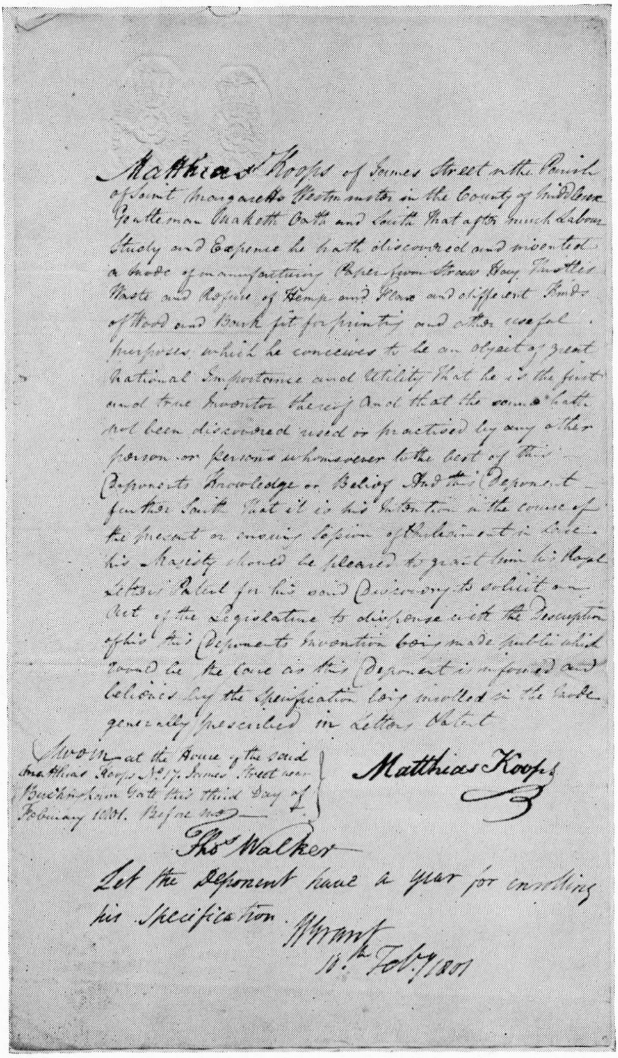

Fig. 252   *The original application by Matthias Koops for a patent covering the making of paper from ". . . different kinds of wood and bark." The application gives the address of Koops as "No. 17, James Street, near Buckingham Gate," with the date February 3, 1801. The patent was granted February 17, 1801, Number 2481. This was the third patent granted to Matthias Koops.*

was in 1801 that Matthias Koops set up a company for the making of paper from straw, and it would appear from the newly discovered documents that Samuel Lister, Norfolk Street, Strand, and James Forbes, Nassau Street, Soho, were the two men directly responsible for the financial development of the establishment of the company. In the earliest group of stockholders Koops's name heads the list with 356⅔ shares of the total number of one thousand shares,* the balance of the stock being in the names of twenty-four other investors, including William Tate, Edward Ravenscroft, General Bennet DeBoigne, Richard Twiss, and John and James Hunter, with goodly proportions of the holdings.

A new building was erected to house Europe's first paper mill in which materials other than linen and cotton rags were to be extensively used. From the old mill documents we find that the stone for the foundations was brought from Scotland at a cost of £150 17s. 4d.; the brick and tile were made locally. One item of timber used in the construction of the mill is set down in the expense account as costing £44 5s. 1d., while Thomas Terry, a carpenter, received 700 pounds for his labour. J. Nichols, a bricklayer, was paid 500 pounds, and the pipe-fitting and plumbing in the mill came to £354 17 s. 6d. From these figures it may be seen that the building for the Koops mill was of considerable proportions, larger than any other paper mill in England up to that time.† Even more

---

I made every effort to ascertain the exact location of the Koops straw-paper mill, but so many changes had taken place it was impossible to determine even the approximate setting of this historic property.

* Apparently the original holdings of Matthias Koops amounted to this figure, but in a statement dated January 1804 the stock belonging to Koops and J. W. Tate, both listed together, amounted to 429⅔ shares. At this date the money owed by these two stockholders to the Straw Paper Company was the sum of 7,552 pounds, of which the amount of 6,939 pounds and 9 shillings was in arrears. For the most part the other stockholders had paid their just proportions of the total of 71,525 pounds, with the exception of the Earl of Wigtown, who was still owing for all his stock, 1,666 pounds, 13 shillings, and 4 pence.

† An idea of the size of these buildings may be had from the descriptions given in an eight-page brochure issued at the time of the sale by auction of the property, dated October 27, 1804. The list embraces buildings reputed to be worth "one hundred thousand pounds," including "an elegant small bow-fronted dwelling-house, three stories high, with an observatory and flat lead roof." This was evidently the superintendent's house and from the description of the interior it was a structure of considerable artistic quality and unusual refinements, including "a patent water-closet, strong room, statuary,

interesting are the costs of the equipment of the mill and we find these listed in detail: There was a "4-horse chain-pump, complete, for the large well" at 200 pounds and two smaller pumps at 50 pounds each. The wooden vats were evidently purchased in sections, for the entry covering these essential handmade-paper appliances reads: "20 Vats for Papermakers, all ready to be put together in our carpentry shop." The vats cost 45 shillings each. The pressing of the newly formed paper was originally done by the use of "6 screw-presses, iron work all complete," at 15 pounds for each press. The lay-stools, upon which the paper was stacked after pressing between the felts, were purchased for two shillings and sixpence for each wooden stool. For forming paper at as many as twenty vats a large number of moulds of various sizes would have been required and these are listed as costing £238 10s. 0d., while the hand-woven felting upon which the individual sheets of newly made paper were "couched" amounted to £93 10s. 9d. For drying the paper there were 450 "tribbles" at two shillings and sixpence each; these drying-racks were placed in "the large room." Cow-hair ropes, also used in hanging paper to dry, came to £5 15s. 8d. There are listed "14 dozen small fools' cap press-boards"

marble chimney pieces and a wine cellar." The mill proper embraced the following buildings:

"Elaboratory or bleaching-house, 60 by 27 feet, with lubber-boarded lanthorn at the top of the roof; a very capital drying-house, 144 by 21 feet, with ten double and single new presses by the ingenious engineer, Mr. Rennie; a preparing-room, 90 by 66 feet, with felt-rooms, etc.; a compleat steam engine of eight horse power, with two beater engines; a chaff-cutting house by Mr. Rennie; a beating-engine house with two large stuff-chests which communicate with the papermaking vats; a papermaking house, 53 by 28 feet, with two wet presses prepared to be worked by the steam-engine, four vats lined with lead, pot holes, and four hog wheels, supplied by a large lead pipe with spring and Thames water, a felt-washing house; a drying and sizing house, 459 feet by 21 feet, two ditto 144 by 21 feet, with two large coppers of 9 and 6 barrels each, a sizing press and sizing vat; a drying-room (above) with treble rails and hair lines, sliding shutters; the centre buildings of twelve-stall stable, cart-shed, five privies; a most excellent turret clock by Twaites, Clerkenwell, four lamp-posts, irons and lamps; a drying-house, the largest and most convenient in the Kingdom, 459 feet by 21 feet; a steam engine of eighty horse power, universally acknowledged to be the most compleat and substantial that ever was made, costing six thousand pounds; a canal has been cut from the river Thames to the manufactory at an expense of seven thousand pounds; the estate consists of fifteen acres of land, four small dwelling-houses; the whole held for an unexpired term of sixty-seven years under the right honourable the Earl of Grosvenor, at the low annual rental of one thousand pounds."

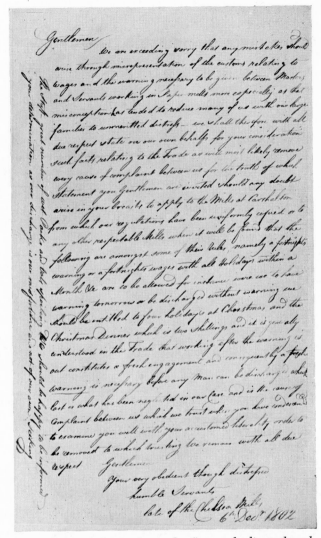

FIG. 253   *A letter from the "very obedient though distressed humble servants," the workers in the paper mill organized by Matthias Koops. This was the earliest commercial mill to make paper of materials other than linen and cotton. This was, of course, a handmade paper mill.*

at 24 shillings the dozen and "12 dozen double fools' cap press-boards" at 30 shillings a dozen. These smooth boards were used in plating, or finishing, the paper. For work around the mill "two old black horses" were purchased for the sum of eight pounds sterling and there is an entry "for horses-oats from L. Turney, £3/7/0."

The stockholders, aside from Mr. Koops, advanced 45,000 pounds for the "buildings, machinery, and utensils." The deed of corporation was made February 26, 1801. On March 27, 1802 Matthias Koops received 50 additional shares of stock from the holdings of William Tate, Neat House Distillery, and a short time thereafter 10 shares of Koops's stock passed to James Stevenson, M.D., Surrey Street, Strand, one of the original stockholders in the straw-paper company.

From the old accounts we learn that considerable paper was made and sold, but evidently not a sufficient amount to prevent the financial rupture of the enterprise, for in less than two years of activity the company went into bankruptcy with debts of 10,500 pounds; the complete assets of the company were listed on November 11, 1802 at 3,500 pounds. Then began the pathetic breaking up of the mill; the cries of the disgruntled workers were heard on every side. In one letter dated December 6, 1802 (Figure 253) from the former papermakers they state that since the mill has ceased to function "a great number of wet packs of paper are spoiling in the vat-house and the pulp is rotting in the vats. We should be happy to be informed of your determination as our discharge is our misfortune and not of our own seeking." This letter is signed: "Your very obedient, though distressed, servants." On December 20, 1802 another letter of grievance from the "distressed" papermakers reached the stockholders. In this two-page communication the erstwhile employees made additional complaints and among other things stated that "each of us is entitled to the sum of 2 shillings and 6 pence for our Christmas dinner, and we trust your own honour, humanity, and feeling will cause our little demand to be discharged without the necessity of appealing to the assistance of the law which being impartial to rich and poor will, we have not the least doubt, be in our favour." This second and last letter from the disgruntled papermakers is signed: "Gentlemen, your late Servants at the Paper-mills." At least one of the buildings of the paper mill was evidently dismantled, for

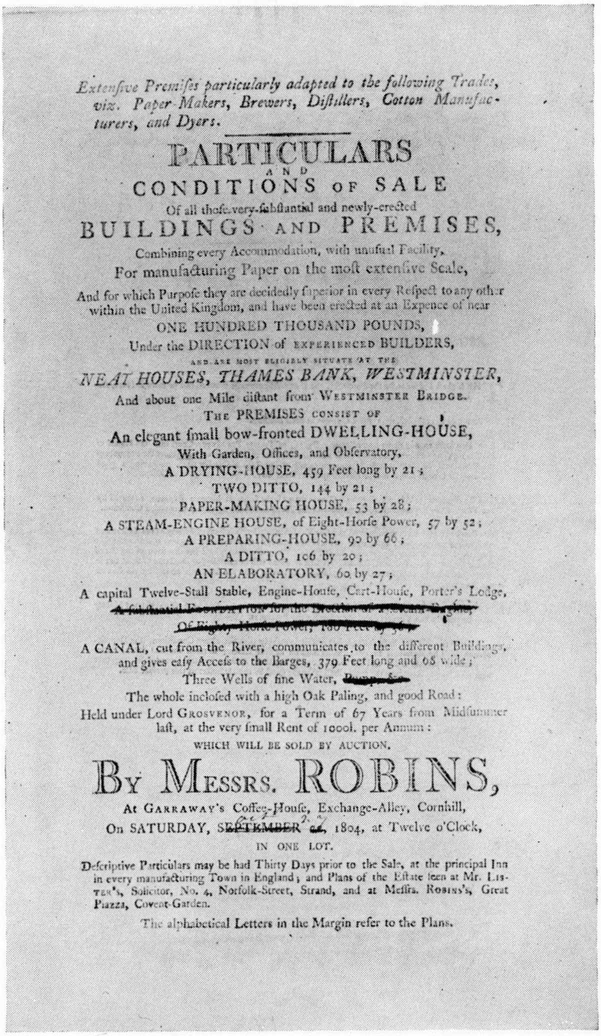

Extenſive Premiſes particularly adapted to the following Trades, viz. Paper-Makers, Brewers, Diſtillers, Cotton Manufacturers, and Dyers.

PARTICULARS
AND
CONDITIONS OF SALE
Of all thoſe ~~very ſubſtantial~~ and newly-erected
BUILDINGS AND PREMISES,
Combining every Accommodation, with unuſual Facility,
For manufacturing Paper on the moſt extenſive Scale,
And for which Purpoſe they are decidedly ſuperior in every Reſpect to any other within the United Kingdom, and have been erected at an Expence of near
ONE HUNDRED THOUSAND POUNDS,
Under the DIRECTION of EXPERIENCED BUILDERS,
AND ARE MOST ELIGIBLY SITUATE AT THE
NEAT HOUSES, THAMES BANK, WESTMINSTER,
And about one Mile diſtant from WESTMINSTER BRIDGE.
THE PREMISES CONSIST OF
An elegant ſmall bow-fronted DWELLING-HOUSE,
With Garden, Offices, and Obſervatory,
A DRYING-HOUSE, 459 Feet long by 21;
TWO DITTO, 144 by 21;
PAPER-MAKING HOUSE, 53 by 28;
A STEAM-ENGINE HOUSE, of Eight-Horſe Power, 57 by 52;
A PREPARING-HOUSE, 90 by 66;
A DITTO, 106 by 20;
AN ELABORATORY, 60 by 27;
A capital Twelve-Stall Stable, Engine-Houſe, Cart-Houſe, Porter's Lodge,
~~A ſubſtantial FOUNDATION for the Erection of a Steam-Engine,~~
~~Of Eight-Horſe Power, 100 Feet by 50;~~
A CANAL, cut from the River, communicates to the different Buildings, and gives eaſy Acceſs to the Barges, 379 Feet long and 68 wide;
Three Wells of fine Water, ~~Pump, &c.~~
The whole incloſed with a high Oak Paling, and good Road:
Held under Lord GROSVENOR, for a Term of 67 Years from Midſummer laſt, at the very ſmall Rent of 100l. per Annum:
WHICH WILL BE SOLD BY AUCTION,
BY MESSRS. ROBINS,
At GARRAWAY'S Coffee-Houſe, Exchange-Alley, Cornhill,
On SATURDAY, ~~SEPTEMBER 22~~ Oct. 27, 1804, at Twelve o'Clock,
IN ONE LOT.
Deſcriptive Particulars may be had Thirty Days prior to the Sale, at the principal Inn in every manufacturing Town in England; and Plans of the Eſtate ſeen at Mr. LISTER's, Solicitor, No. 4, Norfolk-Street, Strand, and at Meſſrs. ROBINS's, Great Piazza, Covent-Garden.
The alphabetical Letters in the Margin refer to the Plans.

FIG. 254 *The cover of the corrected printer's copy of the eight-page pamphlet issued by Messrs. Robins, auctioneers, for the sale of the Matthias Koops mill. The date of the sale was changed from September 22, 1804 to October 27, 1804. The mill was established 1801 with an expense "near one hundred thousand pounds," the largest paper mill in Europe where paper was made from wood, straw, and materials other than linen and cotton.*

under a list of assets to provide payment of debts we find 200,000 second-hand brick and 5,000 tiles. Also a quantity of pot-ash to the value of 100 pounds is listed, as well as paper worth 80 pounds, which was on the premises. Even the two old black horses are entered as assets of the defunct paper company; a later document sets down that these two faithful beasts were eventually sold for seven pounds three shillings.

The ninety or more original documents and letters, until recently buried among piles of early nineteenth-century papers in an old vine-covered English country house, tell the graphic story of the establishment and final demise of this historic mill — the paper manufactory upon which is based the greater part of our modern paper industry, for in this mill from 1801 to the beginning of 1804 was produced the first commercially made paper in the Occident fabricated from vegetable fibres other than those of linen and cotton rags (Figure 254).

XII

The Paper-Machine and Its Inventor, Nicholas-Louis Robert

THE PAPER–MACHINE REVOLUTIONIZES PRINTING

UNTIL the beginning of the nineteenth century, when the paper-making machine was partially perfected, all paper was formed by hand. A skilful worker dipped a flat, sieve-like mould of a given size into a vat filled with macerated fibres suspended in water, and brought forth upon the porous surface of the mould a thin layer of matted fibres — a sheet of paper. In making paper by hand the dimensions of the sheets were limited, as it was not possible for a worker to balance evenly a European mould of great size. In England as late as 1818, to conserve paper, it was a punishable offence to produce a newspaper exceeding 22 by 32 inches. Printing developed naturally along with papermaking, and the methods of printing were governed by the sizes and varieties of paper available. All through the history of printing, in both the Orient and the Occident, paper has been the determining factor, and through the centuries we find the constant influence of paper upon printing.

As outlined in a previous chapter, the increase in the diffusion of knowledge through printing caused a shortage of papermaking materials; the supply of linen and cotton rags was not equal to the demand. This shortage turned scientists toward a solution of the problem, causing them to seek new fibres suitable for making into paper. It is generally assumed that this urgent need for more and cheaper paper was responsible for Nicholas-Louis Robert's invention of the paper-machine. But if we are to accept Robert's own reason for his interest in perfecting a machine for making paper, this idea must at once be relinquished. The inventor himself declared that it was the constant strife and quarrelling among the workers of the handmade papermakers' guild that drove him to the creation of the mechanical device that would replace hand labour.

Nicholas-Louis Robert was born in a small, unpretentious house in the rue Neuve Saint-Eustache, Paris, on the 2nd of December 1761. From birth he was a frail and sickly child. The boy was studious, self-conscious, hiding beneath his fragile body an ambition that was constantly urging him to accomplishment far beyond his physical strength. The sensitive nature of this immature lad gave rise within him to many misgivings, the cruellest of these being that he felt his care and support should not be dependent upon the slender means of his aging parents. When Nicholas-Louis was fifteen he made effort to join the French Army so that his family might be relieved of the burden of his maintenance. Owing to his delicate constitution, to say nothing of his youth, the military officials refused him admission and with heavy heart he returned to his parents' roof again to resume his studies. He was constantly obsessed with the thought that he was an unworthy expense to the family household, and the sensitive young boy suffered untold mental anguish. After four years of study he again turned to the army, and at the age of nineteen, on April 23, 1780, he was given a place in the First Battalion of the Grenoble Artillery and ultimately stationed in a garrison at Calais. A year later, in 1781, the young soldier, now somewhat improved in health, was transferred to the Metz Artillery regiment and within a short time he and his comrades set sail for Santo Domingo, where Robert experienced his first real taste of battle in an encounter with the English. After his return to Paris, at the age of twenty-eight, he gave up the thought of a further military career and immediately set out to seek work as a civilian. Being of a natural mechanical bent, young Robert turned to the craft of printing, and after the customary agreements and indentures he was given a position as clerk with the renowned Paris publishing firm of Didot. After a number of years in the publishing house, Robert tired of his clerkship, and his ambition prompted him to explore other fields in allied arts. He next turned to papermaking and was given a berth in the François Didot (1730–1804) paper mill in Essonnes, a papermaking centre since 1355. This was an important paper manufactory, and much of the paper used by the Minister of Finance for the French currency was made in this establishment. It was while serving in

this mill as inspector of personnel that Robert came in close contact with the handmade papermakers and he was not hesitant in
declaring that he was disgusted with the behaviour of the hand
workers and the lack of discipline among the members of the
papermakers' society. Robert was not many months in the employ
of the paper mill before it occurred to him that it might be possible to manufacture paper without the help of the quarrelling
vatmen, couchers, and laymen of the handmade-paper industry.
Both Robert and his master, François Didot, grew impatient with
the irascibility and ill temper of the workers, and it was this constant wrangling and discord, and not the desire to produce cheaper
and more abundant paper, that gave Robert the impetus to devise
a papermaking machine.

The plans for a machine to supplant the old hand processes were
at first judged "feeble" by Didot, but at the same time he encouraged Robert to proceed with his idea. With the financial assistance and guidance of Didot, Robert constructed a small model
paper-machine, and a trial was attempted. The first model was a
failure and Robert, now thirty-six years of age, became heartily
discouraged; had it not been for the enthusiasm of his employer
he would have relinquished the entire project. Didot implored
Robert to persevere, and to give him more time and opportunity
to work upon the machine the master removed him from the
paper mill and placed him in charge of a flour mill within a short
distance of the paper manufactory. This was in 1797 and for six
months Robert worked contentedly as superintendent of the grain-
grinding establishment. With a relieved mind he gave up his
thought of making paper by mechanical means. This change of
heart was probably brought about by his separation from the papermakers, for he was no longer in daily contact with their strife
and bickering. He was producing flour, not paper, and the plan
of constructing a paper-machine had apparently vanished from
his thoughts. It was at this period that Didot strongly urged Robert to continue his researches in manufacturing paper by mechanical means, and several skilled technicians were placed at Robert's disposal. With his guidance these mechanics either improved
the early model or built an entirely new one. It is unfortunate
that no chronological details relative to these models have been
recorded. In any event, with the improved model there was still

only minor success in actually forming paper, but even this limited progress convinced Robert that the principle upon which his machine was based was sound, and that any practical machine intended for the fabrication of paper must necessarily be built upon the identical rule set forth in his plans. Didot, undaunted, next instructed Robert to make a larger model and incorporate in it everything he had learned through the building of the original small models. The initial trial with the larger model gave renewed hope and encouragement to both Robert and Didot, and upon second trial two sheets of paper were formed, both being well felted and longer than any previously made. The width of the paper was, of course, influenced by the actual width of the model — only the length could be varied at will.

Nicholas-Louis Robert was overjoyed with the success of the trial sheets of paper made on the new model, and when his old Paris employer, St. Léger Didot (1767–1829) saw the paper that he had so recently formed, he insisted that Robert should at once secure a patent. The following day St. Léger Didot accompanied the inventor to Paris, where he introduced Robert to François de Neufchateau, of the office of the Minister of the Interior. The two sheets of paper in the meantime were delivered to the Minister, and on September 9, 1798 Robert formally applied for a patent with the following letter:

For several years I have been employed in one of the principal mills of France. It has been my dream to simplify the operation of making paper by forming it with infinite less expense, and, above all, in making sheets of an extraordinary length without the help of any worker, using only mechanical means. Through diligent work, by experience, and with considerable expense, I have been successful and a machine has been made that fulfils my expectancy. The machine makes for economy of time and expense and extraordinary paper, being 12 to 15 meters in length, if one wishes. In a few words I have set forth the advantages of my machine, which I have built at the home of Citizen Didot, manufacturer at Essonnes. It is here the place to say that in Citizen Didot I have found great help in the making of this machine. His workshop, his workers, even his purse, have been at my disposition; he shares generosity and confidence that one finds only in real friends of the arts. I solicit you, Citizen Minister, for the patent of my invention, which ought to assure me my property, and work for myself. My fortune does not permit me to pay the tax of this patent at once, which I desire to have for fifteen years, nor do my means permit me the cost of a model. This is why, Citizen Minister, I implore you to name a number of commissioners to examine my work and in view of the immense usefulness of my discovery grant me a patent gratuitously. [Signed:] Robert.

The French Bureau of Arts and Trades realized at once that Robert's invention was of tremendous importance and value and it was suggested that a draughtsman be sent to Essonnes to assist in building another model, or to improve upon the model already constructed. The Minister of the Interior approved this move and the result was that M. Beauvelot, an expert draughtsman and a member of the Conservatoire des Arts et Métiers, made a journey to Essonnes, where he drew a detailed plan of the machine. With this plan in hand the Bureau did not hesitate to declare: "Citizen Robert is the first to imagine a machine capable of making paper from the vat; this machine forms paper of great width and of indefinite length. The machine makes paper of perfect quality in thickness and gives advantages that cannot be derived from ordinary methods of forming paper by hand, where each sheet is limited in size in comparison with those made on this machine. From all reports it is an entirely new invention and deserves every encouragement." The commissioners next advised that Robert should be given the sum of three thousand francs, the amount to be later handed to him to make a model for the Conservatoire des Arts et Métiers; the model to be put in action so that the members themselves might see the sheets of paper made.

Before the delivery of the model it was Robert's desire that the scholars of the Conservatory know more of the details and intricacies of the machine so they could judge his invention with intelligent interest. With this thought in mind, toward the close of 1798 he wrote a description of his invention, which he termed: "A general account of the machine for making paper of an indeterminate length." This document comprised a lengthy report of the paper-machine, but inasmuch as illustrations of Robert's machine are here given it will not be necessary to set down this description in full (Figures 255, 256, 257). The principle of Robert's machine — and the same principle holds with all modern papermaking machines — was to form the paper upon an endless woven-wire cloth which retained the matted fibres and at the same time suffered the superfluous water to drain through the meshes of the woven wire.

Fig. 255   *The paper-machine as constructed by M. Alleward, Rives, France, after the original drawings made by Nicholas-Louis Robert.*

In forming paper in the hand-mould the principle of the operation is identical, but with the hand-mould the sheet formed thereon is limited to the size of the mould, while with the machine the paper is formed in an endless length, the width being limited only by the width of the machine. Robert's description in part reads: "At the end of the cloth wire extending on the vat there is a fly-wheel, or cylinder, fitted with little buckets which plunge into the paper stock, or liquid pulp. This cylinder, by its rapid movement, raises the material and throws it into a shallow reservoir in the interior of the head, which recovers it, and thus pours, without interruption, like a sheet of water upon the endless wire cloth. As the material settles on the cloth it receives a side-to-side movement, the wire retaining the fibres and the water draining into the vat beneath. A crank turns the machine and causes the wire cloth to advance, the sheet of newly formed paper finally running under a felt-covered roller. When the paper leaves the first felt roller it is no longer saturated with water, but can be removed from the machine, just as a sheet of handmade paper is taken from the felting after pressing in a press." In Robert's original document he states

FIG. 256   *This photograph shows the traveling endless wire of the Robert machine. This machine in its entirety may be studied in Figures 255, 257.*

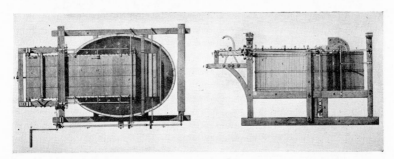

FIG. 257   *Detail of the first paper-machine (Figure 255) constructed by M. Alleward, Rives, France, after the original plans and specifications set down by the French inventor, Nicholas-Louis Robert, about 1798.*

that "the work of operating the machine can be done by children." The first papermaking machine, like the first printing press, was simple in construction. It is only when it becomes necessary to produce paper and printing at low cost and at great speed that these two allied crafts become complex and call for help from the technician and from the laboratory.

The support of Didot and the interest of the commissioners of the Conservatory gave Robert's invention a tremendous impetus, and the Minister of the Interior was so captivated by the machine that on December 4, 1798 he stated: ". . . the machine is useful and deserving all the attention of the government." The recompense of 3,000 francs was accorded the inventor and with encouragement from all sides Robert redrew the plan of the machine and again set down a comprehensive description of the invention. The patent was secured at a cost of 1,562 francs and was dated January 18, 1799.

Robert and the Didots were elated over the invention that would make paper of an "extraordinary length." It must be remembered that the paper was taken from the original machine in laps or sheets while still moist and then hung to dry, just as had been done for centuries with the handmade papers. The thought of passing the paper over a heated cylinder, or even rolling it upon a reel, probably did not occur to Robert. At this period all printing was done on hand presses and therefore paper of an endless length was uncalled for. The paper-machine with its continuous web of paper later suggested and made possible the invention of the rotary press. Here again we see the technique of papermaking having direct influence upon printing. The inventor and his sponsors, St. Léger and François Didot, rightly expected a great future for the paper-machine, but Robert's disposition could not cope with the success that seemed certain. He became over-zealous; the very thought of the acclaim that was bound to be his intoxicated him. He quarrelled with François Didot and several minor disputes had to be settled in court. It was Robert's desire to sell the patent for a huge sum, but as is often the case with inventors, he never realized any remuneration from his mechanical talents.

Owing to the disturbed conditions brought about by the Revolution, little progress was made in France with the Robert-Didot machine, and Robert, becoming financially involved, finally had to sell his patent outright at a not too great figure. The patent was purchased by Didot for 25,000 francs, the money to be paid to Robert in instalments. The payments lagged and Robert became impatient. After much controversy and ill will the inventor took back his patent on June 23, 1801. Meanwhile, in 1799, Didot had written to his brother-in-law, John Gamble, an English paper-mill proprietor, proposing that he ascertain if sufficient money could be raised in England to have a large machine constructed in that country along the lines of Robert's plans. Through the efforts of John Gamble, Henry and Sealy Fourdrinier, London stationers, became interested in the development of the new machine, and upon the suggestion of Gamble, Bryan Donkin, an ingenious mechanic, was induced to build a papermaking machine patterned entirely after the plans of Robert. Several additional patents [1] were procured and in 1803 Donkin had completed a machine that was capable of making fairly good paper. The first machine adapted to the making of usable paper, however, was not constructed until about a year later. This machine was built and set in motion by Donkin at Frogmore mill, Two Waters, Hertfordshire. It had two webs of wire, one over and one under the paper, but the following year Donkin changed the machine so it could be operated with the lower wire only. The Fourdrinier brothers expended about 60,000 pounds on the machine, but, like Robert, never realized any remuneration. The papermaking machine to this day bears the name of the Fourdrinier brothers, the only recognition they received for their part in the perfecting of the machine. By 1807, according to Munsell, paper-machines were being manufactured in England ranging in price from 715 to 1,040 pounds.

The financial loss suffered by the Fourdriniers was attributed to the fact that there was a flaw in their patent of which manufacturers took advantage and erected machines on which they paid no royalties. In Russia several machines were built and installed in the Imperial paper mills at Peterhof at the suggestion of Alexander I, but no royalties were paid to the patentees. Not one of the pioneers in the development of the paper-machine gained anything in the way of pecuniary profit in return for the energy, time, and money expended. They contributed something of inestimable value to the paper industry but nothing to their own material welfare.

THE CYLINDER MACHINE

Another type of machine, the cylinder,[2] was originated and perfected in England and became operative in 1809 in the mill of John Dickinson in Hertfordshire. This machine differs somewhat from the Robert machine in the method of forming the web of paper. A cylinder covered with a woven metal wire screen, and half immersed, revolves in a vat of pulp, and by means of a vacuum within the cylinder, the pulp is made to adhere to the screen on the periphery of the cylinder, thereby forming the paper, which is then detached and passed on to a cylinder with felting.

Aside from the invention of the cylinder papermaking machine, John Dickinson is credited with numerous other patents pertaining to paper. In philatelic history his name will always hold a prominent place, for he was the originator of "silk-thread paper," more commonly known as "Dickinson paper." This invention [3] consisted in introducing a continuous thread of cotton, flax, or silk fibre into the endless web of paper during manufacture. Paper of this kind was used in making the first Post Office envelopes of Great Britain — the famous Mulready envelopes, named after the English artist William Mulready (1786–1863). Also the Dickinson thread-paper was used in the printing of the embossed tenpence and one-shilling postage stamps issued in Great Britain in 1847–8. This type of paper again found use in the printing of the Schleswig-Holstein stamps of 1850; the Prussian stamped envelopes of 1851–2; the Bavarian postage stamps of the years 1854–7; the Swiss stamps of 1854; and the Württemberg stamps of 1857. The Dickinson safety paper was used as a prevention against counterfeiting, and the silk or vegetable fibre threads could be introduced into the paper in any colour and spaced in any desired manner. The Dickinson patents applied to machine-made paper only and it was paper of this kind that was used for making the Mulready envelopes and upon which the 1847 and 1848 British stamps were printed. The paper used in the Prussian stamped envelopes of 1851–2 was also machine-made, with a single thread placed so that it crossed each stamp diagonally. Apparently no patents outside Great Britain were in Dickinson's name, so it may be assumed that paper mills on the Continent were also making paper with embedded threads running through the sheet.

In as much as the work and inventions of John Dickinson have played such a prominent part in papermaking history, a brief outline of his life will not be out of place. He was born March 29, 1782, the son of Captain Thomas Dickinson of the Royal Navy. At the age of twenty-two he established his own stationery business in London, a calling that had also attracted Henry and Sealy Fourdrinier, who had financed the building of the first practical paper-machine patterned after the original invention of Robert. Finding it difficult to procure the constantly needed supplies for his paper-shop, John Dickinson acquired an interest in Apsley mill, near Two Waters, Hempel Hempstead, Hertfordshire. In 1811 he took over the Nash mill, not far from the Apsley mill, and it was here that the safety thread-paper was invented and developed. The business had a steady growth and mills in King's Langley were purchased, all in Hertfordshire. After a full life in the paper industry John Dickinson retired from active duty in 1859; he died ten years later at the age of eighty-nine.[4]

AMERICA'S FIRST PAPER–MACHINE

The first successful attempt to make paper by machine in this country was on one of the cylinder-type machines. This machine began operation in August 1817. It was the outgrowth of the mechanical ingenuity of Thomas Gilpin, and was erected in his own mill with considerable secrecy. Gilpin had doubtless obtained some idea of the working of the Dickinson machine. The Gilpin mills were situated on Brandywine Creek, a picturesque spot about two miles above Wilmington, Delaware (Figure 258). The product of Gilpin's cylinder machine was noted for its fine uniformity of texture and freshness of colour. There remains today evidence of this in some paper which still retains a firmness of texture and a good tone.* It speaks well for the honest rag stock

---

* The first successful paper manufactured on the Gilpin cylinder machine was used in printing Poulson's *American Daily Advertiser*, published in Philadelphia. It was not long before this machine-made paper was being sought after by other newspaper publishers; also book publishers wished to adapt it to their work and the well-known book-printing firm of Matthew Carey and Son, Philadelphia, used the Gilpin paper for the text, charts, and maps of the 1820 and 1821 editions of N. Lavoisne's *A Complete Genealogical, Historical, Chronological, and Geographical Atlas,* probably the first publication to be printed on American machine-made paper.

Fig. 258   *The Gilpin mill on the Brandywine, Wilmington, Delaware, where the first paper-machine in America was put in operation, 1817. From the steel engraving entitled* The Battlefield of Brandywine *by James Smillie after Thomas Doughty (in* Graham's *Lady's and* Gentleman's Magazine, *Philadelphia, 1844).*

from which it was made and the careful processing it underwent in a mill noted at the time for the cleanliness of its manufacturing methods.

The original public announcement of the Gilpin machine was probably an article in the *American Watchman and Delaware Gazette,* a newspaper published in Wilmington, Delaware, from 1809 to 1828, under slightly varying titles. The first national publicity of this momentous event in American papermaking was given in the November 29, 1817 issue of Niles' *Weekly Register,* Baltimore, and was credited to the *Delaware Watchman.* The *Register* article reads:

We have lately visited the paper mills of Thomas Gilpin & Co. on the Brandywine, and witnessed the performance of their new machine for manufacturing paper on an extensive scale, which promises to be an important addition to the arts and manufactures of our country. This process of making paper delivers a sheet of greater breadth than any made in America, and of *any length* — in one continued unbroken succession, of fine or coarse materials, regulated at pleasure to a greater or lesser thickness. The paper, when made, is collected from the machine on reels, in succession as they are filled; and these are removed to the further progress of the manufacture. The paper in its texture is perfectly smooth and even, and is not excelled by any made by hand, in the usual manner of workmanship — as it possesses all the beauty, regularity and strength of what is called well closed and well shut sheets. The mills and engines now prepared, are calculated to do the daily work of *ten paper vats,* and will employ a water power equal to about 12 to 15 mill stones, of the usual size.

The apparatus and machine are on a principle and construction entirely new, and are patented by the inventors here. It has been very expensive, and has been brought to its present state of perfection with much labour, ingenuity and perseverance.

It is with much pleasure that we announce the success of this machine; and we hope it will tend to secure our country against the importations from abroad, which have so much interfered with our own domestic arrangements; and we are also much gratified in believing, that its establishment on our own stream in the neighbourhood of this place, will aid its improvement, and add to the valuable manufactories on the Brandywine.

An interesting account of Gilpin's pioneer paper-machine appeared in an issue of the *Federal Gazette and Baltimore Advertiser* of February 1818:

The following short notice of a very valuable improvement in papermaking, is copied from a letter just received from a gentleman near Wilmington, Delaware, which is another evidence of the progress of American genius. The Messrs. Gilpin who have their paper mills on the Brandywine, near Wilmington, have so far completed this valuable machinery that it makes three reams per hour. The person who attends the machine, puts in the rags, which are not touched again by man till he lays hold of the perfect paper, at the opposite side, to direct the end of it to the Receiving Reel — where it winds on with great velocity what may be termed one endless sheet. The sheet which was thus winding in my presence was thirty inches wide: he can reduce the width at pleasure, and can cut the sheets to any length. The paper thus made, from the finest bank paper to coarse printing, comes out of the rollers as smooth as satin. At common speed this machine makes, attended by two men and one boy as much as the old machinery by twelve men and six boys. With all common paper, such as for printing, all the time for pressing, &c. is saved. This improvement will save to Gilpins 6 to 12,000 dollars a year in wages only: they will, of course, require an increased number of engines to prepare the pulp. They have secured the patent.

This same article, credited to the *Federal Gazette,* was copied in the *Weekly Recorder,* Chillicothe, Ohio, in the issue of April 3, 1818, and this is no doubt the earliest reference to America's first paper-machine in a publication in the "western country."

In regard to the cost of the mill and the quality of the paper manufactured on Gilpin's machine, Niles' *Weekly Register,* Baltimore, has this to say in the issue of August 5, 1820: ". . . Among these were the Gilpins, on the Brandywine, whose establishment for the manufacture of paper, we suppose must have cost between three and four hundred thousand dollars, and is said to be without a superior in the world; though several others of our papermakers manufacture goods equal to theirs, and have for several years made papers which, with the same advantage of age before using, would compare with any furnished from England, and at 25 per cent. less price than they can be sold at, in that country. Paper is a dear article in England, though exceedingly cheap in France, Germany, Italy, &c."

The Gilpin paper-machine of 1817 was, as indicated in one of the foregoing quotations, capable of forming paper about thirty inches in width, but the speed of the machine is not mentioned. After a thorough search through numerous newspaper and magazine files of the period the only reference to the capacity of this pioneer machine was found in a publication entitled the *Casket of Flowers of Literature, Wit & Sentiment,* issued in Philadelphia for the month of March 1828. A woodcut of Gilpin's paper mill is shown and on page 125 appears a brief account of the machine: ". . . the mills of Messrs. Gilpin are situated about two miles above Wilmington and are now solely employed for the manufacture of paper. By the introduction of machinery, about ten years since . . . the very finest sheet of paper is produced in an almost instantaneous process of *sixty feet per minute.* . . ." Basing our information on various contemporary descriptions, from which quotations have been made, it may be stated that the first papermaking machine installed in an American paper mill was capable of forming paper about thirty inches in width and at a speed of sixty feet each minute. (In 1941 the largest paper-machine in the world was located in Sittingbourne, Kent, England, and had a capacity of producing paper 320 inches in width at the rate of 1,400 feet per minute.)

The quality and quantity of the Gilpin paper and the mill's prosperity became the envy of other papermakers, and in spite of the secrecy with which Gilpin guarded his machine, other machines began to appear. Gilpin was soon to lose his monopoly of the machine-made-paper field. A foremost competitor of Gilpin was John Ames of Springfield, Massachusetts. Ames was clever at invention and possessed a genius for mechanics. He had heard about the Gilpin machine, learned something about its principle of operation, appropriated the idea, and was reputed to have improved upon the Gilpin construction and produced a better machine.

THE FIRST FOURDRINIER MACHINE IN AMERICA

What is generally considered to be the first paper-machine of Fourdrinier design to be erected in this country was imported by Henry Barclay of Saugerties, New York. The machine, which was sixty inches in width, was built in England by Bryan Donkin. It was put into operation on October 24, 1827 in a mill owned by Beach, Hommerken and Kearney. After this machine was completed in England and ready for shipment and the contract money had been paid, English paper-manufacturers made strenuous objections to its leaving the country, as they feared competition from America. Parts of this historic machine were still in use as late as 1872, when the remaining sections were destroyed by fire.

The second Fourdrinier paper-machine installed in America had been made in France to the order of the Pickering paper mill, North Windham, Connecticut. The huge Fourdrinier, packed in many crates and boxes, arrived at an American port in December 1827. The machine was eventually erected for the Pickerings by a mechanical genius, George Spafford (1795–1855), who, although not versed in such complicated machines, undertook the enormous task fully confident that he could erect the French-built Fourdrinier and cause it to function properly. In 1828 this machine produced paper successfully, and the young mechanic, Spafford, delighted and encouraged by his important part in the enterprise, conceived the plan of actually building a machine in this country, without the aid of European skill or materials. The future looked bright for such an undertaking: sailing ships were slow and freight transporation from France and England expensive, and George Spafford knew that the making of paper by machine was certain to supplant the old traditional hand method. He was resolved to build a complete paper-machine, founded on the Fourdrinier principle, in this country, and with this end in view he sought a partner who had both mechanical skill and at least a little aptitude for business. Spafford soon found James Phelps (1802–60), a mechanic who had been engaged in the construction and fitting of handmade-paper mills, and the firm of Phelps and Spafford was not long in being formed. In South Windham, Connecticut, these two determined men acquired an old schoolhouse, which they moved to a near-by millstream so that power might be developed for actuating their limited power-driven equipment. A young mechanic named Charles Smith (1810–97), a boy of nineteen, was hired by the newly established firm, and Smith assumed the responsibility of superintendent of the foundry and machine shop. Here, with a lathe turned by water of the stream, and with tools they had themselves made, the partnership of Spafford and Phelps, assisted by Charles Smith, constructed the first Fourdrinier paper-machine to be made in America. Inasmuch as the plans for this machine were drawn on smooth pine boards and the designs planed off as soon as used, nothing remains of the original drawings of this American-built machine. Upon completion of their marvel of engineering skill, Phelps and Spafford sold their paper-machine to Amos H. Hubbard, who had been operating a hand-made-paper mill in Norwich Falls, Connecticut (Figure 259). The machine commenced making usable paper in May 1829 (Figure 260). The Hubbard mill was on the Yantic River and the location had been the original site of the Christopher Leffingwell mill, the earliest papermaking plant in Connecticut, established in 1767.

A second machine was completed by the firm of Phelps and Spafford in 1831 and was installed in the mill of Henry Hudson, East Hartford, Connecticut (Figure 261). According to an old

Fig. 259   *The paper mill of Amos H. Hubbard, Norwich, Connecticut, where was installed the first Fourdrinier paper-machine to be built in America. The machine was completed in 1829 by Phelps and Spafford, South Windham, Connecticut. From a contemporary ream label of R. & A. H. Hubbard, Norwich, Connecticut.*

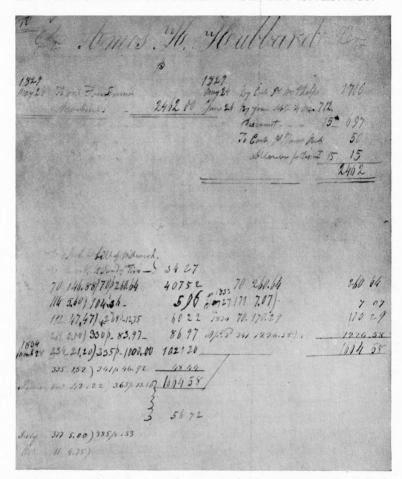

FIG. 260   *The page from the account book of Phelps and Spafford showing the cost of the first Fourdrinier machine built in America, and sold to Amos H. Hubbard, Norwich, Connecticut. The account is dated May 24, 1829 and the cost of the machine is stated to be $2462.*

account-book, this Fourdrinier was sold for $2,000, with "one Drying Machine" at $1,000 additional (Figure 262). During the following years a number of paper-machines were constructed by this South Windham foundry and machine shop, but the financial crash of 1837 proved too severe for them to withstand and the company was forced to suspend operations. Charles Smith, the

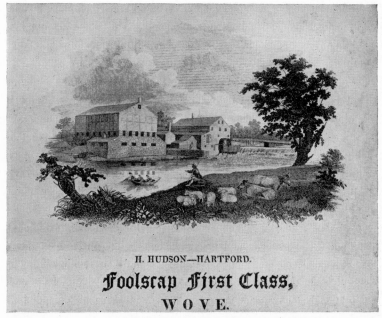

H. HUDSON—HARTFORD.

ffoolscap ffirst Class,

WOVE.

Fig. 261   *The paper mill of Henry Hudson, Hartford, Connecticut, where in 1831 Phelps and Spafford installed the second Fourdrinier paper-machine they had built. Reproduced from a contemporary engraved ream label used by this mill.*

young superintendent, was able to purchase what remained of the company's tools and equipment and with Harvey Winchester (1818–88) formed the firm of Smith and Winchester, a well-known establishment still building paper-machines in South Windham, Connecticut.

All of the early papermaking machines used in America were fitted with wires that had been woven abroad. It was not until the year 1847 that suitable wires for the machine were woven in this country. While it is probable that the early American makers of handmade paper wove their own felts in comparatively small individual pieces, it is stated that the first successful felts woven in this country for use on the paper-machine did not appear until about the year 1864.

During the period of the development of the paper-machine in England, France, Germany, and America, the frail, ingenious

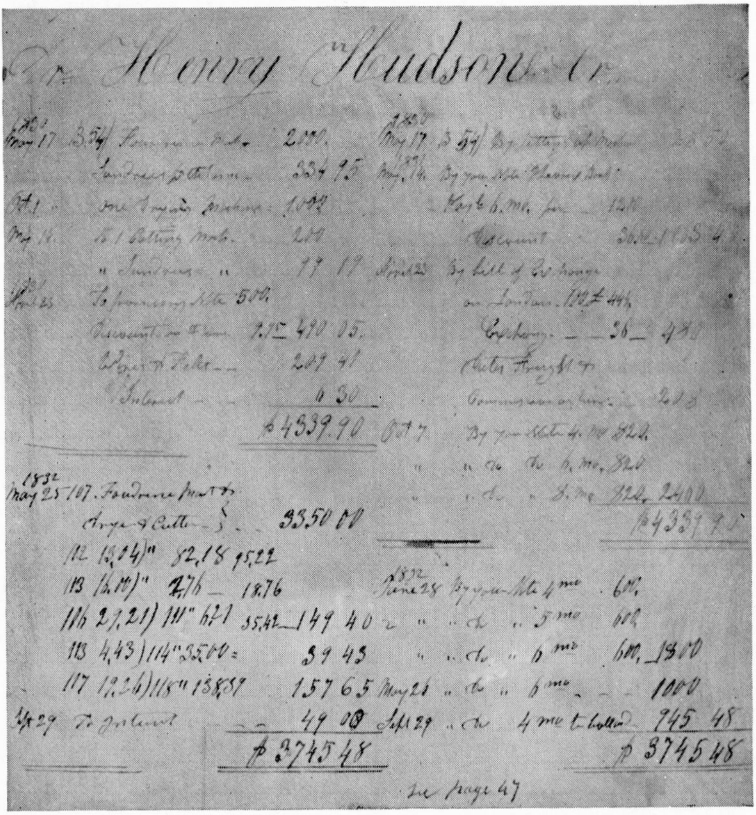

FIG. 262   *The cost of the second Fourdrinier paper-machine built in America and installed in the mill of Henry Hudson, Hartford, Connecticut, is preserved in an old account book of Phelps and Spafford. The list reads: "May 17, 1830, Fourdrinier machine $2,000; Sundries to the same 334.95; Oct. 1, One drying machine 1000; May 14, One cutting machine 200; Sundries on cutting machine 99.19; Wires and felts 209.41." The cost of the entire machine to Henry Hudson was $4339.90. This illustration and Figure 260 are reproduced through the courtesy of the Smith and Winchester Company, successors to Phelps and Spafford.*

Nicholas-Louis Robert was living quietly in France. He realized no monetary remuneration from his invention, and even the glory of originating a machine that was destined to revolutionize civilization was denied him. When the first commercial paper-machine was set up in France in 1811, Robert, its originator, was fifty years of age, a broken, discouraged man. Robert'died on August 8, 1828, in Vernouillet, a poorly paid teacher in a modest primary school. Even if this destitute inventor did not realize any financial gain or recognition during his lifetime, the name of Nicholas-Louis Robert will be perpetuated by papermakers and paper-users the world over, for to him must go the credit of originating the now indispensable machine that furnishes the paper of "an indefinite length" employed in printing all modern newspapers, magazines, books — in fact, practically all paper that is consumed today.

The early paper-machines were incomplete in their conception, there being no suction under the wire; the paper was wound up while still moist, cut into sheets, and hung in the drying-loft as had been the practice with handmade paper. Drying cylinders * in connection with the paper-machine were first used in England about 1821. In America the earliest drying cylinders were made by George Spafford, of the firm of Phelps and Spafford, in 1830. Drying rolls of the Crompton-Spafford type accomplished the drying of the paper in a few minutes, while with the old method of hanging the paper to dry after it left the machine, the time required might have been days or even longer, depending upon the weather. The drying cylinders were originally heated by wood or charcoal fires placed within the metal rolls, but in later years steam was introduced. Even as late as 1834 direct charcoal fires were in use in America in heating the drying cylinders, and in some parts of Europe this method was employed until the fifties and sixties. The English inventor of the drying cylinders, Thomas

---

* The first drying cylinders were invented and patented by Thomas Bonsor Crompton. The patent (dated November 1, 1820, No. 4509) reads: "Drying and finishing of paper by certain means hitherto unused for this purpose; and this is effected by conducting the paper by means of cloth or cloths against heated cylinders, which cloth may be of any suitable material, but preference is given to a cloth of linen warp and woolen weft. Attached to this machine is a cutter or shears to cut the paper off in suitable lengths as it comes from the rollers."

Bonsor Crompton, also conceived the first cutting device to be placed on a paper-machine.

The improved driers invented by Robert Ranson did not come into use until 1839.* An unusual letter dealing with the Ranson drying cylinders was received a number of years ago from the grandson of the patentee, Robert Gill Ranson. Owing to the interesting contents of this letter it is given here verbatim:

My father told me the following story as to the matter of his father sending him to France in 1842 with a shipload of machinery to exhibit to the French papermakers. He arrived at Boulogne sur Mer and set up all the machinery, but after it was in place he could find no engine capable of setting it in motion. He then had a huge wooden flywheel constructed and went to the docks along the sea where he employed all of the wharfmen he could get together. These men were put to turning the huge wooden wheel which was geared to the machinery. These men worked so irregularly that the web of the paper was broken. The hiring of these men was unsuccessful. He next visited the mayor of Boulogne, who gave him a letter to the captain of a local company of soldiers. These men, about fifty in number, went to work to actuate the great wooden wheel. They were all used to working at the word of command. My father stood by the captain and gave the orders, — start — slow — faster — steady — halt, etc. The huge wheel and the machinery turned at exactly the right speed and the papermaking was a decided success, or possibly the paper was already made and it was only sized and dried upon the machinery that had been transported from America. All of the principal papermakers of France attended the demonstration. One by one they came to my father and made offers for the use of the drying cylinders. The offers increased until the sum of sixty-five thousand pounds was reached. He told the papermakers that he was not empowered to accept any offers, but would have to communicate with his father before anything could be determined. Immediately after this most successful demonstration word was received that Robert Gill Ranson, the inventor, was very ill and he died just as his son reached the American shore. The English bank in which my father had an interest became financially involved, and as the Ransons had no money to fight the infringements, the French papermakers made use of the patents without authority. However, the English papermakers paid my grandmother about $5,000 a year as long

---

* The original English and Scotch patents relating to the Ranson drying cylinders, as well as many letters, documents, specimens of the first paper from the Ranson driers, etc., are now housed in the Paper Museum of the Massachusetts Institute of Technology.

FIG. 263   A paper-machine of 1829, in the Russian Imperial paper
mill, Peterhof. (From Mechanics' Magazine, Museum, Register, Journal and Gazette; London, December 12, 1829.)

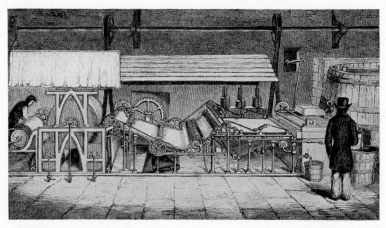

FIG. 264   *A paper-machine with three drying cylinders, from the period 1835–40.* (*From* The Useful Arts and Manufactures of Great Britain; *London, 1840.*)

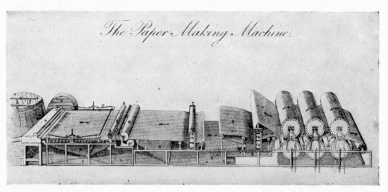

FIG. 265   *A paper-machine with six drying cylinders from the period 1850–60.* (*From* Paper and Papermaking, Ancient and Modern, *by Richard Herring; London, 1856.*)

as she lived. My father, although financially ruined, again went into papermaking and built a new mill, but his workmen were so fearful the new machinery would rob them of their positions, they burned the mill. My father becoming discouraged he gave up the paper business entirely and went in the lumber trade. He died at the age of eighty-eight.

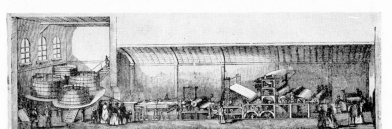

Fig. 266   A paper-machine from the 1860 period, in a Netherlands mill. (From Het Boek der Uitvindingen, Ambachten en Fabrieken; Leiden, 1864.)

Fig. 267   The "wet-end" of a modern Fourdrinier paper-machine. This huge machine is founded upon the same principle as the ancient hand-mould of China shown in Figure 47. (Courtesy, Mead Pulp and Paper Company)

Nicholas-Louis Robert formed paper on his original model in a size of "12 to 15 metres" in length, and about 24 inches in width, termed at that time of "extraordinary" dimensions. The world's largest paper-machine of today, operating in Sittingbourne, Kent,

Fig. 268   *The drying cylinders of a modern paper-machine.* (Courtesy, Hammermill Paper Company)

England, and working on the same principle as Robert's original model, will produce newsprint paper 26 feet 8 inches in width at the rate of 1,400 feet per minute— more than a quarter of a mile of paper every sixty seconds! In Figure 263–6 are reproduced contemporary woodcuts of the paper-machine showing four periods of development: 1829, 1840, 1850, and 1860. In Figures 267, 268, and 269 American paper-machines of the most modern type may be studied.

The *principle* of making the paper is precisely the same on all Fourdrinier machines, no matter how small or large the machine may be, or the period of its construction. The mission of the paper-machine is to transform the wet macerated vegetable fibres into a thin web of dry paper. This forming process is accomplished upon an endless wire screen, which travels continuously over rollers. The fibres are flowed to the screen in water, and in turn much of the water is removed by suction and drainage through the meshes of the metal screening. The forming of the fibres into a

FIG. 269   *The "dry-end" of the same machine as pictured in Figure 267.* (Courtesy, Mead Pulp and Paper Company)

continuous sheet, or web, of paper on the wire of the machine is the same function that is performed by the vatman when he dips his wire-covered mould of limited proportions into the vat containing beaten fibres suspended in water. From the moving wire screen of the machine the moist web of matted fibre is transferred to an endless woollen blanket, termed a felt. This blanket carries the newly formed web of paper through the press rolls, eliminating still more moisture; by the time this stage of the operation is reached, the matted, intertwined fibres have assumed sufficient strength and formation to withstand being carried over the steam-heated cylinders for drying. In making paper by hand these functions also have their counterpart in the worker, called a coucher, transferring the moist individual sheet of paper from the mould to the felt, and in the pressing and exchanging, and finally in hanging the paper in the loft for drying. The machine imitates mechanically all of the operations that are performed in the hand process by the vatman, coucher, and layman and through the action of the standing press and drying-loft.

IMITATION HANDMADE PAPER

During the past thirty-five years machines have been constructed for the purpose of imitating genuine handmade, or vat, papers. These special machines are known as "cylinder-mould," or "cylinder and vat," machines. They are so made that the sheets of paper formed upon them have four deckle edges. Previous to the invention of this machine the four-deckle sheet had been possible only by forming in the hand-mould, as described in previous chapters. The deckle edges formed on the paper made upon one of these machines differ materially from the deckles produced by the hand-mould, but the difference is not easily described. The cylinder-made deckle is more even in appearance than the edge of a genuine handmade sheet, the former having that machine-made quality that always separates the mechanically made thing from that fashioned by the hand of man. A machine may be made to imitate hand work up to a point, but the product is obviously machine-made. Power looms have been constructed to imitate ancient Chinese and Persian rugs; but the genuine rugs always embody an indefinable technique that a machine can never duplicate.

The cylinder-mould paper-machine is shown in detail in Figure 270A. It consists of two horizontal stuff-chests (A, A), fitted with agitators (B) and lifter wheels (C), from the buckets of which the pulp, after being diluted, flows over a sand table (D), through a flat strainer (E), to the vat (F), in which the cylinder mould (H) revolves. The vat is made of heavy sheet copper, and the cylinder is of brass; all the piping used in the machine is also of non-rusting material. The couch felt (K) passes between three presses (L, L, L), and the paper is carried between felt K and an upper felt (M); hence, a felt is on both sides of the sheet. Both felts are fitted with washers (W), and a suction box (N) helps to dewater the paper; P is a suction pump. The presses consist of a bronze top roll and a rubber-covered bottom roll, driven by machine-cut gears; thus they both start and stop simultaneously,

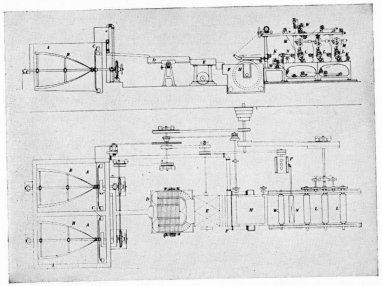

FIG. 270A   *A cylinder-mould machine used in making imitation handmade papers.*

and there is no slip between them. After passing through the presses, the paper is led over four drying cylinders, placed in one row and furnished with one felt. This makes the paper smooth on one side only; but this one-sidedness disappears later, since the paper is usually sized or otherwise treated afterward. The paper is formed by the deposit of fibres on the surface of the wire-covered cylinder (H), the white (or waste) water passing through and being conserved for diluting the stock. The felt (K), pressed against the cylinder by the couch roll (G), picks up the paper and carries it between the press rolls (L).

When the paper is not taken off the machine in single sheets (as described later), it runs onto a reeling apparatus for further treatment. In this form the machine is adapted to the manufacture of endless paper or webs; and as the cylinder rotates in the stock, currents are set up that tend to lay the fibres in the direction of rotation. This causes the paper to be much stronger in the running direction than in the cross direction. It is this characteristic that should be prevented in imitation handmade papers; and it can partially be overcome by using agitators, which maintain even distri-

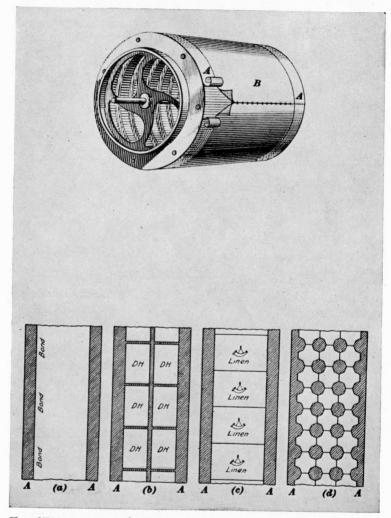

FIG. 271A   *The cylinder of a mould-machine and the methods of dividing the sheets.*

bution of fibres, and also by operating the machine at a low speed. The slower the cylinder revolves, the smaller will be the difference in strength and stretchability of the paper in the two directions. The production of the machine, therefore, is limited. The machine can be operated successfully as low as forty feet per minute.

Fig. 270   *The cylinder and vat machine for making imitation handmade paper in individual sheets, with deckle edges on all sides. The single sheets may be seen travelling on the felt. Paper made on this type of machine is known commercially as "mould-made" and cannot be sold in America as genuine handmade paper. (Courtesy Eynsford Paper Mills, Eynsford, Kent)*

Fig. 271   *Removing the individual sheets of paper from the felt of a cylinder and vat machine. These sheets have four deckle edges and are supposed to emulate genuine handmade paper. It is always possible to discern the difference between paper formed at the vat by a skilled worker and that manufactured on a mould-machine. Photograph taken in the Eynsford Mill, Kent, England, probably the only mill in England where the three types of paper are made: genuine handmade, imitation handmade, and Fourdrinier machine-made.*

The *cylinder mould* is an ordinary cylinder (Figure 271A) composed of brass ribs which support a coarse, "laid" covering, also of brass. The covering acts as a support to the removable outside covering (B), on which the wire watermarking designs are fastened. The watermarks made in the paper produced on one of these machines are clear and brilliant and are decidedly superior to the watermarks produced by the use of the "dandy-roll" on the regular paper-machine. In some respects, however, they do not compare with the finest watermarks produced through the use of a hand-mould. The covering for the cylinder used in forming a continuous sheet, or web, of paper is shown in (a), Figure 271A. All the parts marked A are waterproof cloths and they determine the width of the sheet and cause the deckle edges of the paper. At (b),

Figure 271A, the covering is shown arranged with the waterproof, or waxed cloth, so as to form separate sheets, each sheet having deckle edges on all four sides. It is understood, of course, that the pulp will not form upon the waterproof cloth. At (c), Figure 271A, the sheets are separated by means of a thread of cotton tissue, extending from one waxed, or waterproof, cloth of the cylinder to the other. With this arrangement the paper is torn into sheets, along the lines impressed in the paper by the cotton thread, after the paper has passed through the driers. The making of envelopes with deckles on all sides is shown in (d), Figure 271A. With the separate sheets as shown in (b) the sheets must be taken, one after the other, from the wet felt (Figures 270, 271). They are placed in piles and subjected to pressure in the hydraulic press, and are usually dried in the manner of genuine handmade papers. The cylinders are made from 45 to 60 inches in width, the 60-inch being a practical size. So that the paper may as closely as possible resemble handmade paper, cylinder papers are usually sized after they are formed, and not in the beater as is usually the practice with other makes of machine papers.[5]

XIII

Printing Revolutionizes Papermaking, and the World-Wide Quest for New Papermaking Fibres Begins in Earnest

IN both Europe and America the development of the paper-machine was comparatively rapid. The widths of the machines were constantly increased and every effort was made to acquire more and more speed of production. Improvements were made in the drying mechanism and in the surface finishing of the paper, all of which made for a greater diversity of product and an expansion of the paper industry. With this growing efficiency and the constant increase in productive capacity, there became more apparent the ever threatening shortage of rags as a raw material. It spurred the manufacturers in the search for a new papermaking material, a vegetable fibre in compact form, easily gathered and handled and furnishing the highest average yield per acre of growth. Wood seemed to answer these requirements, but it was long of realization. As stated in a previous chapter, Réaumur, in 1719, in his treatise on the habits of the American wasp, relates how the wasp fabricates its nest by using the fibres of wood. He observed how the sheets that form the structure were a type of paper. Réaumur reasoned that the ingenuity of man could surely produce usable paper from these same wood fibres. Nearly a quarter of a century later he bemoaned the fact that nothing had been done with respect to his discovery and reproached the papermakers for their apathy and their failure to appreciate and attach some value to his observation.

EARLY EXPERIMENTS WITH WOOD PULP

There did follow several pioneer attempts in an experimental way to make paper of wood fibre. Chief of these and still in evidence in the six volumes, described previously, published in Germany in 1765–72, is the work of Dr. Jacob Christian Schäffer, who made some crudely formed paper from wood fibres taken from many different kinds of vegetation. Among the woods chosen by Schäffer were beech, willow, aspen, mulberry, spruce, and others. Copies that remain of these books printed on these experimental papers are in a comparatively good condition today. Dr. Schäffer in his papermaking attempted nothing more than a matting of the fibres, which was a sufficient test of their papermaking properties.

Later, in 1800, Matthias Koops, previously mentioned, had published in London a book printed on paper that he made by his own process from straw. In this book were also a few leaves of paper made from wood, for which Koops made the claim that it was "Paper made from wood alone, the product of this country, without any intermixture of rags, waste paper, bark, straw or any other vegetable substance, from which paper might be, or has hitherto been manufactured; and of this the most ample testimony can be given." The author-inventor claimed it was the first *practical* paper made from wood. It surely proved to be a most "practical paper," as copies of the book remain today to bear testimony to that fact.

The Koops book bears the formidable title: *Historical Account of the Substances Which have been Used to Convey Ideas from the Earliest Date to the Invention of Paper,* a learned treatise prefaced by a most respectful exposition to King George III of the wider field for the gathering of papermaking materials which straw and wood afforded. Koops's work was prophetic, but apparently the English manufacturers were too conservative for such a radical departure in papermaking. In his book Koops pleaded with the King for better protection for English inventors, insisting that the English method of publishing the details of patents offered the inventor no protection for an idea that had been the result of much labour and study, and which might be readily appropriated by persons in another country.

Koops did not regard his paper as a vehicle for printing only, but declared that wood fibre could be converted into a substance of great strength consisting of layers of paper. He even went so far as to predict that paper would become valuable as a building material when treated so as to become impenetrable and incombustible, and would displace tiles and slates. When one considers that the largest tonnage of paper produced today is in paper board, and no small portion is used as building material, Koops's voice is recognized as that of a prophet.

WOOD PULP COMMERCIALIZED

It is an interesting coincidence that at the time of the Koops experiments the papermaking machine was undergoing its initial development in England. Both inventions, or discoveries, were the most important factors in enabling the paper and printing industries to make their marvellous expansion in succeeding years. The apathetic attitude of the English papermaker toward the use of wood let slip an opportunity that was later seized upon in Germany, but not until 1840. In that year Friedrich Gottlob Keller, a German weaver in Hainichen, Saxony, secured a German patent for a wood-grinding machine. This machine was destined to undergo a wonderful development and give to the world cheap ground-wood papers, and chiefly newsprint paper as we know it today. It made possible the high-speed rotary printing press and the modern newspaper with its practically unlimited dissemination of the news.

Keller defibred blocks of wood by pressure against a revolving wet grindstone, and the first ground-wood paper had in it an admixture of forty per cent rag fibre to give it strength. It was made as newsprint by K. F. G. Kuehn, a papermaker at Alt-Chemnitz. In 1846 Heinrich Voelter, a paper-mill director in Bautzen, Saxony, bought the Keller patent and devised practical machines for quantity production. These machines were built by the machinist I. M. Voith in Heidenheim, Württemberg, in 1847, who began production in Voelter's near-by mill. For an interval of five years Voelter devoted his time entirely to the practical and commercial promotion of the new process. By 1852 ground-wood pulp was being regularly produced in the mill of H. Voelter's Sons in Heidenheim, and also by a mill in Giersdorf, Silesia. The product of both plants had a percentage of rag fibres to strengthen the paper.

Contemporaneous with Keller, but working entirely independently, was Charles Fenerty, a Nova Scotian, who was first to make paper on the American continent from ground wood. Fenerty began his experiments in 1839 and produced a ground-wood sheet in Halifax in 1841. He lacked the support and faith of the Canadian papermakers, but did receive a degree of credit from a Halifax newspaper which endeavoured to obtain a subsidy for Fenerty on patriotic grounds. In a letter written in 1844 to the *Acadian Recorder* he made the following comment on his works:

> Enclosed is a small piece of paper, the result of an experiment I have made in order to ascertain if that useful article might not be manufactured from wood. The result has proved that opinion to be correct, for — by the sample which I have sent you, gentlemen — you will perceive the feasibility of it. The enclosed, which is as firm in its texture, as white, and to all appearances as durable as the common wrapping-paper made from hemp, cotton, or the ordinary materials of manufacture, is actually composed of spruce wood reduced to a pulp, and subjected to the same treatment as paper is in course of being made, only with this exception, viz: my insufficient means of giving it the required pressure. I entertain an opinion that our forest trees, either hard or soft wood, but more especially the fir, spruce, or poplar, on account of the fibrous quality of their wood, might easily be reduced by a chafing, and manufactured into paper of the finest kind. This opinion, sirs, I think the experiment will justify, and leaving it to be prosecuted further by the scientific or the curious, I remain, gentlemen, your obedient servant. . . .

It reveals Fenerty as a man of foresight, not a visionary, although he was something of a poet and indulged a fancy for writing verse about his beloved forests. His invention might be regarded by some as their betrayal.

It is recorded that John Beardsley, of Buffalo, New York, attempted to make paper from basswood. On December 26, 1854 he is said to have submitted three samples of his product to the editor of the Buffalo *Democrat*.

GROUND WOOD COMMERCIALIZED IN THE UNITED STATES

The first ground-wood pulp produced commercially on this continent was the output of a machine based on the Voelter patents. In 1867 Albrecht Pagenstecher founded at Curtisville (now Interlaken) near Stockbridge, Massachusetts, the first ground-wood pulp mill in the United States. Here, with an initial output of a half ton per day, was produced a marketable, mechanically prepared wood fibre. The first sale of the pulp was made to the Smith Paper Company of Lee, Massachusetts, at eight cents per pound. The Smith Paper Company, under the management of Wellington Smith, made a practical paper of it and introduced in this country ground-wood paper as a salable commodity. It did not spring suddenly into general use, and newspaper publishers were reluctant to accept the new material. It was considered "shoddy" and an inferior stock and condemned as bad and unfit for use by the daily newspaper. This prejudice was eventually overcome, and it was discovered that the paper had good printing qualities and another point of importance in that it lowered the cost of their white printing paper.

Ten years previous to the Pagenstecher venture, Platner and Smith had at Lee, Massachusetts, made some paper from ground wood in an experimental way, but had given up the idea as their method proved too costly and the process too lengthy in reducing the wood to pulp. The method was the same in principle as that later used, but the paper made was so coarse that it proved to be a poor printing medium.

Two persons foremost in introducing ground-wood paper here were Albrecht Pagenstecher and Frederick Wuertzbach. Wuertzbach, thirty-one years of age, an all-round mechanical genius, came over with the first wood-grinder in order that it might be properly erected and operated. His services were so valued that he was retained as superintendent for the entire life of the mill. It is interesting to note that in relating the story of his first labours, and how the idea came to him, Albrecht Pagenstecher gives a certain amount of credit to Theodore Steinway of the well-known firm of piano-manufacturers. Steinway mentioned to a cousin of Pagenstecher, Alberto Pagenstecher, that paper was being made successfully in Germany by a ground-wood process. At that time Rudolph Pagenstecher, a brother of Albrecht, was in Germany and correspondence on the subject was opened with him, with the result that it was decided to import two wood-grinders and to engage a competent man to set them up and supervise the operation. The "competent man" proved to be Frederick Wuertzbach.

The two machines arrived in December 1866 in charge of Wuertzbach, who installed them and had them in full production by March 5, 1867. For more than a year the Smith Paper Company at Lee enjoyed a monopoly in the use of the new raw material, but were somewhat secretive about it, realizing that it was still in the early stages of development. By 1868 other mills in Lawrence, Fitchburg, and Lee, Massachusetts, Norway, Maine, and Lanesville, Connecticut, became interested. Another mill was started by the Pagenstecher interests at Luzerne, New York. This mill was the pioneer in using grinding machinery made in this country. In later years this became the Hudson River Pulp and Paper Company and developed into one of the foremost paper mills in America.

The mill at Lawrence was instrumental in acquainting William A. Russell with the possibilities of the new raw material. He obtained the rights to build two large pulp mills, one at Franklin, New Hampshire, and another at Bellows Falls, Vermont. Later he bought the rights to manufacture ground wood under the Voelter patents in six New England states. About this time Warner Miller, an influential paper-manufacturer, also became interested. He had learned of the successful operation of wood-grinders in Germany. At Herkimer, New York, Miller had endeavoured to make use of a patent he had bought from Henry Lowe of Baltimore, who had invented a method of converting reeds into paper pulp, but had not made a commercial success of it. Miller went to Baltimore to see the machine and then set up one after his own ideas, but based on the Lowe patent. Some wood pulp was made with it, but evidently not entirely satisfactorily. Miller then decided to join forces with the Pagenstechers and obtained an interest in the mill at Luzerne, New York. Here pulp was made in the form of "cheeses"; that is, water was drained from the pulp as it left the grinders, and it was shovelled into small bags and then put in a heavy hand press. The pulp was thus pressed in blocks ten by twelve inches and two inches thick. The blocks of pulp were shipped in that form to the paper mills.

This process of separating the pulp from the water proved to be inefficient, stood in the way of quantity production, and was too costly a method of handling. A cylinder machine was devised and Miller demonstrated to the satisfaction of Albrecht Pagenstecher how it was possible to get a measure of mass production by running the pulp in quick-forming sheets five feet by three and as thick as sole leather. This was a happy solution and an aid in lowering the cost of production.

Not far from the site of the Pagenstecher mill was that of Benjamin Franklin Barker. It was situated on the same stream at Curtisville that furnished the power for the Pagenstecher grinders. The Barker mill was upstream and possessed prior water rights. Patent records show that Barker held four patents covering wood-grinders of his own design. These were dated September 19, 1871, May 19, 1874, March 23, 1875, and August 10, 1875. In his application for his second patent Barker mentions the use of poplar wood and says: "I get by means of my improvement, much longer fibres than heretofore, and this further improves the resulting pulp." In a later application the inventor intimates that his grinder is of such nice adjustment, so automatic and of such gentle feeding force, that "a delicate female or other attendant with little strength can maintain the proper action in a considerable number of these feeders without severe labour." Barker seems to have been less celebrated than Voelter in papermaking history, but he deserves to be numbered among those pioneers who made valuable contributions to the development and advancement of the paper industry.

In the early 1860's newsprint paper was selling for about twenty-five cents per pound. Ground-wood pulp was first sold at eight cents per pound, and soon dropped to four and five cents, where it remained for a time. It then fell to as low as a cent a pound and reduced the price of newsprint from fourteen cents in 1869 to two cents and less in 1897. In the matter of cost alone the effect of the new ground-wood paper was revolutionary.

It has long been stated that the earliest use of wood-pulp paper in American newspaper printing was the October 28, 1830 issue of the *Crawford Messenger,* published in Crawford County, Pennsylvania. It is also stated that the paper was made by Joseph E. Holmes and Lewis Wooster, Meadville, Pennsylvania, and the material was lime and aspen wood. An analysis of the paper used in the *Messenger* for the date of October 28, 1830, recently made, showed that the material is not wood, but very short rag (linen) fibre. Apparently the first use of wood-pulp paper for newspaper printing in this country about which we may be certain was the

January 14, 1863 issue of the *Boston Weekly Journal;* the *Daily Journal* of the same date was printed on the regulation all-rag paper. There is considerable difference in the quality of the paper used in the two issues, the rag paper being much finer than that produced from wood. The following appears on the editorial page of the *Journal* for January 15, 1863: "The entire edition of *The Journal* of today will be printed on paper made from wood, by a new process. We bespeak for it a fair criticism from our readers, and all those interested in the use of and the manufacture and sale of printing paper. This paper is not a fair test of what the manufacturers propose to do when their arrangements are fully perfected, but it will certainly prove that there are other materials than rags which can be used successfully in the manufacture of white paper. We have been experimenting with this paper on portions of our editions for several days past, and the results have been highly satisfactory. Thus far it has exceeded our most sanguine expectations. . . ."

According to the research [1] made by Mr. John Archer and Mr. William R. Thurman, of the New York Public Library, the first New York City newspaper to use the newly invented wood-pulp paper for its regular editions was the *New Yorker Staats-Zeitung;* in going through the files they found the issues of January 7, 8, and 9, 1868 printed upon paper made from this material. This newspaper was using all-wood paper entirely by 1870. The *New York World* followed the German newspaper in the use of wood-pulp paper; the edition of June 22, 1870 is printed on paper of this kind. Inasmuch as the ground-wood process was perfected in Germany it is perhaps appropriate that the *Staats-Zeitung* was one of the earliest American newspapers to make use of it.*

---

* A summary of the first use of wood-pulp paper by United States newspapers, compiled by Mr. John Archer and Mr. William R. Thurman, New York Public Library, follows:

Newspaper	First issue on wood	Wood used entirely
Staats-Zeitung (New York)	Jan. 7, 1868	1870
World (New York)	June 22, 1870	1881
Providence Journal	April 5, 1871	1880
Brooklyn Eagle	July 28, 1871	1884
Evening Express (New York)	Sept. 6, 1872	1876
Albany Argus	March 20, 1873	1880
New York Times	Aug. 23, 1873	1874

STANWOOD AND HIS MUMMY PAPER

Apparently little is known of the experiments of I. Augustus Stanwood (born December 7, 1839) in the manufacture of paper by the ground-wood process. Stanwood and William Tower began their papermaking in Maine in 1863 and it is claimed by the Stanwood family that their mill produced ground-wood paper in January of that year.

The most interesting phase of Stanwood's career, however, was his use of Egyptian mummies for making wrapping paper. The information here set down regarding the mummy paper was given to me by Stanwood's son, Daniel, a retired professor of international law, living in Massachusetts. During the Civil War, according to Professor Stanwood, his father was pressed for raw material to keep the Maine mill in operation and he had to use his ingenuity to overcome the difficulty. This he did by importing mummies from Egypt for the sole purpose of stripping the dried bodies of their cloth wrappings and using the material for making paper. Professor Stanwood informed me that his father brought several shiploads of mummies to his mill in Gardiner, Maine, and threw the woven wrappings as well as the papyrus filling into beaters and manufactured from these substances a coarse brown wrapping paper, which eventually found its way into the shops of grocers, butchers, and other merchants who used paper of this kind. It was further stated that the rags stripped from the long-dead Egyptians caused an epidemic of cholera among the rag-pickers and cutters in the Maine mill, for at that period there was no regulation regarding the disinfection of rags. Professor Stanwood also related that the only competition his father encountered in purchasing the mummies was the Egyptian railroad, for during a ten-year period the locomotives of Egypt made use of no other fuel

Newspaper	First issue on wood	Wood used entirely
Weekly Times (New York)	Feb.　4, 1874	. . . .
Verbote (Chicago)	Feb.　14, 1874	1880
Sun (New York)	May　20, 1874	1880
New York Tribune	Dec.　8, 1874	1879
New York Herald	Dec.　31, 1874	1882
Journal of Commerce (New York)	April　1, 1875	1875
New York Evening Post	Aug.　17, 1875	1878
Cincinnati Daily Gazette	Dec.　7, 1878	1881

than that furnished by the well-wrapped, compact mummies, the supply of which was thought at the time to be almost unlimited. Stanwood the papermaker died March 6, 1914, and in the various obituaries published by New York newspapers accounts were given of his experiments with ground wood and his unusual manufacture of wrapping paper from the wrappings of Egyptian mummies. It would appear, however, that Stanwood was not the first American papermaker to use this novel material. In the Syracuse, New York, *Daily Standard* * of August 19, 1856 the following may be found in the editorial page:

An Onondaga county man, worshipful of the golden Eagle and not of the Egyptian Ibis, has put upon the market "paper made from the wrappings of mummies." Could anything better illustrate the practical character of this age, and the intense materialism of America?

With an intense materialism that shears right through sentiment, and world's ideas and usages, this American sees fibre in all the mummied dead of Egypt. He would not ask for nor accept moral instruction, political teaching, artistic suggestions, or historical learning from the preserved and garnered generations of the rulers, warriors, architects, and mechanics of the foremost state of the Old World. It is fibre he

---

* Joel Munsell in his *Chronology of Paper and Papermaking* (Albany, N. Y., 1870) states that the Syracuse *Standard* "boasted" that one of its issues was printed on paper made from the wrappings of Egyptian mummies. A diligent search through the files of this publication did not reveal a copy of this newspaper printed on paper manufactured from this unusual material. The only reference to mummy paper found in the files of the *Standard* was the article of 1856 (herewith given), and this was reprinted from the Albany *Journal*. These two references led to an investigation of the making of mummy paper in New York State, and through the interest of Miss Ida Benderson of the Syracuse University Library the Syracuse *Post-Standard* reprinted the original 1856 story in its issue of December 22, 1940. This article brought forth a communication from Mrs. John Ramsey of Syracuse, the interesting contents of which are here set down: "Upon reading the article in the *Post-Standard* recently about paper made of wrapping from mummies, I am reminded of a story told me about forty years ago by an old friend of my father. His name was Dr. Myron K. Waite, and he came from Northfield, where he lived, from the neighbouring town of Broadalbin, N. Y. Dr. Waite said that when he was a young man (about 1855–1860) he worked in a paper mill in Broadalbin where they received great bundles of old linen wrappings from Egyptian mummies, which they made into paper. He said that the rolled-up vestments retained the shape of the mummy, so that when the workmen tried to straighten or unroll the 'cocoon,' as it might be called, it sprang back at once into the shape of the mummy it had encased so long. He described the material as cream-coloured linen and fragments of the embroidery still remained on some of the edges, somewhat like modern cross-stitch borders."

wants, and nothing but fibre. He would pass the cerements of Cleopatra through a paper mill as quick as he would the shirt of Winnebago. Pharaoh would be to him but so many reams of "demy," "commercial post," or "satin note." He would not question him about the first Fugitive Slave Law, nor the Nile granite quarries, nor the Pyramids. He would curtly ask him for his fibre, and would inform him that his mill was idle while he delayed producing his fibre. If Potiphar's wife tendered to his ear a whispered confession, he would interrupt her with a decisive — "your fibre, madam, if you please, the mill is idle!"

In 1855, a year earlier than the short article appeared in the Syracuse *Standard*, a New York scientist, Dr. Isaiah Deck, compiled a manuscript in which he advanced the idea that the wrappings of Egyptian mummies could be used in making paper. In regard to the scarcity of material for paper at that time Dr. Deck stated that 405,000,000 pounds of rags were required in the eight hundred paper mills operating in the United States. In pointing out the great store of papermaking material lying idle in ancient Egyptian tombs Dr. Deck wrote: "At this period of sepulture it is by no means rare to find above 30 pounds weight of linen wrappings on individual mummies; one from the collection of Mr. Davidson yielded, when unravelled, nearly 300 yards, and weighed, when bleached, 32 pounds. A princess, from the late Mr. Pettingrew's collection, was swathed in forty thicknesses, producing 42 yards of the finest texture." In his manuscript Dr. Deck lays further stress on the abundant quantity of mummy wrappings by stating: "The supply of linen rags would not be limited to the mummies of the human species alone; independent of that obtainable from this source, a more than equal amount of cloth could be depended on from the mummies of the sacred bulls, crocodiles, ibides, and cats as all of these animals were embalmed and swathed in a superior quality of linen . . . some bandages, from 5 inches to 5 feet wide and 9 yards long, have been stripped from mummies their entire length without tearing." In regard to the cost of this grewsome material Dr. Deck has this to say: "The question, Will it pay? may be readily answered by assuming the value of rags to be from 4 to 6 cents per pound; in the United States this is considered under the market estimate of fine linen rags; the cost of purchasing, collecting, and transportation of the Egyptian material would be under 3 cents per pound, while on the other hand the substances used in the process of embalming would be far more valuable than the swathing cloths — aromatic gums of the rarest and most expensive qualities, and such as are now used in preparing incenses for the Catholic Church: olibanum, labdanum, issoponax, ambergris, etc." It is possible that the actual use of mummy wrappings by Stanwood for papermaking was an outgrowth of the suggestions set forth by Dr. Deck in 1855.

During the Civil War and immediately thereafter research in wood-fibre development went hand in hand with experiments in the manufacture of all manner of articles made of paper. This was the commencement of the Paper Era. In 1853 the first paper collars, cuffs, and shirt bosoms appeared in New York City, and such finery created a sensation among the dandies of the day. The largest firm engaged in making this paper habiliment was Ray and Taylor, Springfield, Massachusetts, and according to old trade cards a few of the names given to their men's paper collars were: "Lord Byron," "Longfellow," "Shakespeare," and "Dantè." The first "turn-down" paper collar made in the United States was a product of this Springfield concern and it was given the name "Persigny," in honour of Jean Gilbert Victor Fialin, Duc de Persigny (1808–72), French Minister of the Interior. Another appellation used by this firm for their paper collars was "Beecher," which became known among the wits as the "Beecher garrote." The letter from Henry Ward Beecher giving his consent to use his name on paper collars is still preserved, and reads: "Brooklyn, N. Y., March 3, 1869, Messrs. Ray and Taylor: Gentlemen: My name has been used so much for all sorts of things that I doubt whether I could substantiate, in a court of justice, any claim to it; and, of course, it would not be fair to forbid you the use of it. I hope your enterprise may be successful, and that the paper collars may be good enough for the name, and the name never disgrace the collars. Respectfully yours, Henry Ward Beecher."

Ten years after the original development of paper collars, cuffs, and shirt bosoms the use of paper became almost universal in making waistcoats, bonnets, aprons, hats, tapestry, curtains, and carpets; also roofing and building papers had their beginning, and boxes, buckets, cuspidors, and barrels were formed of paper.*

---

* The use of paper in Europe in the manufacture of various commodities had its origin a hundred years previous to 1870, but it was at this later period

By 1870 a Boston manufacturer was producing 75,000,000 paper collars a year. For the purpose of making collars various layers of paper were pasted together and the material was treated with transparent waterproof enamel; the laminated paper was finally passed between heated rolls upon which linen cloth had been wound, thus giving the paper a woven-appearing surface resembling linen (Figure 272). In England at the same period the use of paper for everyday commodities became so generally accepted that a song entitled *The Age of Paper* (Figure 273) was popular in London music halls. The words were sung by Mr. Howard Paul, "attired in a suit of paper."

Perhaps the most unusual use of paper at this period was its employment in making coffins. M. Szelelmey, the inventor of various paper products, believed in the universal adaptability of

---

that paper developed into an important factor in the manufacturing of products other than for writing, printing, etc. The following abridgments of English patents attest the activity in the utilization of paper for industrial purposes during the latter part of the eighteenth century:

A.D. 1772, November 20, Henry Clay. "Making in paper high varnished pannels or roofs for coaches, and all sorts of wheel carriages and sedan chairs, pannels for rooms, doors, and cabins of ships, cabinets, book-cases, screens, chimney-pieces, tables, tea-trays, and waiters, by pasting several papers upon boards or plates of regular thicknesses on each side of the same until the thickness required is attained; the edges are cut off or planed until the board or plate appears and the papers taken off such boards or plates, and are rendered inflexible by drying in a hot stove, while at the same time they are rubbed with or dipped in oil or varnish, which drenches into them, and secures them from damps, etc. The papers so made are worked in every respect like wood, and into such articles as tea-trays and dressing-boxes. The articles may be coated with colour and oils sufficient to make the surface even, and are then japanned and high varnished."

A.D. 1788, August 12, Lewis Charles Ducrest. "Making paper for the building of houses, bridges, ships, boats, and all sorts of wheel carriages, sedan chairs, chairs, tables, and book-cases, either entirely of paper, or wood and iron covered with paper, and this may be done either by pasting over a mould of the article required covered with canvas layers of paper until the necessary strength is acquired. The mould is then disjointed and taken out and the canvas taken from the paper. After strengthening the edges by wood and pasting paper over this wood, the damp and moisture are entirely extracted, by drying in a hot room or stove, when five or six coats of common varnish are laid on and well dried in; afterwards a new coat of varnish is added, and whilst wet a fine powder of pumicestone and steel filings in certain proportions is to be sifted on; after thorough drying new coats of varnish are laid on. In constructing bridges, the ropes are covered with layers of paper and treated as above; and if articles of wood or iron are employed, they are covered with paper and submitted to similar treatment."

Fig. 272   *By 1870, paper collars were universally worn; one Boston manufacturer made 75,000,000 a year. This was the beginning of the "paper age." (Photograph courtesy New-York Historical Society, New York, N. Y.)*

paper to all needs of civilization. He used the material for coating ships to render them impervious to shot; he employed paper in the manufacture of railway carriages and drain pipes. His idea of making coffins of paper was to procure a perfectly air-tight, waterproof, and damp-defying case, into which nothing from without could penetrate and nothing from within could escape. The so-called Zopissa paper casket of the late sixties was a solid and compact structure resembling to a marked degree the ancient mummy cases of Egypt. Working at the same time, Stanwood, the papermaker, was making Egyptian mummies into wrapping paper while Szelelmey, the inventor, was manufacturing laminated and compressed paper into coffins that closely resembled the mummy boxes of the Egyptians. The use of paper in the construction of coffins dates from a remote period as the Persians formed caskets of laminated paper many hundreds of years ago. The Paper Museum possesses a small paper coffin that was used by an ancient Persian nobleman in the preservation of a favourite falcon that had been mummified and is still in perfect condition. The inner casket in which the wrapped bird lies is of laminated paper, about a quarter inch in thickness and enamelled black. The outer coffin is formed of the same material, somewhat heavier, and painted in a highly decorative pattern depicting the art of falconry. These double caskets are not composed of papier mâché, which is in-

FIG. 273   *The coloured lithograph cover of the song* The Age of
Paper *as sung in 1860 in the music halls of London by Howard Paul,
"attired in a suit of paper."*

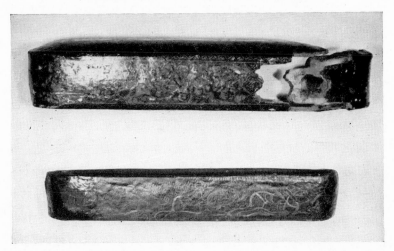

Fig. 274   *The two sections of a coffin made of laminated paper.*
The coffin was made in Persia and antedates the use of laminated paper
in Europe by many hundreds of years.

deed an exceedingly ancient art, but they are actual laminated
sheets of paper put together in the same general manner as some
wall boards are made at the present time (Figure 274).

THE FIRST CHEMICAL PROCESS

While perhaps not imbued with quite the same degree of romance as the ground-wood industry, still the beginnings of the
chemical processes for the preparation of wood for papermaking
are not without interest. These beginnings are characterized by
the same lack of material reward for the discoverers and inventors. Many of them spent comparatively large sums of money
and much time and effort in furthering their ideas, only to have
failure follow and others take up the work where they left off
and, profiting by previous mistakes, carry the project through to
a successful and profitable conclusion.

While the ground-wood process gave the paper industry a cheap
paper in vast quantity for a large variety of uses, there remained
the necessity for a more durable and lasting paper at a cost intermediate between paper made from rags and that made from
ground wood. It called for the purification of the wood fibre, some-

thing that would act gently on wood cellulose in eliminating the lignin — the intercellular tissue of the wood — and the resinous matter that binds the wood fibres together in their natural state. The best method proved to be that brought about by chemical action.

The earliest work that proved capable of development was the process originated by Hugh Burgess and Charles Watt. White paper suitable for printing was made by them in a paper mill at Boxmoor, Hertfordshire, England, in 1851. Part of a weekly edition of the *London Journal* was printed on this paper and proved its practicability. But the interest in England was not sufficient to secure for it a healthy development, so the inventors left England for this country and secured their American patent in 1854. In brief, the patent consisted in producing pulp by boiling wood in caustic alkali at a high temperature, and became known as the soda process.

A plant was established at Gray's Ferry on the Schuylkill near Philadelphia. The process, according to patent specifications, called for boiling the wood, after it had been cut in small chips or shavings, in a solution of caustic alkali, in a closed boiler, under high pressure of steam at a high temperature. After having been boiled to a fibrous mass, the pulp was washed with water, and if the wood used was of a resinous character, the pulp after having been washed was subjected to the action of chlorine or its compounds, with oxygen. In the Manayunk works only non-resinous woods such as poplar, hemlock, and whitewood were used, these being plentiful and of comparatively little value for other purposes.

After experimenting with straw, cornstalks, bamboo, and cane, wood was found to be the most suitable. The first pulp made by the Watt and Burgess process was made into paper in the near-by Warren mill at Maylandsville, and also by the Megargee brothers in another mill in the same locality. Larger pulp mills were built, of which Burgess became the manager. As with ground-wood paper, this new wood-pulp paper did not meet with ready acceptance, and its general use was only brought about by a battle against a stubborn and undeserved prejudice. The American Wood Paper Company, formed in 1863 and incorporated with a capital of $2,000,000, erected works on a large scale at Manayunk with a daily productive capacity of twenty tons of wood pulp, considered a large volume at that time, in the infancy of the industry. In the face of much litigation the organization held its own as the leading manufacturer of soda pulp and paper. It gave the needed impetus to that branch of papermaking and achieved its successful establishment, regardless of the fact that the company eventually failed financially.

THE SULPHITE PROCESS

A pioneer in another chemical process for the preparation of wood fibre for papermaking was Benjamin C. Tilghman (in collaboration with his brother Richard), who also at Manayunk, near Philadelphia, made a suitable wood pulp for paper. Tilghman was the originator of the sulphite method, an acid process. He began his experiments somewhat accidentally in Paris in 1857. Tilghman's procedure embodied the application of sulphurous acid to wood to effect the dissolution of the intercellular matter, leaving a fibre sufficiently strong to felt properly in sheet form. Tilghman's own story of his discovery tells how in Paris in 1857 he was making some experiments with fats in sulphurous acid. The solution was kept in wooden barrels, and to indicate the depth of the liquid in these containers, small holes were bored a few inches apart. These holes were closed by removable conical pegs made of soft wood. After a period of immersion it was observed that the ends of these plugs, which were constantly wetted by the solution, became soft and fuzzy. At the time Tilghman paid little attention to this chemical action, but a few years later, on visiting the pulp works of W. W. Harding at Manayunk, he recalled the experience.

Tilghman then began experimenting and found that a solution of sulphurous acid, kept at a high temperature and pressure, dissolved the intercellular matter of wood, but the fibres left were red-coloured and had to be bleached. Analysis showed that the sulphurous acid had been partly converted into sulphuric acid, and it seemed probable that the red colour came from the secondary action of the latter. The constant pressure of an excess of sulphite of lime would prevent the existence of the sulphuric acid, as it would immediately combine with the lime and drive out the weaker sulphurous acid, precipitating neutral sulphite of lime.

Further research confirmed this idea, and pulp was obtained which was pronounced by experts to be suitable for papermaking.

Tilghman's chief obstacle in putting his process into practical operation lay more in the failure of his equipment. His own statement was to the effect that he and his brother battled for months against leaks in the digester caused by faulty lining. He finally became thoroughly discouraged in the face of dwindling financial resources and retired in disgust, having lost twenty thousand dollars and two years of hard work in the venture. Tilghman's efforts were recognized as a technical success, but the inventor failed to succeed with the commercial promotion of his discovery.

THE SULPHITE PROCESS DEVELOPED ABROAD

Carl Daniel Ekman and George Fry * took up the work where the Tilghmans left off. Ekman first carried on his experiments in

---

* Carl Daniel Ekman, one of the most important chemists in the development of the modern paper industry, was born in Sweden, but the date of his birth has not been recorded. In 1871 he was appointed manager of the Bergvik pulp mill, a Swedish plant that was controlled by a London firm. Ekman had previously experimented with the bleaching of mechanical pulp with a sulphite solution under pressure. In 1872 he was successful in producing a new product by cooking the disintegrated wood with a solution prepared from bisulphite and magnesia. Sulphite pulp was used in England on a fairly large scale by the year 1880. The first paper concern to manufacture superior paper from sulphite pulp was the Ilford, Essex, mills that belonged to the same English firm that owned the Bergvik mill in Sweden. Ekman settled in England in 1883, where he acquired a comprehensive practice as a consulting engineer in the erection of pulp mills. The first of these, at Northfleet, Kent, was controlled by the Ekman Pulp and Paper Company. The rights of the Ekman process in America were owned by W. F. and F. C. Sayles, Providence, Rhode Island, and under the sponsorship of this mill Dr. Ekman came to the United States during the early part of 1884 and supervised some of the operations of the Richmond Paper Company, located near Providence. It is stated that the first sulphite imported to this country was made at the Bergvik mill in Sweden. Dr. Ekman died in November 1904, and on November 19, 1934 the Swedish Cellulose Association unveiled in his memory a Swedish black granite monument in Northfleet cemetery. The Paper Museum possesses much of the material used by Dr. Ekman in his experiments, found in his Northfleet laboratory after his death. This collection consists of numerous samples of sulphite pulp and paper dated in his own hand from 1871 to 1886; also blocks of various kinds of wood, wood powder, family photographs, letters, pamphlets, clippings, etc.

George Fry (1843–1934) experimented independently at Arundel, Sussex, with the sulphite process, but later joined Carl Daniel Ekman at Northfleet and together they introduced the Ekman-Fry process of treating wood for papermaking on a commercial scale.

Sweden and later moved to England, where Fry joined him in perfecting the process. The first American papermaker to make use of the new process on a commercial scale was Charles S. Wheelwright, who had a mill at Providence, Rhode Island. About this time Professor Alexander Mitscherlich, a German, secured patents on his indirect cooking method. In 1883 these patents were contested by Behrend and found invalid by the German courts. But these findings were not upheld by United States courts, and later August Thilmany purchased the Mitscherlich patent. In 1887 Thilmany transferred the rights for the United States and Canada to the International Paper and Fibre Company. A mill was erected at Alpena, Michigan, by G. N. Fletcher and Albert Pack, a partnership of lumbermen, with the idea of making use of lumbermill waste. This was the first sulphite mill to institute operations in the United States, and it employed the Mitscherlich process. But this initial use of sulphite in this country was preceded by a successful attempt to make sulphite at Cornwall and Merriton, Ontario, by one Captain Ellis in 1885, and two years later production on a commercial basis was accomplished.

The increasing interest in promoting the use of the sulphite process was advanced by the work of such pioneers as Francke, Partington, Graham, Cross, Flodquist, and Ritter and Kellner, all successful in their field. The processes instituted by Partington in England and Ritter and Kellner in Austria have withstood the test of time, and with minor modifications are in use today.

THE EFFECT OF WOOD PULP ON THE INDUSTRY

Wood as a raw material made possible the phenomenal growth of the paper industry and furnished a material that conserved the supply of rags for use in making fine papers. Wood now serves not so much as a substitute for rags, as originally intended, but as a more important material for increasing the scope and variety of papers to meet an ever growing demand for new uses for paper.

In 1897 a writer on the subject of papers made from wood pulp made this observation on the papers of that day: "Endeavouring to make contrasts between the grades of papers of forty years ago and those of today is very difficult for the reason that the requirements of the publishers of today are so much greater than formerly, and it is very doubtful if the all-rag papers made long ago could now take the place acceptably filled by the all-wood papers of the present. The facilities and the art of making paper then were such that no attempt was made, or even required to produce the surface, and so well-made paper that the nice half-tone cuts of today require."

At present there are comparatively few plants and a limited number of trees that will yield cellulose economically for quantity production. The plants are those containing vegetable fibres in the form of cotton, flax, hemp, jute, sugar cane, straw, esparto, and cornstalks. Of the trees there are spruce, balsam, fir, jack pine, hemlock, southern pine, poplar, and cottonwood, with perhaps a few others. Spruce is rather generally given preference owing to its light colour and strength of fibre. Hemlock is by many considered next in importance. Poplar, used in making soda pulp, is short in fibre length and is lacking in strength. In the matter of durability paper made from cotton and linen fibres ranks first, and that from chemically processed wood pulp, straw, and mechanically prepared wood pulp in the order named. (This observation applies, of course, only to Occidental papers.)

Papermaking history is replete with failures by experimenters to heed what had happened to others and to review the innumerable patents for processes and the literature of attempts to make paper from all sorts of vegetable fibres. The fact that there are some two thousand plants that yield fibres which can be felted into a sheet of paper is responsible for the ever increasing "discovery" of new papermaking materials.

STRAW PRECEDED WOOD

Straw preceded wood in its commercialization as a papermaking fibre in this country. It was first converted into paper at Chambersburg, Pennsylvania, in 1829; its papermaking properties were discovered in this instance by Colonel William Magaw of Meadville, Pennsylvania. He conferred with G. A. Shryock of the Hollywell paper mill near Chambersburg, who was quick to see its possibilities, and abandoned the manufacture of paper from rags and devoted himself entirely to making paper of straw on a cylinder machine, producing 300 reams a day. The paper was sold for less than two dollars a ream, Imperial size. In 1871 the production of straw paper in America was estimated at 100 tons a day. At this time newsprint made of straw sold at twenty cents a pound.

The new straw paper was first used for printing. Some of it was employed for decorative purposes, such as wallpaper, and became extensively used as wrapping and binder's board. Straw when digested with caustic soda under pressure yields, if bleached, a white paper pulp, almost pure cellulose. The resultant fibres are fine and shorter than those obtained from wood, and somewhat brittle. The pulp requires an admixture of a stock with longer fibres for strengthening. This type of straw paper has a hardness and a "rattle" that is a property of fine writing papers. It is rather generally conceded that rye straw is preferred; wheat is next in choice, and oat straw is regarded as the least desirable.

The early history of straw paper in other lands begins with its ancient use in China, where the straw from various cereal plants was employed for papermaking. The stuff was soaked in lime water, then boiled and reduced to a fibrous mass by stamping. Dr. Jacob Christian Schäffer made paper of barley straw in an experimental way in 1765. He chopped the straw, scalded it in water for about fifteen minutes, beat it to a pulp, and exposed it to the extraction of a lime lye for two hours. It was then crushed into a flaky pulp and mixed with rag fibre to give cohesion to the finished sheet. This seems to have been the earliest European attempt to make paper from straw.

More practical results were achieved by Matthias Koops in England in 1800. In Koops's book printed on straw paper of his own making, he has this to say for the priority and practicality of his work: "Dr. Schäffer, it is true, worked with perseverance, industry, and ardour, to prove that numerous vegetables were qualified to make paper, and his fame will be immortalized; but notwithstanding that this author theorized upon the subject with great ability, he accomplished nothing satisfactory by his experiments, which only tended to prove that various vegetables could probably be so mollified as to make useful paper with the addition of a small quantity of rags: neither himself, nor any person who has followed him, has ever been able to make it all without rags, or fit for printing, writing, paper-hanging, and other purposes."

The production of straw paper of recent years has been somewhat eclipsed by wood-pulp papers for both wrapping and printing. About ninety per cent of the total quantity of fibrous raw material used in the manufacture of paper has been derived from wood. But there continues to be a comparatively large production of strawboard. Straw is likely to be more widely employed owing to the great draft upon wood by the growing demand for cellulose for the manufacture of rayon, cellophane, synthetic fibres, lacquers, plastics, and finishes. All these products are constantly increasing the demands for cellulose from the best softwoods. Manufacturers of these new products can outbid the paper industry, as their commodities command much higher prices than paper.

PAPER FROM PEAT TURF

About 1906 the American Peat Paper Company was incorporated in Maine with a capital stock, according to a contemporary prospectus, of $1,500,000. At its mill in Capac, Michigan, this company attempted to manufacture paper and board from peat, a carbonaceous substance formed by partial decomposition of various plants, more especially certain mosses. The mill was located near a peat bog of five hundred acres. This material had long been used for fuel. While Dr. Schäffer made paper of peat in the eighteenth century, this substance had not been used commercially for papermaking until Christian Esser, of Austria, conceived the idea of making use of the fibre for this purpose. The Esser process was brought to the United States in 1905. It was claimed that paper and board could be manufactured at the Capac, Michigan, mill for $12.50 a ton, the paper being composed of peat fibre mixed with waste paper.

CORNSTALK PAPER

The use of an annual crop in the nature of farm waste is exemplified by the once much-heralded cornstalk paper, which saw its greatest attempt at a boom in 1928–9. There appeared in 1928 a book with the title: *Farm Products in Industry*, by George M. Rommel, a technical chemist. The publication was announced as a book printed on cornstalk paper. An analysis of the paper proved that it was composed of twenty-five per cent cornstalk fibre, fifty-five per cent sulphite fibre, and twenty per cent flax fibre. The small percentage of cornstalk fibre might be considered as merely an admixture or a secondary stock. But where cornstalk paper was to afford the most relief was in the manufacture of newsprint. There were many press notices attesting the successful running of the new stock on newspaper presses, and a serviceable paper was made with sixty-five per cent cornstalk fibre and thirty-five per cent sulphite.

The advent of cornstalk paper was not so sudden as latter-day promoters might make it seem. Jacob Christian Schäffer had made paper in an experimental manner with cornhusks in 1766. As early as 1802 there was an American patent issued to Messrs. Allison and Hawkins for manufacturing paper from cornhusks, and in 1829 J. W. Cooper received a United States patent for making paper from rags, straw, and cornhusks. In 1828 William Cobbett had the title-page and contents leaf of his London-printed book *A Treatise on Corn* imprinted on paper made from the husks of corn that he had himself grown.* Cornhusks being of much less density than wood, the transportation costs to the mill are a factor; to offset this there is the advantage of a rapid-growing crop that can be harvested six months after the seed is planted. While the cellulose content of the cornstalk is only about three fifths that of wood, it is a by-product of a necessary and valuable annual crop. The enthusiasm with which cornstalk paper was hailed about two decades ago seems to have waned somewhat. Interest will probably be revived again with some improvement in the processing which seems to be needed to put it on a better basis to compete with wood-pulp papers.

---

* In the fourth volume of the *Illustrated Catalogue of the Industrial Department of the International Exposition* (London, 1862), the section describing the Austrian exhibits is printed on "Indian-corn paper." This section was printed by the Imperial Royal Court and State Printing-Office, Vienna, and consists of 130 pages, including four pages devoted to an article entitled: "Utility of the Maize-plant," in which is outlined the use of cornhusks and stalks as papermaking material. The article was compiled by Dr. Alois Ritter Auer von Welsbach, chief director of the Imperial State Printing Establishment in Vienna, and director of the Imperial paper mill, Schlögelmühle, near Gloggnitz. The paper is in an excellent state of preservation and appears to have at least a small amount of rag fibre in its formation.

THE SOUTH SUPPLIES A NEW RAW MATERIAL

A new and hitherto unused source of paper pulp which has but recently emerged from the experimental stage is southern pine. While for some years past kraft wrapping paper and fibreboards have been made from the pulp of southern pine, it is only within recent years that a suitable white paper has been produced on a commercial basis. Newsprint of a good clear white colour, light in weight, and with good tensile strength for running on fast newspaper presses is now an actuality. This accomplishment promises to bring to the Southern states a new industry and contribute much to the welfare and industrial progress of the South, all due to the indefatigable work of Dr. Charles Holmes Herty (1867–1938), industrial chemist, whose inventiveness and resourcefulness achieved for him not only a technical success but a commercial one as well.

Southern pine had long been considered as of too resinous a composition to permit its pulping without encountering difficulties from pitch. This notion resulted from a failure to observe that the older growth of trees contained a high resinous content while young trees were without it; that the heartwood, which is highly developed in the older trees, is the cause of the resin content, while sapwood, which is characteristic of the younger trees, is free from resin. In fact, from the sapwood of the yellow pine an almost pure white paper may be produced. Trees which have had as short a growth as six or seven years are usable, and at that age often reach a growth of six inches in diameter.

As long ago as 1931 Dr. Herty made a public statement that within five years from that time the making of newsprint from southern pine would be entirely feasible, and that a new industry of enormous proportions would arise in the South as the result. In 1933 nine Georgia newspapers printed their regular editions on newsprint made from southern pine. The wood from which the pulp was made was taken from trees fifteen years old. This pulp, consisting of seventy-five per cent ground wood and twenty-five per cent sulphite, was processed at a laboratory plant in Savannah. There being no mill in the South at the time equipped to run newsprint, the pulp was shipped to Thorold, Canada, and converted into newsprint there.*

On January 17, 1940 the newly completed Southland Paper Mills at Lufkin, Texas, with a potential output of 150 tons daily, produced the first newsprint made from southern pine for continuous commercial consumption. This paper met every test of the fast-running newspaper presses and received high praise from the pressmen for its excellent running and printing qualities. Thus began a new phase of industrial development in the South.

---

* The following editorial regarding paper made from east Texas pine appeared in the Dallas *Morning News*, February 17, 1939: "Texas newspaper history is made with this edition of *The News* printed in small part on paper from the first roll of newsprint made from East Texas wood pulp. The pulp was shipped to Savannah from the same East Texas pine acreage that will serve the newsprint plant in Lufkin. The entire carload shipment was used in varied experiments by the Herty Foundation Laboratory and only part of it manufactured into newsprint. Of this, however, this first 17½-inch roll rushed to Dallas from Savannah is a part. From a 17½-inch wide roll of newsprint weighing 73 pounds approximately 2,500 pages can be printed. *The News* utilized the available supply to print as many copies of the editorial page as possible in the first run of today's issue. So that for the first time in Texas newspaper publication, East Texas wood pulp has served the purpose for which in the course of the near future there is every reason to believe that it will be used daily. *The News* is proud of adding another historic 'first' to the many that have stressed this paper's pioneering since its birth under the Republic of Texas. It is glad to give this convincing demonstration of the utility of the late Dr. Charles H. Herty's experiments which with development will serve alike the pine wood producers of the state and the newspaper field." Along with the article in the *News* there is a cartoon of a cowboy, on his horse, with outstretched hand holding a copy of the newspaper, on which appears: "Part of this paper is printed on paper made from East Texas pine."

XIV

The Watermarking of Machine-Made
Papers and the Use of Watermarks
in Detecting Forgery

As stated in other parts of this book, the principle of the paper-machine was conceived in France in 1798, but it remained for English engineers to perfect the machine to a point where it was capable of producing usable paper on a commercial scale. The first commercially practical English-built machine was in use about the year 1812; the earliest paper-machine in America was put in operation in 1817.

The introduction of the continuous papermaking machine led to attempts to produce watermarks similar to the devices, symbols, and letters that had for more than five centuries been used in handmade papers. The problem of marking machine-made paper was finally solved by John Marshall with his invention of a wire-covered roll, with the designs upon it in wire, which rode over the tender sheet of paper just after it left the travelling wire-cloth of the machine. This invention took place in 1826 (Figure 275) or about fourteen years after the first commercially successful paper-machine was in operation in England. Therefore there was a short period when all paper produced by machine was totally unwatermarked, either with the "laid" pattern or with any emblems or lettering. The watermarking device became known almost immediately as the "dandy-roll." * Various types of these

---

* There has been considerable controversy relative to the origin of the so-called "dandy-roll" used in the watermarking of machine-made papers. The invention of this marking device is usually attributed to John Marshall, a member of the family firm of T. J. Marshall, London, paper mould-makers, established in 1792. When I was working in the Stoke Newington shop of this firm in 1912, Mr. Dudley Marshall, a direct descendant of the original inventor of the dandy-roll, was connected with the small office of the concern. Mr. Marshall told of the invention by his ancestor, but apparently the

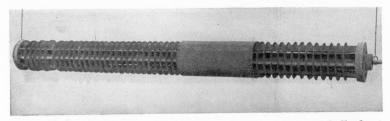

FIG. 275   *The original dandy-roll made by John Marshall about 1826. The construction consists of wooden ribs, like those of a hand mould, running lengthwise, with round metal disks to support the "wove" cover, part of which remains; a brass tube runs through the centre into which the axel is inserted. (Courtesy T. J. Marshall & Company)*

rolls are shown in Figures 276A, 276B, 277, 278, 279, 280. The construction of the dandy-rolls appears simple, but the manufacture of a workable roll involves considerable knowledge of metal and unlimited engineering skill.

The actual watermarking wires were originally bent by the use of pliers, as had long been the practice in forming the letters and

watermarking roll was not patented by Marshall as no specifications are recorded under his name in the Great Seal Patent Office. Mr. Dudley Marshall thought that the unusual name of the roll originated when one of the workmen upon first seeing the skeleton roll expressed his delight by exclaiming: "Isn't that a dandy!" and from this casual remark the name was derived. During my several months' work in the Marshall establishment it was not my privilege to see the first dandy-roll made by Mr. Dudley Marshall's ancestor, but a short account of this device was given at a later date in a communication from Stoke Newington: "We have what we believe to be the first 'dandy-roll' that was ever made. It is partly of wood and is really copied from the hand-mould in which the wooden bars, or ribs, of the mould are fixed horizontally across the 'dandy-roll' making it round instead of flat, as is the case with the hand-mould. We look upon this roll as showing the change-over from handmade to machine-made paper. This wooden 'dandy-roll' was probably constructed about 1826."

The earliest English patent relative to the dandy-roll for marking paper on the paper-machine was granted to John and Christopher Phipps on January 11, 1825. An abridgment of this patent reads: "An improvement in machinery for making paper by employing a roller the cylindrical part of which is formed of 'laid' wire. The effect produced by the said cylindrical roller is that of making an impression upon the sheet of paper, or pulp, upon which the said roller passes, & thus the paper so made has the appearance of 'laid' paper" (like that manufactured by hand). Therefore, the paper formed on the paper-machine before the year 1825 was of the "wove" type, so marked from the travelling wire of the machine.

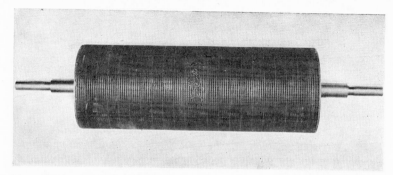

Fig. 276A   *A dandy-roll, used in watermarking machine-made paper. After formation, the paper stock passes under the watermarking roll; in handmade paper the paper stock lies over the watermarking wires during the entire moulding of the sheet. The "laid" design of this roll had its origin in China over seventeen hundred years ago. See Figure 51.* (Courtesy Joseph J. Plank)

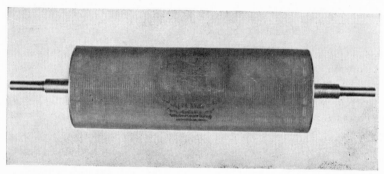

Fig. 276B   *A dandy-roll of the "wove" type used in watermarking machine-made paper. The "wove" style of mould was used in China during the first years of papermaking. See Figure 47. In Europe handmade paper of the "wove" design came into use about the year 1755 and was first conceived either by John Baskerville, the Birmingham printer, or by the James Whatman paper mill, Maidstone, Kent (Figure 101). The European invention was a rediscovery, as the Chinese originated the "wove" mould.*

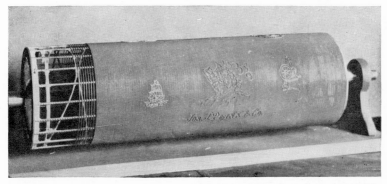

Fig. 277   *The construction of a dandy-roll used in the watermarking of machine-made papers. This picture gives a clear conception of the skeleton roll that supports the wire gauze upon which the watermarking devices are secured.*

Fig. 278   *A modern dandy-roll used in the manufacture of extremely light-weight papers, such as air-mail. A break in the "laid" wires causes a pattern to appear in the sheet of paper. The "chain" marks on this roll are made by disks, as seen by looking inside the dandy-roll. (Courtesy The Sinclair Company)*

FIG. 279　*A dandy-roll used in the manufacture of writing-paper. This is a journal-type roll, a model that is being replaced by the open-end roll as shown in Figures 278 and 280. (Courtesy The Sinclair Company)*

FIG. 280　*A dandy-roll used in the making of cigarette paper. The construction of this roll is similar to that shown in Figure 278. The "laid" lines in this particular roll are extremely fine, varying from 29 to 38 mesh, and the "chain" lines, as shown by the edges of the disks, are very shallow, protruding above the "laid" bars about .003". Such rolls as this must be built with great accuracy. (Courtesy The Sinclair Company)*

F<small>IG.</small> 281   *The watermarking wires being bent by hand to form letters, emblems, and devices. Although this photograph was made in a modern dandy-roll factory, the same process was used in forming the watermarking wires for hand moulds. (Courtesy Joseph J. Plank)*

designs that were sewed or laced with fine wire to the surface of hand-moulds (Figure 281). According to the Science Museum, South Kensington, London, the first use of solder in fastening the wire letters or designs to the rolls was the result of experiments made by Messrs. T. A. and C. D. Marshall, of the same firm responsible for the invention of the dandy-roll. The change from sewing to soldering took place in 1870 (Figure 282). In late years duplicate watermarking devices and designs have been made by the process of electrotyping. In applying the wire designs to modern hand-moulds the old sewing-on process is still used; with this method the watermarks may be changed from time to time and the same pair of moulds used for any number of different markings.

In dandy-roll watermarking, as with the hand-mould, it is possible to use the invention of William Henry Smith's light-and-shade marks (Figure 283); or simple wire marks and the light-and-shade type may be used in combination (Figure 284). Naturally, the finest results in watermarking are to be found in papers

FIG. 282   *Soldering wire trade-marks to the surface of a dandy-roll requires skill and patience as each emblem must be accurately placed and the solder joints executed with dexterity. Photograph made in the plant of Joseph J. Plank, Appleton, Wisconsin.*

made on the hand-mould, or upon the cylinder of the mould-machine as described in Part XII, an imitation of the hand process. In both of these methods of forming watermarks the paper stock, or macerated fibre or pulp, is held *upon*, or *over*, the face of the embossed wire design during the entire formation of the sheet of paper, while in watermarking with a dandy-roll on a paper-machine the roll as well as the design upon its face passes *above* the newly formed web of paper *after* the fibres have been inter-twined and felted. With the employment of the dandy-roll it is only natural that the finished paper will lack the clear-cut shad-ing found in marks produced on the hand-mould. To achieve a distinct, well-defined watermark the paper pulp, or stock, should lie *over* the embossed wire during the complete process of paper formation. Also, much of the sharpness of a watermark, by hand or machine, depends greatly upon the kind of stock and upon its beating. As has been previously stated, the strength and endur-ance of handmade papers are often sacrificed in acquiring a bril-liant and sharply modelled watermark; it is not to be expected

Fig. 283   A pressed "wove" wire watermark made in the manner invented about 1845 by William Henry Smith, England. This particular mark is for the paper used by Northwestern University. (Courtesy Joseph J. Plank)

Fig. 284   A light-and-shade watermark of a ship used in connection with wire lettering. The ship design is pressed into the woven wire, and the bent-wire lettering is soldered to the "wove" covering of the dandy-roll.

that long, drawn-out fibre will produce a clear watermark in the paper.

The forming of the watermarking wire emblems and letters for use on a hand-mould does not involve any calculation as to the shrinkage or stretch of the paper, as the sheet is formed flat upon the mould. There are, to be sure, slight variations both ways, but these do not in any perceptible manner distort the mark in the finished paper. The same cannot be said in regard to the watermarking wires applied to a dandy-roll. As an example, in making a watermark of a four-inch circle to be used on a hand-mould, the wire circle would be made perfectly round, and in the paper formed on the mould the watermark would also be perfectly round. On a dandy-roll, however, a wire circle of this size would have to be distorted about three eighths of an inch. There is no definite scale upon which the amount of allowance for shrinkage and stretch may be determined, as so much depends upon the weight and grade of paper being made. It is only through experience that the maker of dandy-rolls is able to arrive at the amount of distortion to place in the watermarking wires; no set formula for calculation is possible. To some extent the correctness of a circular watermark can be controlled by the operator of the paper-machine, by adjusting the "draws" on the machine, which may be set for normal stretch or to "pull" the sheet, which in turn causes excessive shrinkage.

PAPER AND WATERMARKING IN DETECTING FORGERY

In the seventeenth century within the old stone cloister of their Sicilian monastery the devout Camaldulians, a branch of the Benedictine monks, exhibited in a crystal case a much-worn letter bearing a printed label stating that the epistle had been written by the Virgin Mary, inscribed in her own hand. A most casual examination of the creased and folded letter, so carefully protected from the rays of the sun, would have revealed that it was written not upon parchment or papyrus, as it well could have been, but upon linen rag paper — a substance that did not come into existence until years after the death of the Virgin.

THE SHAKESPEARE FORGERIES

The eighteenth-century exploits of Thomas Chatterton (1752–70) and William Henry Ireland (1777–1835) will long remain the most interesting as well as the most incomprehensible of all literary forgeries. The work of Chatterton in producing spurious documents purporting to have been the writings of one Thomas Rowley, an imaginary fifteenth-century monk, were executed upon parchment and vellum, strips of which the young Bristol poet had rescued from the muniment room of the Church of St. Mary Redcliffe. Our primary interest in Chatterton, however, lies in the influence his forgeries may possibly have had upon Ireland rather than upon his actual counterfeits, inasmuch as Chatterton made use of the skins of animals for his forged calligraphic undertakings; he did not set down his fraudulent writing upon paper, and it is with paper that we are concerned.[1]

William Henry Ireland was born in London, the son of Samuel Ireland, engraver, author, and occasional trader in rare books, manuscripts, and curios. In 1794 Samuel Ireland, accompanied by his son, journeyed to Stratford-on-Avon, where young Ireland became acquainted with John Jordan, a local poet of sorts, who had forged the last will and testament of Shakespeare's father. This companionship and a knowledge of Chatterton's work put ideas in young Ireland's fertile mind. Knowing of his father's deep interest in anything pertaining to Shakespeare, William Henry Ireland, seventeen years of age, undertook to produce forged manuscripts in imitation of Shakespeare's unsteady hand, for no other purpose than to please and ingratiate his gullible father. Samuel Ireland incredulously accepted as authentic the forged leases, contracts with actors, letters, notes, and receipts, all supposedly in the calligraphy of William Shakespeare; the leading bibliophiles of London passed judgment upon the paper, ink, and writing of the documents and pronounced them genuine. Encouraged by the reception of his dexterity, young Ireland even forged a love letter of Anne Hathaway and enclosed a lock of hair with the note, all to the delight of his unsuspecting father and the deception of numerous experts of the day. Spurred by the success of his deceit, William Henry Ireland became so bold in his dubious undertaking that he compiled a complete new play which he attributed to Shakespeare's pen, and the counterfeit production, *Vortigern and Rowena*, was given to a crowded audience in Drury Lane Theatre, London, on the night of April 2, 1796. All of these false documents supposedly unearthed by young Ireland were said by him to have been discovered in an old chest that had belonged to an ancestor, "William Henrye Irelaunde," who existed only in the imagination of the adolescent forger. According to the story told by the young man, the papers had been bequeathed to his ancestor in gratitude for having rescued Shakespeare from drowning in the Avon. It is needless to state that the forgeries were eventually discovered and the disgrace was no doubt responsible in hastening the death of the father, Samuel Ireland, who passed away in July 1800. Five years after his father's death William Henry Ireland, filled with remorse, compiled his complete *Confessions*, which were published in London,[2] a book of 317 pages with a number of plates giving reproductions of the manuscripts he had so skilfully falsified. In reference to the paper and watermarks used by Ireland in his undertaking, the twenty-eight-year-old forger set down in his *Confessions* (pages 70–2) the following enlightening account:

> . . . Being thus urged forward to the production of more manuscripts, it became necessary that I should possess a sufficient quantity of old paper to enable me to proceed: in consequence of which I applied to a bookseller named Verey, in Great May's Buildings, St. Martin's Lane, who, for the sum of five shillings, suffered me to take from all the folio and quarto volumes in his shop the fly-leaves which they contained. By this means I was amply stored with that commodity: nor did I fear any mention of the circumstance by Mr. Verey, whose quiet unsuspecting disposition I was well convinced would never lead him to make the transaction public; in addition to which, he was not likely even to know anything concerning the supposed Shakesperian discovery by myself; and even if he had, I do not imagine that my purchase of the old paper in question would have excited in him the smallest degree of suspicion. As I was fully aware, from the variety of watermarks which are in existence at the present day, that they must have constantly been altered since the period of Elizabeth, and being for some time wholly unacquainted with the watermarks of that age, I very carefully produced my first specimens of the writing on such sheets of old paper as had no watermark whatever. Having heard it frequently stated that such marks on paper would have greatly tended to establish their validity, I listened attentively to every remark which was made upon the subject, and from thence I at length gleaned the intelligence that a *jug* was the prevalent watermark of the reign of Elizabeth: in consequence of which I inspected all the sheets of old paper then in my possession; and having selected such as had the jug upon them, I produced the succeeding manuscripts upon these; being careful, however, to mingle with them a certain number of blank leaves, that the production on a sudden of so many watermarks might excite suspicion in the breasts of those persons who were most conversant with the manuscripts.

Much of Samuel Ireland's correspondence in regard to his son's forgeries, as well as numerous specimens of the Shakespeare counterfeits, are preserved in the British Museum.

THE CASE OF THE REVERSED WATERMARK

In more recent times a watermark in the paper of a will proved the deciding factor in a Tennessee court of law, the famous Cloth-

Garrett case of 1913. The will, which was at first accepted by the court, disposed of the one-million-dollar estate of Mrs. Caroline Cloth, widow of Herman Cloth, of Shelby County, naming Bruce Garrett as a beneficiary for a quarter of the total sum. The will as offered was dated 1898, which was correct and proper, the paper upon which the will was written was watermarked "W S & B REGENT BOND," and from all outward appearances every detail seemed in perfect order; the witnesses of the will had long since passed on. The paper had been made by the Southworth Paper Company, Mittineague, Massachusetts, for a New York firm: Wycoff, Seamans and Benedict, succeeded by the Remington Typewriter Company, with offices at 327 Broadway. The attorneys for the contestants asserted that the watermark proved the will a forgery, as through an extended investigation they had ascertained that previous to the year 1900 this paper had always been watermarked "REGENT BOND W S & B," or the reverse of the manner in which the mark appeared in the paper of the forged will. Here was a case in which the forger, whoever he may have been, no doubt thought he had thoroughly protected himself, but he had not taken into account that paper mills have records of all the watermarks they use and can usually give the date of any changes made in the lettering or form of the marks.

THE KOESTER–JENNINGS CASE

Another interesting will dispute in which the watermark in the paper influenced the court's decision was the Koester-Jennings case, Chicago. The estate of Edwin B. Jennings, an aged recluse, involved the dispersement of five to six million dollars, and a last will and testament, dated October 9, 1918, was offered by Edward C. Koester, of Detroit, purporting to prove that he was the sole heir to the vast fortune. The will was written upon paper bearing the watermark "ARTESIAN BOND," made by the Whiting-Plover Paper Company, Stevens Point, Wisconsin. A discerning attorney became suspicious of the authenticity of the will, which led to an investigation of the paper on which it had been written. An official of the paper mill willingly agreed to testify and the court was soon shown that the particular watermark in the paper of the will, dated 1918, had not been used until 1920, two years after the will was supposed to have been written. When the five attorneys employed by Koester, the claimant, were confronted with such deciding evidence, they immediately withdrew from the case. Probate Judge Henry Horner of the Chicago court was not long in dismissing Koester and his false will. It behooves the forger to look well to his paper, as there are many concealed factors continually lurking in the background over which the unwary swindler may stumble to his downfall.

THE CASE OF THE MISSING "B"

The Sudland case involved another forged will, which was said to have been found in an old trunk in 1923, "about 21 years after the death of the testator." In so far as the testator was concerned, the will was properly dated, January 24, 1902, Shreveport, Louisiana, and to the casual untrained observer the paper, watermarked "ERKSHIRE BOND U S A," was apparently in order. The paper had been manufactured for Eaton, Crane and Pike, Pittsfield, Massachusetts, and, of course, the watermark should have been "BERKSHIRE BOND U S A," a watermark that was not originally drawn until December 19, 1905. The paper bearing this mark was first placed on sale early in 1906. According to the records of the mill, between December 12, 1907 and October 11, 1909, the letter "B" in the word "Berkshire" accidentally became unsoldered from one of the individual markings on the dandy-roll; five different lots of paper were made before the missing "B" was discovered. The omission of the letter "B" would appear only in one sheet in a certain number, depending upon how many individual watermarking designs were on the dandy-roll. Regardless of the missing letter in the watermark, the paper used in writing this will was not made or marketed until four or five years after the death of the alleged testator and therefore it was obvious that the will was spurious.

SLIGHT CHANGES IN WATERMARKS

In innumerable instances watermarks have played their part in the detection of forged wills, documents, bills of sale, patents, and so on. Recently a will case involving millions of dollars hinged upon the changes in a watermark over a period of years. First the mark was of fairly large size; later it was reduced, but retained all of its former design; next a monogram was added; the monogram was then slightly changed; and still later the wording "MADE IN U S A" was added to the mark. All of these apparently minor changes had been carefully set down, with dates, in the records of the paper mill. In checking the watermark in the paper of the questioned will it was proved beyond doubt that the paper the forger had used had not been made until several years after the date of the document, and the fraud was immediately traced.

In another instance of a forged document the same watermarked paper had been made by four or five different mills, in various states of the Union. This involved considerable accurate measuring of the lettering and spacing, and through the slight curl of a single wire letter on the dandy-roll and the position of the design on the sheet of paper the date of manufacture was definitely established, and again the document was found to have been dated prior to the time the paper was actually made and in use. It is not unusual for letters and devices to come loose from dandy-rolls, or for letters and designs to become twisted and distorted, but such accidents are repaired as soon as possible. The paper already made, however, is sold and may in a few instances eventually lead to the discovery of fraud.

Several wills have been declared false through the forger's premature use of paper bearing the well-known "Rag Content" watermark. In a disputed-will case in Texas a document dated in the twenties was written on paper bearing the legend "Rag Content." This will was obviously detected as a forgery, as this mark was not registered with the United States Patent Office until December 23, 1930, and did not appear as a watermark in paper until January 15, 1930. The mark is the property of the Rag Content Manufacturers Association, and any paper so marked must contain at least twenty-five per cent rag fibre. The earliest use of the "Rag Content" watermark by the American Writing Paper Company was during October 1933. The term is fast becoming obsolete owing to the present-day use of linen and cotton fibres derived directly from the plants. For this reason the word "rag" has been deleted from fibre requirements in Federal specifications, and "linen and cotton" substituted. The term "linen" applies both to the bast fibres from the flax plant from which linen cloth is made and to fibres derived from the cloth.

THE THOUSAND–DOLLAR–AN–HOUR CASE

Perhaps the greatest legal case of all time that hinged on paper and watermarking was that involving manufacturing rights on washing machines, and known in legal circles as " The thousand-dollar-an-hour case." This case centred on the Bendix Home Appliance Corporation, South Bend, Indiana, as plaintiffs, the Chamberlain-Bassett Corporation, Chicago, Illinois, as defendant, and the Boorg-Warner Corporation, Chicago, as intervening defendant. The case, tried in 1939, concerned a document that purported to have been drafted during December 1935, but through an examination of the paper used in writing the document the attorneys endeavoured to prove that this particular paper was not in existence at that date. The paper had been manufactured by the Southworth Paper Company, Mittineague, Massachusetts, and had been watermarked "GENUINE TRUSSELL." The case hung upon a broken letter "T" in the watermarking wires of the dandy-roll. In contemporary newspaper accounts of the lawsuit it was stated that the attorneys visited the paper mill and solicited the testimony of expert dandy-roll makers, papermakers, and chemists in an endeavour to prove through certain defects in the watermark and chemicals used in the paper that the document in question had not been written until 1939, or four years after the time it was dated. The master in this interesting case took testimony in the loft of the paper mill for several weeks, and an article in a local newspaper stated that $75,000 was expended on this case during the testimony carried on in the mill relative to the paper on which the allegedly forged document was written. Aside from the minute examination of the fifty-one slight variations of the watermarks, this case also involved the use of titanium dioxide, used by papermakers to give the paper more opacity. Apparently the earliest use of this chemical by the Southworth Paper Company was on November 26, 1935, but this particular paper was not shipped from the mill until February 21, 1936, or about two months after the date set down on the disputed document. In chemical tests the paper used in writing the document showed the presence of titanium, which again gave convincing evidence that was introduced in court.

Almost every piece of paper, no matter when or where made, has its own peculiarities, and under the microscope and through chemical tests it may reveal many things that the layman never suspects. Therefore, it behooves the falsifier of documents, wills, letters, and the like to choose his writing material well; even the plainest and most harmless-appearing sheet of paper may hold elusive evidence that could readily be turned to the undoing of the most careful and painstaking forger.

For the modern plagiarist even to hope to succeed in perpetrating a series of perfect forgeries he would need to be a diligent student of paper and watermarking history, vegetable fibres and fibre formation, paper-sizing materials in all countries and periods, as well as a competent papermaker. He would necessarily be an ink-maker versed in the long history of ink, brushes, quills, pens, blotting sand, blotting paper, sealing wax, wafers, adhesives, stamps, seals, metal clips and pins; he would need to be experienced in the various printing processes, in printing inks and their application, with an expert knowledge of the characteristics and imperfections of all typewriters, type, spacing, and ribbons, to say nothing of years of study in the eccentricities of handwriting from all times, countries, and civilizations. Sooner or later the work of the most skilled and adept forger is detected by some slight detail inadvertently overlooked.

THE LANCASTER CASE

For the most part, the falsification of documents involving watermarks have been cases in which the malefactor has been apprehended through his unwitting use of paper that bore a watermark not in existence until after the date placed upon the spurious will, letter, or document; several such cases have been outlined.

It is indeed seldom that the counterfeiter is sufficiently versed in his "art" actually to have watermarked paper manufactured for the express purpose of carrying on his criminal practices. Individually watermarked paper is not easily obtained, and can only be had at great expense. The making of a watermark is an undertaking of complicated nature, involving the manufacture of a special dandy-roll; also the paper mills must be guaranteed the purchase of a great quantity of paper to justify a special run. In the so-called "Lancaster case" of almost fifty years ago we have an example of expert counterfeiting in both paper and printing. In 1899, in an old weather-beaten tobacco barn near Lancaster, Pennsylvania, two skilled workers, Taylor and Bredell, engaged in one of the most amazing forgeries in the annals of American crime. Every detail of the execution of this forgery was brazen in the extreme, embracing as it did the making of United States revenue stamps, a type of counterfeiting that any cautious and prudent forger would avoid with all his iniquitous will-power. Messrs. Taylor and Bredell, criminals extraordinary, engaged in the printing of false tobacco stamps, and as they were dextrous workers, they were not content with the use of any good, workaday bond paper that would have been acceptable to less skilled men of their particular calling. These two counterfeiters actually had a dandy-roll made to their order for the watermarking of the letters "U S I R," the initials used in the paper of all genuine stamps – United States Internal Revenue. Paper of the proper tint and weight with the correct watermark was procured by the forgers; both the dandy-roll and the paper were innocently made for these two arch counterfeiters by reputable American firms. The unsuspecting maker of the dandy-roll and the manager of the paper mill, both honest and upright manufacturers, were blindly led into the web of these clever counterfeiters through their explanation that the tinted paper with the "U S I R" watermark was desired by Messrs. Taylor and Bredell for wrapping bottles containing a special patent medicine of their own invention and concoction, which they blandly explained was called "Uncle Sol's Indian Remedy," hence the letters "U S I R." The famous Lancaster case is probably the only counterfeiting on record in which false revenue stamps were printed on watermarked paper bearing the proper initials.

COUNTERFEITING DURING PROHIBITION

In 1920, under the eighteenth amendment to the Constitution, the United States applied prohibition on a national scale. The Prohibition Act applied to such a tremendous and complex population extending over such a large territory that this period is now known as the greatest social experiment of modern times.

During this national experiment the Federal Prohibition Director issued various types of engraved "Permits to Purchase," "Withdrawal Permits," "Physicians' Prescriptions," and so forth. These handsomely engraved papers were used in the legitimate procurement of spirits for medical and other necessary purposes if properly endorsed and signed by a registered physician. Every year a newly designed prescription blank was introduced, each more elaborately engraved than its predecessor. All of these blanks from year to year, however, were printed on the same type of paper, bearing the watermark "PROHIBITION" in outline letters, three eighths of an inch in height, distributed throughout the sheet in an all-over pattern. The complicated engraving and this watermark were intended to prevent counterfeiting of the blanks, which, it is needless to say, were in considerable demand, for only with one of these blanks, properly filled out and signed by a physician, could liquor be legally procured. The engraving could be duplicated by photographic methods and the endorsements and signatures would be only a routine matter for a forger, but to procure the "PROHIBITION"-watermarked paper presented a real problem. At least half a dozen large-scale cases of falsely duplicating this watermark are recorded by the Treasury Enforcement Agencies of the United States Treasury Department. This series of forgeries in the manufacture of counterfeit liquor-withdrawal certificates represented an "investment" of thousands of dollars. During prohibition days there was probably more money involved in making feigned watermarked prohibition paper than in all previous counterfeiting in the United States combined. In but one instance $12,000 cash was paid for watermarked paper, a tidy sum that gives a little conception the part "big business" played in the liquor-permit forgeries that were perpetrated from 1920 throughout the period of prohibition. In recording these cases of counterfeiting, all names of dandy-roll makers, paper-manufacturers, and paper dealers have been omitted, as our interest lies in the method of accomplishing the forgeries and not in the manufacturers of the paper or the makers of devices used in its watermarking.

FIG. 285   *A sheet of the counterfeit paper made in 1922 as a ruse for procuring "prohibition" watermarked paper for use in printing spurious physicians' prescription blanks, so much in demand during the era of prohibition in the United States.*

PHYSICIANS' PRESCRIPTIONS BY THE TON

The earliest case of attempting to counterfeit physicians' prescription certificates on a gigantic scale occurred in November 1921, when two men called at the office of a paper mill in Massachusetts and negotiated with the sales manager for one ton of sixteen-pound bond paper at thirty-six cents per pound. The paper was to be watermarked "VANCOUVER BRITISH COLUMBIA DOM. OF CANADA PROHIBITION INTERNAL REVENUE PROHIBITION" (Figure 285). The paper company, in all innocence, had a dandy-roll constructed with the watermarked letters as desired and the paper was manufactured. When completed, the cases of paper were shipped by express to the address given by the forgers: 150 Broadway, New York City. Later it was removed to a warehouse lo-

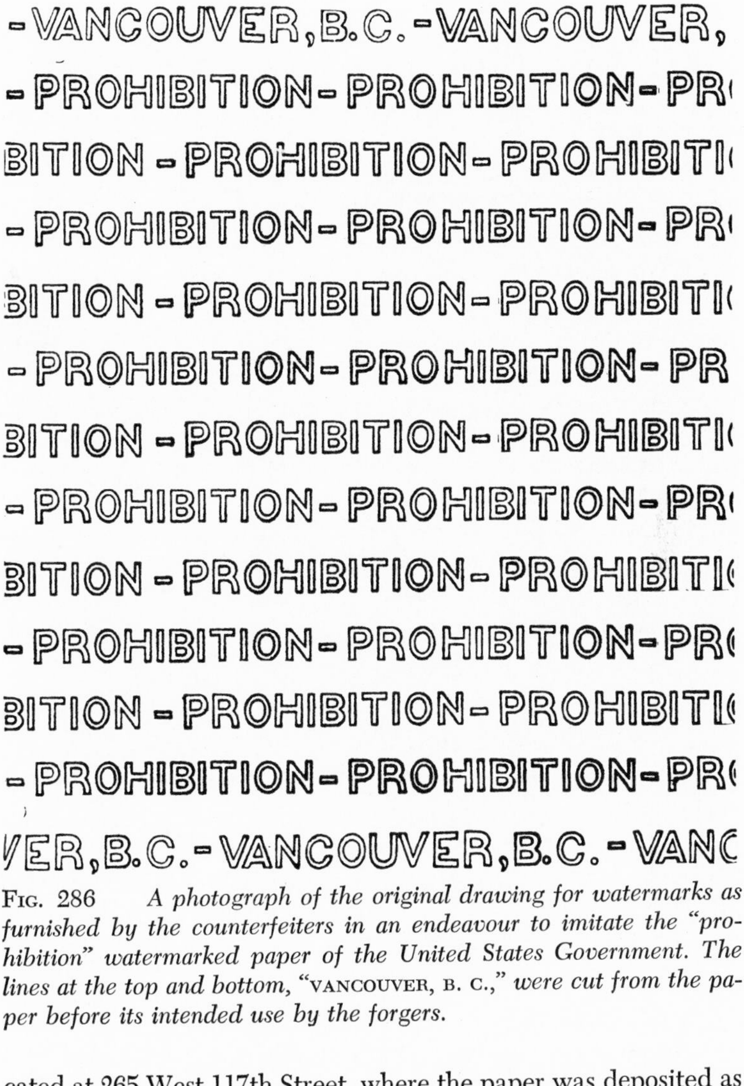

- VANCOUVER, B.C. - VANCOUVER,
- PROHIBITION - PROHIBITION - PR
BITION - PROHIBITION - PROHIBITI
- PROHIBITION - PROHIBITION - PR
BITION - PROHIBITION - PROHIBITI
- PROHIBITION - PROHIBITION - PR
BITION - PROHIBITION - PROHIBITI
- PROHIBITION - PROHIBITION - PR
BITION - PROHIBITION - PROHIBITI
- PROHIBITION - PROHIBITION - PR
BITION - PROHIBITION - PROHIBITI
- PROHIBITION - PROHIBITION - PR
VER, B.C. - VANCOUVER, B.C. - VANC

FIG. 286   *A photograph of the original drawing for watermarks as furnished by the counterfeiters in an endeavour to imitate the "prohibition" watermarked paper of the United States Government. The lines at the top and bottom, "*VANCOUVER, B. C.," *were cut from the paper before its intended use by the forgers.*

cated at 265 West 117th Street, where the paper was deposited as household goods. On April 5, 1922, the cases of paper were moved to 232 Dumont Avenue, Brooklyn, and placed in a cellar under the pretext that the six cases contained sewing-machines. It is assumed that this particular lot of paper had apparently been ordered by the professional counterfeiters as a subterfuge, or perhaps certain parts of the paper were to be cut and used in counterfeiting. In any event, the paper was seized by special agents of the Internal Revenue Bureau on May 9, 1922.

Not to be outdone, the counterfeiters, during July 1922, ordered another ton of sixteen-pound bond paper from the same Massachusetts paper mill that had furnished the previous two thousand pounds. With this second order, however, the watermark was to be changed on the dandy-roll to the regulation all-over pattern of the word "Prohibition" exactly as used on the legitimate withdrawal permits of the Prohibition Act. To this end the bold counterfeiters furnished an original drawing of the precise watermark they wished placed in the paper (Figure 286). Here again the wording "Vancouver B. C." was introduced in such a manner that these lines could be cut from the sheets, and the balance of the watermarked paper used for false certificates. This paper was also actually manufactured and on September 27, 1922 was shipped by rail to 113 Lincoln Street, Boston, Massachusetts, where the band of counterfeiters had borrowed a chair and a table, rented a room for a period of one month, and set up an "office." Just as the packing cases containing the paper were to be transferred to an address in Washington Street, Boston, the would-be forgers were arrested by internal revenue agents and the paper was returned to the Massachusetts paper mill where it had been made; here it was destroyed under the supervision of government agents. In the numerous cases of the counterfeiting of "prohibition" paper it is not difficult to perceive the gullibility of the papermakers; but in every instance mentioned the paper was actually manufactured by a reputable paper mill and apparently there was no suspicion of fraud. On the other hand, the apparent ease with which the internal revenue agents worked and in all cases caught the culprits deserves the greatest commendation.

THE CASE OF THE CHANGED WATERMARKS

In 1922 a paper-manufacturing company in Wisconsin received an order from a Chicago paper dealer, who in turn had received the order from a supposed printing firm, for 2,000 pounds of white bond paper to be watermarked with the lettering: "International News Internal Revenue Prohibition." The dandy-roll bearing

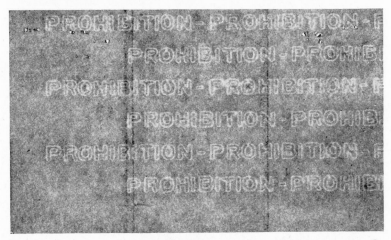

FIG. 287   *A watermarked counterfeit "prohibition" paper innocently manufactured by a Wisconsin mill in 1922. All but 125 pounds of the original ton of spurious paper was seized and destroyed by Internal Revenue agents.*

this lettering in wire was made by a watermarking firm in the same state and eventually delivered to the paper mill. A few weeks later the paper mill received a communication from the paper dealer with instructions to change the wording on the dandy-roll to an all-over pattern of the word "PROHIBITION." This was accomplished and the finished watermarked paper reached a Chicago storage company on June 28, 1922; two days later, on July 1, the cases containing the ton of paper were transferred to an address in Carpenter Street, Chicago. It was established by the United States Secret Service that two rum-runners and forgers were responsible for the attempt to defraud the United States by purchasing the dandy-roll and the "Prohibition"-watermarked paper. On December 13, 1922, when these men were arrested by Secret Service officials, one of them had in his possession a single sheet of the counterfeit watermarked paper, a complete book of false Physicians' Prescriptions No. A–42944, and a check from a dentist for $225. At the Carpenter Street address the internal revenue agents seized fifteen cases containing 1,875 pounds of the original 2,000 pounds of counterfeit paper. One of the cases had been previously removed, so it is assumed that 125 pounds of this Wisconsin-made paper found its way into false certificates. A photograph of the paper made for these two forgers is shown in Figure 287. The International News Company, of course, had nothing to do with this case.

THE LEAGUE FOR THE ENFORCEMENT OF PROHIBITION

One of the few instances of counterfeiting the withdrawal certificates during prohibition days that were at least partially successful in so far as the counterfeiters themselves were concerned occurred during the autumn of 1922. Two men, representing themselves as officials of an Illinois organization known as the "League for the Enforcement of National Prohibition," called at the office of one of the leading Chicago paper dealers and submitted an order calling for 11,000 pounds of watermarked paper. The sheets were to be 17 by 22 inches and were to be used, according to the self-styled representatives of the "League," for diplomas for the members and also for a frenchfold circular advancing the strict prohibition tendencies of the "organization." Naïvely enough, the paper was to be watermarked with the heading "LEAGUE FOR THE ENFORCEMENT OF NATIONAL PROHIBITION," followed underneath by an all-over pattern of the word "PROHIBITION" (Figure 288). The dandy-roll was constructed according to the instructions furnished, and the paper was manufactured by a well-known and highly regarded Wisconsin paper mill. The paper dealer, the dandy-roll maker, and the paper mill, all firms of integrity, did not question the authenticity of the order, and the work progressed without suspicion. Of course, the top line of the watermark, "LEAGUE FOR THE ENFORCEMENT OF NATIONAL PROHIBITION," was trimmed off, and then the balance of each sheet was practically a counterpart of the genuine government prohibition paper such as was used for printing physicians' prescription blanks. At least a portion of the paper was used by the counterfeiters in printing spurious withdrawal certificates, but it was not long before the Federal agents had uncovered this gigantic project of forgery, and the balance of the watermarked paper was immediately destroyed. Also the dandy-roll was totally demolished, although the paper dealer pleaded that at least the brass skeleton

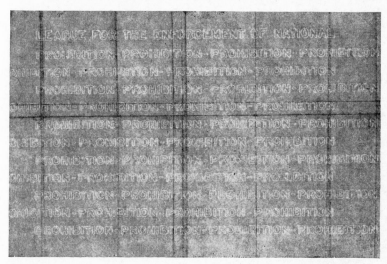

Fig. 288   *A sheet of the League for the Enforcement of National Prohibition watermarked paper. In this paper the top line was cut off and the balance of the sheet intended for the printing of false physicians' prescriptions.*

of the roll be preserved so it could again be used for more legitimate watermarking; but the Federal representatives were unmoved and insisted that the entire dandy-roll be completely and thoroughly destroyed.

THE MONTREAL CONSPIRACY

The most prodigious of all attempts to obtain watermarked paper for the printing of false physicians' prescriptions occurred in Canada in 1926. As previously outlined, these certificates were used during the days of prohibition for the withdrawal of intoxicating liquor. The legally issued withdrawal blanks were in quintuplet, there being a copy for the distillery or bonded warehouse, a copy for the permittee, a copy for the director's office, and two carriers' copies. The so-called "Montreal conspiracy" constituted a greater attempt at fraud than any like counterfeiting committed in the United States. In this particular case, however, the forgers were not so clever as they thought and their plot was actually discovered almost before it began.

In the autumn of 1925 an executive of a Beauharnois paper mill was confidentially approached by the Royal Canadian Mounted Police, who told him that they had reason to believe the paper mill would shortly be tendered an order for watermarked paper that was intended for use in counterfeiting United States physicians' prescriptions. The police impressed upon the mill executive that if such an order was offered, it was their desire that it be accepted and filled. The United States Treasury Department also communicated with the mill executive expressing the same request, at the same time keeping the Royal Police advised as to the progress of the work. The plan was that the paper be manufactured and shipped, and when it eventually reached the United States, the cases of paper would be seized and the conspirators arrested.

In due course the Canadian paper mill was approached by a representative of the counterfeiters, and an order for more than seven tons of high-grade paper was accepted and $12,000 in cash paid. As requested by the unwary forgers, the paper was to be watermarked "PROHIBITION," but in a somewhat awkward effort to avoid any suspicion in the minds of the manufacturers of the dandy-roll, it was arranged that the roll should contain the words "SUFFOCATION," "PROHIBITION," and "APPLICATION," each word occupying one third of the watermarked face of the roll. The counterfeiters were willing to discard two thirds of the paper in their effort to procure the "Prohibition" watermark on the remaining third. This subterfuge in itself was a clumsy attempt at deception.

From the time the completed dandy-roll reached the Beauharnois mill until the paper was manufactured and shipped, one or more United States prohibition-enforcement agents was always in the paper mill so that the watermarking roll and the paper would be under their constant observation and no paper could be removed from the mill without their knowledge. The executive with whom the Mounted Police and the United States Treasury Department had communicated was the only person connected with the mill who was aware of what was taking place. The paper was completed March 5, 1926, some of the watermarked sheets were shipped April 7, 1926, and a subsequent shipment was made April 26, 1926. Both shipments were eventually consigned to the Place Viger Station, Montreal, billed as cement to be forwarded to St. Johns, where the cases were to be placed aboard a rumrunner destined for the United States. The amount of paper would have been sufficient to allow the withdrawal of liquor to the value of from six to nine million dollars. The Royal Mounted Police seized the paper before it left Canada and arrested three men who were charged by the crown prosecutor at Montreal with conspiring with others in New York and New Jersey for the purpose of securing watermarked prohibition paper to print forged liquor permits. Bail was set at $3,000 each.

The case came to trial in Montreal on July 8, 1926, on a charge of conspiracy to defraud and to forge, and of forgery. The attorney for the defendants argued that the possession of such paper in Canada was no crime. He stated that the Quebec Liquor Commission had liquor valued at millions of dollars, which if shipped to the United States would be illegal, but it was not so in Canada. The same applied to the watermarked "Prohibition" paper, he maintained. The court took the matter under advisement and on November 16, 1926 handed down a decision in French that the defendants had violated no Canadian law, and they were immediately dismissed. It is assumed that the counterfeit paper was ultimately destroyed. Thus ended an attempted forgery of such proportions that it no doubt exceeded in the amount of paper and money involved any other case in the entire history of counterfeiting.

WATERMARKING AS A SAFEGUARD AGAINST ESPIONAGE

In the many great American plants manufacturing vital war equipment and materials it is absolutely essential to restrict entrance to authorized employees only, numbering hundreds of thousands of workers. Such caution calls for an identification card for each employee. These cards have to be so complicated in their entire formation that they are beyond the possibility of forgery — merely the photograph, fingerprint, and signature of the worker are not sufficient. It remained for Ned Whitehead, of Los Angeles, California, to originate a method of making identification cards that consist of watermarked paper enclosed between two sections of transparent seamless plastic. The individual cards measure 3 ⅝ by 2⅜ inches, each sheet of paper making thirty-two cards. The

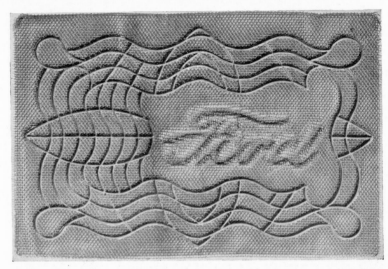

Fig. 289   *A single section of the wire form such as used on the dandy-roll for watermarking paper to be used for identification cards. Both the light-and-shade and single-wire techniques are employed. (Courtesy Harry Bennett, Ford Motor Company)*

watermarking wires on the dandy-roll embrace both the light-and-shade and the single-wire techniques (Figure 289). A full sheet of the paper, before cutting into individual cards, is shown in Figure 290. The firm of Whitehead and Company have made and supplied almost eight million of the watermarked cards to the Army, the Navy, Ford, Standard Oil, Bell Telephone, Timken, Anaconda, Kaiser Industries, California Shipbuilding, Consolidated, Martin, Lockheed, Pratt and Whitney, Douglas, and other manufacturing plants. Millions of the Whitehead watermarked cards have been issued, but there has not been a single instance of successful counterfeiting, although numerous attempts have been made. This good fortune is due largely to the watermarked paper, a method of preventing forgery that is almost impossible to duplicate, as the equipment for such work is well beyond the reach of the average counterfeiter.

F<small>IG</small>. 290   *A complete sheet of the watermarked identification cards, each sheet making 32 individual cards. The round, dark spots in the paper are different-coloured pieces of confetti, an extra precaution against counterfeiting. (Courtesy Harry Bennett, Ford Motor Company)*

XV

Present-day Papermaking by Hand
in Europe

THE MAKING of paper by hand is still practised in many mills in England and on the Continent. These mills do not all necessarily date from the pre-machine age, but in numerous instances they were established previous to the invention of Nicholas-Louis Robert. The hand mills of Europe have been equipped with modern and efficient appliances and are up to date in every way possible consistent with hand work. In making paper by machine it would not be profitable to operate carelessly and inefficiently, and the same would apply to the present-day handmade-paper industry.

THE MATERIALS

In most European countries only pure rag pulp is used in making handmade papers, and for the very finest sorts of paper only white rags are employed (Figure 291). Inasmuch as hand work is expensive, it would be most shortsighted to make use of any but the best materials throughout the entire process. Therefore in many of the European countries the handmade papers are made from the most superior linen and cotton rags; inferior material is discarded. The rags to be used in the making of paper by hand are subjected to practically the same treatment as like material would undergo for making all-rag machine-made paper. But in the handmade-paper mills the quantity of rags is much smaller and the material can therefore be more carefully sorted, boiled, and beaten. The cleaner and whiter the rags, the less severe the boiling and bleaching, the better will be the finished paper. The boiling of rags for fine paper is usually carried on without pressure, and only limited amounts of caustic soda and lime are used. This permits the strength of the linen and cotton fibres to remain unimpaired.

FIG. 291   *The rag storing- and cutting-room of a modern handmade paper mill; only the finest linen and cotton rags are used in making high-grade handmade papers. Photograph made in the mill of W. S. Hodgkinson & Company, Wookey Hole, near Wells, Somerset, England, where paper has been made since 1610.*

After boiling, the material is again inspected by experienced sorters to be certain that no foreign substances are present.

WASHING AND BEATING

After the rags are boiled, they are placed in "engines" equipped with cylinder washers (Figure 292), and in these low, oblong tubs the loosened dirt is washed from the material, the dirty water leaving the beaters through the screens of the cylinder washers, which do not permit the macerated fibres to escape. Clear water flows into the beaters during the entire process of washing, and when the water leaving the screen cylinders is as clear and fresh as that which enters the beater, it may be assumed that the rags have been cleansed. If bleach is to be added, it is put into the beater at this stage, but the stock must be further washed until tests show that no trace whatever remains of the chlorine. The washing completed, the cylinder is raised and the same beater may be used for

Fig. 292   *After boiling, the rags are placed in "engines" equipped with cylinder washers, and the loosened dirt is washed from the material. (Courtesy W. S. Hodgkinson & Company)*

Fig. 293   *The Hollanders, or beaters, of handmade paper mills are small, holding from two to three hundred pounds of dry stock. They are fitted with light-weight rolls so that freer and longer stock is the result. (Courtesy W. S. Hodgkinson & Company)*

macerating the material, although in some mills a breaker is used for the washing process, from which the material is run into special beaters, or Hollanders. These beaters (Figure 293) are small, holding about two hundred pounds of dry stock, and are fitted with light rolls so that freer and longer stock is the result. The beaters in a handmade-paper mill are usually lined with sheet lead or copper and equipped with beater-knives and bed-plates of bronze. It is possible to draw out the fibres to such length that the stock could not be run successfully on a paper-machine, but fibre of this kind makes the strongest handmade paper. It is in the beating process that the strength and enduring qualities of the finished paper are determined.

THE STUFF–CHEST AND VAT

The beating completed, the stock, or stuff, flows by gravity, or is pumped, into the stuff-chest, where the fibrous material is kept from settling by the action of a slow-moving, upright agitator. From the stuff-chest the stock runs through a pipe into the lifting-box, or bucket-pump, by the vat, which in turn lifts it and throws it into the knotter. This appliance is a boxlike apparatus with a

F𝐈𝐆. 294   *Looking into an empty lead-lined vat from above.*
This photograph shows the knotter in the foreground. The knot-
ter, agitated by two tappets, separates the knots, specks, and
foreign matter from the stock before it enters the vat. The agi-
tator, or "hog," used in preventing the stock, or pulp, from
settling, may be seen across the bottom of the vat; the drain-off
pipe, at the far end of the vat, may be raised or lowered. A
mould, with deckle, rests upon the stay, while another mould,
without deckle, leans against the asp. The bridge along which
the moulds slide is plainly visible.

FIG. 295   A scale model of a present-day handmade paper mill in the Science Museum, South Kensington, London. This model shows the stuff-chest, lifter-box, knotter, vat equipment, and hydraulic press. The model was built in 1910 by T. J. Marshall & Company, London.

floor made up of a series of slitted brass plates through which the stock passes, removing the knots, flecks, and foreign matter from the flowing pulp. From the knotter the stock flows into the vat through a regulating cock which to some degree determines the consistency of the stock in the vat. A lead pipe at the back of the vat carries the pulp back to the lifting-box so the stock in the vat is in constant movement and is continually being strained through the knotter. When the stock leaves the beater, it is warm through circulation and agitation, and this heat is retained in the vat through the action of a steam pipe; warm stock facilitates the vat-man's work. The stock is kept stirred while in the vat by means of a horizontal agitator, termed a "hog."

During the making of paper, the temperature of the pulp in the vat should be from 80° to 95°F.; never should the temperature be allowed to go above about 112°F. The vat (Figure 294, Diagrams

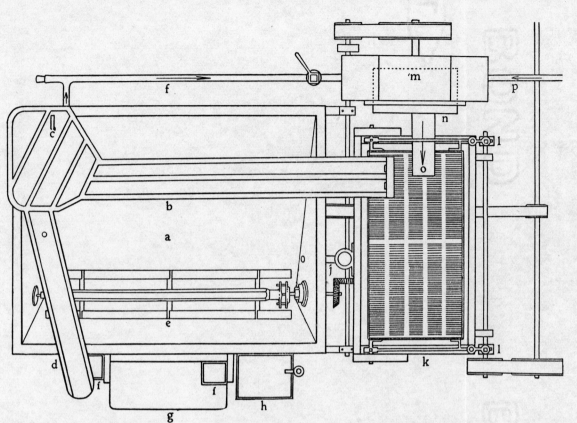

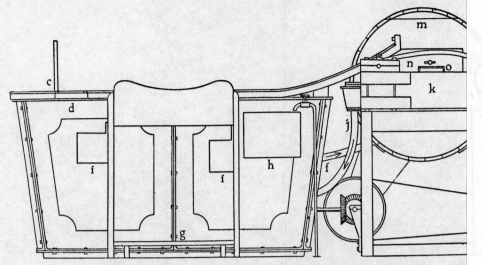

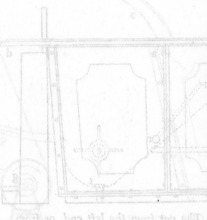

FIG. 294 (II)   The vat equipment from the front, or from the positi[on of]
the vatman. The same letters apply that are shown in Figure 294 (I). [A view]
of the cam and tappet devices that agitate the knotter is shown at (1). S[cale:]
½ inch to 1 foot.

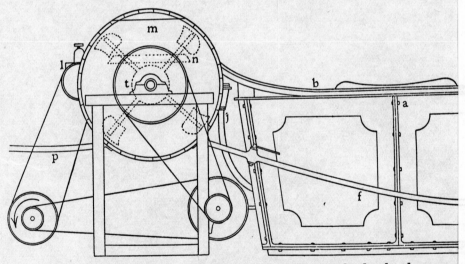

FIG. 294 (I)   The vat, lifter-box, and knotter equipment of a modern
English handmade paper mill. The various parts are designated by letters:
(a) the vat made of iron, lined with lead; (b) the bridge upon which the
coucher slides the moulds; (c) the asp, or horn, against which the coucher
leans the moulds for draining; (d) the stay, upon which the vatman places
the moulds before they are leaned against the asp; (e) the agitator, or "hog,"
revolving paddles that keep the stock in suspension in the vat; (f) back
water pipe; (g) stool where the vatman stands at his work; (h) fresh water
cistern for supplying hand boxes and washing-moulds; (i) vatman's hand
rinsing-boxes; (j) pipe to vat from knotter-box, and cock for regulating flow
of stock; (k) the knotter used for separating the knots, specks, and foreign
matter from the stock; (l) the two tappets that agitate the knotter; (m) lifter-
box containing the four bucket pumps; (n) drawer that catches stock delivered
by bucket pumps; (o) chute for delivering stock from drawer to knotter;
(p) pipe that conveys the stock from the stuff-chest to the lifter-box. Scale:
½ inch to 1 foot.

FIG. 294 (III)   The apparatus of a present-day handmade paper m[ill]
viewed from the rear. The four bucket pumps (t) lift the diluted sto[ck, or]
pulp, from the bottom of the lifter-box (m) after it enters from the [stuff-]
chest through the pipe (p). The bucket pumps throw the stock into the d[rawer]
(n) from where it travels to the knotter. Scale: ½ inch to 1 foot.

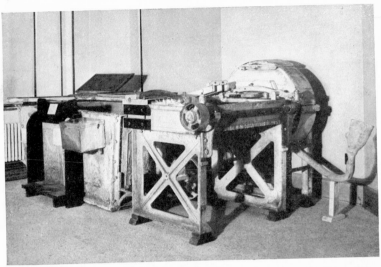

FIG. 296   A full-size handmade paper equipment in the Paper Museum of the Massachusetts Institute of Technology, Cambridge. The finest book, writing, drawing, water-colour, etching, architectural, and engineering papers are still made by hand by using appliances of this design. This equipment was originally in the mill at Wookey Hole, Somerset, England.

I, II, III, IV, and Figures 295 and 296) may be made of stone, copper, or iron; in the latter case it is lined with lead to prevent rust. The vat is about 5 by 6½ feet with a depth of 38 inches, the front and back walls slanting toward the bottom, as shown. When made of stone, the walls are about three inches thick, with the joints mortised and leaded; if made of metal, the corners are bolted; the lead lining, about one-eighth inch in thickness, is soldered at the joints. The "hog," before mentioned, extends the full length of the vat and is used to prevent the fibres from falling to the bottom; the "hog," or agitator, is operated at slow speed. Each vat in a mill is supplied with its own stuff-chest. Across the top of the vat, toward the back, is a wooden platform fitted with rounded brass rails; this is termed the "bridge." At the left end of the bridge there is a wider portion which supports the "asp" or "horn" and the "stay." The other essential appliances directly connected with the vat are the "couching tray," the press, and the

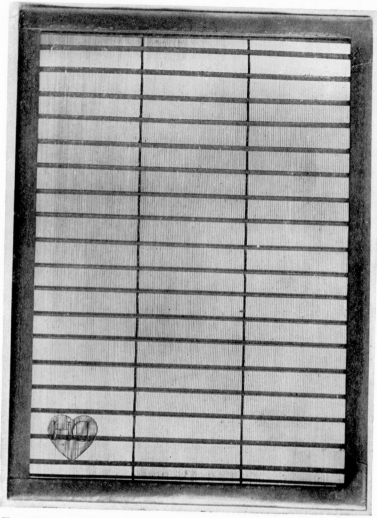

FIG. 297   *A hand mould with deckle. This mould is of the "antique" pattern, without underlying wires between the ribs and the face. Moulds of this type are used at the present time to emulate old paper. This mould is capable of forming a sheet 23 by 16 inches, an ideal size for either a folio or a quarto book.*

"lay stool." The last is used to support the moist sheets of paper after they are taken from the felts immediately after pressing.

FORMING AND COUCHING THE SHEETS

In making paper at the vat three workers are required. The most skilled of these is the vatman, who forms the sheets upon the moulds. Next in importance is the coucher, who removes the sheets from the moulds by "couching" them upon the felts. The third workman is the layman, whose duty it is to separate the sheets of paper from the felts, after pressing, lay the paper in a neat pile, and return the felts to the coucher for further work. Each step in the process will be described in the order in which it is performed:

The vatman stands on a platform in front of the vat and grasps the mould (Figure 297), with one hand on either side at a convenient point of balance. With the deckle in position, his thumbs extend along the top of the deckle, and his fingers are under the mould. He should hold the mould firmly, but not in a tense manner, since a great deal depends upon the freedom of the muscles under his control. The vatman now holds the mould nearly at arm's length over the vat in an almost vertical position, and with a quick, but steady, scooping movement, he plunges it into the vat, bringing it out again covered with pulp into a horizontal position close to his body, a few inches above the surface of the vat. By an almost imperceptible tilt forward, he causes a wave of pulp to flow across the surface of the mould from back to front, and this has the effect of levelling the pulp. As this wave flows across the mould, a few rapid side shakes are imparted to it, which causes some of the fibres to set in a cross direction, and as the wave reaches the far side, the mould is shaken several times somewhat vigorously, first toward the vatman and then away from him, until the bulk of water in the pulp has passed through the wires of the mould and the fibres appear set in the form of an even sheet on top of it. This manipulation of the mould is called the "vatman's stroke" (Figures 298, 299, 300). In the course of practice the vatmen become so dextrous that the formation of a sheet from the time the mould is dipped to the time the final shake is given occupies only a few seconds. Some vatmen pick up on the mould

Fig. 298   *The vatman has just formed a sheet of paper upon the mould; the next step is to place the mould, with its newly formed sheet, upon the stay and remove the deckle. The coucher next places the mould against the drainage asp. Photograph made in the mill of J. Barcham Green and Son, Maidstone, England.*

only sufficient pulp to make a sheet of the required weight, while others pick up more than is sufficient and throw off the excess at the end of the stroke, just before the fibres become "set." The thickness of the sheet of paper being made depends upon the consistency of the pulp in the vat and also upon the vatman's knowing just how much stock to pick up upon his mould. Except in the case of small moulds, great care must be taken not to submerge the mould completely when making a sheet of paper; if the mould is entirely submerged, a little difficulty would be experienced in bringing it out, owing to the suction. This not only would make the work extremely laborious, but would also interfere with the vatman's stroke and prevent a well-formed sheet being made. To avoid the suction, only about three fourths of the mould should be actually submerged.

After the sheet of paper has been formed upon the mould, the

FIG. 299   *The mould has just been shaken from side to side, and in this revealing photograph the camera has caught the elusive ripple in the moist pulp as the sheet is being formed. This picture was made in 1945 by Springer Pictures, Inc., as part of a coloured motion picture depicting the history of papermaking. The vatman is Robert Robertson, the last remaining handmade papermaker of a family that carried on the craft for many generations. Mr. Robertson came to America from Maidstone, Kent, England, to work in the Dard Hunter mill, Lime Rock, Connecticut, where this photograph was made.*

mould, with its thin deposit of pulp, is laid in a level position on the stay at the vatman's left. Here it remains until the stock is sufficiently hard to permit removing the deckle. The degree of solidity is determined by the peculiar appearance that gradually comes over the sheet, which dries from the edges to the centre of the surface, as the water drains from underneath and evaporates from the top. The vatman then removes the deckle and passes the mould holding the semi-wet sheet to the coucher, who leans the mould against the asp or horn at the proper angle and leaves it there until it has drained sufficiently to couch, or lay, on the felt.

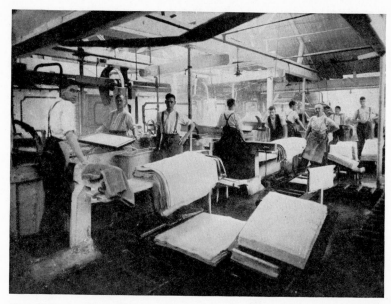

FIG. 300   *The vatman, at the left of the photograph, is placing the mould upon the stay. The next operation is to remove the deckle and pass the mould to the coucher, who will lean it against the asp previous to couching upon the felt. (Courtesy J. Barcham Green and Son, Maidstone, Kent, England)*

In the meantime another mould has been pushed along the bridge by the coucher to the vatman, who now places the deckle on the second mould and proceeds as before to make another sheet (Figure 301). When the mould just used, which leans against the horn with the semi-wet sheet on it (Figure 302), has had a few moments for draining, the coucher grasps the upper edge of it with his left hand and swings it across in front of him, seizing the other side with his right hand, at the same time releasing it with his left. The mould is now held in a vertical position, with the lower edge on the right edge of the post of felts; it is then turned over so that the semi-moist sheet comes in contact with the uppermost felt (Figure 303). By giving the requisite amount of pressure on the mould during the turning-over movement, the sheet of paper adheres to the felt and detaches itself completely from the face of the mould. The mould is now turned up again into a ver-

FIG. 301   *The vatman is in the act of placing the deckle upon the mould in preparation for forming another sheet. The left hand fits over the lower left corners of both deckle and mould, eliminating lost motion. (Courtesy J. Barcham Green and Son, Maidstone, Kent, England)*

tical position on the left side of the post, and from this position it is raised and pushed along the bridge until it comes to rest in front of the vatman. The coucher usually shoves the empty mould along the bridge with considerable energy, and to enable the mould to find its proper position directly in front of the vatman, the far end of the bridge has a slight incline, which causes the mould to slide back into its right place. The coucher's next duty is to "pitch" a felt on top of the sheet he has just couched. This motion requires a great deal of skill and accuracy. Catching up a felt from the felt board on his right side, he grasps one of the short ends with both hands; holding it up in front of him well clear of the post, and with an outward swinging movement, he drops the felt squarely upon the wet sheet, without dragging or wrinkling; otherwise the newly couched sheet would be ruined. He then proceeds to couch another sheet on top of the preceding one, and in this manner the post is built up to a height of about eighteen inches, every sheet

FIG. 302   *In this photograph, made in the Hodgkinson Wookey Hole mill, the three couchers are about to lift the pulp-covered moulds from the asps before couching. The moulds, with their deposits of pulp, will be turned over on the felts, leaving the moist sheets smooth and unwrinkled.*

of moist paper interleaved by a felt. When extra-large sheets of paper are being made, a boy is required to help the coucher in handling the mould and in pitching the felts. It is advisable to place three or four felts on the couching tray to receive the first sheet of paper inasmuch as it would be difficult to couch a sheet of paper on a single felt laid directly upon a hard surface.

The vatman and the coucher must regulate their movements so that they work in perfect unison, which involves much more hardship than might be imagined (Figures 304, 305). The number of sheets that can be made each hour depends upon the size of the moulds, the thickness of the sheet, and the grade of pulp. The two workers should shake their hands at their sides after each sheet has been formed, as even a small drop of water on the surface of a newly formed sheet will cause a transparent spot in the finished sheet of paper. With all the precautions exercised by careful workmen these spots are common in both old and modern handmade papers.

FIG. 303   *The mould, with the thin layer of moist fibre upon it, is turned over on a felt, leaving the newly formed sheet upon the felt's surface. Photograph made in the Hayle mill, operated since 1811 by the Green family, Maidstone, Kent, England.*

Fig. 304   *The vatman and coucher must regulate their movements so they work in perfect unison. This photograph was made about 1900 by Edwin Hale Lincoln in the L. L. Brown paper mill, North Adams, Massachusetts. The four workers are members of the William Norman family, English papermakers, who came to America in 1880. The Brown Company made paper by hand from 1881 to 1907.*

PRESSING THE POST

The couching tray, holding the completed post, is rolled on a track to the hydraulic press, where the pile is subjected to a pressure of from 100 to 150 tons, which expels a large proportion of the water (Figure 306). Before opening the press it is well to scrape off the excess water from the edges of the felting with a wooden paddle, as when the press is opened this water would have a tendency to run back into the felts and paper. When the post is removed from the bed of the press, the third workman, called a layer or layman, separates the sheets of paper from the felts (Figures 307, 308, 309). This is done by taking each sheet by the two corners nearest to him and lifting the sheet so that it pulls away from the felt evenly and without strain. He places the sheets of paper in a pile, taking care that the four corners of each sheet fall directly over the corresponding corners of the sheet underneath. The worker places the felts upon the felt board, ready for the

quirements. The varieties of finish and texture that may be imparted to handmade papers are practically unlimited and any taste may be satisfied.

THE WASTE IN MAKING PAPER BY HAND

There is considerable loss in making paper by hand, owing to tears in the sheets, knots, water drops, hairs from the felts embedded in the paper, drops of size, bubbles, holes, blurred watermarks, ruffled laid-lines, and pieces of rust from some part of the vat, but particularly the steam pipe. It is not unusual to discard as imperfect about twenty per cent of the paper produced. The best of the discarded sheets are sold as "seconds," or "retree," and the remainder is repulped and made into paper for wrapping the perfect reams.*

AMATEUR PAPERMAKING

It is feasible to make paper by hand by the use of a small vat and miniature mould as a hobby or diversion, but this manner of working should not be confused with professional papermaking by hand. With the most limited skill it is possible to make a few hundred small sheets of paper in an improvised vat and without proper equipment, but this sort of dilettante papermaking is far removed from the actual work of a regulation handmade-paper mill. To produce paper in ream lots, day after day, in usable sizes, in equal weight and thickness, it is absolutely essential to have

---

* The term "retree" is no doubt a corruption of the French *retrait* (withdrawal, shrinkage), from *retraire* (to withdraw), and is used to designate sheets of paper that bear slight imperfections such as short tears, small holes, wrinkles, blurred laid- and chain-lines, vatman's drip, etc. The retree is usually sold at ten per cent less than the good paper, and it is customary for a customer having a specially watermarked handmade paper manufactured to accept from ten to twenty per cent retree at the lower cost. Retree is indicated on the ream packages by two crosses (XX) or the letter "R." The defects in paper classed as retree are usually so slight that they pass unnoticed, especially after printing. The paper that is more severely harmed is termed "outsides" and is placed at the top and bottom of the reams when wrapped. The price of outsides is twenty per cent that of good paper. The term "cassie," or "casse," from the French word *cassé*, meaning broken, is now seldom used, but the term "broke" is common in even machine mills. The sorters of handmade paper do not always agree on what may be classed as retree, outsides, and broke, and variations may be expected.

full-size equipment and appliances, with an abundance of clear water, considerable power, and, what is most important, highly skilled workers. A handmade-paper mill is not a matter of an expenditure of a few hundred dollars, but represents an investment running into the thousands. The one-vat mill that was established in Connecticut more than a dozen years ago represented an expenditure, all told, of close to thirty-five thousand dollars. The setting up and operating of a handmade-paper mill should not be undertaken without long experience and the same careful planning that would be given to the establishment of any modern industry.

For experimenting in the use of various fibres, if only test sheets are required, a small ten- to twenty-pound beater, a miniature vat, and a small mould are most useful; in the laboratories of large machine mills such equipment is usual. As previously outlined, it is not possible to manufacture usable paper by employing small, home-made appliances. The making of paper in limited dimensions at a small vat enables the amateur to study fibre formation, and much can be gleaned about paper and watermarking through working in this limited manner. Such procedure, however, has but little relationship to real papermaking by hand with large moulds and proper equipment.[1]

XVI

Handmade Papers vs. Machine-made Papers

PAPER MADE BY THE ANCIENT TRADITIONAL

METHODS STILL HAS A LIMITED USE, BUT

THE PAPER–MACHINE HAS ALTERED

EVERY PHASE OF LIFE

A GREAT deal has been written relative to the merits of handmade paper formed in individual sheets in hand-moulds as compared with paper made on a machine in a continuous web. We are led to believe that paper shaken by hand in a mould will endure for a much longer period than that formed on the travelling wire of a paper-machine. This assumption is no doubt based on the fact that the oldest existing papers are handmade — the machine is a comparatively recent invention. If a paper-machine could be furnished with exactly the same stock, or pulp, that is used in making paper by hand, there is no reason why the machine-made product would not last as long as that formed in a hand-mould. It is seldom, however, that such a "furnish" is the case. The maceration of rags in handmade mills is usually accomplished in smaller beaters and with infinitely more care than in the machine mills. But, what is more important, the handmade-paper workers are not so inclined to use chemicals in their paper stock, while many machine-made papers are overcharged with bleach and other chemical admixtures that are employed for quick and cheap operation. The preparation of the paper stock rather than the method employed in its formation influences the life and durability of the paper, be it by hand or by machine. Owing to the use of poor raw materials and chemicals, some of the handmade papers produced in Italy will last no longer than much of the mediocre paper fabricated in America on machines. Indeed, it is questionable if many of the so-called "all-rag" papers will endure for the hundreds of years that are expected of them. In laboratory testing it is doubtful whether it is possible to emulate artificially the effects of time on paper. The only real time test that can absolutely be relied upon is the actual endurance of paper through the centuries. No matter how superior papermaking fibres may be in their original state, the material may be ruined before being made into paper by the use of fibre-destroying chemicals. This detriment is not evident immediately, but makes itself known only after the paper has been in existence for many years.

If paper of genuine permanence is desired, it is necessary to imitate as closely as possible the ancient methods of fabrication, for only in this manner is there assurance that the paper will endure. No more durable paper of the European type has ever been made than that used in printing the Gutenberg forty-two-line Bible of 1450–5. This paper has definitely lasted for five hundred years, and from all appearances it will remain in this unchanged condition for hundreds of years to come. We are not satisfied to make paper by these old methods, even though we are convinced that only paper made in this same tedious manner, without the aid of chemicals, will endure for countless centuries. It is admitted that modern paper produced on the machine is far more perfect in formation and in mechanical development than the paper made by hand in the fifteenth century, but the endurance and lasting quality of present-day paper are often sacrificed for speed of production.

A number of years ago I attempted to produce handmade paper commercially by using the same methods employed by the papermakers of the incunabula period. The finest rags were gathered, no chemicals were introduced, the beating was executed with care, and the sheets were formed separately in hand-moulds; the drying and finishing were undertaken with assiduous caution. Apparently, however, there was no demand for paper of this quality and the mill was forced to close through lack of support. Perhaps it is a saving grace that many modern books — to say nothing of magazines and newspapers — will not exist beyond a few decades. Could this be nature's subtle way of eliminating from posterity the records of an uncouth and slipshod age?

Provided precisely the same stock is used, the greatest advantage in quality handmade paper would have over paper formed on the machine would be that the fibres of handmade paper are shaken four ways, causing them to cross and intertwine in formation. On the travelling wire of the machine the course of the fibres is limited to the side-to-side shake, which has a tendency to throw the fibrous material in one direction only. For this reason paper formed on the machine has a "grain" and tears more easily one way than the other, while handmade sheets will tear with almost the same resistance in all directions. Also, in handmade paper the individual sheets are allowed to shrink naturally, but with machine-made paper the artificial drying on heated cylinders produces paper that has not been permitted natural shrinkage.

The machine-made thing may always be more perfect technically and mechanically than that made by the hand of man. With the present-day glorification of the handmade thing, however, it would seem that there were but few hands and fingers left in the world, while in reality there are more than ever before. The difficulty is that workers are not trained in the hand crafts — an absolute necessity before the advent of the machine. I have long been an advocate of hand work and have consistently tried to carry out my convictions, but I am well aware that there are many instances where the handmade thing has been discordantly employed, and printing is no exception. The use of handmade paper in book-printing is perfectly proper when all materials and methods are in accord with it, but does it not seem an anachronism to print a volume on handmade paper when the text of the book has been composed on the Linotype or Monotype? The type-setting and type-casting machines are marvellous inventions, and so is the paper-machine with its production of miles and miles of paper of an even thickness and weight. If handmade paper is to be used consistently in book-printing, the type should rightfully be hand-cut, hand-cast, and hand-set, and the printing executed on a hand press. Handmade paper is too often used for an "effect," an endeavour to gain a certain superficial aristocratic veneer that has no right to exist. If the mechanical type-setting machine can take the place of punch-cutting by hand, matrix-adjusting, and hand casting, then the paper-machine should be looked to for the paper, if there is a sincere desire for harmony and consistency. No matter how perfectly a book may be designed and printed, it will always be incongruous if the modern machine and the old hand methods are forced to form a partnership. The two distinctly different schools of production will not blend.

Since the invention of papermaking in the second century after Christ, workers in this craft have had to contend with mechanical imperfections due to the construction of the hand-mould and the limitations of human skill. Most pronounced among these imperfections were the deckle edges caused by the moist fibrous pulp running against the boundary frame, or wooden deckle, of the mould. The Oriental papermakers cut away these rough edges, leaving a clear-cut edge on each of the four sides of the sheet. In Europe also during the early centuries of book-printing the deckle edges were eliminated in many cases. The rough edges were regarded as blemishes in the making of the paper and therefore were discarded. It was not until the beginning of the machine age that deckle edges on paper began to be considered artistic and desirable. At the present time probably more handmade paper is sold on account of the deckle — or uneven — edges than for any other single characteristic. As a matter of fact, if the four deckle edges were cut away, it is doubtful if there are a half dozen printers or bibliophiles in America who could distinguish handmade paper from that made on a machine. During the early years of printing in Europe the deckle edges on paper were looked upon with disdain. Now these same rough edges are the label of respectability and recall to mind private presses, limited editions, and all manner of book snobbery. It is doubly offensive, however, to see deckle edges on the four sides of paper that has been formed on a machine, for here we have the deliberate imitation of an imperfection! There have even been machines invented to put mechanical "deckle" edges on cheap paper by means of a rotating cutting device, and a New York firm was at one time listed as doing artificial "deckling" for the trade. The deckle edges on paper could be compared to the selvage on cloth — something that is essential in fabrication, but a defect that should be hidden or eliminated from the finished book or garment.

Aside from the deckle edges on genuine handmade paper, which make registration in printing difficult, unless the hand press with pin register is used, there are numerous other imperfections in handmade paper that cause difficulties to the printers who utilize paper of this kind. Probably the most annoying of these defects is a disparity of thickness in the separate sheets, as it is humanly impossible for a vatman to guage each sheet of a ream so it will weigh exactly the same as every other sheet. In forming paper in a hand-mould, the worker has only his sense of weight and balance to guide him, and the thickness of each individual sheet of paper depends entirely upon the skill of the craftsman. It would be rare indeed to find a workman who could always dip precisely the same amount of liquid pulp with his mould, for the weight of each sheet must be judged while the fibre is saturated with water. A newly formed sheet of moist rag fibre weighing several pounds might after drying weigh only as many ounces. Only a superhuman artisan could be expected to form all sheets of a ream identical in weight, but it is surprising how dextrous the vatman becomes after many years of practice. The difficulty of moulding paper, however, does not lessen the trouble and worry involved in printing upon paper that is uneven in thickness and lacking in uniformity. If one sheet of paper is thin and another heavy, there is certain to be a difference in the impression when the paper is put through the press. A far more exasperating defect, sometimes present in handmade paper, is that one portion of a single sheet is heavier than another. While this difficulty is not so common as variation in the weight of separate sheets, it is nevertheless prevalent to some extent in the finest handmade papers and the result is that undue hardship is caused the pressman when he prints upon it, either on a hand press or one operated by power. Inasmuch as the weight and thickness of handmade paper is so irregular, paper of this kind is seldom sold by weight, the tendency being to list the paper as bulking so much to the ream.

Another characteristic of handmade paper that makes for difficulty in printing is that the sheets are not always square. The moulds upon which the paper is formed are perfectly true, as well as the wooden deckle boundary rims, but it is seldom that the finished paper dries absolutely square and even at the four corners. In folding a sheet of handmade paper in the centre for a folio, it will be noticed that the four corners do not always fall one upon another, and if the top edge of a sheet be brought in perfect alignment in folding, it is likely that the watermarked "chainlines" will not be absolutely perpendicular. While this lack of squareness may not be offensive from an æsthetic viewpoint, it does, nevertheless, give both the printer and the bookbinder considerable annoyance. The technical faults of not being truly square, along with the rough deckles and uneven thickness of handmade paper, are conditions that have always been present in paper of this kind and it is not likely that they will be overcome.

With all the various uncontrollable imperfections that are present in handmade paper, there is a particular fascination about the product that makes it desirable and suitable for the printing of certain books, but paper of this kind should not be used indiscriminately, without regard for its traditions. In many instances where handmade paper has been used in an endeavour of the printer to acquire "class," it would have been far more appropriate to have used a well-made machine paper. Even among the leading book-designers and typographers it is sometimes amazing to see the lack of knowledge displayed in the selection of paper for specific work. It is not unusual to find books of the highest workmanship and scholarly attainment printed on paper that is totally unsuited to the work in hand. The makers of machine-made paper have made decided æsthetic progress during the past decade and many pleasing tones and finishes have been devised. The greatest fault of the makers of machine-made papers is perhaps their endeavour to imitate certain elusive qualities that only handmade papers rightly possess. The machine should be confined to its legitimate work and not be forced to make artificial deckle edges, imitation "laid-" and "chain-lines," and antique finishes. This is an outright confession of the machine's limitations in the creation of what is commonly considered artistic value, and an acknowledgment that the technical blemishes and imperfections of genuine handmade paper are highly desirable from a selling standpoint. Papers made by hand have qualities that are peculiar to this type of paper; machine-made papers possess qualities that are not possible to duplicate by the old hand methods; the two products are distinctive and one should not be an imitation of the other.

Book-printers too often regard paper as simply a necessary background for their type and composition, very much as a painter looks upon his canvas. No matter how beautiful the typography of a book may be, if the paper is not in keeping with the complete scheme of design and purpose, the undertaking loses much of its real value. This does not mean that all handmade paper is suitable for all fine work — indeed, many books have suffered because handmade paper was used. Moreover, as outlined at the beginning of this chapter, the fact that paper is handmade does not necessarily mean that the product is lasting and enduring, and therefore suited for fine printing. In some parts of Europe, especially Italy, good papermaking materials are exceedingly expensive, while labour is exceedingly cheap — an economic condition that brings forth hand work with inferior material. Finer papermaking rags are to be had in America than in almost any other part of the world, and the machine-made-paper mills of the United States have this advantage over even the European handmade-paper mills. Workmen from European handmade-paper concerns, upon seeing the fine American rags, have expressed themselves forcibly on the excellence of the material and have stated that they never previously encountered such superior quality.

For the general run of fine bookmaking, much of the imported handmade paper from Europe is sized too heavily and gives considerable difficulty in dry printing. For damp printing the sizing does not matter to such an extent, as the tough resistance of the paper's surface is reduced considerably by the humidity. In printing dry, hard-sized handmade paper on a hand press, it would not be an exaggeration to say that almost twice as much ink would be consumed as in printing the same paper after it had been dampened.

The Chinese and Japanese papers made of mulberry, mitsumata, and gampi barks all have beautiful printing qualities and embody characteristics that make them admirable for woodblocks, etchings, photogravures, and so on. These papers, when free from foreign wood pulps and chemicals, are just as enduring as any rag papers of the Occident; in fact, paper made from pure mulberry bark and hemp fibre has remained in perfect condition for over fifteen hundred years. Papers made from unadulterated mitsumata and gampi barks seem almost to improve with age, specimens several hundred years old retaining their original freshness and giving the appearance of being able to endure for all time. Owing to the nature of the fibres, the handmade papers of China and Japan are not suited to the Occidental form of writing, but their printing possibilities are various. The most serious objection to many of the Oriental papers is that their surface becomes rubbed more readily than that of papers made in the European manner from linen and cotton rags.

It is always difficult to decide upon the proper paper for a specific book or piece of printing and there are no set rules to follow precisely. The decision should rest largely upon the typography of the book and the purpose of the volume. Both handmade and machine-made papers have their places in modern printing, and the typographical designer should study carefully the utilitarian and artistic requirements of a book before the final selection of the paper. While handmade paper from a reliable mill may be stronger and more durable than any paper made on a machine, it would not be practical to use it to any extent in modern book work. Handmade paper should never be used merely for its appearance of luxury and splendour, without any thought as to its artistic appropriateness or requirements from a utilitarian point of view.

Chronology, Bibliography, Notes, and Index

XVII

Chronology of Papermaking, Paper, and the Use of Paper

It would be presumptuous to bring forth a chronology of paper-making without generous reference to the work of that interesting old typographer of Albany, Joel Munsell. It is indeed a tribute to this American printer and publisher that his *Chronology of the Origin and Progress of Paper and Papermaking*, first issued in 1856, has so long endured and remains an interesting, but not always accurate, compilation to the present day. Joel Munsell was the only American chronicler of the middle of the nineteenth century possessing sufficient vision and foresight to record the happenings in the field of papermaking that occurred during his own lifetime. In many instances he assembled useful and worth-while contemporary information that otherwise would have remained unrecorded.

Joel Munsell was born in Northfield, Massachusetts, in April 1808. His earliest work in the printing craft was as an apprentice in the office of the *Franklin Post and Christian Freeman*, a newspaper in Greenfield, a thriving town ten or twelve miles south of his birthplace. In 1827, at the age of nineteen, young Munsell, ambitiously seeking a more likely field for his endeavours, crossed the Hudson river to the growing city of Albany. Here he worked as a journeyman printer until 1836, by which time he had acquired sufficient capital to enable him to set up his own printing business. Through diligent work, saving, and a keen interest in and appreciation of the art of typography, rare at that time, Mr. Munsell gradually developed his printing office into one of the most successful concerns in Albany. In 1839, when Munsell was but thirty-one years of age, he wrote his first book, *Outline of the History of Printing*, followed in 1850 by his *Typographic Miscellany*. Six years later came his well-known *Chronology of Paper* (1856), with enlarged editions in 1857, 1864, 1870, and 1876. Mr. Munsell died on January 15, 1880, aged seventy-two. His extensive collection of books on the subjects of printing and local history were acquired by the State Library.

Joel Munsell's *Chronology of Paper* in its various editions has to a limited degree influenced the form of the present chronology, and, after verification, a few of his entries, especially covering his own period, have been incorporated. For the most part, however, this compilation has not drawn upon Munsell or any other chronology, but is the result of personal research in books, pamphlets, contemporary newspaper and magazine files, patent records, local histories, manuscripts, letters, and documents; also through many years of correspondence with old-time American and European papermakers whose memories have retained interesting information and anecdotes relative to their beloved craft.

The present chronology does not profess to be complete in all phases of papermaking; the foremost intention has been to enumerate the important steps in the development of this craft without resorting to incidental material that has little relation to papermaking technique, paper history, and the use of paper. To a great extent the material comprising this chronology has been suggested by the foregoing text in this book, where many of the entries will be found enlarged upon in accordance with their individual importance.

B.C.

2700   *Chinese characters conceived; Ts'ang Chieh credited with the invention.*

2200   *Prisse manuscript on papyrus, probably the oldest Egyptian document. The Great Harris Papyrus, in the British Museum, measuring 133 feet in length and 16¾ inches in breadth, is one of the largest in the world. It is dated in the XXXIInd year of Ramses III, Epiphi 6 (April 14). Papyrus is a built-up, laminated material and should not be confused with true paper, which was not invented until about* A.D. *105.*

1400–1300   *The earliest actual evidence of writing in China is the incised divination bones discovered in Hunan Province*

B.C.

in 1899, dating from the fifteenth and fourteenth centuries B.C. *These writings upon bones consist of short sentences addressed to the spirits. It was, no doubt, the long, narrow form of the bones that influenced and suggested the method of Chinese calligraphy, vertical in form, from top to bottom.*

900   *True felt made by the Greeks, but not used as a "couching" material by papermakers until the introduction of papermaking in Europe.*

500   *During the life of Confucius (551–478* B.C.*), China had no true ink and no true paper. Scholars wrote on strips of bamboo with a paint-like pigment held on the points of wooden sticks or reeds.*

400–300   *Silk as a material for writing and books was used at this period, perhaps even earlier. While silk was light in weight and could be rolled into scrolls, it was too expensive for general use, and strips of wood and bamboo remained in favour. In the official Han Catalogue, compiled in the first century* B.C., *more manuscripts and records on wood than on silk are listed.*

255   *First mention of the use of seals for impressing in clay, without the use of ink.*

250   *Invention of the camel's-hair brush by Mêng T'ien, eventually revolutionizing the writing of Chinese characters.*

200   *An improved method of refining parchment from sheepskin thought to have been introduced by the King of Pergamum (197–158* B.C.*). This led to the supposition that parchment was invented in Pergamum, from whence the name is derived.*

A.D.

82   *The Chinese philosopher Wang Ch'ung wrote: "Bamboo is cut into cylinders, which are split into tablets. When brush*

A.D.

and ink marks are added we have writing — the classics being inscribed on long tablets, the historical records on shorter ones." The long bamboo tablets measured about twenty inches.

100   *The Chinese dictionary,* Shuo-wên, *described books written upon narrow strips of wood held together by cords, in the manner of a Venetian blind. The third-century lexicon* Shih ming *likens the arrangement of the strips of wood to the teeth of a comb.*

105   *During the period of Chien-ch'u, Ts'ai Lun was made one of the Imperial Guard. Later Ho Ti (*A.D. *89–105) appointed him privy councillor and it was during this reign that Ts'ai Lun,* A.D. *105, announced the invention of papermaking to the Emperor. The paper was made from mulberry and other barks, fish nets, hemp, and rags.*

106   *Paper used in lieu of metal coins for placing in the tombs of the dead; the beginning of the use of "spirit-paper," used to the present day in Chinese ceremonial and religious rites.*

142   *According to a work compiled by Yü Shih-nan (*A.D. *558– 638), a scholar, Ts'ui Yüan,* A.D. *142, wrote: "I send you the works of the Philosopher Hsü in ten scrolls — unable to afford a copy on silk I am obliged to send you one on paper." This would suggest that by thirty-seven years after the invention of paper this substance was cheaper than silk, a writing material previously used.*

150   *Papermaking improved by Tso Tzŭ-yi, after its invention by Ts'ai Lun.*

Paper dating from this period found in the Great Wall of China by Sir Aurel Stein. Made from rags.

175   *Text of Chinese classics cut in stone, which later gave impetus to the stone rubbings, a form of printing.*

A.D.

250–300   *Paper from this period found at Niya, Turkestan, by Sir Aurel Stein.*

264   *Earliest clearly dated paper. Found in Loulan by the Swedish explorer Dr. Sven Hedin.*

300   *According to Chinese records, it was about this period that paper began to be universally accepted as a substitute for wood, bamboo, and silk as a writing material.*

390   *A letter written by St. Augustine (*A.D.*354–430) makes an apology for using papyrus instead of parchment, the papyrus being considered less formal and desirable.*

399   *Most ancient paper discovered in Turfan, Chinese Turkestan, by the Russian expeditions under Dr. Grünwedel and Dr. von Le Coq, from 1902 to 1907, dates from this period.*

400   *Invention of true ink from lamp-black, used in China for brush writing and later for wood-block printing.*

406   *The commencement of the Tun-huang papers. These manuscripts date from* A.D. *406–1035, all written upon paper. Ten thousand rolls were found in one cave on the border of Chinese Turkestan.*

445   *Fan Yeh, the first scholar to record the invention of papermaking by Ts'ai Lun, died.*

450   *For the first time the Chinese made use of true ink in printing seals. The seals were engraved in stone, metal, wood, jade, bamboo, and horn and were used in the manner of a modern rubber stamp. This was the earliest instance of actual printing with an incised stamp with ink upon paper.*

General use of paper in Eastern Turkestan, replacing all other materials for calligraphy. The paper was made from rags and barks, with improvements in sizing with pastes made from grains.

A.D.

470   *The* History of the Later Han Dynasty (A.D. *25–221*), *written about* A.D. *470, states: "From this time on it [paper] was used universally." Other references likewise attest that the making and use of paper spread rapidly throughout China.*

575   *Introduction of Taoist seal charms, or temple blocks, used in the same manner as the smaller seals. This was the second step in the art of printing following the use of the small seals. Genuine wood-block printing remained to be conceived.*

610   *Papermaking introduced into Japan from China, the country from which Japan received all of her cultural and artistic development.*

627–49   *Between these dates was made the earliest inscription extant from a stone monument. Found in 1901 at Tunhuang by M. Paul Pelliot. This rubbing on paper dates from the period of T'ai Tsung of the T'ang Dynasty.*

650   *Chinese Buddhist monks experimented with the duplication of images by the use of rubbings, charm blocks, stencils, and textile prints. These experiments were the forerunner of true block printing in the ninth century.*

Earliest use of paper in Samarkand, the paper imported from China, the world's most highly developed Empire.

674   *A Chinese edict made it compulsory to use a toxic substance rendered from the berries of the* Phellodendron amurense, *commonly known as the Amoor cork tree, for the colouring of certain types of Chinese paper. Paper so treated was immune to the ravages of insects.*

700   *About this time a few papers began to be sized: first with gypsum, followed in succession with glue or gelatine made from lichen, then starch flour and other sizing agents rendered from grains.*

A.D.

707   *Earliest use of paper in Mecca, the material brought from the seat of its invention, China.*

751   *In this year paper was made in Samarkand, the first place outside China to understand the secrets of the craft, revealed by Chinese prisoners of war.*

770   *The earliest instance of text printing upon paper, the million printed* dhāranī *of the Empress Shōtoku. The paper was made from hemp and the blocks used in the printing may have been of wood, metal, stone, or porcelain. A number of the* dhāranī *are still extant, but no printing block used in this work has ever been found. While the work was actually executed in Japan, it was accomplished under Chinese influence and therefore this earliest of all text printing upon paper should be regarded as almost purely of Chinese origin.*

793   *Paper fabricated for the first time in Baghdad, introduced by Harûn-al-Rashid (766?–809), who acquired skilled artisans from China for the purpose.*

800   *Earliest use of paper in Egypt, probably imported from Samarkand or Baghdad.*

Egyptian paper of the Erzherzog collection, Vienna, dating from A.D. *800–1388, examined in 1885 by Dr. Karabacek and Dr. Weisner, found to contain rags. Until the discovery of Chinese rag paper in 1904 by Dr. Stein it was generally believed that the use of rags in papermaking was originated by the Arabs of Samarkand.*

807   *Paper made for the first time in Kyōto, the art centre of Japan.*

About this time, during the reign of Emperor Hsien Tsung of the T'ang Dynasty, it is recorded in Chinese texts that paper money was used, termed "flying-money." No genuine notes of this issue are known; there is nothing to indicate that the notes were produced by printing and it is possible they may have been in manuscript, if they actually existed.

850 *Gampi* (Wikstrœmia canescens) *bark used for the first time in Japan as a papermaking fibre.*

868 *The earliest printed book, the Diamond* Sutra, *printed by Wang Chieh. The book was found at Tun-huang by Sir Aurel Stein. The roll, the original form of true Chinese book, is sixteen feet in length. The Diamond* Sutra *was first printed in Japan in 1157.*

875 *Arab travellers in China report having seen toilet paper in use in that country during the ninth century.*

883 *An Egyptian letter of thanks dating between this year and 895 closes with these words: " Pardon the papyrus." Inasmuch as the letter is written on a handsome piece of papyrus it is inferred that the apology was made for not making use of paper, this substance having but lately been introduced into Egypt.*

For the first time block prints are mentioned in literature, by Liu Pin, who had examined specimens of wood-block printing in Szechwan.

900 *True paper made in Egypt for the first time, the methods of the Chinese employed.*

932–53 *Fêng Tao began his large-scale printing of the Chinese classics.*

950 *Earliest use of paper in Spain.*

About this time the Chinese made use of the first folded books. Previous to this period only rolled books had been used in China.

A.D.

953 *The block printing of Confucian classics as ordered by Fêng Tao completed after twenty-one years of labour. With this impetus the craft of printing began on a much larger scale than at any previous time.*

960 *During the Sung Dynasty* (A.D. *960–1126) the highest development of printing took place, with a perfection of technical excellence never surpassed. All forms of literature were printed and much of this fine work remains in public and private collections.*

969 *Earliest recorded mention of playing cards, China.*

972 *The printing of the Buddhist Canon, comprising 130,000 pages. This was the* Tripitaka, *the three divisions or "baskets" of Buddhist scriptures: Discipline, Discourses, Metaphysics (China).*

994–1063 *Printing of the great dynastic histories, during the period of the Sung Dynasty.*

998 *By this date the amount of paper money in circulation in China had reached a total of 1,130,000* tiao. *A* tiao *was a string of 1,000 cash, equivalent to about thirty cents in United States money, but having a far greater buying power. In 1022 there was an additional issue of 1,130,000* tiao.

1000 *The manuscripts* Gharibu-el-Hadith *and* Umdet-el-Kuttab *and others were written from the ninth to the twelfth century and are probably the earliest compilations to deal with paper. The material in these ancient manuscripts throws but little light on the actual technique of early papermaking.*

1035 *The Persian traveller Nasiri Khosrau, on a visit to Cairo, was astonished to see "sellers of vegetables, spices, hardware, provided with paper in which all they sold was im-*

mediately wrapped up, if it were not so already." Probably the earliest recorded instance of "packaging," so much in evidence today.

About this time waste paper was repulped and again used as material for papermaking. In Japan the paper made from this material was known as Kamiya-gami.

1041–9   *Invention of movable type in China by Pi Shêng. The Chinese language with its myriad characters did not lend itself to the use of movable type and therefore the invention had but little use in China.*

1100   *Su Tung-p'o (*A.D. *1036–1101) recorded that bamboo was used as a papermaking material in China.*

The earliest instance of papermaking in Morocco, having been introduced from Egypt.

First use of paper in Constantinople.

1102   *Earliest use of true paper in Sicily.*

1109   *Earliest existing European manuscript on paper, a deed of King Roger, written in Arabic and Greek, Sicily.*

1116   *The Chinese made use of the first stitched books, printed on one side of the paper with "French fold," sewed with linen and cotton thread.*

Earliest of the Buddhist printed books in Chinese and Tangut, found at Kara-Khoto, Mongolia.

1140   *A physician of Baghdad writes of the source of the wrapping paper used by the grocers: "The Bedouins and fellahs search the ancient cities of the dead to recover the cloth bands in which mummies were swathed, and when these cannot be used for their own clothes, they sell them to the*

A.D.

mills, which make of them paper destined for the food markets." (See: 1855.)

1147 *According to legend Jean Montgolfier on the Second Crusade was taken prisoner by Saracens and forced to labour in a Damascus paper mill. He is supposed to have returned to France and in 1157 set up a papermaking establishment in Vidalon. (See: 1189.)*

1150 *El-Edrisi said of the Spanish city of Xátiva (now Játiva or S. Felipe de Játiva): "Paper is there manufactured, such as cannot be found anywhere else in the civilized world, and is sent to the East and to the West."*

1151 *A stamping-mill for the maceration of rags for papermaking was put in operation in Xátiva, Spain. This type of mill was adopted from the Orient and was used in Europe until the invention of the Hollander. (See: 1680).*

1154 *First use of paper in Italy, in the form of a register written by Giovanni Scriba, dated 1154 to 1166. It is thought that this particular paper had been imported from the East. No other specimens of paper are found in Italy until 1276, the date of the first mention of the Fabriano paper mills.*

1189 *The date usually given as the commencement of papermaking in France, in the town of Lodève, in the department of Hérault. This assertion is now considered an error and was based on an incorrect translation and a mistaken date. (See: 1348.)*

1221 *Emperor Frederick II (A.D. 1194–1250), King of Naples and Sicily, prohibited the use of paper for public documents, but the edict was not entirely effective.*

1228 *Earliest use of paper in Germany.*

1250 *Block printing executed in Egypt. The existing prints show Chinese influence.*

A.D.

1276 *First mention of the Fabriano, Italy, paper mills.*

1282 *Watermarks used in Europe for the first time. They consisted of simple crosses and circles (Italy).*

1285 *Earliest use of the fleur-de-lis as a watermark in paper. Shortly after this date initials of the papermakers appeared in watermarks.*

1293 *First paper mill in Bologna, Italy.*

1294 *Paper money issued at Tabriz, Persia, in Chinese and Arabic texts.*

1298 *After visiting China, Marco Polo wrote regarding the paper money he had seen in use in that country. Paper money was the first form of printing seen by European travellers, and at least eight pre-Renaissance European writers mentioned it. The description given by Marco Polo was the most comprehensive and most widely read.*

1300 *Use of wood type near the borders of Turkestan by Uigur Turks. A fount of type of this kind in the Uigur language was found in Tun-huang by M. Pelliot.*

1309 *First use of paper in England.*

1319–27 *Earliest use of paper money in Japan. The Japanese notes were smaller than those of China, being about 2 by 6 inches. This paper money was secured by a gold or silver or other metallic reserve.*

1322 *Usually given as the date of the first use of paper in Holland. According to J. H. de Stroppelaar* (Het Papier in de Nederlanden Gedurende de Middeleeuwen, Inzonderheid in Zeeland, *Middelburg, 1869), the oldest paper found in the archives of Holland is dated 1346, and is preserved at The Hague.*

A.D.

1337 *Probably the earliest use in Europe of animal (gelatine) sizing for paper.*

1348 *Under this date it is recorded that a paper mill was established in the Saint-Julien region near Troyes, perhaps the earliest mill in France.*

1368 *Many specimens of Chinese paper money of this period (Hung Wu, Ming Dynasty, 1368–98) are in American collections, as this was apparently the most abundant issue. These notes measure 8¾ by 13½ inches.*

1390 *The King of Korea ordered the establishment of a typefoundry.*

First paper mill in Germany, established by Ulman Stromer, Nürnberg. A woodcut of this mill is given in Schedel's Nürnberg Chronicle, 1493. The watermarks of the Stromer mill consisted of the letter "S" and the arms of Nürnberg. Before the commencement of this mill the paper used in Germany was imported from Italy. The first recorded labour strike in the paper industry took place in the Stromer mill. The earliest recorded labour strikes in the printing industry occurred in France, dating from 1539.

1403 *Movable type produced in the royal typefoundry, Korea. Specimens of this type are in the museum in Seoul.*

1405 *In Flanders a papermaker named Jean L'Espagnol mentioned at Huy, probably the first maker of paper in this locality.*

1409 *Earliest known book printed in Korea from movable type.*

1420–70 *Papermaking introduced into Kashmir, India, from Samarkand, by King Zanulabin, popularly known as Budshah.*

A.D.

1420 *The second fount of movable type produced in Korea.*

1423 *The beginning of block printing in Europe, by use of the ancient Chinese technique. Image prints and playing cards were printed from wood-blocks and coloured by hand.*

1434 *The third fount of movable type produced in Korea.*

1450–5 *Johann Gutenberg's 42-line Bible produced. The beginning of book-printing in Europe and the commencement of the use of paper on a comparatively large scale. The paper used in the printing of this Bible has never been excelled for durability and remains to this day a monument to the papermaking craft.*

1450 *The earliest known use of an "ex libris," a bookplate or label printed upon paper and pasted in the front of books to show ownership.*

1465 *Earliest mention of blotting paper in the English language. The following reference to blotting paper appears in Horman's* Vulgaria: *"Blottyng paper serveth to drye wette wryttynge, lest there be made blottis or blurris" (1519).*

1470 *A bookseller's advertisement issued by Peter Schöffer is considered to be the first printed poster upon paper to be produced in Europe.*

1476 *William Caxton established his printing office in Westminster and produced thirty books during the first three years. All of the paper used by Caxton was procured in the Low Countries. (See: 1495.)*

1480 *Anthony Koberger, printer of Nürnberg, distributed a printed circular to his customers, probably the first use of this form of advertising.*

A.D.

1482 *Venetian papermakers separated the initials of the paper-maker from the device or symbol of the watermark; introduced in France about 1567.*

1486 *The unknown schoolmaster printer of St. Albans issued the first English book printed on paper in which coloured inks were used in the illustrations:* The Bokys of Hauking and Huntyng *by Juliana Berners.*

The earliest European book to use folding plates was probably Breydenbach's Peregrinationes, *the woodcuts by Erhart Reuwich, Mainz.*

1487 *By this year almost every country of Europe had adopted printing, and large quantities of paper were consumed in the printing of books.*

1491 *The first paper mill in Poland, in Prądnik Czerwony, near Kraków. The finest paper of Poland was made by Frédéric Szyling in Prądnik Duchacki about 1495; another mill was located in Poland's second capital, Wilno, in 1522. The first Warsaw paper mill was set up in 1534 on the river Dona in Gaj Królewski, near the present Powązki, a Warsaw cemetery. By the year 1546 there were thirty-five paper mills in Poland. (Lucia Merecki Borski.)*

1493 Nürnberg Chronicle *issued by Schedel, a pictorial history of the world embracing 645 woodcuts of 1,809 subjects. In the double-page delineation of the city of Nürnberg is shown a small picture of the Ulman Stromer paper mill (lower right corner). This was the first picture of a paper mill to be used in a European book. (See: 1390.)*

1495 *First paper mill established in England, by John Tate, in Hertfordshire. The first printer to make use of Tate paper was Wynken de Worde in the English edition of* Bartholomæus: De proprietatibus rerum, *1496.*

A.D.

1497 *Paper used for the first time in producing a guide-book,* Mirabilia Romæ, *printed in Rome by Stephen Plannck, the most prolific printer of Rome in the fifteenth century.*

1508 *Earliest use of paper in Scotland for book-printing, Chaucer's* Maying and Disporte, *printed in Edinburgh by Chepman and Myllar.*

1521 *The earliest recorded use of rice straw in Chinese papermaking.*

1535 *The first complete Bible in English, Myles Coverdale's translation, probably printed in Zürich by Christopher Froschover. In an examination of eleven copies of this Bible ten different watermarks are found: seven forms of a large crown, one small crown, and two bull's-heads, one with snake and the other surmounted by a rose of bliss. The first Bible to be actually printed in England dates from 1537.*

1540 *The glazing- or pressing-hammer introduced in Germany, taking the place of the old method of burnishing the paper by hand in the Oriental manner.*

1545 *The earliest use of paper in issuing a book catalogue,* Bibliotheca Universalis, *printed by Christopher Froschover, Zürich.*

1549 *The Spanish missionary Diego de Landa, of the Monastery of Izamal, Yucatán, burned the library of the Mayas in Mani. According to Dr. Victor Wolfgang von Hagen (The Aztec and Maya Papermakers, New York, 1944), the Mayas were making a sort of bark paper as early as the ninth century of our era.*

1550 *Earliest use of "smalts" in colouring paper blue. Prussian blue was discovered by Diesbach in 1704; ultramarine has been made since 1790, and synthetic ultramarine was first made commercially by Guimet in 1828.*

A.D.

Wallpaper introduced into Europe direct from China by Spanish and Dutch traders.

Probable date of the origin and use of marbled papers, a Persian invention.

1565   *Jacques Besson in his book dealing with mathematical instruments shows for the first time in Europe a theoretical design of a stamping-mill for the maceration of paper stock.*

1568   *The date of the first delineation of a papermaker at work to appear in Europe, the picture by Jost Amman with a short poem by Hans Sachs. This book of trades was published in Frankfurt in 1568, with an edition in Latin in 1574. The first edition (German) contains 115 cuts of trades and callings and the later edition 132 woodcuts.*

1570   *About this time the earliest extra-thin papers were produced in Europe.*

1575–80   *According to Relación del pueblo de Culhuacán desta Nueva España, written January 17, 1580, the first paper mill in Mexico was established in Culhuacán, it being "a mill with a hammer in which paper was made." This reference was probably made to the concession granted by royal deed to Hernán Sánchez de Muñón and Juan Cornejo, and dated at the Forest of Segovia on June 8, 1575, to "manufacture paper in New Spain, utilizing material they had found." A twenty-year privilege was granted these papermakers. The location of the village of Culhuacán is southeast of Mexico City in the Federal District at the foot of Estrella Hill. At the present time nothing remains of the first paper mill of Mexico.*

1576   *The first paper mill in Russia was probably established in Moscow this year.*

A.D.

1580 First commercial pasteboard manufactured in Europe. In China and Persia board of this kind had been made centuries earlier.

1586 The earliest mention of national papermaking in Holland was contained in a decree authorizing Hans van Aelst and Jan Luipart to manufacture paper near Dordrecht.

1588 John Spilman, a German, one of the goldsmiths to Queen Elizabeth, established a paper mill in Dartford, Kent, England. In 1589 Spilman was granted a patent which gave him a monopoly in the collecting of rags and the making of paper in the Kingdom.

1589 European printing introduced into China by Jesuit priests. In 1591 Japan received printing from the West for the first time.

1590 Approximate date of the introduction of Persian marbled papers into Europe. The first papers were of the "fine-combed" variety.

1591 Newly discovered records show that the first paper mill in Scotland was established at Dalry, near Edinburgh, by Mungo Russell and his son Gideon, assisted by Michael Keysar and John Seillar, Germans, probably papermakers.

1592 Paper used in printing the earliest typefounder's specimen sheet in Europe, issued by Egenolff-Berner foundry, Frankfurt am Main.

1593 Earliest European type printing in the Philippine Islands, two books issued by the Dominicans. The paper came from Spain.

1595 About this time the first "paste papers" (papers decorated by the use of coloured rice paste) were in use in Germany, France, and Italy. Paste papers made their initial appearance in America about 1750.

A.D.

1597   *Mitsumata* (Edgeworthia papyrifera) *first recorded used in Japan as a fibre for making paper.*

1607   *The first picture of a set of practical papermaking stampers to appear in a European book:* Novo Teatro di Machine et Edificii, *by Vittorio Zonca, Padua.*

1609   *The earliest newspaper with regular publication dates,* Avisa Relation oder Zeitung, *published in Germany. The first English newspaper was issued in London in 1622. The earliest Russian newspaper appeared in 1703.*

1610   *Papermaking at Wookey Hole, Wells, Somerset, recorded for the first time. The W. S. Hodgkinson and Company mill, one of the five surviving handmade-paper mills in England, is an outgrowth of this original establishment.*

1630   *Paper cartridges first used by Gustavus Adolphus (1594– 1632), King of Sweden from 1611 to 1632.*

1634   *The first book to appear in China in which the art of paper- making is treated in both text and illustrations:* T'ien kung k'ai wu, *by Sung Ying-hsing.*

1636   *E. and R. Greenbury granted the first English patent for the decorating of "paper for hanging."*

England visited by a plague thought to have been brought into the country through linen and cotton rags imported by the papermakers.

1638–9   *First printing press set up in North America by Stephen Daye, at Cambridge, Massachusetts. The first printing exe- cuted was a broadside on paper:* The Freeman's Oath; *first thing in book form, Peirce's* Almanack *for 1639; earliest ex- isting specimen of Cambridge printing: John Eliot's* Bay Psalm Book, *dated 1640.*

A.D.

1650   *Printed papers of the "all-over" pattern in various colours and used in the binding of books were in use in Germany and Italy.*

1661   *First New Testament printed in America, John Eliot's translation into Algonquin, printed at Cambridge, Massachusetts, by Samuel Green and Marmaduke Johnson.* The Old Testament *was issued in 1663, the two making the first Bible printed in this country. The paper was of European manufacture.*

1662   *The publication in England of Thomas Fuller's* The History of the Worthies of England, *in which the author outlines his unique observations relative to English, Dutch, and Italian papers. (The reference to paper will be found on pages 144 and 149, the latter number being a misprint for 145.)*

     The great work on machinery issued by Georg Andreæ Böckler, Nürnberg, gives a delectable engraving of a paper-maker at work and a good rendering of a stamping-mill operated by water-power, the latter founded on the Zonca engraving of 1607.

1665   *The first English patent pertaining to papermaking was granted Charles Hildeyerd: "The way and art of making blew paper used by sugar-bakers and others." The second English patent was given Eustace Burneby in 1675, the specification reading: "The art and skill of making all sorts of white paper for the use of writing and printing, being a new manufacture and never practiced in any way in our kingdomes or dominions."*

1666   *To save linen and cotton for the papermakers a decree was issued in England prohibiting the use of these materials for the burial of the dead; only wool could be used for this purpose. In England at this time 200,000 pounds of linen and cotton were saved annually in this manner.*

A.D.

1678   William Rittenhouse, who established the first paper mill in America, was working as a papermaker in Amsterdam, Holland, at this time.

1679   The first "Dutch gilt" papers, originated in Germany, imported to the New World.

1680   The "Hollander," or beater, used in the maceration of materials for making into paper, invented in the Netherlands.

1682   Johann Joachim Becher recorded for the first time a brief description of the "Hollander" as he had seen it used in Serndamm, Holland.

1683   The earliest treatise on typefounding, Mechanick Exercises, by Joseph Moxon (1627–1700), published in London.

Birth of René Antoine Ferchault de Réaumur, the French scientist who first suggested (1719) the use of wood as a papermaking fibre. Réaumur's observations were made after a study of the wasp in making its nest, a form of paper. Réaumur died in 1757.

1687   Earliest use of ochres, umbers, and vermilion in the colouring of European paper.

1690   First paper money in the colonies, issued by Massachusetts Bay Colony. The next locality to issue paper currency was South Carolina, in 1703; followed by New York, New Jersey, and Connecticut, 1709; Pennsylvania, Delaware, and New Hampshire, 1723; Maryland, 1733; North Carolina, 1748; Georgia, 1749. The first "greenback" paper money appeared February 25, 1862.

William Rittenhouse established the first paper mill in British America, near Germantown, Philadelphia, Pennsylvania. (See text for description.)

A.D.

1691   *On November 6 a patent was granted to Nathaniel Gifford, England, for "a new, better, and cheaper way of making all sorts of blew, purple, and other coloured paper." The first English patent pertaining to the colouring of paper.*

1692   *The earliest reference to the Rittenhouse paper mill appeared this year, a poem of twenty-six lines compiled by Richard Frame, published in Philadelphia by William Bradford, a partner in the establishment of the mill.*

1693   *Father J. Imberdis, Claromonti, a Jesuit priest, wrote his curious observations on papermaking as carried on in Ambert in Auvergne:* Papyrus sive Ars conficiendæ Papyri.

1696   *According to the* Case of the Paper Traders *there was produced in England 28,000 pounds' worth of paper; at this time there were 100 paper mills in England as recorded in the same report.*

John Holme wrote twelve lines of verse about the art of papermaking in America; the verse was not published until 1847.

1697   *At this time William Bradford, Philadelphia printer, arranged to purchase paper from the Rittenhouse mill at ten shillings sterling a ream. This price prevailed in this country until as late as 1750.*

1704   *The* Boston News Letter *established in Boston by John Campbell, the earliest permanent newspaper in America.*

1710   *The second paper mill in the colonies set up by William De Wees, an outgrowth of the original Rittenhouse mill, established in 1690 near Philadelphia. (See text.)*

1712   *In Bavaria the Hollander superseded the old stamping-mill for the maceration of rags for papermaking.*

Peter the Great (1672–1725), Czar of Russia, visited Dresden and after seeing paper being made in the Schuchart mill procured workmen in Germany and returned to Moscow, where he established the first extensive paper mill in Russia. By 1801 there were twenty-three paper mills in the Russian Empire.

1714 *Invention and patent of a typewriter for "transcribing of letters, one after another, as in writing on paper." The patent was issued in England, January 7, to Henry Mill.*

1715 *Death brought to a close the unworthy pursuits of John Bagford (1675–1715), who, during his day, was supposed to be the greatest authority on paper who had ever lived. Bagford gathered his specimens of early paper and printing by mutilating books and documents in public and private libraries. In 1707 he proposed a history of papermaking and printing, but his work was not published. Some of the material that this "wicked old biblioclast" had filched is now in the British Museum under the title of "Bagford's Collectanea," numbered 5891–5988.*

1718 *Birth of Jacob Christian Schäffer, the German clergyman who between 1765 and 1772 was destined to make use of more than eighty different vegetable fibres in the fabrication of paper. Schäffer died 1790.*

The first illustration of the Hollander to appear, in the work by Leonhardt Christoph Sturm, Vollständige Mühlen Baukunst, *published in Augsburg. The first Hollander used in Germany was set up in this year.*

First coloured printing (red and black) accomplished in America, by Andrew Bradford, Philadelphia.

1719 *Establishment of* American Weekly Mercury, *Philadelphia, the first newspaper in Pennsylvania.*

A.D.

1720 *Pressing-hammers gave way to wooden glazing-rolls for finishing paper with a smooth surface.*

1722 *During this year Great Britain produced 300,000 reams of paper, averaging 2 pounds 10 shillings a ream.*

1724 *First English patent for "staining, vaining, spotting, and clouding paper in imitation of marble, tortoishell, etc.," granted to R. Redrich and T. Jones.*

1725 *From this year to the present day Messrs. Portal have manufactured the paper upon which the Bank of England notes are printed.*

Between this year and 1730 Ernst Brückmann, a German, published his work on geology in which part of the paper used was made from asbestos.

1726 *The beginning of papermaking in the state of New Jersey is more obscure than that of any other Eastern state, but the first paper was probably made in Elizabethtown between this year and 1728. The owner of the Elizabethtown mill was William Bradford (1663–1752), the son of a London printer, also named William. The younger William did not learn the trade of printing in his father's shop, but in the London establishment of Andrew Sowle, a Quaker, who during young Bradford's apprenticeship printed a book entitled* The Frame of the Government of Pennsylvania in America. *It was probably the influence of reading this book that led young Bradford, when nineteen years of age, to join William Penn's group in emigrating to the New World. Bradford evidently laid his plans well, for after a few years in America he returned to London and married Sowle's daughter Elizabeth; he and his bride came to the country of his adoption in 1685. This same year William Bradford, when but twenty-two, executed the first printing in Pennsylvania. It was only natural that young Bradford, being engaged in printing, became associated with William Rit-*

tenhouse in the establishment of his paper mill, in 1690, the first in the colonies. Three years later, however, Bradford incurred the displeasure of the dominant party in Pennsylvania and he was compelled to leave the state. He moved to New York City, where he established the New-York Gazette *in 1725, and with the knowledge of papermaking he had gained from Rittenhouse, Bradford set up a paper mill in Elizabethtown, New Jersey, with the plan of supplying his New York publication with the necessary paper. The earliest contemporary mention of Bradford's Elizabethtown paper mill was in the* American Weekly Mercury, *Philadelphia, a newspaper operated by Bradford's son, Andrew. The notice is dated July 3 and 10, 1729, and reads: "An indented Servant Man named James Roberts, is run away from William Bradford's Paper Mill at Elizabeth-Town in New Jersey. . . . He is a West-Country Man, has been about one year in the Country and is a Paper-Maker by Trade." From the following advertisement in the* New-York Gazette *for March 31, 1735 we may assume that the mill was in operation at this time, but it is not known whether or not William Bradford was still the owner: "On Wednesday the 23 of April next at the Paper Mill in Elizabeth-Town, there will be Sold at Public Vendue to the highest Bidder, all sorts of Household Goods, Cattle, Horses, Hogs, Cart, Plows, Harrows with Iron Teeth, and other Utensils: The Plantation adjoining to the said Mill will also be sold, which contains about Ninety Acres. . . ." The notice of 1729 and the advertisement of 1735 are the sole contemporary references that can be found in connection with the earliest paper mill in New Jersey; it is upon these meagre accounts that practically all the history of this mill is based. A search in the New Jersey Historical Society, Newark, collection of imprints and the Library of Rutgers University reveals no watermarked paper from Bradford's mill, the first in the state. The paper used by Isaac Collins, the founder of the* New Jersey Gazette, *1777, in printing the New Jersey Revolutionary money was made in Spotswood, New Jersey.*

A.D.

1728 *The year of the establishment of the first paper mill in the state of Massachusetts. This mill was located in the town of Milton on the bank of the Neponset River, near Boston. The mill building used in this undertaking had originally been the Joseph Belcher textile mill, constructed about 1717. The paper company, composed of prominent Boston men, secured a lease on this mill, and after it had been equipped with appliances for papermaking, operations commenced under a "grant for the encouragement of a Paper Mill," passed by the General Court of Massachusetts, September 13, 1728. The five men who made up the company were Daniel Henchman, Gillam Phillips, Benjamin Faneuil, Thomas Hancock, and Henry Deering. Henchman, the leader of the group, was a well-known bookseller and publisher, with a shop in Cornhill, Boston. Hancock was also in the bookselling and publishing trades, with his headquarters in Anne Street. He had served his apprenticeship with Henchman and had learned the craft of bookbinder, but what was probably more important, he married Henchman's daughter, Lydia. Of the other members of this papermaking company, Benjamin Faneuil was the father of Peter, who built Faneuil Hall in 1740 and presented the building to the town of Boston; Gillam Phillips was a brother-in-law of Peter Faneuil. Henry Deering was the superintendent and agent of the mill, but nothing is known of his previous experience in making paper. The foreman of the mill was Henry Woodman, who had learned his trade in his native England. This newly established company was given the sole right to manufacture paper in Massachusetts provided the proprietors lived up to certain productions of paper that were set down in the agreement. The mill continued without interruption until 1737, when Woodman, the foreman, severed his connection with the company. Also, Deering, the superintendent, wished to engage in other work, so the owners of the mill secured Jeremiah Smith, an Irishman, to become overseer, although Smith was not an experienced papermaker. In the place of Henry Woodman, an Englishman named John Hazleton was made foreman. By diligent*

A.D.

work and perseverance Jeremiah Smith eventually became sole owner of the mill as he, little by little, acquired the interests of Henchman, Hancock, Phillips, and Faneuil. In 1741 Smith was able to purchase the mill building and real estate from the heirs of Joseph Belcher. It would appear that Smith acquired the title to the mill and equipment, as well as ownership of the company, through prudent management rather than from any great financial success of the undertaking. For the most part only coarse paper of a common kind had been produced, as the early printers of Massachusetts relied upon the more developed paper industry of Pennsylvania, also Europe, for their book-printing. The greatest difficulty experienced by Smith was in procuring adept papermakers who could mould even sheets of usable paper. It was not until about 1760 that Richard Clark, a skilled English worker, was induced to take over the management of the Milton mill, and with the making of better paper than had previously been produced, the mill commenced to enjoy considerable prosperity. In 1769 Daniel Vose, a son-in-law of Jeremiah Smith, was permitted to purchase a half interest in the mill, and six years later Vose acquired the other half, Jeremiah Smith retiring on a substantial fortune he had amassed through almost forty years' connection with the paper mill.

The invention by Claude Genoux, a French printer, of the papier-mâché, or wet-mat, stereotyping process.

1729   *Third paper mill in Pennsylvania established in Chester County by Thomas Willcox of Devonshire, England. (See text).*

1731   *The renowned James Whatman paper mill established in Kent this year. Many of the original mill properties along the river Lea had been used as cloth mills, but when the cloth trade ceased to be profitable, the buildings were taken over for the making of paper. As early as 1719 one of these converted mills was used for making brown paper, another for the production of white paper; both mills belonged to William Gill, who in 1731 sold them to James Whatman and W. Brookes. Eight years later Whatman became the sole owner and it was not many years before the watermark "J WHATMAN" was known throughout the world. Whatman rebuilt the mills and gave them the name "Turkey Mills," a trademark that he took from the old fulling cloth mill, which made a richly coloured cloth, called Turkey red. In 1830 this mill was operating nine vats, but on November 14, 1848 the old hand process was abandoned and the Turkey Mills were devoted exclusively to making paper by machine. The Turkey handmade-paper trade was then carried on at the Springfield mill, near Maidstone, Kent, where the number of vats increased from twelve in 1860 to sixteen in 1880. At the present time the well-known "J Whatman" drawing, engineering, water-colour, writing, and account-book papers are made by W. and R. Balston, and about four hundred workers are employed at this handmade-paper mill, the largest in England.*

Samuel Pope granted an English patent, May 20, for "a new art for marbling paper with a margent [margin] never practiced by any person whatsoever before he invented it."

1733 *The discovery of China clay by William Cookworthy, England. Clay was first used in "loading" paper about the year 1807; by 1870 this method of "loading" was a common practice.*

1734 *The Hollander pictured for the first time in the country of its invention, in* Groot Volkomen Moolenboek, *published in Amsterdam.*

The probable beginning of papermaking in the state of Maine. Between 1731 and 1734 Jonathan Belcher (1681–1737), colonial Governor, reported to the Lords of Trade that a paper mill had been established at Falmouth, in Casco Bay, now Portland, Maine. Samuel Waldo and Thomas Westbrook no doubt supplied the capital for the enterprise, and Richard Fry, who had learned the craft of papermaking in his native England, was in charge of technical operation. The workers were also English, probably friends of Fry. The mill was either located "across the Presumscot River" or on the banks of the Stroudwater, a small brook near Falmouth, according to latter-day records. The work of this pioneer paper mill of Maine is obscure and for the most part the only contemporary records that exist are documents relating to lawsuits that were brought about by debts contracted by the papermaker, Richard Fry. In 1734 Waldo and Westbrook leased the mill to Fry for twenty-one years at an annual rental of forty pounds. Richard Fry continued to operate the mill until 1736, but in lieu of rent he delivered to the mill-owners fifty reams of paper, valued at ten pounds, sufficient to pay the rent for only a quarter year. The non-payment of rent brought on a lawsuit against Fry, which resulted in the English papermaker spending the following several years in a debtors' prison. After this incarceration he apparently took up business in or near Boston, as is evidenced by advertisements for rags. Richard Fry died in 1745, and in administering his estate his wife, Martha, described herself as a "papermaker," so we may assume that Fry was engaged in this craft until his death. No watermarks that can be identified as having been used by the pioneer paper mill of Maine can be found. A search through the personal papers of Samuel Waldo from 1731 to 1750 reveals no watermarks of local origin; most of the marks are of English and Dutch paper mills.

Between this date and 1765, there was published in Amsterdam a four-volume set of books by Albert Seba (1665–1736), Flemish writer on natural history, in which he suggested the use of Algæ marina (seaweed) as a material for making into paper.

1735 *The original English patent for the fireproofing and waterproofing of paper, granted Obadiah Wyld, March 17.*

A.D.

1736   *The fourth paper mill in Pennsylvania, established by a branch of the Pietists of Germany, at Ephrata, Lancaster County. (See text for description.)*

1737   *The earliest advertisement for foreign wallpaper to appear in America; the material was termed "stained-paper" and sold by the booksellers. Previous to this date wallpaper was not commonly used in this country. In 1763 decorated wallpaper of domestic manufacture was presented to the Society of Arts, Manufactures, and Commerce, New York. Twenty years later there were wallpaper printers in Pennsylvania and New Jersey; the large output of Boston supplied Massachusetts as well as other states. In 1789 Philadelphia was making 10,000 pieces a month. The first patterns with glazed grounds were produced in the United States in 1824. Previous to the invention and introduction of the paper-machine which made paper in a continuous web, all wallpapers were printed on individual sheets as formed in the hand-mould, or the sheets were pasted together at the edges to form larger sheets.*

1740   *The first papermaking moulds produced in the colonies, the work of Isaac Langle, an immigrant from Germany, living in Pennsylvania. Langle died 1744.*

French laws set down the sizes and weights, also the watermarks, of paper to be sold. The list embraced 53 different names, and with additions like Large, Small, Medium, etc., the total amounted to 85 sizes of paper.

First use of the Hollander in France, at Montargis.

1741   *Jean Étienne Guettard (1715–86), French scientist, suggested the use of conferva (swamp moss) and other forms of vegetation as suitable material for papermaking.*

1743   *America's earliest complete Bible in a European language published in German by Christopher Sauer, Germantown,*

A.D.

Pennsylvania. It is thought that at least a portion of the paper used in this printing was made in the mill conducted by the Seventh-Day Baptist brotherhood at Ephrata, Lancaster County, Pennsylvania, established about 1736.

1744   *The date of the establishment of the first paper mill in the state of Virginia. The earliest mention that paper should be a product of this colony was in a book by the Reverend Hugh Jones, published in London in 1724, entitled* Present State of Virginia. *Jones wrote: "Paper-Mills I believe would answer well there; for there are good Runs of Water with Timber for nothing for building them, and I am sure the Negroes would supply them with Rags enough for Trifles; to which add the Advantage of Water Carriage; these need not interfere with the English Paper-Mills, but only supply us with such Quantities of Paper, as we buy from foreign Countries." It was not until 1742, however, that plans for the building of a Virginia mill were actually commenced, for in the* Pennsylvania Gazette, September 23, 1742, *we find the following advertisement: "An honest and diligent Person, that is capable of building a good Paper-mill, and another that understands the Making of Paper, are wanted to undertake and carry on that Business in a neighbouring Colony. Any such Persons that want Employment, will meet with a Person who will give good Encouragement, if they apply to the Printer of this Paper on the 25th Instant." The* Pennsylvania Gazette *was founded by Samuel Keimer during the month of December 1728, but by October 1729 Benjamin Franklin had become owner and editor of this influencial newspaper. It was no doubt Benjamin Franklin who inserted the "help wanted" advertisement in the* Gazette *with the hope of finding a papermaker who was capable of erecting a paper mill in Williamsburg, Virginia; the mill was to make paper for Franklin's friend William Parks, who established printing in the colony in 1730. The notice in the* Gazette *(September 23, 1742) was answered by a member of a well-known Pennsylvania papermaking family, Johann Conrad Scheetz (Schultz or Shütz), who eventually travelled to Williamsburg and built the first paper mill in Virginia. Inasmuch as Scheetz had returned to Pennsylvania by March 1744, it may be assumed that he had built the mill and placed it in charge of local workers whom he had trained as papermakers. Benjamin Franklin apparently gave considerable attention to the setting up of the Parks mill and during September 1744 he credited*

the Williamsburg mill with £55 12s. 9d. for delivery of paper, which it may be assumed was produced in the newly established Virginia paper mill. In the Virginia Almanack, for the year 1749, printed and sold by William Parks, the following advertisement for rags appeared: "THE Printer thereof; having a PAPER-MILL, now at work near this City, desires all Persons to save their old Linen Rags, for making Paper. All Sorts are useful, from the coarsest Crocus or Sail-Cloth, to the finest Holland or Cambrick; and he will give a Price in Proportion to the Fineness, from a Half-penny to Three half-pence, per Pound. Old Thread Stockings, which can be used no other way, will make good Paper. As this is the first Mill of the Kind, that ever was erected in this Colony, and has cost a very considerable Sum of Money, he hopes to meet with Encouragement suitable so useful an Undertaking. Persons who will save their Rags, and send them to the . . . with their Tobacco, may have ready Money for them of the Inspectors, who are requested to take them in." *The watermarks used by this paper mill were the arms of Virginia, a harp within a crowned escutcheon, and the initials "W P" either alone or under a crown.*

A.D.

1750   First use of cloth-backed paper in Europe, used for maps, charts, etc.

So-called "India" paper first brought to Europe from China during this year. Probably the earliest use of the "India" paper for Bible printing was in 1841, by the Oxford University Press. Paper of this kind was made in England by machine in 1875. Science and Health was first printed on English-made "India" Bible paper in 1894 in an edition of twenty-five copies, by John Wilson and Company, Cambridge, Massachusetts.

Marbled papers, invented in Persia, used in American bookbindings.

1754   The polishing of paper by the old glazing-stone prohibited in Austria, the pressing-hammer being recommended as a better means of "finishing" paper.

1755   The earliest English printing of gold upon paper for the making of wall hangings. A patent was granted Joachim Andreas Bähre, July 22, for his method of sizing paper to be printed upon in gold and silver.

First definite date of the establishment of the Eynsford paper mill, Eynsford, Kent, England. Here the well-known "Unbleached Arnold" papers are made. A mould-machine was introduced in 1895, one of the earliest machines in England for the manufacturing of imitation handmade papers. The large-size genuine handmade paper used by William Dana Orcutt in printing the monumental edition of Science and Health (1941) was a product of this mill, the sheets measuring 28 by 40 inches.

1757   "Wove" paper used for the first time in European bookprinting. John Baskerville, Birmingham, England, printed his Virgil using the newly conceived type of paper, but paper of this kind had been made in China hundreds of years previous to the rediscovery in Europe.

A.D.

1758 First forgery of English bank-notes.

1760 It is recorded that Jacob Rittenhouse, of the first American papermaking family, invented slanting plates in the beater for macerating rags. The information is meagre and lacking in technical detail.

1761 On December 2 was born in Paris Nicholas-Louis Robert, the inventor (1798) of the paper-machine.

1763 The first Bible to be printed in America in which American-made paper was extensively employed. This was the Germantown, Pennsylvania, Bible printed by Christopher Sauer, Jr.; the paper was made in the Williamsburg, Virginia, mill of William Parks and is watermarked with "W P" and crown and the arms of Virginia. The page size is 8 by 10 inches and 2,000 copies were printed.

1764 The second great work on typefounding, Manuel Typographique, by Pierre Simon Fournier (1712–68) published in France. (See: 1683.)

John Strange, an English diplomat living in Italy, suggested the use of broom, a fabaceous shrub, and other plants, for papermaking fibre.

George Cummings granted an English patent for the coating of paper. The "coating" was composed of white lead, plaster of Paris, stone lime, mixed with water in such consistency "as to lay on with a brush." This would seem to be the first instance of coating paper in Europe, a method first used by the Chinese.

On March 25, 1764, articles of partnership were signed by John Waterman, printer, his father-in-law, Jonathan Olney, Jonathan Ballou, and William Goddard, printer, for the establishment and operation of the first paper mill in Rhode Island. A mill was built on the Woonasquatucket River, near the present Olneyville, and the making of paper began in 1765. John Waterman, operator of the mill, used as a watermark in the paper the single word "PROVIDENCE" in outline letters. This mark appears in the paper of William Goddard's Providence Gazette. The Waterman management of the mill eventually passed to the Olney family, and about 1788 Christopher Olney used the watermark "C OLNEY" in outline lettering. A few years later the paper-

mark "C C O" (Christopher C. Olney) with a foul anchor on a shield (the arms of the state) appeared in the paper made at the mill. In 1780 Samuel and Martin Thurber set up a rival mill in Providence, on the banks of the Moshassuck River. In 1791 the Thurbers were using as a watermark a foul anchor, without a stock, and the initials "S T & Co" in outline letters. (Rhode Island Historical Society.)

1765   The monumental work dealing with vegetable fibres for papermaking was begun by Dr. Jacob Christian Schäffer, and between this year and 1772 his six-volume treatise was issued in Regensburg, Germany.

1767   "A method, entirely new, of dicing, flowering, colouring, or marking playing cards so as to render them easily distinguishable from the white cards now in use"; the earliest English patent pertaining to the decoration of playing cards.

By this year the first paper mill in Connecticut was in operation. The mill, on the Yantic River, Norwich, was owned by Christopher Leffingwell. Apparently the mill did not *prosper, for in 1769 the Connecticut government granted a bounty of twopence a quire on all writing paper and one penny a quire on all printing paper that Leffingwell was able to manufacture. After three years the bounty was discontinued. From the recorded production of this mill it may be assumed that two vats were in operation. Leffingwell, a man of considerable prominence in the state of Connecticut, was also engaged in the weaving of stockings, gloves, and purses. The watermarks used in the Leffingwell paper were the simple initials "C L" in the regulation outline lettering, and a more elaborate watermark with the initials*

C L

"C L" and "Norwich" with a floral ornament, all enclosed in a double-line elliptical border measuring 3¼ inches in width. In a Connecticut deed dated 1777 we note the initials had been applied to the mould on which the paper was formed in reverse, making the watermark read: "L C Norwich," but this was no doubt a mistake, which was corrected before much paper had been made. Christopher Leffingwell took his son-in-law, Thomas Hubbard, into partnership with him in the operation of the Norwich paper mill. This family later established the firm of R. and A. H. Hubbard, papermakers, and upon the site of the original Leffingwell mill the Hubbard concern set in motion the first Fourdrinier paper-machine to be built in America.

1769–73 *The precise commencement of the actual making of paper within the state of New York is a subject of controversy. Two different mills claim priority in this manufacture: the paper mill of Hugh Gaine, Hendrick Onderdonk, and Henry Remsen at Hempstead Harbour, Long Island, and the mill of John Keating located in New York*

City. According to Dr. Lawrence C. Wroth in his excellent book The Colonial Printer (*1938*), *the first proposed plan for a mill in New York State was that of William Bradford, who established a paper mill in New Jersey between 1726 and 1728. On pages 129–30 Dr. Wroth says: "Bradford's need for paper in the later years of his career as a New York printer was not satisfied by the supplies he continued to obtain from the Rittenhouse and De Wees mills. In 1724, he petitioned the New York Assembly for the sole privilege of making paper in that colony, but adverse to the encouragement of local manufacturers, the Governor and Council refused to admit to a third reading the bill for the establishment of Bradford's mill that had already passed the Lower House. Bradford was forced to turn his attention elsewhere. . . ." The earliest mention in contemporary New York newspapers of the possibility of papermaking in New York State we find in the* New-York Mercury, *March 7, 1760, as follows: "This is to give Notice, that there is come to the Place, last Month from England, a Person that knows the Preparation and making of all sorts of Paper, and it appearing to him that that Branch of Business will answer to good Profit in this Place; any Gentleman that has a good and constant Stream of fresh Water, and will erect a Paper-Mill thereon; that the Proposer will go half with him; the Gentleman to receive all the Profits, only subsistence Money, 'til the Proposer's Half of the Building shall be discharged, also an Allowance for the Water. He may be heard of at Mr. Anneyley's Gun-Smith, in New-York." From the tone of this notice it could be inferred that there was no paper mill in the immediate locality at that time. In the* New-York Gazette and Weekly Mercury, *August 15, 1768, we find this notice: "Thomas Shaw and Nathaniel Sedgfield, lately arrived from England, takes this method of acquainting the public, that they are capable of building most sorts of mills, as grist-mills, paper, and oil-mills. . . ." In the same newspaper for October 31, 1768 an advertisement appears which further shows that there were men in the vicinity capable of erecting paper mills. This advertisement* reads in part: "*Dominicus Andler, Wheelwright, from Germany, Acquaints the public, That he can make most sorts of mills, such as grist, oil, fulling,* paper, *and saw-mills. . . .*" The earliest "save rags" advertisement to appear in a New York newspaper was that of Hugh Gaine in the New-York Mercury for December 17, 1764. This notice, however, makes no mention of a paper mill in actual operation and it is possible that the rags were desired for use in New Jersey or Pennsylvania mills. The first "save rags" advertisement of John Keating appeared in the New-York Journal or the General Advertiser, February 18, 1768. Neither the advertisement of Hugh Gaine nor that of John Keating makes any reference to having paper mills in actual operation. It was not until August 17–24, 1769 that John Keating in the New-York Chronicle definitely mentions having a paper mill in operation. This advertisement reads: "*The New-York Paper Manufactory. John Keating, Takes this Method to inform the Public, that he manufactures, and has for sale, Sheathing, packing, and several Sorts of printing paper. Clean Linen Rags, are taken in (for which ready Money will be given) by said Keating, at his Store, between the Fly and Burling's-slip; and by Alexander and James Robertson, at their Printing-Office. . . .*" The first intimation in a New York newspaper that the Long Island mill of Hendrick Onderdonk was in actual operation appeared in the New-York Gazette and the Weekly Mercury, October 11, 1773, as follows: "*The printer of this paper* [Hugh Gaine], *in conjunction with two of his friends* [Hendrick Onderdonk and Henry Remsen], *have lately erected a Paper-Mill at Hempstead Harbour, on Long-Island, at a very great expense, the existence of which entirely depends on a supply of Rags, which at present are very much wanted; He therefore most humbly intreats the assistance of the good people of this province, and city in particular, to assist him in this undertaking, which, if attended with success, will be a saving of some hundreds per annum in the colony, which has been constantly sent out of it for Paper of all sorts, the manufacturing of which has but very lately orig-*

A.D.

inated here; but should the publick countenance the same it is more than probable that branch will be brought to considerable perfection in this place. The highest price will therefore be given for sorts of Linen Rags, by the Public's Humble Servant, HUGH GAINE." An interesting sidelight on the wages paid a papermaker appears in an advertisement of John Keating in the New-York Gazette and the Weekly Mercury for October 7, 1771: "Sixty Pounds per Year, with Meat, Drink, Washing and Lodging, will be given by John Keating, to a Man who understands the Paper-making Business well, in all its Branches, and good Encouragement for Journeymen Papermakers; likewise ready Money for good clean Linen Rags." In the issue for May 21, 1772 of the New-York Journal or the General Advertiser John Keating lists the kinds of paper he was making in this manner: "John Keating, at his Paper Manufactories, At and near New-York, makes All sorts of Paper and paste board; viz. Brown, whited brown; Blue, and Grey; Purple sugar loaf; Cartridge and press; waste or wrapping, different sizes. Printing and writing paper of various sorts and sizes Paste board of all qualities and sizes. Which are to [be] sold at the lowest prices, at his store in Queen-street, near Burling's slip, where he gives the best prices for Linen Rags. . . ." These various notices and advertisements from contemporary New York newspapers do not necessarily determine whether the Onderdonk mill or the Keating mill was the first in New York State; but both were apparently set up about the same time and it is difficult to say which establishment actually produced the first paper. From all indications the John Keating mill used no watermarks; at least, none has been discovered. The Onderdonk mill used the single name "ONDERDONK" in outline letters; also in a volume printed by Hugh Gaine in 1774, under the title Laws of New York, 1691–1773, the watermark shows two single circles enclosing the name "HAMSTEAD H" and the letters "O," "G," and "R," the initials of Onderdonk, Gaine, and Remsen. In 1790 a watermark used by this mill consisted of an eagle with shield clutching arrows and olive branch,

all enclosed within a circle, with the lettering "A ONDER-
DONK" *in outline underneath. By the latter quarter of the*

*eighteenth century, papermaking in and near New York
City had developed to such an extent that it was apparently profitable for wiredrawing firms to advertise that they
were able to supply papermaking appliances. In the July
10, 1775 issue of the* New-York Gazette and the Weekly
Mercury *we are informed that Richard Lightfoot, from
Dublin, at the Crown and Cushion, makes ". . . pins for
linen printers and paper stampers; laying and sewing wire
for paper makers. . . ." Also, in the* Constitutional Gazette
*for June 22, 1776, Joseph Plowman, pinmaker, in Water-
Street, advertised that he ". . . makes moulds for paper
makers with sewing wire. . . ."*

1770   *About this time came into use the first machine for the ruling of music paper and paper for account-books. An English
patent was granted John Tetlow on June 15 of this year.
Previous to this time all music and account-book paper was
ruled by hand.*

*An abridged edition of Dr. Schäffer's great work was issued
in Amsterdam, in one thin volume, now the rarest of all
the books compiled by this German scientist.*

*The second maker of papermaking moulds in North Amer-
ica was Nathan Sellers, a metal-worker living in Philadelphia. Previous to the time of Isaac Langle (see: 1740) and
Nathan Sellers all moulds used by the papermakers had
been imported from Europe.*

A.D.

1772   *First use of paper in Europe for building coaches, sedan chairs, cabinets, bookcases, screens, etc.*

1773   *An act was passed in England that decreed the death penalty for copying or imitating the watermarks in English bank-notes.*

The earliest English treatise regarding the papermaking of the natives of India. The article is entitled: "Of the culture and uses of the Son- or Sun-plant of Hindostan, with an account of the manner of manufacturing the Hindostan paper." By Lieutenant Colonel Ironside, communicated by Dr. Heberden. The paper was read December 23, 1773 and printed in Philosophical Transactions, *pages 99–104. The most complete description of Indian papermaking to appear in the eighteenth century. From Colonel Ironside's report it may be learned that papermaking in India has undergone no change to the present day. The communication suggested that the sun-plant be introduced into the West Indies as a useful fibre.*

1774   *This year Mrs. Patrick Delany began her so-called "Paper Mosaick," which soon became the talk of England and the Continent. The work consisted in making boxes, tea-caddies, etc., through the building up of myriad small rolls of coloured paper. Mrs. Delany's work received the acclaim of George III, and many examples of her work were exhibited in public museums. Her sight failed in 1784, terminating her unique career.*

Karl Wilhelm Scheele (1742–86), a Swedish chemist, discovered chlorine, which was in later years used in the bleaching of paper stock.

1776   *The earliest paper mill in central Massachusetts. This mill was established by Abijah Burbank, Sutton, Worcester County, and was located on the outlet of what was then known as Crooked Pond. In the pamphlet entitled* Early Paper Mills in Massachusetts, *by Ellery B. Crane (Worces-*

ter, 1887), the following description of this mill is given: "*It was a two-vat mill, arranged after the style of the largest and most approved plan then in use in this country. A breast-wheel twelve feet in diameter furnished the power to drive the greater portion of the machinery in the mill, which, previous to the year 1828, was composed of two engines with rolls two feet in length and twenty-six inches in diameter, one duster and one grindstone with which to sharpen the bed-plates to the engine. The rags were cut by hand on a scythe fixed in a post, or a long knife, and five men with ten or twelve girls made up the required quota of help. By running two engines to their full capacity, the accustomed fifteen hours per day, they were able to turn out from 230 to 250 pounds of paper daily, or about 1500 pounds per week.*" *This is one of the few mentions of the equipment of early New England paper mills, but the author does not state where he procured such precise information. In 1783 Caleb Burbank, the son of Abijah, took over the operation of the mill, and in 1788 Caleb and his brother, Elijah, purchased their father's property for six hundred pounds. In 1804 the Burbank brothers were using two separate watermarks:* "C BURBANK" *and* "E BURBANK" *on the left side of the sheet of paper, each with a finely executed seal of Massachusetts on the right side. The Paper Museum possesses a mould from this mill with the watermark* "C BURBANK," *the date 1804, and the Massachusetts crest done in fine wires. This mould is capable of forming sheets of paper measuring 19 by 23 inches. According to Ellery B. Crane, the Burbank mill introduced a cylinder machine in 1828, the cylinder being* "30 inches in length and 26 inches in diameter." *For seventeen years this was the only paper mill in Worcester County and during this period it was the chief source of supply for Isaiah Thomas, the renowned printer and publisher of Worcester, and founder and first president of the American Antiquarian Society. The Burbank mill could not withstand the financial panic of 1836–7 and it then passed into other hands, but continued in operation until about 1857.*

The date usually given by historians for the first paper-making in the state of Maryland, but it is possible they have been misled as to the actual maker of the first paper produced in this state. The hitherto accepted information regarding Maryland's pioneer papermaker has rested on two things: a grant of money by the Maryland Convention and a newspaper advertisement pleading for rags. Historians have long given the credit to James Dorsett as the original maker of paper in Maryland, for on June 5 or 6, 1776 he was granted the sum of 400 pounds to pay for the erection of a mill. It is likewise assumed that Mary Goddard, of the Maryland Journal, sponsored the Dorsett mill, for in the issue of her newspaper for November 8, 1775 the following advertisement appeared: "Cash given at the printing-office, for clean linnen Raggs for the use of the Paper Manufactory, now erecting near this Town. — By the Fabrick of Paper here, a vast saving will accrue, and save as much Money in the Country as the Quantity made will amount to. — The most respectable Families are encouraging the saving of Raggs for this Manufactory." Neither of these records furnishes decisive proof that James Dorsett had a paper mill in operation in Maryland in 1776. Even after the granting of the money to Dorsett it would have required considerable time to erect and equip a workable paper mill. Although the advertisement of Mary Goddard reads: ". . . now erecting near this Town," there is no positive assurance that this request for rags referred to the Dorsett mill. The compiler is indebted to Mrs. May A. Seitz, of Towson, Maryland, for a vast amount of information relative to the William Hoffman paper mill, which she contends was the first to be established in the state of Maryland. Mrs. Seitz is a direct descendant of the Hoffmans, an old paper-making family of Maryland. Mrs. Seitz quotes the following from the Maryland Archives to substantiate her claim that William Hoffman was responsible for making the first paper in Maryland: "Tuesday, 27th of May, 1776, Ordered the said Treasurer pay William Lux, for use of William Hoffman, Five Pounds, Fourteen Shillings for

Nineteen Reams of Cartridge paper." The Mr. Lux mentioned was a general storekeeper and it is assumed that he acted as selling agent for William Hoffman. The date of May 27, 1776 was at least a few days previous to the time (June 5 or 6, 1776) the money was granted to James Dorsett for the erection of his mill. According to Mrs. Seitz, the William Hoffman paper mill was actually established in 1775. William Hoffman arrived in Philadelphia from Germany in 1768 and learned the papermaking craft with the Scheetz (Sheetz, Schultz, or Shütz) family of Pennsylvania papermakers before going to Maryland to set up his own mill. The original Scheetz family is thought to have emigrated to Pennsylvania from a village near Frankfurt am Main, Germany, where they had long carried on the art of papermaking. It was probably a member of this well-known family, Johann Conrad Scheetz, who was responsible for the erection of the first paper mill in Virginia for William Parks. In turn, William Hoffman learned his trade at the Scheetz mill in Pennsylvania, and Johann Schmidt, also a German, gained his knowledge of papermaking from Hoffman. This same Johann Schmidt, about 1810, was head  vatman at the Christian Waldschmidt mill in Ohio, the second paper mill to be established in that state. We can therefore trace the direct influence of the Scheetz family of Pennsylvania papermakers in Virginia, Maryland, and Ohio. The most common watermark of the William Hoffman mill was a fleur-de-lis with the initials "W H" and a line underneath. The fleur-de-lis is of great size, measuring six inches in height and four inches in width, with the initials in proportion.

Stephen Crane, the brother of Zenas, sold on January 4, 1776 thirteen reams of "money paper" to Major Fuller and John Brown; the payment was made in 1778 by Paul Revere, who probably engraved the notes. This was the earliest instance of the Crane family making paper for money.

A.D.

Crane and Company commenced the making of bank-note paper in 1857–8 and in the "Government Mill," Dalton, Massachusetts, continues to manufacture the United States money paper to the present time.

By this year linen and cotton rags for papermaking had become so scarce that the Massachusetts General Court appointed a Committee of Safety in each locality to encourage the saving of rags. So great was the need for paper in America at this time that legislation obtained exemption from military service for all skilled papermakers. This same exemption prevailed in 1812.

1777   *In central Massachusetts the price paid by the papermakers for their rags was about threepence a pound; the following year (1778) the price had risen to eightpence and by 1779 it varied from twelvepence to two shillings a pound. By the year 1780 the price had reached three shillings and in 1781 clean rags soared to ten shillings a pound. In 1792 the price became normal, with prices from twopence to threepence being customary.*

The first paper mill in North Carolina may have been established this year, although the record is not clear and no authentic information has been forthcoming after considerable research. The statement that paper was made in North Carolina in 1777 rests upon the two following statements: in August 1775 the Provincial Congress offered a subsidy of 250 pounds to aid in the establishment of a paper mill; and in the November 14, 1777 issue of the North Carolina Gazette *there appeared an advertisement appealing for rags. The paper mill is said to have been set up near Hillsboro. To rely upon subsidy offers and the numerous "save rags" advertisements as concrete evidence that paper mills have been established may lead to faulty information. The appearance of a "save rags" notice at a certain date does not necessarily mean that a paper mill had been established in the vicinity of the newspaper's influence. Rags were scarce in the eighteenth century and it was not unusual to transport them over long distances, as there was always a*

*ready market at any paper mill. Also, the desire for the
erection of a paper mill might lead local governments to
offer subsidies without results; papermakers were not plentiful in pioneer America, especially skilled workers able to
erect and equip proper mills for the making of usable paper.
It is possible that there was a paper mill in North Carolina as early as 1777, but when we set 1791 as the date when
writing and printing paper was first made in this state, in
the mill of Gottlieb Schober, we are on much firmer ground.
Authentic data regarding this mill are contained in the* Records of the Moravians of North Carolina. *In these* Records
(*Volume V, pages 2269–2326*) *the following occurrences
with dates are set down: "Gottlieb Schober secured the approval of the Church Board to his plan for building a paper-
mill. On September 8, 1789, Christian Stauber left for Pennsylvania to learn the art of papermaking at Ephrata. . . .
Schober secured from the state of North Carolina a loan of
300 Pounds, which he was to have for three years free of
interest. . . . November 11, 1789, Johann Krause, a carpenter, left for Ephrata to find out just what kind of a house
was needed for the work. . . . It was decided that the mill
should be built on the Petersbach, a small stream about
a mile west of the centre of Salem, March 4, 1790. . . .
Stauber returned from Pennsylvania, April 21, 1790. . . .
April 29, 1791, blotting paper will be made this week. . . .
June 30, 1791, printing and writing paper are being made."
The Salem, North Carolina, Moravians were in close contact with the Moravians of Pennsylvania and it is likely that
Christian Stauber journeyed to Ephrata through this connection, but the Brethren of the Ephrata community had
little in common with the Moravians in so far as religious
life was concerned. The North Carolina paper used in early
Moravian diaries and minute-books reveals that the
Schober watermark consisted of a modest letter "S"
sewed to the moulds midway between two chain-
wires. In 1792 this initial was 5/8ths of an inch in
height and by 1806 the size was reduced to barely 9/16ths.
From the minute size of the simple "S" watermark we may*

A.D.

assume that Gottlieb Schober was a man of modesty. In his manuscripts it is noted that when writing in German he spelled his name Schober, but in all of his writings in English he spelled it Shober.

The earliest treatise on papermaking materials appeared in the New World, issued in Philadelphia.

"Wove" paper exhibited in Paris by Benjamin Franklin.

1778 *First spurious watermarks in imitation of English banknotes made by John Mathieson.*

1779 *The "wove" paper exhibited in 1777 by Benjamin Franklin was imitated in France by M. Johannot, Annonay. The paper was so well received that in 1781 Louis XVI presented Johannot with a gold medal. This type of paper was known in France as papier vélin.*

1780 *Earliest use of steel pens for writing upon paper; previous to this date quill pens were in use.*

Charles Price began the counterfeiting of Bank of England notes, which baffled the authorities; Price hanged himself in Bridewell prison.

In America about this time the old stamping-mills gave way to the Hollander for the maceration of materials for papermaking.

1782 *First Bible printed in America in the English language, by Robert Aitken, Philadelphia. The volume embraces more than 1400 unnumbered pages, the page size being 3½ by 6 inches.*

1783 *Joseph Michel Montgolfier (1740–1810), famed papermaker of France, invented first practical balloon.*

1784 *First complete book to be printed in Europe on paper made from material other than linen and cotton. The paper was manufactured from an admixture of grass, lime-tree bark, and other vegetable fibres. France.*

1785   *European printed "all-over" pattern papers identified by the maker's name on the margins were in use in America at this period.*

1786   *The Society of Sciences, Philadelphia, offered a prize for the best suggestion to protect paper from the ravages of insects, for both the American and the West Indian market.*

The Society for the Encouragement of Arts, Manufactures, and Commerce, London, granted its medal for the best English-made paper suitable for copperplate printing. Mr. Lepard and Mr. Bates submitted the finest specimens, which were judged to be superior to the French plate-printing papers that had been previously imported.

In this year there was printed in London a book of poems by C. M. de Villette (1736–93). Part of the edition was on paper made from lime-tree bark, the remaining part on paper fabricated from marshmallow.

1787   *In the September 1, 1787 issue of John Bradford's Kentucke Gazette, Lexington, the following advertisement appeared: "Lincoln, August 15, 1787. The subscriber begs leave to inform the Public that he is now engaged in erecting a Paper Mill, on a branch of Dicks river near his grist mill, and expects to have it fully compleated by the first of November next. He flatters himself that in the execution of an undertaking which promises such advantages to the District, he will meet with the greatest encouragement from every good citizen who wishes to see Arts and manufactures flourish in Kentucke. But as a paper manufactory cannot be carried on without rags, he therefore most earnestly recommends it to all persons to be particular in saving all their old linen and cotton. Proper persons will be appointed in different parts of the county to receive rags, for*

A.D.

which he will give a higher price in cash than is given for that article in Maryland or Pensylvania. JACOB MYERS." *From the text of this advertisement it would appear that Jacob Myers operated the first paper mill in the state of Kentucky; it is definitely stated ". . . he is now engaged in erecting a* Paper Mill. . . ." *Here is another of those harmless-appearing pitfalls into which an over-zealous historian might unwittingly plunge. Jacob Myers did not build a paper mill in Kentucky and there was no paper made in that state until 1793, and then not by Myers. The county records of Kentucky show that Jacob Myers acquired thousands of acres of land in the state, at least* on paper, *and the local historians are not hesitant in calling him a "land hog." He arrived in Kentucky from Philadelphia as early as 1780 and at once began acquiring land and property with the thought, no doubt, of building up a small empire for himself in the "western country." In 1790 he erected an iron furnace on Slate Creek in what is now Bath County, and in 1793 he became interested in a line of packet boats operating between Cincinnati and Pittsburgh. Myers was a pioneer promoter and had many schemes, a few of which he carried to termination, but in so far as his paper mill was concerned the notice itself in the* Kentucke Gazette *was all that materialized of this ambitious undertaking. For the earliest papermaking in Kentucky see 1793.*

The Society for the Encouragement of Arts, Manufactures, and Commerce, London, gave its silver medal to Thomas Greaves, Mill-Bank, near Warrington, for his successful experiments in manufacturing paper from "within twigs . . . with a few green nettles" (? *black willow,* Salix nigra).

This is the probable date of the beginning of papermaking in the state of Delaware. The mill, located on the Brandywine two miles north of Wilmington, was operated by Thomas and Joshua Gilpin. The Gilpins were descendants of an old Norman family with the original name of De Gaylpyn. The land along the Brandywine was acquired by

A.D.

the family as early as 1745 and the original mill was used for grinding corn, the second mill to be located on this part of the stream. The Gilpins, who were inventors of no little accomplishment, devised pumping and dredging machines that were acclaimed by their friend Benjamin Franklin. The approximate time of the beginning of the Gilpin paper mill may be placed about 1787, although there is no definite basis for this date. A letter dated April 30, 1788, written by Joshua Gilpin to Benjamin Franklin, reads: "I beg to present His Excellency, Benjamin Franklin, Esq., with samples of such kinds of paper as have been made at the Brandywine Mill." It may be assumed that specimens of the various papers made by the Gilpins would naturally have been sent to Franklin immediately upon completion of the first well-made paper. No doubt at least a year was required before the mill was in production, hence the probable date of 1787 as the establishment of the first paper mill in Delaware. The watermarks used BRANDYWINE *by the Gilpins were various, with the initials "J G & Co," the name "*BRANDYWINE*," and the well-known post-horn predominating.*

1788   *John Davis, Salisbury-court, Fleet Street, London, was presented a medal by the Society for the Encouragement of Arts, Manufactures, and Commerce, London, for the excellence of his marbled papers used in bookbindings.*

Nicholas Desmarets (1725–1815) issued in Paris his fine work on papermaking: Traité de l'art de fabriquer le papier.

On August 12 an English patent was granted to Charles Lewis Ducrest for his invention of "making paper for the building of houses, bridges, ships, boats, and all sorts of wheel carriages, sedan chairs, chairs, tables and book-cases either entirely of paper, or wood and iron covered with paper." (See: 1772, 1868.)

Benjamin Franklin on June 20 read before the members of the American Philosophical Society, Philadelphia, a treatise

A.D.

on papermaking and stated that the Chinese had overcome the difficulties of making paper in unusually large sheets.

1790 By act of Congress of April 10, 1790, the first United States patent system was founded. From this date until 1812 most of the patents that were issued pertained to agriculture. Owing to the Patent Office fire of 1836 the records previous to this date are incomplete, but the following eighteenth-century papermaking patents were known to be issued; no complete details are extant: J. Biddis, May 31, 1794; C. Austin, December 14, 1798; R. R. Livingston, October 28, 1799.

There is a legend that the first blue paper made in England was the result of an accident: the vatman's wife dropped a bag of blueing in the pulp. The paper so coloured was accepted at an advanced price and the vatman's wife was rewarded with a new cloak.

On April 24 of this year George Washington visited the paper mill owned by Hendrick Onderdonk, Hempstead Harbour, Long Island, an early paper mill in New York State. It is said that Washington formed a sheet of paper at the vat upon this occasion; the sheet was supposed to have been retained in the mill as a remembrance of the visit, but no record of it now exists.

The hydraulic press invented in England by Joseph Bramah. This improved press was not used in English paper mills until about 1800. It then supplanted the ancient screw press for expelling the water from the newly formed sheets of paper as they were held between the felts.

John Phipps, an Englishman, patented a method of teaching writing by means of watermarked lines in paper. (See: 1825.)

Some time between this year and 1795 Vermont's first paper mill was established. The founder of this mill was Matthew Lyon, one of the most discussed American politicians of *the nineteenth century, certainly the most publicized paper-maker of the period; but unfortunately his publicity did not centre on the craft of making paper. Matthew Lyon was born near Dublin, Ireland, July 14, 1750, and in 1763 he was apprenticed to a Dublin printer, where he worked at type-case and hand press for the following two years. He then emigrated to the New World, landing in Connecticut. With his two-year knowledge of printing as a means of live-lihood he journeyed to Vermont, where he settled in a com-munity that became known as Fairhaven, now Fair Haven, Rutland County. Here he set up a printing office and paper mill. According to Joel Munsell (1876 edition, page 52), Lyon manufactured paper from the bark of the basswood tree, but this statement cannot be verified and is most doubtful. In 1793 Matthew Lyon established a newspaper, the Farmer's Library, later the Fairhaven Gazette. The pa-per mill was built for the purpose of furnishing paper for his own publications; apparently no watermarks were used. Lyon is much more fully recorded in history on account of his political exploits than for anything he may have accom-plished in pioneer American papermaking. Through the publicity of a physical encounter with another member of Congress Lyon's prestige began to wane in Vermont and he decided to leave his paper mill and printing office and move west. He settled in Kentucky, where he founded the town of Eddyville and the county of Lyon, named after him. Matthew Lyon later moved farther west, to Arkansas, where he died on August 1, 1822. Eleven years later the remains of Vermont's first papermaker were brought to Kentucky, where they now rest in Lyon County. The files of contemporary newspapers devote columns to the politi-cal adventures of Matthew Lyon in Vermont, Kentucky, and Arkansas, but nothing whatever is mentioned relative to his pioneer papermaking.*

1792   *The date when papermaking is thought to have been in-troduced into the state of New Hampshire. As with the establishment of other paper mills, the information is based* on a *"save rags" advertisement, which appeared in the* Cheshire Advertiser *for March 22, 1792. The proprietor of this paper mill is thought to have been Moses Johnson, who inserted the advertisement in the Keene newspaper (see page 310). The earliest printing in New Hampshire was done at Portsmouth by Daniel Fowle in 1756, and as there was no paper being made in the state at this period, the paper was brought in from New England mills or imported from Europe. In* Ray Nash's Pioneer Printing *at* Dartmouth *(1941) it is noted that some of the paper used by Judah Padock and Alden Spooner at Dresden, Vermont (now Hanover, New Hampshire), bears the watermark of Christopher Leffingwell, the first papermaker in Connecticut, and also the watermarks of French papermakers. In the* Dresden Mercury *and* Universal Intelligencer *for August 9, 1779, apparently the last issue of this newspaper, the following interesting "save rags" advertisement appeared: "Cash Given at the Printing-Office, for Linen Rags fine or coarse. When the great Importance of collecting and saving of such* RAGS *as are entirely useless in Cloathing, and the absolute Necessity we stand in of a Sufficiency of such to furnish Paper for the daily Consumption of this growing Country, are duly considered, the Printers flatter themselves that the good people of this and the neighbouring Towns will manifest their Zeal for the public Good, by saving and supplying them with such Quantities as they may be able to procure, for which a generous Price will be given." Here again we have an advertisement for rags at a time when there was no paper mill in either Vermont or New Hampshire. During the eighteenth and nineteenth centuries there was always a demand for good linen and cotton rags and it was not unusual to haul the bales and bags of rags over long distances to the paper mills; the appearance of a "save rags" notice does not necessarily mean that a paper mill was near by.*

The founding of T. J. Marshall and Company, Stoke Newington, London, makers of moulds for handmade paper.

516 CHRONOLOGY OF PAPER AND ALLIED SUBJECTS

This firm is one of three mould-makers that continue in operation in England. The "dandy-roll" was invented or perfected by this firm between 1825 and 1830.

1793 *The earliest mention of a Kentucky paper mill that actually materialized (see: 1787, Jacob Myers) appeared in the Kentucky Gazette, Lexington, April 7, 1792, and reads: "A* PAPER MILL. *The Subscribers inform the Public, that they have undertaken the building a* PAPER MILL, *at Craig's Fulling Mill, Woodford County. They flatter themselves they will be able to supply the District with Paper the ensuing Winter, if the Public will be so obliging to save their Rags for that purpose, without which (we need not inform them) the Mill will be useless. We therefore earnestly request the considerate part of the people, to encourage so useful a branch of business, by encouraging the less thoughtful part, (servants, etc.) to save them; and that as soon as possible, proper plans will be adopted for collecting them, and a generous price given.* CRAIG, PARKERS & CO." *This mill was erected in Georgetown, in what is now Scott County, and was in actual operation in the spring of 1793. In the* Kentucky Gazette *for March 30, 1793 and several succeeding issues, the following advertisement appeared: "*CRAIG, PARKERS & CO'S. PAPER MANUFACTORY *is now actually making paper, and we make no doubt but that in the course of this spring, we shall be able to furnish this state in all kinds of paper, provided we can get a sufficient supply of rags; nor have we any reason to fear, from the success we have already had in collecting rags, but that we shall be plentifully supplied, provided the good people of this state can be prevailed on to give them, and as the prosecution of this business depends entirely upon that article, we earnestly hope that the importance of the manufactory to the state at large, is a sufficient argument to the individuals to save their rags. Craig, Parkers & Co., March 29, 1793." In the* History of Kentucky *by Lewis Collins (Vol. I, 1882) there is given a description of this pioneer Kentucky paper mill: "The first paper mill was built* *at Georgetown by the Baptist preacher, Rev. Elijah Craig, and his partners, Parkers & Co. The enterprise was begun in the summer of 1791, but the manufacture of paper successfully was not accomplished until March, 1793. The mill house (as seen in 1818 by E. H. Stedman, who is still living (1874) a few miles distant, in Franklin County) was 40 by 60 feet in size, the basement of stone, and the two and a half stories above of wood — the best frame Mr. Stedman ever saw, with not a cut-nail in the building, even the shingles being put on with oak pins. The large volume of clear water from the Royal spring, running over a limestone bottom, was an attractive sight. The mill dam was erected in 1789. Here was turned out the first sheet of paper in the Great West, made by hand, sheet by sheet. . . . This first mill was burnt down in 1837. Some printed sheets of the paper still exist; and one other elegant relic, now in the paper mill of Mr. Stedman, on Elkhorn, in Franklin County — a powerful iron screw, of finished English make, 6 inches in Diameter, 4½ feet long, and weighing 800 pounds. . . ."* The E. H. Stedman mentioned by Collins was Ebenezer Hiram Stedman, whose diary forms one of the most interesting documents in pioneer American papermaking. The *"powerful iron screw"* used in the pressing of paper has long since disappeared and nothing remains today of the old Craig, Parkers & Company mill except a few embedded stones along the brook which may have been the foundation of the dam built in 1789. Elijah Craig was a prominent Baptist minister of Kentucky and he had a wide acquaintance among the preachers of the *"western country."* In the diary of Reverend David Barrow, of Virginia, the entry for June 8, 1795 reads: *"This evening went home with Elder Elijah Craig in Georgetown, Scott County, 12 miles. Elder Craig has been a great blessing to this new country for he has a paper mill, fulling mill, a distillery, merchant mill, tavern, and a store."* The Parkers were evidently merchants of Kentucky, as an advertisement appeared in the Kentucky Gazette, January 1, 1791, setting forth *"A large and general assortment of goods for sale by*

Alexander and James Parker." The most common water-mark of Craig, Parkers & Company consisted of the in-itials "C & P" (1-1/16 inches in height) on the left with a small eagle on the right side of the sheet of paper. The initials are usually carelessly executed and out of position on the moulds, but the eagles, with a wing-spread of one

and one-half inches, were made of heavy wire and show a fair amount of ability in execution. A watermark with the initials "C & P" within a rugged heart is found in papers from the 1812 period. From an examination of manuscripts, deeds, maps, wills, letters, etc., written on paper from this mill, it may be determined that Craig, Parkers & Company possessed at least four pairs of laid moulds previous to the year 1812. Paper manufactured by this pioneer Kentucky mill was used extensively in Kentucky, Tennessee, Ohio, and throughout the West as this was the first paper mill west of the mountains.

A church constructed of paper was built at Hop, near Ber-gen, Norway. The builder was Cancellieraad Christie, who used papier-mâché soaked in vitriol water, then mixed with lime that had been treated with curdled milk and white of egg. This pulpy material was used in the manner of plaster, and even the roof was composed of it. The church was 48 feet in diameter, with a seating capacity of 800. The best description of the church of paper was written by Captain Cornelius de Jong, a Dutchman who visited the paper edi-fice in June 1797. The church of paper was demolished in 1830 after thirty-seven years of service.

Earliest English patent relating to the heating of papermak-ing vats by steam was granted to William Scott and George

Gregory. This was an advanced step in papermaking technique as previous to this invention all vats had been heated by individual charcoal-burners.

Earliest patent to be given in America for improvements in papermaking moulds granted to John Carnes, Jr., of Delaware. The original text of this patent was destroyed in the Patent Office fire of 1836 and no records are extant.

The first English patent pertaining to papermaking moulds followed the American patent by three months, granted to Joseph Moseley Elliott.

1794   *In the issue of the* Centinel of the North-Western Territory, *Cincinnati, the first newspaper in Ohio, for December 20, 1794, the following significant notice appeared: "Being disappointed in getting of paper according to expectations, has obliged us to Print on so bad equallity. We hope our subscribers will consider the great inconvenience that we labour under in procuring paper at so far a distance from where it is manufactured." The nearest paper mill to Cincinnati at that time would have been that of Craig, Parkers & Company, Georgetown, Kentucky, which had been in operation over a year when this notice appeared.*

1795   *Massachusetts had twenty paper mills of two vats each; twenty workers were employed by each mill.*

Isaiah Thomas, printer of Worcester, Massachusetts, used "wove" paper for the first time in an American book, a small volume of poems by Charlotte Smith. (See: 1757.)

1796   *The first English patent granted for the embossing of paper, to John Gregory Hancock. The embossing was produced by placing paper upon an engraved die and subjecting it to pressure.*

The erection of the first paper mill in western Pennsylvania was begun this year. The mill was operated by Jonathan

Sharpless and Samuel Jackson, both Quakers from eastern Pennsylvania. The earliest mention of this paper mill appeared in the January 12, 1796 issue of the Western Telegraphe & Washington Advertiser, *Washington, Pennsylvania: "We are happy in being able to announce to the public with a considerable degree of confidence, that a* PAPER MILL *will shortly be erected on this side the Mountains — that there is little doubt of its being completed by the ensuing fall. The Gentleman who undertakes it, is of an enterprising disposition, and capable of going through with the business with spirit. The work, for which several preparations are already made, will be erected on a never failing stream, in a thick settled part of the country, and close to navigation. The advantages accruing to our community from this addition to its manufactures will be very great, and it behooves every well-wisher to the community, to contribute his mite towards the supporting it. It cannot be carried on without a supply of rags: — Of these every family can supply more or less; and there will be stores in every town, and various parts of the country ready to receive them. Every patriotic family then, will doubtless cause all their Rags to be preserved, and forwarded to some place where they are collected, not so much for the pecuniary advantage to be derived from them, as for the pleasure arising from having deserved well of their Country. . . ." In an advertisement in the same newspaper, May 24, 1796, the names of the proprietors of the mill and its location are given, along with the ever persistent appeal for rags. The notice reads: "To the Public. Samuel Jackson & Co. Inform the inhabitants of the Western Country, that they are making every exertion to forward the Completion of their* Paper Mill, *which they are erecting, on Big Redstone, about four miles from Brownsville, in Fayette County, a never failing Stream; That they have experienced Workmen engaged to carry on the work, and hope to be able before the expiration of the present year to furnish their fellow Citizens with the different kinds of paper usually in demand of their manufacture, and as good quality as any brought from below the mountains. They request their fellow Citizens generally, to promote their undertaking by encouraging the saving and collecting of rags, and inform Merchants and Store-keepers in particular, that they will give them a generous price in Cash for such clean Linnen or Cotton rags as they may collect. Redstone, May 19, 1796." It was probably the summer of 1797 before the first usable paper*

was made, for in the June 20, 1797 issue of the Western Telegraphe & Washington Advertiser *this notice appeared: "The paper which you now read was manufactured at Redstone, by Messrs. Jackson and Sharpless, and forwarded with a request to publish thereon a number of the Telegraphe, that the public might judge of their performance." Also the* Pittsburgh Gazette, *June 24, 1797, states that the paper used was from the Redstone mill and sets down the accustomed appeal to "save rags." It is recorded that the paper mill was 40 by 75 feet, three storeys high, with a half-storey cellar on the creek side. If these dimensions are correct, the Redstone mill was somewhat larger than the Georgetown, Kentucky, mill of Craig, Parkers & Company. These two pioneer mills supplied much of the paper used in western Pennsylvania, Kentucky, Ohio, Indiana, Illinois, and even Missouri during the late eighteenth and early nineteenth centuries; both establishments played a very considerable part in the opening of the West. The watermarks used by Jackson and Sharpless were the initials "J & S" in various sizes in outline letters, along with a well-executed crouching beaver; also a dove and olive branch with the initials "J & S" were used. The dove emblem was no doubt suggested by the abundant use of this mark by eastern Pennsylvania papermakers, as Jonathan Sharpless gained his knowledge of the craft in Chester County, Penn-*

sylvania. The single word "REDSTONE" in neat outline letter-ing was also a familiar watermark of Jackson and Sharpless.

1797   *A pamphlet was issued in London setting forth the use of jute as a papermaking material. The brochure was printed on paper made from this substance.*

Earliest use of yellows and browns (lead chromate) in dye-ing European paper.

1798   *The paper-machine invented by Nicholas-Louis Robert, a Frenchman. The small, undeveloped machine was set up in the Essonnes paper mill and the French government granted Robert a fifteen-year patent and advanced money for the perfection of the machine. Aside from the models made by Robert little was accomplished in France and it was not until a number of years later that a really practical machine was built in England by John Gamble and Bryan Donkin.*

1799   *In France at this time the largest paper mill was located in Montargis, with thirty vats, requiring 810 tons of rags each year. Another large mill in France, at Vougeot, had twelve vats. The capacity of a paper mill of the pre-machine era was computed by the number of vats in operation, each vat capable of producing from two and a half to five reams of paper each day.*

Experiments made in England in imitating the Swedish stone paper, or slate. The material consisted of sheets of paper pulp, bole, chalk, linseed oil, etc. The sheets were made about 14 by 23 inches in size and in the thickness of pasteboard. They were used in sheathing ships and in house construction. An account of this paper is given in the Philo-sophical Magazine, *London, January 1799.*

G. A. Senger, a German naturalist, compiled a pamphlet suggesting the use of conferva ("water-wool") as a paper-

A.D.

making material. The treatise was printed upon paper manufactured from this marine plant.

1800   *Connecticut had sixteen paper mills in operation, employing 160 workmen and consuming 320 tons of rags annually. By 1840 Connecticut was listed as being the fourth state in the country in production of paper. At this time, Hartford, Connecticut, as a publishing centre was surpassed only by New York, Philadelphia, and Boston.*

Matthias Koops, living in London, began his experiments in the use of wood, straw, and the de-inking of paper. Three books were compiled by Koops using these materials for the paper upon which they were printed. The greater part of the present-day paper industry is founded upon the pioneer work of Koops.

The Original Society of Papermakers founded in England, the first organized union of this trade. As early as 1784 there was a labour strike among the papermakers of England, but it was not until 1800 that the artisans were actually organized into a society. (See: 1390.)

Germany operated 500 paper mills, producing 1,250 tons of paper a year; Spain had 200 mills, Sweden 24, and Russia 26. The largest Russian mill of this period operated 28 Hollanders and 70 vats, with a production of 1,100 reams of paper a week. The consumption of rags of this Russian mill was 800 tons annually.

The invention of rosin sizing for paper by Moritz Friedrich Illig (1777–1845), but not mentioned by him until 1807, when he made known his discovery in Erbach, Germany. The earliest practical rosin sizing of paper in the United States was probably done by a German papermaker, Joseph Krah, who emigrated to Baltimore in 1830.

Although blotting paper was made hundreds of years previous to this date, it did not come into general use until the

A.D.

beginning of the nineteenth century. The customary method of blotting ink upon paper was by the use of sand. (See: 1465.)

1801   *First paper mill in Massachusetts west of the Connecticut River, founded in Dalton by Zenas Crane, John Willard, and Henry Wiswell. This was a one-vat mill with a daily production of twenty posts, or between five and six reams of paper. The personnel of this mill consisted of an engineer at $3.00 a week; a vatman and a coucher "at $3.50 per week and board themselves"; a layboy at sixty cents a week and board; and Mr. Crane, the superintendent and general manager, whose partners allowed him $9.00 a week. By the year 1822 Zenas Crane had bought out his partners, as well as another mill that had been established in Dalton in 1809. Zenas Crane continued the business until his death, in 1845, when his two sons, Zenas Marshall and James B., succeeded to the property and carried it on as Crane and Company.*

John Gamble on April 20 received the earliest English patent pertaining to the paper-machine. The title of this patent is: "An invention of making paper in single sheets without seams or joining, from one to 12 feet and upwards wide & from one to 45 feet and upwards in length." The machine is described as follows: "a sheet of copper [screen] joined at both ends, passing round two cylinders, forms an endless web, and this receives the pulp, which, travelling along, passes between two cylinders. The paper is afterwards wound from between the cylinders upon a wooden roller, which, when loaded, another is substituted in its place without stopping the machine." (The paper was dried in lofts, as had been previously done with the handmade product.) (See: 1820, Crompton.)

Johann Christoph Ludwig suggested that the German papermakers adopt windmills for the maceration of paper-

making materials and published a pamphlet in 1820 outlining his proposal.

1802   *The importance of the Craig, Parkers & Company and the Jackson and Sharpless mills (see: 1793 and 1796) to newspaper publishing in the West is shown by the following notice that appeared in the* Scioto Gazette, Chillicothe, Ohio, *for November 13, 1802: "By reason of the Menongehalia River not having been navigable for some time past, we have been disappointed in receiving a supply of paper from Red-Stone, which was contracted for and to have been delivered at the mouth of the Scioto River last month: in order to obtain a supply we sent to the mills at George-Town, Kentucky, but in this effort we were also disappointed, there not being a ream to be had, we have therefore been under the necessity of sending by land to Red-Stone, at a very heavy expense, from whence we shall be furnished in two weeks, our readers will therefore excuse our issuing half a sheet, during that period. From the circumstance of the high price at which paper now comes at, the Editor earnestly calls on those indebted, to come forward and make payment." In the December 18, 1802 issue of this same newspaper it was stated that owing to lack of paper it was impossible to publish for two weeks; the notice further states that arrangements have been made for a constant supply of paper, but does not mention the source.*

Probably the earliest use of bleached wood-pulp paper in English book production. The book, an edition of The Mathematical and Philosophical Works, *to which is prefixed the author's life, by the Right Rev. John Wilkins, was printed in London by C. Whittingham.*

The mechanical agitator, or "hog," for the agitation of papermaking fibre in the vat was introduced in England.

A.D.

1803   On June 7 John Gamble received a supplementary patent to his patent of 1801.

First paper produced in Lower Canada, at Saint André d'Argenteuil (St. Andrews East), Quebec, by New Englanders from Newton Lower Falls, Massachusetts. The enterprise was headed by Walter Ware and the paper was made for printing the Montreal Gazette. (See: 1819.)

1804   The American Company of Booksellers offered a gold medal for the greatest quantity and best quality of paper made from material other than linen and cotton rags. At the same time a silver medal was offered for the best wrapping paper made from materials not before used in the manufacture of paper.

Aloys Senefelder (1771–1834), a Bavarian, accomplished the first successful lithography, thereby creating a demand for still greater quantities of paper.

1805   On April 25 Joseph Bramah, the inventor of the hydraulic press (see: 1790), received an English patent for "an application of machinery by which sheets of much larger dimensions can easily be made than can possibly be done by hand in the usual way." Apparently Bramah's patent was not carried to any termination, as this inventor appears to have had but little influence upon the final development of the paper-machin

In the United Kingdom during this year there were 760 vats in operation, producing 16,502 tons of handmade paper; this same year there were six paper-machines with an output of 557 tons. In thirty years (by 1835) the number of machines had increased to 82, with a production of 24,475 tons, while the number of vats had decreased to 430, with an output of 11,215 tons. In the following thirty years (by 1865) the number of machines had grown to 390, with a production of 103,700 tons; at this time there remained only 109 vats, with an output of 3,310 tons. By the year 1900 the remaining *vats* totalled 104, producing 3,886 tons, but the number of paper-machines had increased to 428, manufacturing 647,764 tons of paper. Thus in ninety-five years of papermaking in the United Kingdom the number of hand-made papermaking *vats* fell from 760 to 104, and the number of paper-machines in operation advanced from 6 to 428. In the early days of the paper-machine, when the widths were comparatively narrow, it was stated that a machine of thirty inches could supplant the work of four *vats*; a machine of forty inches could produce the paper ordinarily made at 6 *vats*; a forty-four-inch machine could duplicate the production of 8 *vats*; and a fifty-four-inch machine the output of twelve *vats*.

1806   The name Fourdrinier appears for the first time in relation to the paper-machine now bearing this well-known appellation. A patent dated July 24, 1806 was taken out by Henry Fourdrinier under the following specifications: "A number of moulds, of the description called laid and wove, are hooked together to form one long mould. A platform to hold the said moulds in such a manner that the moulds shall slide along backwards or forwards, but in no other direction. A vessel or trough from which the paper stuff or material is caused to flow upon the moulds through holes, each provided with one or more registers to limit or mark the flow of stuff. A set of cylinders, upon which is passed, in the manner of a jack towel, an endless web of felting. There is a third cylinder in contact with one of these cylinders, and this third cylinder communicates by means of another web of felt with an additional pair of pressing cylinders. When the moulds arrive at the first cylinder, the felt web takes off the paper and conveys it to the first pair of pressing cylinders, whence it proceeds to the second pair, and afterwards to any fit place of reception, so that continuing the process, paper of any length may be made, and with separate moulds." On August 14, 1807, additional improvements in the machine were granted to Henry Fourdrinier and his brother Sealy.

John Pine established the Hayle mill, Tovil, Maidstone, Kent, England. This mill was acquired in 1811 by the Green family and is now under the firm name of J. Barcham Green and Son. The handmade paper fabricated from Japanese mulberry-bark fibres used in the printing of one copy of the Oxford Lectern Bible (1935), designed by Bruce Rogers, was made in this mill. This copy of the Bruce Rogers masterpiece is in the Congressional Library, Washington, D. C.

A United States patent was procured by Francis Guy, Baltimore, for the manufacture of floor coverings composed of paper. It was claimed that the paper carpets were equal to the regulation product at about half the cost.

The commencement of the use of moiré papers, embossed by heated cylinders, used in bookbindings.

The date of the establishment of the earliest known paper mill in South Carolina. Prior to the American Revolution the provincial governors of South Carolina were constantly assuring the King's Ministry that "positively NO MANUFAC- TURES *of any kind inimical to British commerce are, or are to be, established in the Province." It is only natural that under such conditions had there been a pre-Revolution paper mill in South Carolina the owners would have been reluctant to advertise it widely. On September 8, 1768 Lieutenant-Governor William Bull sent a message to Lord Hillsborough in which it was officially stated that there were "no Paper-Mills" in the province. Through a series of letters still intact in Charleston, the date of the first known paper mill in South Carolina has been established. These letters in the possession of Dr. Joseph I. Waring, a descendant of the original mill-owner, have been copied by Dr. John Bennett, also of Charleston. The first letter relative to the paper mill is dated November 12, 1806, and was written in Columbia, from Benj. Waring to Richard Waring. The letter reads: ". . . I suppose you have heard of my erecting a Paper-Mill. Let me know if it would be convenient for you to purchase or receive old Rags and send up here by boat.*

I would always endeavour to have money in your hands for that purpose, and will allow you ten percent on the cost of the Rags." In this letter is set forth the importance of rags to a paper mill, a plea that is ever present all through the history of pioneer American papermaking. The next letter shows that paper was being made on a fairly large scale and gives the price of the paper. The letter is dated Columbia, March 30, 1809, from George Waring, Benjamin's son, to Messrs. Waring & Hayne, the mill agents: "Gentlemen: By the bearer, W. Powell, Patroon of Capt. Wade's boat, you will receive Seventeen Reams of large printing Paper . . . when I was in Charleston I enquired the price of that size Paper, and was informed that they sold it at Four Dolls. and a quarter per Ream; and I think mine is full as good as what I saw. But don't take less than Four Dollars per Ream." It appears that Waring was experimenting with the use of raw cotton for making into paper, for a letter dated, Columbia, October 10, 1809, reads: ". . . With respect to the Cotton Mr. I. Robertson has, — it does not answer for Paper as well as Rags, unless for Wrapping Paper; though, if it is clear of sticks, motes, etc., I may put a proportion of Rag with it to make it answer for coarse Printing Paper. If that is the case I will give him his price of Three Dollars per cwt.; but if it is not clear of trash, I could not afford to give him more than one or two Cents per lb., according to the strength and cleanness of it. The Strength I would make no objection to, if it will answer for coarse Printing Paper; but Wrapping Paper requires principally to be strong." The Waring mill made paper for at least four years, but a search has found no paper that could positively be identified as having been made in South Carolina's first mill; naturally there are no records of watermarks if such were ever employed.

1807   *Additional improvements in the paper-machine were patented by Thomas Cobb, an Englishman; and Léger Didot, a Frenchman, received further English patents in 1812 and 1817.*

The first paper mill in Ohio was established this year by Jacob Bowman, Brownsville, Pennsylvania, John Bever, George Town, Beaver County, Pennsylvania, and John Coulter, Brook County, Virginia. An agreement among these three men was drawn August 1, 1806 ". . . for the erection of a paper mill near the mouth of Little Beaver Creek. . . ." Perhaps the earliest mention of this pioneer Ohio mill in a contemporary publication appeared in Zadok Cramer's Navigator, *published in Pittsburgh in 1808. The notice appears on page 44 and reads: "Little Beaver Creek, left side. A quarter of a mile below George Town. Near the mouth of this creek are two grist, one saw, and a paper mill erected in 1807–08 by Messrs. Coulter, Beaver* [sic] *and Bowman." This would place the mill in Ohio, near Fawcettstown, now East Liverpool, Columbiana County. Both Bowman and Bever came to Ohio from western Pennsylvania, not far from the Jackson and Sharpless "Redstone" mill, and it is reasonable to surmise that they were influenced by the success of this mill. The only contemporary description of the building of the Fawcettstown mill or the paper made there is given in Browne's* Cincinnati Almanac *for the year 1810, after John W. Browne, the publisher, had made a visit to the vicinity some time previous to 1809, when the* Almanac *was actually printed. Browne's description reads: ". . . the creek is full of large rocks, and affords a romantic scene. About 2 m. up from the mouth is a paper mill, built of stone, and admirably calculated to perform a great deal of business. The paper made at this mill is equal, if not superior, to any made this side the mountains; and there is every reason to suppose, from the attention paid to the manufactory, that a large stroke of business will be satisfactorily carried on. How strange to say, that though there are not less than ten or twelve printing presses in the state of Ohio, yet the only paper mill in the state is situate within one mile of its eastern boundary. There does not appear a better, or more sure and lucrative speculation, than what might be deserved from a well conducted paper mill; and it is sincerely to be wished, that some adventurous*

A.D.

gentlemen would permit their attention to be directed to that object." The watermark used by Coulter, Bever and Bowman consists of a badly drawn eagle with spread wings, the eagle claws clutching a branch; underneath the eagle is the word "OHIO" in outline letters, also crudely executed. This emblem appears on the right and the initials "C B & B" on the left side of the sheets of paper; the "&" is usually placed backwards on the moulds. The spread of the eagle wings is about 2¾ inches, but a decided variation in the twisting of the wires makes it possible to determine the number of moulds possessed by the mill. For the most part the moulds were of the "wove" style capable of forming paper measuring approximately 13 by 16 inches. The paper produced by this pioneer Ohio mill is of very good quality, having been made from well-selected linen and cotton rags without being subjected to detrimental chemical treatment. What was probably the second paper mill within the confines of Ohio was the mill of Christian Waldschmidt, the son of Simon Waldschmidt, the master of a paper mill in Gengenbach, on the Kinzig, Germany. Young Waldschmidt (Anglicized to Waldsmith) emigrated to America in 1786 and readily found work in a paper mill in Montgomery County, Pennsylvania. The Ohio Waldsmith mill was established on a bend of the Little Miami River, near a locality known as "Germany," but during the Civil War the name of the settlement was changed to Camp Dennison. The earliest contemporary mention of this mill may be found in the January 16, 1810 issue of Liberty Hall, *Cincinnati, which states: "Christian Waldsmith announces his intentions of building a paper mill on the Little Miami River." It was not until a year later, however, that the mill was in actual operation, as is evidenced by the following editorial in the* Western Spy, *Cincinnati, January 26, 1811: "Our impression appears for the first time on paper manufactured at Mr. Waldsmith's new paper mill in Sycamore township. Much praise is due Mr. Waldsmith for his unremitted exertions to furnish the neighboring printers with*

an early and constant supply. Nothing appears to be wanting to render this establishment of the greatest utility, except the care of the industrious housewife in saving her
rags. The ladies of the community are informed that we
shall hereafter give three cents a pound for rags in cash,
W & Cº   or four cents in books and stationery." The
watermark used by the Waldsmith mill
M I A M I   was the single word "M I A M I" on one
half of the sheet of paper and the letters "W & Co" on the
other half, in the regulation outline lettering, well executed
for the period.

1809   Samuel Green, New London, Connecticut, was given a
United States patent for making paper from seaweed, and
Francis Bailey, Salisbury, Pennsylvania, received a patent
for the hot-pressing of paper, a method still in use.

John Dickinson, an English papermaker, invented and patented the cylinder paper-machine.

1810   It was probably this date before the Fourdrinier paper-
machine reached any degree of perfection, after patient
work by John Gamble and Bryan Donkin. It was not until
January 13, 1812, however, that the machine was started
on a thorough commercial basis, the machine on this date
being operated by Marchant Warrell, in the mill at Two
Waters, Hertfordshire. It has been stated that many of the
handmade papermakers regarded the advent of a perfected
machine as a detriment to their craft. Riots are thought to
have taken place outside the mill, and in anticipation of
trouble the windows had been boarded; also as an extra
precaution large carboys of vitriol were placed on the roof
of the mill so that the liquid might be poured upon the disgruntled handmade-paper workers should they attempt to
harm the newly perfected machine. There is no authentic
record upon which this information might be based.

According to The History of Printing in America by Isaiah
Thomas, there were the following paper mills in America:
"New Hampshire 7; Massachusetts 38; Rhode Island 4;

Connecticut 17; Vermont 9; New York 12; Delaware 4; Maryland 3; Virginia 4; South Carolina 1; Kentucky 6; Tennessee 4; Pennsylvania about 60; in all other states and territories, say 16." These figures are taken from Vol. II, page 530, of the 1810 edition of the Thomas work. In Lawrence C. Wroth's excellent book The Colonial Printer (1938), page 152, also quoting from Thomas, the number of mills credited to Massachusetts is 40; Delaware 10; and all other states and territories 18. This makes a difference of ten mills, but Thomas gives the total number as 185, so it is possible that the number of mills was changed in the volume examined by Mr. Wroth. Isaiah Thomas does not mention a mill in Ohio (see: 1807). The mills listed by Thomas (1810) manufactured 50,000 reams of paper annually, which was consumed in the publication of 22,500,000 newspapers. This paper averaged about three dollars a ream. The paper made for book-printing was about 70,000 reams, which sold for approximately three dollars and fifty cents a ream. Thomas also states that about 111,000 reams of writing paper and 100,000 reams of wrapping paper were probably manufactured in 1810. Some of the mills in New England had two vats, but there were mills in New York, Pennsylvania, Delaware, and Maryland that operated three or more vats, according to Thomas. A mill with two vats meant a capital investment of about $10,000 and such a mill employed twelve or more persons. A two-vat mill was capable of producing 2,000 to 3,000 reams of paper a year. Thomas further states that the collecting of rags, making paper, etc., gave employment to at least 2,500 persons in the United States.

In Europe and America the Fatsia papyrifera pith "paper" of Formosa was seen for the first time when it was brought from China by sailing-ship captains and sailors. Western people thought the material a manufactured substance and mistakenly gave it the name "rice-paper" on account of the resemblance to rice and to true paper. The material is used in the Orient for painting and for the making of artificial flowers; also it is used in China as a tea in the healing of lung and throat diseases.

This date was the probable beginning of papermaking in the state of Georgia. In Augustin Smith Clayton's Compilation of the Laws of the State of Georgia, from 1800 to 1810 (page 697), we find the following "Resolutions" relative to the earliest paper mill in the state: "The select committee to whom was referred the petition of Zachariah Sims, praying a loan of four thousand dollars, to enable him to complete the establishment of a paper manufactory in Greene county in this state, are of opinion, that the prayer of the petitioner is reasonable and ought to be granted. . . . Resolved that there shall be appropriated to the said Zachariah Sims, out of any monies unappropriated, the sum of three thousand dollars, to enable him to carry into operation a paper manufactory, upon his giving bond and sufficient security to his Excellency the Governor for the return of the said money with interest, into the treasury of this state, at the expiration of three years next after the said Zachariah Sims shall receive the same. Approved, 10th December, 1810." It is not definitely known whether this mill actually made paper, or exactly where it was located. It is a matter of record that the sum stated was turned over to Sims, and his paper mill was supposed to be almost completed when he asked the state for aid. The records of the Clerk of Courts of Greene County show that Governor David B. Mitchell brought suit against Sims and his bondsmen in 1814, and that the paper mill was sold by "public outcry" and was bought by Thomas Stocks, President of the Georgia Senate. The description of the property purchased by Stocks would indicate that the mill was in Greene County, on the Oconee River, near Scull Shoals. The earliest printing to be executed in Georgia was in 1763, so the date of 1810 as the commencement of papermaking in the state does not appear unreasonable. The making of paper in each state naturally followed the introduction of printing, and even with the date 1810 there was a lapse of forty-

A.D.

seven years between the earliest printing and the establishment of the first paper mill. Regardless of the date of the
pioneer handmade-paper mill in Georgia, it may be definitely stated that the first machine-made paper was produced in 1849, in a mill erected at Marietta, Cobb County,
on Soap Creek, a rocky tributary of the Chattahoochee
River. The name Soap Creek is probably a corruption of
Old Sope, the title of a Cherokee chief who remained in
the locality after the removal of the Cherokee in 1838. This
old Indian chief is said to be buried at Sewell's Cemetery,
not a great distance from the paper mill. During the War
Between the States the Marietta mill was operated by
James Byrd, an uncle of William S. Whiteman, who owned
a paper mill in Tennessee where was made much of the
paper used in printing the Confederate money and bonds.
It is said that the first twisted paper twine to be made in
the South was produced by Byrd in this mill. At this period
it was not possible to procure woven wire or felting in the
South, and as these materials were essential to the operation of a paper-machine, it was necessary to smuggle them
through the Union lines. This was done by blockade-
runners who brought the wire and felt in wagons over the
rough roads of Virginia, Kentucky, Tennessee, and Georgia.
On his march to the sea General Sherman commanded his
soldiers to destroy all the records of Cobb County and to
burn the Marietta mill, which he said was too valuable to
the Southern cause to be allowed to remain. The mill was
built of granite and the ruins stand to the present day.

1811 The date of the establishment of the first paper mill in Tennessee has not been definitely determined, but the following enlightening advertisement appeared in the March 11,
1811 issue of the Carthage Gazette: "The subscriber informs his fellow-citizens that his paper mill is now in operation. He will give three cents per pound for linen and
cotton rags, delivered at his printing office or at the paper
mill." The owner of the mill was probably William Moore,
publisher of the Gazette. If the files of the Carthage Gazette

A.D.

can be relied upon, this mill was built by funds collected through a lottery, as the "Paper Mill Lottery" was first mentioned in Moore's newspaper in the issue of May 25, 1809 The last drawing of the lottery was announced in the Gazette for June 8, 1810. From the above rag advertisement and from an appeal for "a good, sober Papermaker capable of carrying on the business . . ." we may assume that this paper mill actually existed. According to the pamphlet compiled by R. H. Halley entitled Papermaking in Tennessee (Nashville, 1904), the pioneer papermaker in Tennessee was William S. Whiteman, who established his mill on Middle Brook Creek, about four miles from Knoxville, "many years previous to 1837." Halley states that Whiteman went to Tennessee from Philadelphia about 1806, having been a papermaker in Pennsylvania previous to journeying south. The equipment for this mill was brought by horse and wagon from Philadelphia, there being no other means of transportation. This was, of course, a hand mill. Whiteman died in 1840 and the mill was continued in operation by Gideon Hazen. Isaiah Thomas stated that there were four paper mills in Tennessee as early as 1810, but this assertion cannot be authenticated.

First paper-machine set up in France, by the Berthe and Grevenich establishment at Sorel (Eure-et-Loir). In 1827 there were four paper-machines in France; in 1833 the number exceeded twelve, according to Proteaux. For the most part these machines were built in England.

1812   From 1803 to 1812 there were ten paper-machines constructed in England, and from 1812 to 1823 twenty-five. The making of paper by machine was yet to become a reality in America. (See: 1817.)

In England between this year and 1818 there were circulated 131,331 pieces of forged bank paper. This abundant counterfeiting gave rise to the invention by Sir William Congreve. (See: 1819.)

A.D.

1814 *The London* Times *for November 29 was the first newspaper to be printed on a cylinder press with the aid of papier-mâché matrices (stereotyping by the use of paper).*

1815 *The French paper mills began the manufacture of specialties in paper, thus eliminating competition between mills.*

The date of the first paper mill in Steubenville, Ohio, probably the fourth to be established in the state. Zadok Cramer in his Pittsburgh Almanac, 1815, *page 62, says: "Steubenville . . . a steam paper mill with three engines is erecting here, which will shortly be in operation, owned by Messrs. Scott and Bayless." This mill, without the benefit of steam, was probably operating on the banks of the Ohio River several years previous to 1815, but this was the earliest mention of it. William Cooper Howells (the father of William Dean Howells) in his book,* Recollections of Life in Ohio, *gives the year 1813 as the commencement of this paper mill. This mill is of particular interest because it furnished the paper for the wall hangings designed by Thomas Cole (1801–48). Cole's father emigrated from Chorley, England, to Steubenville, Ohio, in 1819, and began the making of decorated paper wall hangings. Young Cole cut the wood blocks, mixed the colours, and printed the papers, each sheet separately, as was necessary before the introduction of the paper-machine with its continuous web of paper. Thomas Cole later became a well-known American artist and founded what is now known as the "Hudson River school," perhaps the most representative style of painting to have its origin in this country. In later years the Steubenville paper mill was taken over by Messrs. Holdship, Hanna, and Turnbull, a firm that published* The United States Spelling-Book *in 1830 with the imprint on the title-page "at the Clinton Paper-mill."*

1816 *By act of Congress of April 26 a thirty-per-cent duty was placed on all imports of paper into the United States. By 1820 there was being made in this country $3,000,000 worth of paper; by 1830 the volume had risen to $7,000,000.*

A.D.

Bishop records that the first steam paper mill in the United States was put in operation in Pittsburgh, Pennsylvania. The engine was of 16 horse-power and the mill employed 40 workers. The engine required 10,000 bushels of coal annually. The rags consumed amounted to 120,000 pounds, which were made into paper valued at $30,000 a year. (See: 1815).

1817　First paper-machine erected in America, a cylinder machine operated in the mill of Thomas Gilpin, near Philadelphia. The machine was based on the Dickinson principle (see: 1809). The first newspaper to make use of the Gilpin machine-made product was Poulson's Daily Advertiser, Philadelphia. The original machine did the work of ten vats of the handmade mills.

1818　In England, to conserve paper, it was made a punishable offence to produce a newspaper exceeding 22 by 32 inches.

In April of this year Benjamin Owen Tyler produced his quasi-facsimile of the Declaration of Independence, at the price of $5 a copy; in November 1819 a facsimile of the Declaration was issued by John Binns, selling at $10. These facsimiles were printed upon American-made paper, said at the time to have been the finest paper ever produced in this or any other country.

1819　Sir William Congreve (1772–1828) submitted his experiments in watermarking for bank-notes to the Bank of England and a few of his inventions were adopted and are still used.

A. M. Sinisen published in Copenhagen a pamphlet dealing with his experiments in making paper from the fibre of beet-root. To prove the practicability of this fibre as a paper-making material the pamphlet was printed on paper manufactured from beet-root.

A.D.

During this year began a heated controversy regarding the use by Congress of foreign-made paper, and a series of indignant letters and editorials appeared in Niles' Weekly Register, *the most popular and universally read publication of the period. In the issue of August 5, 1820 an editorial said in part: "Last winter we indignantly noticed the receipt of a letter from the clerk of the House of Representatives of the United States, written on paper stamped and marked with the royal crown of England . . . a friend in the Senate sent us a sheet of the paper usually laid on the desks of its members, dignified with the same emblem of royalty, at which we were again mortified. The paper was of a very fine quality, better, perhaps, than four-fifths of the members of Congress ever used, perhaps ever saw, before their arrival at Washington. . . ." In his tirade against the crown watermark Niles goes on to say: "Let it take any shape but that, — a codfish or a hoe-cake — a yoke of oxen or a race horse — anything but the regal crown of England." During the same period newspapers were complaining that Congress was using writing paper watermarked* Napoléon empereur et roi. *The first American-made writing paper to be used by the U. S. Senate is thought to have been manufactured by Simeon and Asa Butler, Suffield, Connecticut.*

The second paper mill established in Canada (see: 1803), at Bedford Basin, near Halifax, by R. A. Holland, who published the Halifax Record. *In the village known as Crook's Hollow the first paper mill in what was then known as "Upper Canada" was built in 1825. Here in a building about 30 by 40 feet James Crooks made paper by hand and earned the bounty of 100 pounds offered by the government for the first paper manufactured in Upper Canada. John Eastwood and Colin Skinner succeeded only a few days later in making paper at their mill on the Don River, a few miles from Toronto, and the government recognized their enterprise by remitting the duty on the equipment they had to import from the United States. The first paper-machine to*

*be set up in Canada was no doubt installed in the Don
River valley.*

1820   *In Niles' Weekly Register, Baltimore, January 15, 1820, under the heading of "Domestic Industry," the following account is given of American papermaking: ". . . The paper
manufacture of the United States produces an annual average value, as to the amount consumed, of about three million of dollars, of which cost of the raw materials, and the
labour employed thereon, is estimated at two millions, —
giving employment to about 5,000 persons, of whom only
about 1,700 are believed to be males over 16 years of age,
the rest being women and children." At this period (1820)
there was but one paper-machine in operation in the United
States (see: 1817), therefore the majority of these workers
were engaged in making paper by hand.*

*In the issue of Niles' Weekly Register, January 22, 1820, an
article gives some interesting details relative to papermaking in Pennsylvania and Delaware; these states "pray that
Congress will lay a duty of 25 cents per pound on all writing, printing, and copperplate papers, and 15 cents on all
others." The article further outlines that "in the districts
represented, it appears there were 70 paper mills, with 95
vats, in full operation, until the importation after the late
war. These establishments cost about 500,000 dollars, and
employed 950 persons, whose annual wages amounted to
217,000 dollars, consuming 2,600 tons of rags a year, and
producing paper worth 800,000 dollars — but now only 17
vats are at work, the wages paid amount to only 45,000 dollars; the production no more than 136,000 — leaving 775
persons out of the employ, with the loss of 2128 tons of rags
unconsumed, and a manufactured amount of 624,000 dolls.
When paper was taxed, the average amount paid by a vat
was from 200 to 250 dollars."*

*The first ivory paper, made by S. Einsle, used by miniature
artists to take the place of genuine ivory. The paper was*

made an eighth of an inch in thickness and was said by prominent English painters to be superior to ivory. The invention was sponsored by the Royal Society of Arts.

Thomas Bronsor Crompton granted a patent in England for drying cylinders for the paper-machine. Previous to this time the semi-moist paper was taken from the machine, cut into sheets, and dried in a loft as had long been the procedure with the handmade product.

1821 *First important book to be printed on American machine-made paper manufactured on the Gilpin cylinder machine:* A Complete Genealogical, Historical, Chronological, and Geographical Atlas, *by N. Lavoisne, published by Matthew Carey and Son, Philadelphia.*

1822 *The completion of Rees's* Cyclopedia, *Philadelphia, up to that time the largest work in the English language. The printing of this 41-volume work with 147 engravings required 30,000 reams of paper.*

1823 *Gypsum* (calcium sulphate) *used for the first time in Europe as a "loading" material.*

1824 *The first machine for pasting sheets of paper together, forming cardboard. The patent was granted to John Dickinson, the inventor of the cylinder machine.*

1825 *John and Christopher Phipps were granted an English patent for what purports to be the original "dandy-roll" for watermarking paper. The specifications read in part: "the employment of a roller the cylinder part of which is formed of 'laid' wire . . . the effect produced by said roller is that of making impressions upon the sheet of paper upon which said roller passes and thus the paper so made has the appearance of 'laid' paper."*

About this time, when cloth bookbindings were first being used, a heavy coated paper with each side a different colour began to appear as end-papers in the larger books.

The first paper-machine in India was set up this year, by Mr. Marsham of Serampur. This was a cylinder machine, but apparently the venture did not prove successful. By the year 1880 machine mills were operating in Lucknow, Gwalior, and Calcutta. In 1903 there were nine machine mills in India, employing 4,500 workers with a yearly production of 22,000 tons of paper. In 1937 British India produced 60,268 tons of paper and imported 140,727 tons, mostly from Japan and Great Britain; no Indian paper, either hand- or machine-made, was exported.

1826 *First use in the Occident of the divided papermaking mould, making possible the formation of two sheets at one dipping of the mould into the vat. This type of mould had long since been used in China.*

M. Canson, Annonay, France, applied to the Fourdrinier machine suction pumps, which caused a suction under the travelling wire on which the paper was formed, to help in removing the water. In 1840 M. de Bergue suggested the employment of sand-traps on the paper-machine, which, as the name implies, removed sand, gravel, and heavy particles of dirt from the pulp, which previously had ruined type, copperplates, etc., when printed upon the paper.

The earliest paper mill in the state of Indiana. The paper used in Indiana previous to the erection of this mill came from the several Ohio, Kentucky, and western Pennsylvania mills. The difficulty of procuring paper from these mills is shown by the following notices in the Vincennes Western Sun and General Advertiser. *In the issue of September 11, 1819, we read: "We are compelled to present the* Western Sun *to its patrons this week on a writing sheet — we expect a supply of paper in a few weeks, when it will again resume its usual appearance." In the issue of December 18, 1819, we find the following: "In consequence of numerous disappointments we have not been able to procure paper of the usual size, and we have been compelled to let our paper appear on a sheet much smaller than we would have wished. We shall, however, after our next publication, receive a supply which is now ascending the Wabash, after which we shall use every exertion to make a proper remuneration to our patrons for their indulgence." It was not until March 18, 1826 that this same newspaper proudly stated: "The* Indiana Republican, *printed at Madison, on the 9th inst. says the Editor, 'is printed on paper made in that county,' it is the first paper mill erected in the state, and the proprietors have my warmest wishes for their success." The pioneer paper mill of Indiana was operated by John Sheets and was located in Jefferson County, on Indian-Kentucky Creek, below Manville. William Hughes, an experienced papermaker from Ireland, acted as the superintendent of the mill, which was "one and a half stories and stood erect over the mill-race, visible all the way down the valley to the curves." It is recorded that the mill was built by Nathaniel Bayless, a carpenter and millwright, who was born in Hartford County, Maryland, March 12, 1796, and journeyed to Indiana in 1817. John Sheets, in common with all other papermakers of the period, was constantly in need of rags, and in the Indianapolis* Indiana Journal, *May 15, 1828, we find the usual appeal: "Paper Manufactory — The Subscriber takes this method to give general notice that his Paper Mill in the neighbourhood of Madison, is now in complete operation, and he is prepared for making Letter, Writing, Printing and Wrapping Paper, of every description, and he flatters himself, from the particular care which he has taken in the selection of workmen, that the paper will not be inferior to any that is made in the western country. . . . Cash will be given for all kinds of Rags and also for coarse tow. . . . John Sheets." The first paper-machine set in motion in Indiana, a Fourdrinier, was probably by Phillips and Speer, of Cincinnati, about the year 1837.*

Papermaking by machine established in Denmark, the Fourdrinier machine having been built in England by Bryan Donkin.

1827 *First Fourdrinier paper-machine set up in America, built in England by Bryan Donkin. The machine was put in operation at Saugerties, New York, in the mill of Henry Barclay, on October 24.*

The first enamelled paper produced and patented by John George Christ, England. The enamelling was accomplished by using a mixture of animal size, isinglass, gum, and white lead. The liquid was applied to the cardboard or paper at three separate times, and finally given a high finish by using a polished steel plate run through a press.

This year David Kizer patented a transparent paper that may well have been the predecessor of Cellophane. Contemporary notices of this material appeared in the New York Enquirer and in that storehouse of useful information, Niles' Weekly Register. In the latter publication for October 27, 1827 the following account of the newly conceived transparent paper is given: "The paper is well suited to cover prints and paintings in place of glass; if put on well there will be but little difference in the appearance of a picture from one covered with glass. The cost of covering a picture with transparent paper will not exceed 50 cents for a frame three feet by four feet; it is also used as a covering for windows, to prevent the rays of the sun from passing through, at the same time to admit as much light as if no paper was on. It can also be used as a cylinder or tube, to put round a lamp or candle, and cause it to emit a more agreeable light. These, are only a few uses to which it can be applied; many more will gradually develop themselves when artists are aware that such an article is to be obtained."

1828 *Second Fourdrinier paper-machine in America installed in the mill of Joseph Pickering, North Windham, Connecticut.*

William Magaw, Meadville, Pennsylvania, began the making of paper from straw. It is said that an edition of the New Testament was printed upon this cheap yellow paper that sold for five cents a copy. This same year straw paper was also made in Chambersburg, Pennsylvania, the amount being 300 reams daily, selling for less than two dollars a ream for imperial size (22½ by 29 inches). (See: 1800, Koops.)

On August 8 Nicholas-Louis Robert, the French inventor of the paper-machine, died in Vernouillet, France, a poorly paid school-teacher. (See: 1798.)

William Cobbett made paper in England from cornstalks. In America a patent was granted for making paper from this material as early as 1802. In 1834 Dr. Jones, of Mobile, Alabama, also made paper from Indian-corn stalks and husks.

1829 *Of the sixty paper mills in Massachusetts, only six had paper-machines; the rest were handmade-paper mills. By this time many of the rags were imported from Germany and Italy. The consumption of rags for these Massachusetts mills was 1,700 tons, producing paper to the value of $700,-000 for the year.*

Montgolfier, French papermaker, introduced paper table-cloths and paper hangings with embossed designs, known as papier-linge.

John Dickinson, the inventor of the cylinder machine, patented a process for running a silk or other kind of thread through the length of paper as it was formed on a paper-machine. This type of paper is known as "Dickinson thread paper," and its latest use is in the modern English ten-shilling and one-pound notes.

First Fourdrinier papermaking machine to be built in America made in South Windham, Connecticut, and in-

*stalled in the mill of Amos H. Hubbard, Norwich Falls,
Connecticut. This machine produced usable paper during
the month of May of this year.*

1830   *Commercially made sandpaper produced about this time,
one side of the paper being brushed with glue, and sand,
ground glass, or emery dusted upon the paper. Previous to
this date most workers made their own abrasives by coating
ordinary canvas or heavy paper with glue and sprinkling
sand upon the surface.*

Joel Munsell records (1876) that an issue of the Crawford
Messenger, *Meadville, Pennsylvania, was printed on paper
made from lime and aspen wood. The paper used in printing the edition of October 28, 1830 appears different from
all other issues, but inasmuch as the paper has not been
analysed, it is not possible to state definitely that it is wood-
pulp paper. It has not been possible to procure a specimen
of the paper for examination. If Munsell is correct, this
would be the first instance of the use of wood-pulp paper
in printing an American newspaper. (See: page 380.)*

*Bleach, invented by Scheele in 1774, first used by American
papermakers in bleaching rags for making paper.*

According to Julius Grant, writing in Books and Documents
(*London, 1937*), *paper was first calendered in England this
year.*

*The "knotter" used for the removal of knots and lumps in
paper stock invented in England by Richard Ibotson. The
earliest patent for a knotter in America is dated March 12,
1831, and was granted to Solomon Stimpson, Newbury,
Vermont.*

1831   *Hall, of Dartford, England, used for the first time washing-
screens on the Hollander, enabling the water to be constantly changed while washing paper stock.*

A.D.

*One of the earliest paper-machines in the "western country."
Under date of July 16, 1831, the Chillicothe, Ohio, Weekly
Advertiser had the following advertisement: "Machine Paper Mill. H. & I.* INGHAM, *Respectfully inform their friends
and the public that their Machine Mill is now in successful
operation, and that they will supply at the shortest notice
any orders for* WRITING PAPER, *Nos. 1 2 3* CAP, *Nos. 1 2* POSTE.
*Also, Printing and Wrapping of any size and quality, per
order, upon as reasonable terms as paper of the same quality can be had from any other establishment in the Western
country. The highest market price will be allowed for* RAGS,
*either in cash or in exchange for paper." This was probably,
if not the first, one of the first paper-machines in the West.
Hezekiah and Isaiah Ingham went to Ohio from Bucks
County, Pennsylvania, about 1810 and established a handmade-paper mill on Kinnikinnick Creek, Ross County. By
1812 they were making writing and printing paper equal to
any manufactured in the East. Their watermark was "H & I
INGHAM" in the regulation outline letters.*

*A cylinder machine made by John Ames, of Springfield,
Massachusetts, was installed in the mill of Zenas Crane, established 1801, at Dalton, Massachusetts. The first Fourdrinier machine to be used in the Crane mill was not installed until about 1840–5, previous to the death of Zenas
Crane in 1845.*

1833 *The earliest use of drying-rolls on a paper-machine in
France, in the Firmin Didot mill at Mesnil-sur-l'Estrée
(Eure) (Proteaux).*

1834 *The earliest papermaking in the state of Missouri. Printing,
however, was accomplished in this state as early as 1808
by Joseph Charless, but the paper used by this pioneer
Missouri printer came from Craig, Parkers & Company,
Georgetown, Kentucky, or from Jackson and Sharpless,
Redstone mill, as evidenced by watermarks in early Missouri printing. The* Missouri Gazette, *established by Char-*

less, had no end of difficulty in procuring paper for publication, and in March 1809 the newspaper was printed on letter paper; in the issue for October 9, 1813 it was stated that the newspaper was so small in size owing to the scarcity of suitable paper; in the publication of January 1814 the editor complained that there was no regular trade with Kentucky, where funds had been sent and the paper awaited a trader bound for Missouri. As early as January 1834 the newly established Missouri mill advertised for rags: "good, clean linen and cotton rags 3 cents per pound, for woolen 10 cents, and jeans rags 1 cent per pound." But apparently it was not until the latter part of the year that the mill was actually in operation, when the Missouri Intelligencer, *December 27, 1834, announced the event in the following manner: "The paper on which this number of the* Missouri Intelligencer *was printed, was made at the paper mill of Messrs. Lamme, Keiser & Company (David and William Lamme, John W. Keiser and Thomas Cox), in this county (Rock Bridge, near Columbia, Boone County). It is a fair specimen of what may be expected when the mill has been longer in operation. This is the only establishment of the kind in Missouri or Illinois, and the worthy and enterprising proprietors, who have expended a large sum in the undertaking, merit, and we sincerely hope, will receive a liberal and general support from the printers and merchants of the two States, — particularly Missouri. The machinery is entirely new, and the whole establishment is on an extensive scale. We have no doubt that as good paper as printers and others may wish will be manufactured here. Our own manufacturers ought to be encouraged by us, in preference to those of other parts of the Union. We are sorry to see that the new* Journal *at Fayette, only 25 or 30 miles from the mill in Boone, is printed on something probably called paper, but possessing neither soul nor body, of which we understand, the editor procured a large supply from Cincinnati! We hope we will not have occasion hereafter to say the same in reference to any other editor in Boon's Lick." The first paper manufactured in Missouri was, of course, made on a paper-machine, but it is not known whether the machine was of the cylinder or Fourdrinier type.*

Michigan's first paper mill was erected this year in the village called Raisinville, three or four miles west of Monroe. Christopher McDowell was the owner of this pioneer Michigan mill, and the original building, which was of wood, housed a paper-machine about thirty feet in length with a width of thirty-eight inches. The paper was dried by running the web around a metal drum ten feet in diameter which contained a charcoal fire. The mill was known as the River Raisin Paper Company. The mill-owner lived on a farm across the river from the mill. The first product of this mill was butchers' paper manufactured from straw. (Michigan History Magazine, Vol. XXII, page 363; Michigan Manufacturer and Financial Record, 1924, page 112.)

Dr. Daniel Stebbins, Northampton, Massachusetts, imported mulberry trees (Broussonetia papyrifera) *from China with the thought of using the inner bark for the making of paper, as in China and Japan. A few reams of excellent paper were made, but the growing of the trees for this purpose evidently proved unsuccessful, as nothing more was heard of the venture.*

1837   *The first use of old manila rope as a papermaking fibre in the United States. Owing to the depression Lyman Hollingsworth, South Braintree, Massachusetts, was forced to use this material as a substitute for linen and cotton rags, and a new source of material was inaugurated.*

1839   *Improved drying cylinders for the paper-machine invented and patented by Robert Ranson.*

1840   *Mulready paper envelopes adopted by the English Post Office. The "Dickinson thread paper" was used in making these envelopes (see: 1829). These envelopes were released on May 1, 1840, when 2,500 were sold, but they were not*

used until May 6, 1840, when the "penny black" stamps
made their memorable appearance.

Watermarking used in postage stamps, the "penny black"
of England, 240 small watermarked crowns on each sheet
of handmade stamp paper. This was the first issue of adhe-
sive postage stamps.

Friedrich Gottlob Keller, a German weaver of Saxony, procured a German patent for a wood-grinding machine. Keller's work was no doubt based on the practical experiments
that Matthias Koops carried on in England as early as 1800.

Between 1835 and 1840 the cylinder washer for attaching
to the Hollander was invented and used successfully. The
invention is attributed to Breton frères. This style of washer
enabled papermakers to cleanse the surplus bleach from
the rag stock more thoroughly than formerly. The same
invention was later perfected through the efforts of M.
Blanchet, Rives, France.

The earliest papermaking in the state of Illinois. The actual
beginning of the industry in this state is somewhat obscure,
but apparently the first mill made paper by hand. In Henry
B. Pierce's The Past and Present of Kane County (1878) the
following account is given: "In 1840 Read Ferson built a
blacksmith shop on the East Side, which was converted in
the following year into a paper mill by William Debit. Paper is said to have been made in it for some time by hand,
but Debit soon quit the business, when the property was
owned for a short time by R. J. Haines and P. C. Simmons,
and at length by Butler and Hunt, who first fitted it with
suitable machinery. The West Side paper mill was built by
Butler and Hunt, 1847–48. . . ." In regard to the Butler and
Hunt mill, Frank O. Butler, a descendant of the well-known
papermaking family, has furnished the following further information: "The Butler and Hunt mill, built on the Fox
River at St. Charles, presumably started in 1840 was un-
questionably the first erected within the State. Oliver M.

A.D.

Butler came to Illinois in 1839–40, both he and his father, Zebediah Butler, Jr., were handmade paper producers. Neither, however, practiced this method after leaving New England. In youth Oliver M. Butler served his apprenticeship with the Hurlbut Paper Company, South Lee, Massachusetts. It was from this mill that he made his first shipment of paper to Chicago, the beginning of the present-day Butler Paper Corporations. . . . In 1839, prior by one year, to Oliver M. Butler's journey west, a man named Devitt (William Debit?) attempted in Chicago to produce power by windmill sufficient to operate a beater. Failing in this he went to St. Charles in the hope of stabilizing wind power with paddle-wheel help from Fox River flow. This was his second attempt at producing power by the wind, but this also failed and nothing more was heard of him. Within the next year or so Butler and Hunt built the first dam, of log construction, at St. Charles." It is recorded that the paper-machine set up in the Butler and Hunt mill was built at Brattleboro, Vermont, by Thomas and Woodcock. The machine comprised one cylinder, three thirty-six inch driers, with a cutter operated direct from the driers. The production was 400 pounds of paper each day, with twenty-five per cent newsprint and the rest wrapping paper. According to Frank O. Butler, this machine was dismantled in 1847–8 and shipped to Wisconsin, where it was used in one of the early paper mills in that state.

1841   *Charles Fenerty, a Nova Scotian, produced in Halifax the first ground-wood paper made in the Western Hemisphere.*

1842   *Will Egley, an English artist, produced the original Christmas card, an idea that was eventually to consume prodigious quantities of paper and cardboard in all countries where Christmas is celebrated. (See: 1874.)*

1843   *About this time the earliest "safety paper" was produced in England. The paper was printed on both sides in all-over patterns with special inks subject to erasure, etc.*

A.D.

1844 *The first commercial paper boxes made in America, by Colonel Andrew Dennison, a cobbler, at his home in Brunswick, Maine. This was the commencement of the Dennison Manufacturing Company.*

The first use in America of silk threads in paper was accomplished by Zenas Marshall Crane, who made bank-note paper for a bank in Northampton, Massachusetts. It is said that the placing of silk threads in paper was the invention of Crane. By the year 1847 this type of protected paper was in use by various banks in the United States.

1845 *Massachusetts had 89 paper mills producing 600,000 reams of paper a year; in Connecticut there were 37 mills. By this year only two handmade-paper mills remained in America; all other mills were operating paper-machines.*

1846 *Heinrich Voelter, of Saxony, purchased the Keller patent (see: 1840) and began making ground-wood paper on a fairly large commercial scale.*

While only two handmade-paper mills remained in the United States, Germany was operating 1,043 vats for forming paper by hand.

1847 *The first Fourdrinier wire to be woven in the United States was produced in September of this year by William Staniar and Cornelius Van Houten. The wire was 52 inches wide and 24 feet 10 inches long. It was woven in the shop of Stephens and Thomas, Belleville, New Jersey, on a loom made by Van Houten from a model brought from England by Staniar.*

First postage stamps used in the United States, founded on the George Plitt report on the "penny black" of England, used in 1840.

1848 *About this time W. H. Smith, an Englishman, invented but did not patent light-and-shade watermarks, which enabled papermakers to produce portraits and other shaded pictures in watermarks. Before this date all watermarks were made of single wire, sometimes with a "wove" background such as the early nineteenth-century marks of Johannot, Annonay, France.*

The first paper mill in Wisconsin was established by Ludington and Garland, in Milwaukee. In 1855 paper mills were built in Beloit and Appleton; in 1857 the first mill was erected in Whitewater, and the first in Neenah in 1865. The first ground-wood paper was made in this state in 1872 by Colonel Frambach, who built the Eagle mill at Kaukauna on the Fox River. The Beloit and Whitewater mills made strawboard; the other plants produced rag-stock newsprint. In the pamphlet by Francis F. Bowman, Jr., entitled Ninety-Two Years Industrial Progress (1940), *the following relates to Wisconsin paper mills: "Today over ninety years have passed since Ludington and Garland established the first Wisconsin paper mill. In that time no less than 131 papermaking firms have been organized. Of these original firms 39 now represent the Wisconsin industry. Thirteen were merged with the present concerns and 79 failed to survive the many risks of industrial enterprise."*

1849   *The earliest paper mill in the state of Alabama was set in motion this year. In the* Alabama Beacon, Greensboro, March 10, 1849, *the following account of this mill appeared: "Tuscaloosa papers announce that the Paper Mill, recently erected in that city, has commenced operations, and is now engaged in manufacturing an article of wrapping paper. . . . Having found it impossible to get, either in Mobile, or any other market we have tried a good article of printing paper, of the size we use, we shall try the Tuscaloosa Factory, as soon as it goes to manufacturing Printing paper, — and if the article and price suit, shall supply ourselves altogether from that source. Our Tuscaloosa contemporaries would oblige us, and no doubt others, by stat-*

ing when the Tuscaloosa Factory will commence the manufacture of Printing Paper." The date of the opening of this mill is further verified in the State Guard, Wetumpka, Alabama, for in the issue of March 27, 1849, we read: "The Tuscaloosa Observer of the 19th inst., says: 'we announced the week before last, that the Paper Mill in this city had commenced operations, and that it would shortly make paper suitable for newspaper printing. Our edition of the Observer is printed today on paper manufactured in this city, and those of our brethren of the press have now an opportunity of judging of its merits. The price, according to quality, we think, is as cheap, if not cheaper, than it can be had in any market of the South. Considering the newness of the machinery, the inexperience of most of the hands employed in its manufacture, and the numerous little difficulties attending a new enterprize of this kind, we think the first effort at papermaking here is an excellent one. Whatever it may lack now, a little time and experience will soon give.'" According to the Memorial Record of Alabama, Vol. I, this pioneer paper mill of Alabama did not survive the Civil War.

The earliest known American photograph on paper, the Talbot invention of "taking impressions on paper . . . portraits from life on paper without the least aid of the pencil, etc." The process was perfected by W. and F. Langenheim (? Philadelphia).

1850   First use of "ribbed" paper in printing postage stamps, Austria.

At this date the English "Whatman" handmade papers had become so renowned that they were imitated on the Continent. German and Austrian papermakers forged the watermark "Whatman" and sold the paper as genuine.

The "lace" paper valentines, cards, envelopes, letter paper, bands, labels, etc., originated about this period. The first

A.D.

English patent for making perforated or lace embossed paper was given John Evans, May 29, 1854. The lace papers had considerable vogue for the following twenty-five years.

Paper bags made for the first time, entirely by hand. The earliest automatic paper-bag machine was built in 1876. (In the United States during the year 1941, 50,000,000,000 paper bags of all sizes were consumed. Paper twine was first made in America in 1862. At the present time this material is used almost exclusively in the tying of wool, as it gives off no lint. For this one purpose 20,000,000,000 feet, or 57 carloads, of paper are used in America annually.)

1851 *The use of paper money resumed in China. The last former use of money of this kind was during the time of Yung Lo (1403–25), when its use gave way to metallic money entirely.*

The year of the Great Exhibition, London, the firm of Byran Donkin, the builders of the first practical paper-machine, made their 191st machine for fabricating paper in an endless reel. Of these machines 83 remained in Great Britain, 23 were exported to France, 46 to Germany, 22 to the north of Europe, 14 to Italy and the south of Europe, 2 to America, and 1 to India.

First useful paper made from chemical wood fibre originated by Hugh Burgess and Charles Watt. The process was patented in the United States in 1854.

First postage stamps used in Canada, printed by Rawdon, Wright, Hatch, and Edson, on paper probably made by the Willcox mill, Pennsylvania.

1852 *Ground-wood pulp produced regularly in the mill of H. Voelter's Sons in Heidenheim; also in a mill in Giersdorf, Silesia. A small percentage of rag fibres was used to give the paper strength.*

A.D.

1854 *The earliest paper to be made in Utah was formed by hand by Thomas Howard, an English Mormon, assisted by Thomas Hollis. The small beginning was sponsored by Brigham Young (1801–77) and the Mormon Church. The original equipment for the handmade-paper mill was converted from beet-sugar machinery, which furnished the rag-cutter and hydraulic press. The first sheets of paper were produced on June 27, 1854 and probably found their original use in the printing of the* Deseret News, *Brigham Young's newspaper, which began publication in Great Salt Lake City, June 15, 1850; the newspaper was an eight-page quarto measuring 6½ by 8½ inches. There was great difficulty in getting raw material for the mill, although Brigham Young, in anticipation of a paper mill, began advertising for rags as early as November 30, 1850, when this notice appeared in his newspaper: "Rags! Rags! Rags! Save your rags, everybody in Deseret, save your rags; old wagon covers, tents, quilts, shirts, etc., are wanted for paper. The most efficient measures are in progress to put a paper mill in operation the coming season in this valley and all your rags will be wanted. Make your woolen rags into carpeting and save importations." Even with this appeal there were only one hundred and fifty pounds of rags available when Howard and Hollis commenced their papermaking by hand. This hand mill continued operation for about six months, when the sugar company demanded its machinery, which had been brought west for making sugar, not paper. This brought the making of paper by hand to a conclusion, as without a hydraulic press, or a pressure press of some description, it was impossible to make paper. In 1860 Brigham Young and his Mormon group purchased a 36-inch paper-machine from Nelson Gavitt, Philadelphia. This machine, probably the second in the Far West (see: 1856), was hauled from the Missouri River to Salt Lake City by ox teams. In January 1861 the sugar mill, a building 20 by 100 feet, was converted into a paper mill by Thomas Howard, the original vatman of the old handmade-paper mill. The first machine-made paper was produced in Utah*

A.D.

on July 24, 1861. The machinery was eventually moved from the old sugar mill to the Granite mill at the mouth of Big Cottonwood Canyon, thirteen miles from Salt Lake City. In addition to the original 36-inch machine a 66-inch Fourdrinier was put into use; also six rag engines. The Granite mill was destroyed by fire on April 1, 1893. The stone walls of the building have since been renovated and the graceful structure is at present used as a clubhouse.

John Beardsley, of Buffalo, New York, submitted to a local newspaper three specimens of paper he had made from basswood.

1855 *Henry Fourdrinier, the brother of Sealy, the last surviving partner of the Fourdrinier brothers, who financed the Bryan Donkin and John Gamble paper-machine, died in England, aged ninety years.*

About this time Egyptian mummies were imported to America, the wrappings and other fibres to be used in the making of wrapping paper for grocers, butchers, etc.

Dr. Lloyd, of England, contributed to the Journal of the Society of Arts *his proposal for making paper from the fibrous substance of cow dung. In 1879 the* Scientific American *proposed the use of this material for making into paper in this country.*

Even in the Far West there was an early search for fibres that could be converted into paper, as is evidenced by the following taken from the Journal of the Sixth Session of the Legislature of the State of California *(Sacramento, 1855):* "A great portion of the land acquired by the State under the Act of September, 1850, as is well known, is covered with a luxuriant growth of Tule (Scirpus lacustris and S. tatora), indigenous to the soil, and averaging at least two tons to the acre. During the past autumn, this Tule has been carefully examined by experienced manufacturers, and the*

A.D.

opinion expressed, that paper of good, if not superior quality, can be made from it. . . . Several parcels of Tule have been forwarded to manufacturers in the Atlantic States, for the purposes of testing, by actual experiment, its adaptation to the making of paper, and we shall soon learn the results of these interesting and important experiments."

1856   *Discovery of aniline dye (Perkin's mauve), used in colouring paper, etc. By 1870 dyes of this type were in common usage.*

First English patent covering corrugated paper granted to Edward Charles Healey and Edward Ellis Allen, July 7. The corrugating was accomplished by passing the paper between corrugated rollers or by pressing between corrugated dies.

By this year the consumption of paper in the United States had reached a point where it equalled that of England and France combined. The newspapers of New York City required 12,000 tons of paper for the year, and by 1864 newsprint had reached the price of twenty-eight cents a pound.

During this year was produced the British Guiana postage stamp which may be now termed the most valuable piece of paper in existence. This stamp was printed at the office of the Royal Gazette, *Georgetown, on paper of a deep magenta colour. The only known copy was sold at the Ferrary sale, 1921–5, to the American philatelist Arthur Hind for $32,500. Another extremely valuable piece of paper was the Swedish 1855 stamp that was printed in orange instead of blue-green; this minute bit of paper sold for £5,000. The highest price ever achieved in America for one of these "scraps of paper" was $27,000, paid for a block of eight 24-cent United States air-mail stamps with inverted centres.*

1856–7   *The first paper-mill to be established in California and the second in the Far West (see: 1854). The early newspapers in California were small in size, no doubt owing to the difficulty in procuring paper from Eastern mills. The California, the first newspaper in the state, made its initial appearance on August 15, 1846 in a size of 10¼ by 11¾ inches, printed upon paper that had been made for writing and for cigarette wrappers. The California Star, established January 9, 1847, was printed on paper brought from the East in nearly a two years' supply, but by 1851 the Star was being issued irregularly printed upon half sheets of coloured paper and brown paper used in cigar manufacture. The usual size of the Star was 13 by 18 inches. The earliest notice of a paper mill in the state of California appeared in the San Francisco Alta, August 3, 1852, and told of the proposed mill as follows: "It will be no less gratifying to the readers than the publishers of newspapers in California to know that there is now about being shipped at New York a splendid paper-mill. It was manufactured by a practical and enterprising gentleman, expressly for this city, who intended to have shipped it by the Flying Cloud, when she made her 89 days run, but was prevented from doing so by the narrow minded and officious interference of a paper warehouse in New York. The mill was built at an expense of eighteen thousand dollars, and is calculated to turn out 3000 pounds daily of every variety of printing paper. . . . In six weeks after its arrival the owner will guarantee to supply every paper in the State with whatever size and description it requires, thereby relieving publishers from the necessity of assuming the risk of shipments by Cape Horn. . . ." The Sacramento Union, October 17, 1856, sets down the first definite information regarding the progress of the mill: "A paper mill, the first one in California, has been built and nearly completed near Tomales Bay, some eight or ten miles above Bolinas. The mill is owned by Messrs. V. B. Post and Samuel Taylor, and the machinery put up under the superintendence of Henry Russell, a practical millwright, from Massachusetts. It is not yet fully done but will be ready in a month or two to commence work. The situation is about six miles from the bay, upon a small creek, the water of which will be used to drive a thirty-five horse power breast wheel. The main building is thirty-five feet square and two stories high, and intended to contain four engines with two and a half foot rolls, two of which are completed. An addition to the above building, fifty feet long by thirty-five feet wide, and two stories high, is intended to contain two machines, one of which, a Connecticut machine, has already arrived, and is nearly fixed in its place. . . ." Evidently it was not until the spring of 1857 that paper was actually being made, as is evidenced by the following in the San Francisco* Bulletin, *April 1, 1857: "We yesterday received a specimen of printing paper, made at the new mill of Messrs. Taylor and Post, at Bolinas. It seems to be of fair quality. As it has been a point with us to encourage California manufactures, the* Bulletin *will, probably, soon be printed upon some material from the first paper mill in California. . . ." The first publication actually to use the California-made paper was the* California Farmer; *in the issue of April 17, 1857 the following notice appeared: "It gives us much pleasure to announce that the* Farmer *is this week printed entirely on California-made paper, from the New Mill of Messrs. Taylor & Post, at Bolinas. So we have at length what has long been needed, a paper mill in full operation in this State, and it is another advance in prosperity, as it will save to our own citizens a large amount of money which has formerly been sent out of the country for printing paper. We are gratified to state that the appearance of the* Farmer *will be much improved in future, as we have made arrangements for a regular supply of this Home Production, and intend to use it exclusively." The initial use of the local paper apparently proved satisfactory, for the editor of the* California Farmer *in the next issue (April 24, 1857), had this to say: "We again call attention to our journal, which is printed on California paper. Although at an extra cost to us weekly, we most cheerfully adopt it . . . by direct information we have received, we learn that the mill now turns out 6,000 pounds of paper, per week, of large size, and measures are in prog-*

A.D.

ress to increase the manufacture as fast as material can be had, from which good paper can be made. Eighteen workmen are employed; and the best prices will be paid for rags at the office of the manufacturers. . . . We have the pleasing consciousness of having contributed the FIRST MONEY *for* CALIFORNIA PRINTING PAPER *on the Pacific coast. We have the agreeable fact from the books of the new Paper Mill, that the first money received for paper was received from the office of the* California Farmer, *thus showing that we do mean to sustain home industry." It is not recorded the length of time this mill continued in operation, but it probably ceased during the depression of 1893. In Mildred Brooke Hoover's* Historic Spots in California *(1937) this description is given: ". . . Rags to supply this mill were gathered by Chinese in San Francisco, made into great bales, and shipped by schooner to the head of Tomales Bay. They were then loaded on a scow and floated on the tide to Taylor's warehouse, whence a team of oxen completed the transportation to the factory. . . . The undertaking was prosperous from the beginning and was especially so during the Civil War period. . . . After lying idle for several years, the red-painted building with windows and doors outlined in white was mysteriously burned. Now only the damaged foundations remain; the columns that acted as supports for the water wheel are still standing and crumbling brick walls outline the space where the boiler was located. These ruins are about two miles above Camp Taylor on the road from San Rafael to Olema."*

1857   *Experiments in the sulphite process for the preparation of wood fibre for papermaking begun in Paris by Benjamin C. and Richard Tilghman.*

To compete with the fine English paper sized in the machine with animal glue, the French mill of Outhenin Chalandre, Savoyeux (Haute-Saône), adopted this method of sizing their papers.

A.D.

1857–60 *Esparto grass* (Stipa tenacissima) *used in England for the first time in making paper, introduced by Thomas Routledge. Esparto grass is a perennial plant that grows without cultivation in semi-arid parts of Spain and North Africa. The Algerian name for esparto is alfa. It grows wild from Morocco to Tripoli, but most abundant in Algeria. It requires twelve years to mature the roots and produce fibre suitable for making into paper. Oran, the French port of Algeria, is the chief shipping point to England. The paper made from esparto grass is smooth, with a soft printable surface, and is suited for reproducing fine screen half-tones and colour work. Such well-known periodicals as the* Illustrated London News, Graphic, *and* Sphere *are printed on paper made from this African material. Esparto grass was first used in the United States by the Smith Paper Company, Lee, Massachusetts, in 1869.*

1859 *On July 4 was published in New York by George Roberts the world's largest newspaper, the sheet measuring 70 by 100 inches, with thirteen columns to the page. The paper was said to have cost the publisher $60 the ream, each ream weighing 300 pounds. It was intended to print 28,000 copies, but the press broke down before the task was completed. Only one issue of this newspaper is recorded.*

The first printed sheets of an American book to be folded mechanically was a thick quarto volume concerning the Rosetta Stone, *published in Philadelphia. The folding equipment was devised by Cyrus Chambers of Philadelphia.*

The earliest paper mill in the state of Minnesota was established at St. Anthony by Jonathan Chase and C. C. Secombe. The first printing to be executed in this state was by James G. Goodhue, who established the Minnesota Pioneer, *the first issue of which appeared on April 28, 1849. From an examination of old invoices it has been found that Goodhue procured his paper from St. Louis, probably from the mill of Messrs. Lamme, Keiser & Company (see: 1834).*

The earliest mention of the paper made in Minnesota's pioneer mill appeared in the periodical entitled the Minnesota Farmer and Gardner, *Vol. I, No. 2, St. Paul, December 1860. In this issue the editor says: "This number of the* Farmer and Gardner *is issued upon the first printing paper manufactured in Minnesota or the North-west. Messrs. Cutter and Secombe of the St. Anthony mill gave us the preference. . . . They promised to give us a good article and they have redeemed their promise as our readers will readily discover by comparing this number of our paper with the past." In the same magazine for July 1861 the following comment is made: "The paper mill of Cutter and Secombe is really a good institution and is one of the many things that has long been needed in our State. Burbank and Company of St. Paul take all they make of white paper including printing and book paper. They also make superior wrapping paper which is quite equal to any made at the old mills East." In George E. Warner's* History of Hennepin County and Minneapolis *(1881), an account of the owners of this mill is given: ". . . The mill was built at the upper end of Hennepin Island in 1859 by Jonathan Chase and C. C. Secombe. In 1860 Mr. Chase sold his interest to W. W. Eastman who in turn sold to E. W. Cutter. In 1861, H. M. Carpenter joined the firm of Secombe and Cutter."*

1860   *In New York City alone the census of this year recorded the use of $5,000,000 worth of paper and ink, producing $11,000,000 in books, newspapers, etc., employing more capital than any other single industry.*

About this time the original Jordan engine, for refining paper stock, was made by the Smith and Winchester Company, for the Boswell Keene Company, East Hartford, Connecticut. Joseph Jordan, the inventor of this machine, died on November 25, 1903, at his home in Bridgeport, Pennsylvania. For two years previous to his death Jordan had been receiving a pension from the American Pulp and Paper Association.

As late as this date rags formed 88 per cent of the total papermaking material.

Probably the first cigarette paper to be made from the fibre of the tobacco plant, the manufacture taking place in Algiers. In 1854 an English patent was granted John Adcock for the use of waste tobacco for making into paper to be employed in wrapping cigars.

1861   *In August of this year the* New York Tribune *adopted the papier-mâché method of stereotyping, followed soon after by the* Times *and the* Herald.

All stamp paper used by the government of France was required to be beaten by the old stamping-mills; it was thought that better and stronger paper was the result of this form of maceration.

In Dunbar Rowland's Encyclopaedia of Mississippi History *it is stated ". . . in 1861 the South was cut off from its paper supply," and then began a period when many newspapers discontinued altogether and the few that did appear were at times printed on wallpaper. The earliest Mississippi printing preserved in this country is the 209-page* Laws of the Mississippi Territory, *printed by Andrew Marschalk in Natchez, 1799, on foreign-made paper. There was no paper mill in Mississippi until comparatively recent times.*

1862   *The earliest manufacture of tracing-paper as a definite commodity for professional use.*

The Harper papermaking machine patented by James Harper, East Haven, Connecticut. This machine was founded on a combination of the Fourdrinier and the Dickinson cylinder machines. By the year 1873 only eight Harper machines had been built.

A.D.

Owing to the high cost of cotton during the Civil War it was necessary to find a substitute for cotton twine. The result was that paper was twisted into twine, cord, and string and became a standard product. (See: 1850.)

In searching for new and plentiful papermaking fibres that could be harvested in New England, the Smith and May paper mill, Lee, Massachusetts, made successful paper from the life-everlasting plant, also known as cudweed (Gnaphalium).

About this time the use of cactus (Cactaceæ) as a papermaking fibre was undertaken in San Jose, California, in a mill that had originally been built for grinding grain. The mill was located on Alviso Creek and was fitted with machinery for making cactus pulp and converting it into paper, but the experiment did not prove successful. The mill was later used in making paper from straw and waste paper. This may have been the second paper mill in California. (See: 1856–7.)

1863   *It is claimed that I. Augustus Stanwood and William Tower produced ground-wood paper in their mill in Gardiner, Maine, in January of this year.*

The Boston Weekly Journal for January 14 printed on paper made from wood-pulp. The Daily Journal of the same date appears to be on paper of the regulation sort. It is stated editorially that the entire edition of the Journal for January 15 was printed on "paper made of wood, a new process."

1864   *Piece felts for papermakers were made as early as 1854 in the United States by Asa Shuler, Hamilton, Ohio, but it was not until 1864 that paper-machine felting was manufactured. This was accomplished at Camden, Maine, by a firm that became known as the Knox Woolen Company.*

About this year the United States Government established a paper-machine in the basement of the Treasury Building,

A.D.

Washington, D.C. This machine was used in making paper for bank-notes and for whisky stamps. The paper was known as "membrane" owing to the silk threads interspersed through the sheets. Because of the complaints of the occupants of the Treasury Building concerning "their health being impaired by inhaling the pestilential vapors and odors developed by the process of papermaking," the project was abandoned in 1869 and the machinery removed from the building. The manufacture of bank-note and stamp paper was then entrusted to a commercial mill under government supervision.

1865 *Between this date and 1885 a larger number of patents relating to papermaking were issued by the United States Patent Office than had ever been known in the history of any country.*

1866 *In October of this year was established the first paper mill in the state of Oregon, at Oregon City. The mill was primarily intended for the manufacture of newsprint, and the man responsible for the activity was Henry L. Pittock (1835–1919), who began his long career with the* Oregonian *in 1853, at the age of eighteen. Regarding this mill the* Daily Oregonian, *April 19, 1866, has this to say: "The organization of the Oregon City Paper Manufacturing Company was perfected on the 18th inst. . . . We are informed that the company has already purchased the necessary machinery, and that is now in San Francisco. The building of the factory is to commence at once and be completed by the first of September. The location is one block below the woolen factory, and the power comes from the basin. . . ." In the October 29, 1866 issue of this same newspaper we find the following: "The building of the pioneer paper mill in Oregon is now completed and the machinery well advanced preparatory to active operations. . . ." Apparently the mill was not in operation until early the next year, for in the* Daily Oregonian, *January 12, 1867, these hopeful comments are made: "We have on our table some samples of Oregon* *made paper, the first ever manufactured in the State. They are from the Oregon City paper mills, and at the hour of writing are not more than twenty-four hours old. The mill, after considerable delay, and a few alterations in the machinery, as first set up, was started yesterday, the 10th inst., on brown, straw wrapping paper, and samples of the result are before us. The paper has not been submitted to pressure and is, consequently, rough in surface, but we have never seen straw paper of tougher texture. . . . We are informed that the mill will be worked right along on this kind of paper for two or three months, and that then, it will undertake newspaper, for which its machinery is well adapted. The price of brown straw paper made by the California mill, 20 by 30, is $2.00 per ream for wrapping. . . ."*

From all indications this mill was not a success, perhaps because the machinery was second-hand, as it was probably bought from an Eastern mill where it had been discarded. It is recorded that Henry L. Pittock again ventured into papermaking when he was responsible for the erection of the Clackamas mill, on the Clackamas River, in 1868. This mill, unlike the first attempt, was a pronounced success, according to a review of papermaking history in the state that appeared in the Oregonian, *October 1, 1905.*

The earliest paper mill in Iowa was established in November of this year at Coralville, near Iowa City. In the State Historical Society, Iowa City, there is preserved a sheet of paper that is said to have been made in this mill. In July 1875 the mill was wrecked by an explosion, and seven workers were killed. The mill was rebuilt by M. T. Close, who operated it for several years. The United States Census for 1870 lists three paper mills in Iowa — one in each of the following counties: Clinton, Johnson, and Jackson.

First ground-wood pulp mill in Canada, the Buntin mill at Valleyfield; the material, maple blocks.

The Willcox mill of Pennsylvania ceased making paper by hand, the last of America's handmade-paper mills except two revivals that did not continue long in operaticn. (See: 1729.)

First use of "batonné," "quadrille carré," and "oblong quadrille" paper in the printing of postage stamps, the Guadalajara issue of Mexico, 1866–7.

1867   *"Pelure" paper used for the first time in the making of postage stamps, used by the Dominican Republic.*

Albrecht Pagenstecher, Curtisville, Massachusetts, established the first ground-wood mill in the United States. (See: 1863.)

1868   *By this time paper was being converted into articles for almost every conceivable purpose: boxes, cups, plates, wash-bowls, barrels, table tops, window blinds, roofing, collars, vests, cuffs, aprons, towels, napkins, shirt bosoms, buttons, hats, handkerchiefs, raincoats, corsets, slippers, petticoats, curtains, carpets, machine belts, etc. Paper had become so commonly used in making dozens of different articles that a song entitled* The Age of Paper *was popular in London music halls. The words were sung by Mr. Howard Paul "attired completely in a suit of paper." (See: 1788, Ducrest.)*

The New Yorker Staats-Zeitung *in its editions of January 7, 8, and 9 was printed on American newsprint made from ground-wood pulp, the first New York City newspaper to use paper made of this material.*

The making of fine paper for printing and writing began near Melbourne, Australia. Previous to this time the supply was imported from the United States and Europe.

1869   *Paper coffins were manufactured in the United States at this time, laminated sheets of paper lending themselves to this purpose. This was not a new departure inasmuch as the*

Persians had made and used laminated-paper coffins hundreds of years previous to this date.

The original use of okra (Hibiscus esculentus *or* Abelmoschus esculentus) *on a commercial scale in American papermaking.* In the Weekly State Journal, Montgomery, Alabama, March 20, 1869, *the following account of the okra plant and its use in Southern papermaking is given:* "The Okra plant is indigenous to the South and anybody who can grow cotton can raise the Okra. The Okra is the same family as cotton, but is free from the insects which attack that plant. It can be produced so easily that an acre of good land will yield from five to eight tons of the stalks, and a ton of the stalks is worth twenty dollars. . . . The owners of the Chickasabogue paper mill, a few miles above Mobile, have lately made experiments which prove satisfactorily the great value of this plant as a papermaking material. It makes a paper as soft as rag paper, and as strong as that made from pure linen, thus affording the two essential qualities, flexibility and strength. The Okra can also be used to give strength to the paper made from cotton rags. . . . The Chickasabogue paper mill will commence using this new material as soon as they are assured of a sufficient supply, and their consumption will, of itself, amount to one hundred tons a month. . . ." In 1870 the Mobile Register *was printed on paper made from the okra plant, but the use of this material was apparently not continued.*

The first set of paper car wheels manufactured in the United States was made in Brandon, Vermont, by Richard N. Allen, the inventor. These wheels were used on a wood-car on the Central Vermont Railway for six months. In 1871 the Pullman Company gave its first order for 100 paper wheels. Ten years later the Allen Paper Car Wheel Company, Hudson, New York, produced 13,000 paper wheels in one year. One set of these wheels travelled 300,000 miles. It is the body of the wheel only that is composed of disks of rye-

straw paper board laminated together; the tire and the hub of the wheel are of metal.

1871   *The earliest use in America of toilet paper in roll form, a United States patent issued to Seth Wheeler this year (see: A.D. 875). The use of toilet paper did not progress rapidly, but by 1899 it was used universally. In 1940 there were consumed in the United States 300,000 tons of toilet paper.*

"Building paper" was first extensively used in America directly after the Chicago fire, when the Western Paper Company made the paper for lining 10,000 houses to accommodate those made homeless by the conflagration. Each house measured 16 by 20 feet and the cost of the paper was five dollars for each small building. The building, or lining, paper was composed of waste paper and straw.

1872   *Carl Daniel Ekman and George Fry, working in England, continued the experiments in the sulphite process begun by the Tilghmans (see: 1857).*

During this year the original Ford handmade-paper mill, Little Chart, Kent, England, was acquired from Waterloo and Sons by the present firm of Joseph Batchelor and Sons. It was in this mill that the paper for the William Morris Kelmscott books (1891–8) was fabricated. This mill also made the paper for the Ashendene (1894), Essex House (1898), Doves (1900), and other well-known English private presses. The paper for 200 copies of the Oxford Lectern Bible (1935) designed by Bruce Rogers was a product of this mill.

The original establishment of a machine-made paper mill begun in Japan. The small mill was set up near Tōkyō by Marquis Chokun Asano upon the recommendation of Thomas Waters, an Englishman, in the service of the Japanese Ministry of Finance. The machine was of British construction and John Rogers, an Englishman, was the superin-

tendent. The mill was known as the Yuko Company and actual production of paper commenced in 1874.

1874   *Although the first Christmas card was printed in England as early as 1842, the use of English-made cards did not become general in the United States until about 1860. A contemporary notice of greeting cards reads: "It is a happy form of business which can soothe and charm the cares and situations of social life." The earliest American-made Christmas cards were the product of Louis Prang, the Boston lithographer, who in 1874 was reproducing the works of celebrated painters for this purpose. By the year 1942, a hundred years after the original English Christmas card, the industry in the United States produced three billion cards with a value of $50,000,000.*

The first paper mill in the state of Kansas was probably erected this year at Blue Rapids. The mill was put in operation by G. and J. Greene, and printing and wrapping paper was manufactured until the mill ceased manufacturing in 1877. (See The History of Marshall County, Kansas *by Emma E. Forter, 1917.)*

1875   *First instance in the United States of coating paper on both sides, accomplished by Charles Gage, Springfield, Massachusetts. This paper, to the extent of 100 reams, was made at the request of Theodore DeVinne, New York bookprinter, to be used in printing a catalogue containing many coloured wood-engravings. The earliest coating of paper on one side in America was in 1852, by William Waldon, New Brunswick, New Jersey. (See: 1764, Cummings, and 1881.)*

During this year there appeared a pamphlet entitled Bamboo, as a Papermaking Material, *by Thomas Routledge (see: 1857–60). This booklet of 40 pages is printed on paper made from bamboo, probably the first use of this material in the Occident for papermaking. In 1876 at Arnhem a book under the title* Bamboe en Ampas als Grondstoffen voor Papierbereiding *was also printed on paper manufactured from bamboo. Routledge states that the rapidity of the growth of bamboo is unequalled and says in his pamphlet: ". . . at Gehzireh, the gardens of the Khedive of Egypt in Cairo it has grown nine inches in a single night and at Syon House, the Duke of Northumberland's, stems of* Bambusa gigantea *have attained a height of 60 feet in twelve weeks; at Chatsworth, the Duke of Devonshire's, the variety of* Bambusa vulgaris *reached a height of 40 feet in forty days." In 1908 the government of Burma sent eight or nine tons of selected bamboo to England, where it was made into paper by Thomas and Green, Soho mills, Wooburn Green, Bucks. In 1909, R. W. Sindall issued his treatise,* Bamboo for Papermaking, *a booklet of 60 pages on paper made from bamboo. (See: 1100.)*

1876   *Japan established a government mill for the making of paper for Japanese currency and bonds. This was the beginning of the Cabinet Printing Bureau.*

1877   *America introduced bevelled cards with gold edges, a novelty that captured the American and English trade for several decades. The bevel edges were made by fanning out the cards and bevelling them upon an emery wheel.*

At Breslau, Prussia, a factory chimney 50 feet in height was constructed entirely of paper. The chimney was said to perform its duty as well as if made from a more substantial material. In 1885 paper was used in making spokes for wagon wheels and the Germans experimented in making bearings for railroad car wheels of paper. Also in Germany paper was used in constructing piano frames. (See: 1788, Ducrest.)

1878   *The firm of Elisha Waters, Lansingburg, near Troy, New York, made a paper dome for the observatory of Rensselaer Polytechnic Institute, Troy; this dome was removed in*

1899 when the building was changed for another purpose. In 1881 this firm constructed a paper dome for the observatory at West Point, New York. This dome was composed of 36 sections and contained 2,500 pounds of paper. A dome made entirely of paper was also put on a building at Columbia University. This dome was in 20 sections and required 850 pounds of paper for its construction.

During this year, or early in 1879, the United States Bureau of Printing and Engraving set up machinery for the repulping of retired paper currency. The equipment was capable of repulping 800 to 900 pounds of old United States paper money daily, representing more than one million bills with a face value of about $12,000,000. The original cost of the paper amounted to about $1,100 a ton. This method of destroying old bills was abandoned in 1943; the retired currency paper is now destroyed by incineration.

According to the Papermakers Monthly Journal, *an English publication, Spanish papermakers were manufacturing paper from watercress (Rorippa nasturtium) for wrapping cigarettes. Cigarettes so wrapped were thought to be of benefit to persons with lung diseases. The paper was of a greenish colour and a heavy texture.*

1880 *About this time appeared the first pictorial end-papers in books.*

At this time there were about 350,000 tons of rags used yearly in the United States in the making of paper; of this amount approximately 85,000 tons were imported from foreign countries. The rags brought from Egypt were considered the cleanest, as the rags were free from grease, owing to the limited meat diet of the Egyptians; on the other hand, the rags from England and Germany were the most filthy, containing the greatest amount of grease and impurities.

The first ground-wood pulp produced on the Pacific coast was made by R. M. Brayne on Young's River, about 12 miles south of Astoria, Oregon. Four years later this ground-wood mill was acquired by the Falls Pulp Company and in 1890 it was taken over by the Willamette Pulp and Paper Company, which operated the small mill for seventeen years, when the four three-pocket grinders were removed and the wooden building allowed to fall into decay.

1881   Probable first employment of "granite" paper in the making of postage stamps, used in Switzerland.

The earliest paper mill in Nebraska established about this year, at Kearney, where cheap brown wrapping paper was made. An early pamphlet relating to papermaking in the West has the following to say about Kearney and its short-lived mill: "It is fair to presume that manufacturing west of the Missouri River must centre at Kearney, With the exception of some few mills engaged in the manufacture of straw boards and cheaper grades of paper, nearly all that is used between Pennsylvania and the Pacific Ocean is shipped from the east, while millions of tons of fine amber straw, flax straw, and other paper material is burnt in this section annually. We have the same pure soft water and water power that has made the manufacturing of paper profitable at Holyoke (Massachusetts), and the time is not far distant when Kearney will be the centre of papermaking in the west as Holyoke is in the east." The paper mill at Kearney ceased operation soon after its commencement.

According to the Paper World, an English publication, paper was being used in the construction of outhouses in the cities and rural districts of England, and they were said to withstand the rigorous climate admirably.

First American commercially-made coated paper, manufactured by S. D. Warren for Theodore Lowe DeVinne, New York printer. (See: 1764, Cummings, and 1875.)

A.D.

1882 *Sulphite pulp first made in the United States on a commercial scale, by C. S. Wheelwright, Providence, Rhode Island. The Ekman process used. (See: 1857, 1872.)*

Senator J. B. Rolland made the first fine paper in Canada, at St. Jerome, Quebec.

1883 *A watch made entirely of paper by a Dresden watchmaker was exhibited in Germany. The watch was claimed to be as serviceable as any timepiece made from more practical material.*

1884 *Sulphate pulp invented by Carl F. Dahl.*

Two specimens of printed paper made from "sugar cane bagasse containing 90% such fibre" appeared in the first number of the National Syndicates of Capital and Labor, *New Orleans. Probably the first actual use of bagasse in Louisiana papermaking. In the North sugar cane was used for making paper previous to this date, as Henry Howe, of Baltimore, is thought to have used bagasse as early as 1856.*

1885 *E. Waters, Lansingburg, near Troy, New York, made the first compressed-paper racing shells. In 1886 Harvard, Yale, and Columbia used shells formed of paper from this maker. The largest paper boat made by Waters measured 42 feet in length, with a 4-foot 4-inch beam.*

The first paper was made in Washington Territory, at Camas, May 5, 1885. The mill was destroyed by fire November 7, 1886, but was rebuilt and again put in operation May 3, 1888.

The original manufacture and use in the United States of vegetable parchment, now universally employed in many branches of the food-packing industry.

1886 *In* The Manufacture of Paper, *by Charles Thomas Davis, there are listed more than 950 materials from which paper could be made.*

A.D.

1887   *The largest paper-machine in the United States at this time was in the Hudson River Company mill at Palmers Falls. The wire was 112 inches wide and 50 feet long and had 22 forty-eight inch driers in two tiers. The machine was operated at 250 feet per minute. The largest paper-machine in England (1889) was at Sittingbourne, with a wire 120 inches wide and 40 feet long, with 20 driers. This machine was operated at 270 feet per minute.*

John W. Mullen, Fitchburg, Massachusetts, made the first paper tester, which was sold the same year to the Parsons Paper Company. The Mullen paper tester is now universally used in all paper laboratories as essential equipment.

As outlined in the Western Paper Trade, *May 16, 1887, the largest "sheet" of paper that had been brought to the editor's attention had been made by the Remington Paper Company, Watertown, New York. The "sheet" in question measured 7¾ miles in length with a width of six feet and a weight of a little over one ton.*

1888   *Sulphite pulp produced in Canada, by Charles Riordon, Merritton, Ontario.*

1889   *For the first time in the United States paper-production exceeded 1,000,000 tons per annum.*

1891   *The Kelmscott Press established in Hammersmith, England, by William Morris. The privately watermarked handmade paper used by this press was made in the Joseph Batchelor mill, Little Chart, Kent. The work of William Morris was instrumental in creating an interest in the revival of handmade paper.*

The earliest papermaking in the state of Colorado. The paper mill, operated by the Denver Paper Mill Company, was located at Manchester. It was opened on August 22, 1891 with two thousand persons present for the occasion;

A.D.

addresses were made by the Governor of the state, the Mayor of Denver, and the president of the newly established company. The paper produced was newsprint. The corporation failed during the financial panic of 1893 and did not resume operation.

Paper as insulation in telephone cables used by the Bell System; the paper was .0025 inch in thickness.

1893   *The largest paper-machine in the world was started running April 7 at the Star mill, Fenniscowles, England. This machine produced paper 140 inches wide, cost 15,000 pounds, and weighed 370 tons. The machine was capable of making between 75 and 80 tons of paper each week.*

The earliest recorded attempt in Europe in moulding paving blocks from paper pulp. In 1894 a section of a Washington, D.C., street was paved with blocks made of paper, but the method used in manufacturing the blocks was undeveloped and the experiment did not have an opportunity to succeed.

1894   *About this time automatic machines for the making of paper boxes were in general use, the beginning of the packaging era. (See: 1035.)*

1895   *According to the* World's Paper Trade Review, *London, a church made of paper was built in England this year. The building material was made of compressed brown paper reinforced with wire. The edifice, the Church of St. Owen, is located in the village of Downham-in-the-Isle. From the account it may be assumed that the building is serving its purpose at the present time and from all indications it is sufficiently durable to withstand the rigors of the English climate for another half century.*

Plain and decorated paper napkins first brought to this country from Japan on a large commercial scale. (In 1940 the United States used 40,000,000,000 paper napkins of all types and from all parts of the world.)

1896 *By this date the largest paper-machine in the United States was at Rumford Falls, Maine, with a wire 162 inches in width and 60 feet long. A year later (1897) machines in New York, New Hampshire, and Oregon were running at the rate of 500 feet per minute. By 1911 the speed of the fastest machine in the United States was 700 feet. In 1941 the largest paper-machine in the world was at Sitting-bourne, Kent, England. This machine is 320 inches wide with a capacity of 1,400 feet per minute.*

Electricity used in papermaking for the first time in the United States, July 10, 1896, in the mill of the Cliff Paper Company, Niagara Falls, New York.

1897 *Charles S. Wood, of Wisconsin, experimented with paper as a mulch in agriculture and was probably the originator of this practice. C. F. Eckhart, Honolulu, H. I., however, was the first to use paper extensively for this purpose when he introduced the practice in 1914 on his sugar plantation. Paper is now exclusively used in Hawaii in pineapple cultivation, the material being impregnated with asphalt.*

Horseshoes made of paper introduced by Chicago blacksmiths. The layers of paper were impregnated with oil to render the material waterproof; the sheets of paper were then laminated together with a cement made of powdered chalk, Venetian turpentine, linseed oil, and lacquer. The holes for nails were stamped in the paper while moist, and the paper was next cut in the desired form and the horseshoes subjected to immense hydraulic pressure. The paper horseshoes could be shaped to the hoofs and were said to be more comfortable for the horses and as lasting as those made of iron. Contemporary with paper horseshoes came the manufacture of paper gas pipes which were made by lapping strong paper around a solid core of suitable di-

ameter, each sheet, or layer, dipped in melted asphaltum. Such built-up paper pipes were impervious to air and water and could endure heavy pressure. The pipes were joined by asphalted paper connections. The advantage was cheapness, light weight, and indestructibility.

1898   *Inasmuch as printing was first accomplished in Louisiana as early as 1764, it would be reasonable to expect to find records of a paper mill operating within the state a few years following. The early Louisiana imprints are on paper imported from France or brought from the North. A considerable search in old files, letters, and documents has not brought forth any evidence that would place paper-making in Louisiana previous to 1898, when a machine mill was set up by an English syndicate at Braithwaite for the manufacture of paper from bagasse (sugar-cane refuse). According to the* Louisiana Conservation Review, *Autumn 1938, this initial experiment in Louisiana with bagasse was a complete failure. (See: 1884.)*

1899   *Production of paper in the United States was 2,167,593 tons, with 22 per cent of the machines idle. The full capacity could have been 2,782,200 tons.*

1900   *A mendicant Taoist priest discovered in Tun-huang caves, Turkestan, the great store of rolled manuscripts on paper dating from* A.D. *406 to 1035. Shortly thereafter Sir Aurel Stein and Professor Pelliot acquired many of these priceless manuscripts for the national institutions of England and France.*

The earliest papermaking in the state of Florida was begun this year in Pensacola, the pulp made from pine. The mill was abandoned after a year or two of unsuccessful operation. Printing was first accomplished in Florida in 1783 by William Charles Wells, when he established the East Florida Gazette *in St. Augustine; apparently no copies of this newspaper exist in America. Owing to the early date of*

A.D.

printing in Florida it was reasoned that paper may have been made by hand in the state previous to the nineteenth century. A careful search in the archives of the state, however, has revealed no papermaking until about 1900. The Yonge Library of Florida History, Gainesville, Florida, definitely states that there was no paper made in the state until the year 1900.

1901   *In England at this time compressed paper had become a standard material for the construction of hansom cabs, interiors of railway carriages, drain pipes, oil drums, and military hospital buildings. In America the use of paper in heavy construction had begun earlier. (See: 1772, 1869.)*

This year died Francis Tempest, an Englishman, who alone for forty-one years operated the Sunnydale paper mill, Beaver Valley, Pennsylvania. The remarkable feature about this mill was that Tempest ran the mill himself, without help, from the year 1860 until the time of his death. The old stone building housed a 36-inch cylinder machine and one 125-pound beater. The machine was operated only in the day-time, but the beater was kept in motion throughout the night. By this method Tempest was able to manufacture 250 pounds of paper each working day. This was probably the longest record of a one-man machine mill in America. More than thirty-five years ago I visited this picturesque old mill, but since that time it has been dismantled.

1903   *First use of corrugated fibre containers, replacing wood boxes to a great extent. The use of fibre boxes was authorized by the railroads of the United States in 1906.*

1905   *Glassine paper introduced into the United States by Olaf Hedstrom through his association with the Hartford City Paper Company, Hartford City, Indiana.*

1906   *The first paper milk-bottles made this year by G. W. Maxwell, San Francisco, California.*

A.D.

1907   *This year terminated the making of paper by hand by the L. L. Brown Paper Company, Adams, Massachusetts. This mill also manufactured machine-made paper, but from 1881 it operated a two-vat handmade-paper department. In 1880 the William Norman family came to the United States from Wells, England, to operate this handmade-paper mill. William Norman died in 1901 and his son Walter Norman continued the mill until 1907, when it was abandoned. Nothing now remains of the original equipment, but for many years the two stone vats that had been brought from England served as watering-troughs for cattle in the Berkshire Hills.*

First kraft (sulphate) pulp made on this continent, at the Brompton paper mills, East Angus, Quebec, Canada.

By this date medicated papers were in universal use. These antiseptic papers included gout papers, Christy's chrome-gelatine for bandaging, East India paper plaster for slight flesh wounds, mustard paper, Ricou's anti-asthma paper, blister paper, Gautier's nascent iodine paper, hygienic paper handkerchiefs, towels, etc. Also paper was used in the making of splints for reducing fractures by treating millboard with shellac, violin resin, pine, etc.

1909   *First kraft paper manufactured in the United States.*

1910   *About this time the wrapping of bread in printed paper became universal in America. Also the wrapping of fruit in paper had its beginning. Apples were wrapped in a specially oil-treated paper to control "scald." In the Northwest of the United States by 1941 there were more than 350 carloads of paper consumed each season in wrapping fruit.*

1915   *The earliest use in California of paper trays for the drying of raisins. In 1940 more than 80 per cent of the raisin-drying trays were made of paper. Previously they were fabricated from wood.*

A.D.

During this year the students of the New York State College of Forestry, Syracuse, New York, planted seedlings of the red pine; a number of years later they harvested the wood and made it into pulp and finally into newsprint, in the school laboratory. The paper manufactured was used in printing the student newspaper of the college. This was the first instance, the school claimed, in which the entire process from growing the trees to making the wood into paper was carried out by an educational institution.

1919   *The most accurate novel in English relating to the hand-made-paper industry published this year:* Storm in a Tea-cup *by Eden Phillpotts. This novel gives an interesting and picturesque insight into the life of English papermakers. The detail is technically correct in every way, which is more than can be said of Joseph Hergesheimer's* The Foolscap Rose, *a papermaking story published in 1934. The mill used as a background by Phillpotts was Tuckenhay Mills, Totnes, Devonshire, now operated by A. Millbourne and Company.*

1920   *Paper was made at a speed of 1,000 feet a minute on October 23, 1920. This speed was attained on a Fourdrinier machine made by Bagley and Sewell, in the paper mill of Wausau Sulphate Fibre Company, Mosinee, Wisconsin. On April 15, 1921 newsprint was made at a speed of 1,000 feet a minute on a 158-inch Rice, Barton and Fales machine in the mill of the Great Northern Paper Company, Millinocket, Maine.*

1921   *First use of Alabama spruce pine for making paper on a commercial scale. The* Birmingham Age-Herald, *June 20, 1921, was printed on paper made from this pulp. The following account of the paper was given in this issue: "Paper made from Alabama spruce pine; wood cut on Yellow Creek, near Warrior River, in December; floated to Birmingport in barges and loaded on cars for Niagara Falls; ground into pulp and made into paper at Defiance mills May second. Experiment initiated, directed and arranged by E. W. Barrett, editor of the* Age-Herald. *Test supervised*

A.D.

by Robert Clade, who says the paper is equal to that made from Canadian spruce."

1927 *There appeared this year in Paris the first edition of* Nouara Chroniques d'un antique village papetier *by Claude Dravaine, an interesting story of old French papermaking. This volume, like the Eden Phillpott's story, is not of a technical nature.*

1928 *The craft of making paper by hand revived in Lime Rock, Connecticut, by Dard Hunter Associates. The equipment for this mill was brought from Downton, Wiltshire, England, and the papermakers came from Maidstone, Kent. For the most part the paper produced in this mill was used by the printing house of the late William Edwin Rudge. The mill ceased operating in 1931, but remains today the only fully equipped handmade-paper mill in America.*

1933 *According to Chinese government statistics there were 24,-437 individual cottage "mills" for the making of handmade paper in the one province of Chekiang, China. These cottage industries gave employment to 127,000 workers in the one province. Most of the paper produced was used in making "spirit-paper" employed in Chinese religious rites and ceremonies. (See:* A.D. *106.)*

1934 *The largest sheet of paper ever made by hand was formed this year in the Iwano mill, Okamoto, Echizen, Japan. Two sheets were made, although only one was required; each sheet measured 200 inches square, or 40,000 square inches. The Iwano paper was too large to be formed in a mould in the regulation manner, so the workers sprayed the pulp, or stock, over a porous surface laid above the floor, forming a thin coating of pulp in a more or less even thickness. One of the huge sheets was used for a painting now in the Memorial Building, Waseda University, Tōkyō, dedicated to the late Okuma, governor of the university, and one-time Premier of Japan. The largest paper ever to be formed in a hand-mould in China measures 84 by 48 inches; in Ja-*

pan 29 by 67 inches; in Tibet 72 by 31 inches; in Nepal 64 by 28 inches; in Siam 80 by 18 inches; and in Europe 53 by 31 inches.

1940 *Production of paper in the United States, 14,372,000 tons, with 14 per cent of the machines idle; full capacity would have been 16,700,000 tons. In the U. S. there were (1938) 125,800 employees; in Canada (1940), 34,719 employees in the pulp and paper industry.*

1942 *It is unofficially stated that the amount of paper used in the building of a battleship of the* Massachusetts *class is 100 tons. Of this amount 16 tons of blueprint paper are used, the balance of the paper being consumed in letterheads, carbon copies, contracts, envelopes, interoffice communications, graphs, stencils, mimeographs, sketches, tracings, routing, crating, packing, and finally the small amount of paper used in actual construction.*

Newsprint to the amount of 8,971,000 tons produced in the world, Canada making two fifths of this. In the United States alone newspaper sales were 44,492,836 copies each day.

1943 *Throughout this year sufficient paper was manufactured in the United States to supply each individual citizen with 287.5 pounds. This was the largest production in the history of the Nation.*

1944 *During the fiscal year ending June 30, 1944 the United States Government consumed 1723 tons of paper in printing the U. S. currency, the amount used in printing postage stamps was 1,045 tons, and United States Government bonds required 1,150 tons of paper. During the calendar year 1944 the cardboard used in making U. S. postal cards was 10,620,109 pounds and in the making of embossed stamped envelopes 19,476,652 pounds of paper.*

1945 *It is stated that there are 14,000 different paper products.*

Bibliography

IN FORMING this bibliography of papermaking and watermarking it has not been my desire to include every book, pamphlet, and article that has been compiled. Such a list would necessarily embrace thousands of titles in all languages and would be well beyond the scope or usefulness of this listing. For convenience this bibliography has been divided into four distinct parts; (1) Oriental papermaking history and practice, (2) Occidental papermaking history and practice, (3) watermarking, (4) paper colouring and surface decoration. In each of these four lists fifty titles have been selected — in all, two hundred books, pamphlets, and articles. These entries have been carefully chosen not only as the most comprehensive works on these respective aspects of paper, but on account of the availability of the material in public libraries. It would not, perhaps, be possible to find every item of this list in any single library, but this bibliography of two hundred entries is more than sufficient for a general study of the history and technique of papermaking, watermarking, and the colouring and decorating of paper in all countries and in all periods. It will be noticed that there is a dearth of material in English, although our own language has been given preference in every instance. Practically nothing has been compiled on early American watermarks, and books and pamphlets in English dealing with early European watermarks are likewise limited. In other languages, however, the watermarks used by early European papermakers have received extended attention, for in French, German, Dutch, and Russian considerable material is available. But even with the reproduction of thousands of old papermarks, the field remains practically untouched when we take into account that there are literally hundreds of thousands of different watermarks in papers extending from the commencement of the art of watermarking, about 1282, to the end of the nineteenth century, when emblems of this kind began to lose their symbolic interest. It is hoped that this short, although comprehensive, bibliography will prove of value to students of papermaking history and technique and that the list will at least serve as a nucleus for further research and study.

I. ORIENTAL

ALIBAUX, HENRI: *L'Étrange Destinée d'une lettre perdue.* 22 pages text; 10 illustrations. In: *Le Papier.* Grenoble, France, 1938.

——: *L'Invention du papier.* 30 pages text; 2 illustrations. *Sonderabzug aus dem Gutenberg-Jahrbuch.* Mainz, 1939.

*ARTS, MÉTIERS ET CULTURES DE LA CHINE: *Papier de bambou.* 71 pages text; 13 coloured engravings showing the use of bamboo in Chinese papermaking. Paris, 1815.

BLANCHET, AUGUSTIN: *Essai sur l'histoire du papier et de sa fabrication.* 44 pages text; 1 illustration; history of paper in the Orient. Paris, 1900.

BLUM, ANDRÉ: *On the Origin of Paper.* Translated from the French by Harry Miller Lydenberg. 79 pages, of which three or four are devoted to Asiatic paper. New York, 1934.

BOCKWITZ, HANS H.: *Zur Kulturgeschichte des Papiers.* 35 pages text; 31 illustrations. Stettin, Germany, 1935.

*——: *Beiträge zur Papiergeschichte: Hat die orientalische Papiermacherei bereits mechanische Stampfwerke gekannt?* 6 pages text; 7 illustrations. In: *Wochenblatt für Papierfabrikation.* Biberach, Württemberg, Germany, 1939.

*BOJESEN, C. C., and ALLEY, REWI: *China's Rural Paper Industry.* 11 pages text; 33 illustrations. In: *The China Journal,* Volume XXVIII, No. 5. Shanghai, China, May 1938.

*BOUVIER, RENÉ: *La Fabrication du papier à la main en Orient.* 10 pages text; 14 illustrations. In: *Le Papier.* Grenoble, France, December 1923.

BRETON, M.: *China: Its Costume, Arts, Manufactures, with Observations Explanatory, Historical, and Literary.* 4 volumes; in Volume II a short description of Chinese papermaking, with 2 coloured illustrations. London, 1813.

CARTER, THOMAS FRANCIS: *The Invention of Printing in China and*

Its Spread Westward. Pages 1–6, invention of paper in China; 3 illustrations. New York, 1925.

*CHAUDHARY, YADAVRAO S.: *Handmade Paper in India.* 8 pages text on paper made in India. Publisher: J. C. Kumarappa on behalf of A.I.V.I.A. Lucknow, India, April 10, 1936.

*DU HALDE, P.: *The General History of China, Including an Exact and Particular Account of Their Customs, Manners, Ceremonies, Religion, Arts, and Sciences.* 4 volumes; in Volume II, pages 415–38: "Of the Paper, Ink, and Pencils, as also of the Printing and Binding the Chinese Books." London, 1736.

*EMERSON, H. W.: *Monograph on Papermaking and Papier Mâché in the Punjab.* 25 pages text. Lahore, India, 1908.

*FAIRBANKS, THOMAS NAST: *A Generalization of the Manufacture of Paper. Modern Papermaking in Japan.* 11 pages text; 15 illustrations. In: *The Dolphin,* No. II (pages 120–30). New York, 1935.

*FRANKLIN, BENJAMIN: *Description of the Process to be observed in Making Large Sheets of Paper in the Chinese Manner, with One Smooth Surface.* (Read by Dr. Franklin, June 20, 1788.) 2 pages text. In: *Transactions of the American Philosophical Society,* Volume III. Philadelphia, 1793.

GEE, W. H.: *Monograph on Fibrous Manufactures in the Punjab.* 52 pages text. Lahore, India, 1891.

HAIBARA, MAOJIRO: *A Collection of 100 Japanese Handmade Papers, including the Most Famous Makers.* 2 pages text; 100 specimens. Tōkyō, Japan, November 3, in the 8th Year of Showa.

*HODGSON, B. H.: *On the Native Method of Making the So-Called Nepalese Paper.* 4 pages text. In: *Journal of the Asiatic Society of Bengal,* Volume I. Calcutta, 1832.

HOERNLE, A. F. RUDOLF: *Who Was the Inventor of Rag Paper?* 22 pages text: In: *Journal of the Royal Asiatic Society of Great Britain and Ireland.* London, October 1903.

*HUNTER, DARD: *Old Papermaking in China and Japan.* 71 pages text; 36 illustrations; 19 specimens. Chillicothe, Ohio, 1932.

*——: *A Papermaking Pilgrimage to Japan, Korea, and China,* 150 pages text; 69 illustrations; 50 specimens. New York, 1936.

*——: *Papermaking in Southern Siam.* 40 pages text; 18 illustrations; 4 specimens. Chillicothe, Ohio, 1936.

*HUNTER, DARD: *Chinese Ceremonial Paper.* 82 pages text; 15 illustrations; 47 specimens. Chillicothe, Ohio, 1937.

*——: *Papermaking by Hand in India.* 129 pages text; 84 illustrations; 27 specimens. New York, 1939.

*JUGAKU, BUNSHO: *Kôgei* (Crafts). Article on Ogawa papermaking. 192 pages text; 6 illustrations; 26 specimens. Tōkyō, Japan, 1935.

*——: *Washi-Dansô* (Symposium on Japanese Handmade Paper). Only Volume I published. 100 pages text: 2 illustrations; 20 specimens. Kyōto, Japan, 1936.

*KAEMPFER, ENGELBERT: *The History of Japan, with a Description of Siam, 1690–1692.* 7 pages text; 3 illustrations devoted to old Japanese papermaking. 2 volumes. London, 1727.

*KHADDARI, MUNNALAL: *Handmade Paper Industry of India* (in Hindustani). 25 pages text. (Textbook of the Kalpi Handmade Paper School.) Kalpi, U. P., India, 1937.

*KHODKE, S. B.: *Handmade Paper, All India Village Industries Association.* (Indian papermaking as practised in the Mohandas K. Gandhi School of Papermaking, Wardha.) 8 pages text; cover printed on Indian paper. Wardha, India, 1936.

*KIRK, R. T. F.: *Papermaking in the Bombay Presidency.* 9 pages text; 10 illustrations. Bombay, India, 1908.

*KÔGEI (Crafts). Articles on Japanese Handmade Papers by Naoyuki Ohta, Kazu Makamura, Muneyoshi Yanagi, Bunsho Jugaku, Naokatsu Nakamura, T. Iwai, and Dr. Torajiro Naitô. 98 pages text; 14 illustrations; 18 specimens. Published by Nippon Mingei Kyokwai, Tōkyō, April 15, 8th Year of Showa.

*KUNIHIGASHI, JIHYOE (or KUNISAKI, JIHEI): *Kamisuki Chôhô-Ki* (Papermakers' Treasury). (The oldest book in the Japanese language devoted to papermaking.) Wood-blocks by Tôkei Niwa. Osaka, Japan, 1798.

LAUFER, BERTHOLD: *Paper and Printing in Ancient China.* 34 pages text. The Caxton Club, Chicago, 1931.

MAUREL, F.: *Le Papier japonais: histoire et fabrication d'après des documents anglais et indigènes.* 12 pages text; 12 specimens. In: *Mémoires de l'Athénée Oriental.* Paris, 1871.

*McCLURE, F. A.: *The Native Paper Industry in Kwangtung.* 10 pages text; 7 illustrations. In: *Lingnan Science Journal,* Volume V, No. 3. Canton, China, December 1927.

*McClure, F. A.: *Some Chinese Papers Made on the Ancient "Wove" Type of Mould.* 13 pages text; 9 illustrations. In: *Lingnan Science Journal,* Volume IX, Nos. 1 and 2. Canton, China, June 1930.

*Mookerjee, D. N.: *A Monograph on Paper and Papier Mâché in Bengal.* 8 pages text. Calcutta, 1908.

*Parkes, Harry S.: *Reports on the Manufacture of Paper in Japan. Presented to Both Houses of Parliament by Command of Her Majesty.* 24 pages text; 20 coloured lithographs of making Japanese paper by hand. London, 1871.

Pearson, R. S.: *The Indian Forest Records.* Note on the *Utilization of Bamboo for the Manufacture of Paper-pulp.* 121 pages text; 2 illustrations; folding map. Calcutta, India, 1916.

*Raitt, W.: *Kashmir Papermaking in Photographs.* 26 illustrations; 1 specimen, n.p., n.d., ?1910.

——: *The Childhood of Papermaking* (Kashmir, India). 3 pages text. In: *The Papermaker and British Paper Trade Journal.* London, February 1, 1930.

Rein, J. J.: *The Industries of Japan, with an Account of Its Agriculture, Forestry, Arts, and Commerce,* 30 pages text; 5 illustrations; 1 specimen devoted to Japanese papermaking. New York, 1889.

Renker, Armin: *Papier und Druck im Fernen Osten.* 53 pages text; 32 illustrations. Verlag der Gutenberg-Gesellschaft, Mainz, 1936.

Royle, J. Forbes: *The Fibrous Plants of India Fitted for Cordage, Clothing, and Paper.* 403 pages text. London, 1855.

Siamese Papermaking. A Lecture on the Making of Khoi (*Streblus asper*) Paper, by Phya Kasikan Banca (in Siamese language). (This pamphlet was distributed at the cremation of Madame Aphiraksh Amphorsathan at Wat Amarintraram, 10th of February B. E. 2477.) Bangkok, Siam.

Stein, M. Aurel: *Ruins of Desert Cathay, Personal Narrative of Explorations in Central Asia and Westernmost China.* 2 volumes; Volume I, 546 pages; Volume II, 517 pages; 333 illustrations, maps, etc. (Deals with Sir Aurel Stein's discoveries at Tun-huang.) London, 1912.

Stevens, Richard Tracy: *The Art of Papermaking in Japan.* 8 pages text; 8 illustrations. Privately printed, New York, 1909.

*Sung Ying-hsing: *T'ien kung k'ai wu*. (The earliest Chinese book to deal with papermaking.) 4 wood-block illustrations with explanatory text, n.p., 1634.

*Venkajee, Tekumalla: *Handmade Paper Industry in India*. 4 pages text; 12 illustrations. In: *Paper Trade Journal*. New York, October 28, 1926.

II. OCCIDENTAL

Alibaux, Henri: *Les Légendes de l'histoire du papier, les moulins à papier sur l'Hérault en 1189, le papier de coton*. 24 pages text. In: *Revue du Lyonnais*, No. III, July–September 1921. Lyon, France, 1921.

——: *Les Premières Papeteries françaises*. 209 pages text; map. Paris, 1926.

*Andés, Louis Edgar: *The Treatment of Paper for Special Purposes*. Translated from the German by Charles Salter. 240 pages text; 48 illustrations. London, 1907.

Barker, Charles R.: *Old Mills of Mill Creek, Lower Merion, Pennsylvania*, 22 pages text. In: *The Pennsylvania Magazine of History and Biography*, Volume L, No. 1. Philadelphia, 1926.

*Bromley, H. A., and Shore, J.: *Articles of Stationery and Allied Materials, Their Chemistry and Technical Examination*. 126 pages text; 7 illustrations and figures. London, 1939.

*Clapperton, R. H.: *Paper: An Historical Account of Its Making by Hand from the Earliest Times Down to the Present Day*. 158 pages text; 143 illustrations; 2 specimens. Oxford, England, 1934.

Crane, Ellery B.: *Early Paper Mills in Massachusetts, Especially Worcester County*. 18 pages text; 1 illustration. Worcester, Massachusetts, 1887.

*Dawe, Edward A.: *Paper and Its Uses, a Treatise for Printers, Stationers and Others*. 160 pages text; 26 illustrations; 34 specimens. London, 1914.

*Degaast, Georges: *Vieux Moulins à papier d'Auvergne*. 13 pages text; 35 illustrations; 2 specimens. In: *Arts et Métiers Graphiques*, No. 53, June 1936, and No. 55, November 1936. Paris, 1936.

*Evans, Lewis: *Ancient Papermaking: A Lecture Given at the*

Dickinson Institute, Croxley Mill, February 27, 1896. 13 pages text; 4 illustrations. In: *The Firm of John Dickinson and Company, Limited.* London, 1896.

*GASPARINETTI, ANDREA: *Carte, Cartiere e Cartai Fabrianesi.* 35 pages text; 25 illustrations; 4 specimens. In: *Il Risorgimento Grafico,* September–October 1938. Milan, Italy, 1938.

Geschichte des Papiers die Roh- und Halbstoffe, by F. VON HÖSSLE, DR. KORN, FRIEDRICH MOSEL, DR. E. OPFERMANN, and DIREKTOR LUDWIG E. WALTER. 278 pages text; 31 illustrations and figures. Berlin, 1929.

GILPIN, THOMAS: *Memoir of Thomas Gilpin, found among the papers of Thomas Gilpin, Jr.* 38 pages text; 2 illustrations. In: *Pennsylvania Magazine of History and Biography,* Volume XLIX, No. 4. Philadelphia, 1925.

GOODWIN, RUTHERFOORD: *The William Parks Paper Mill at Williamsburg.* (Read before the Bibliographical Society of America, June 23, 1937.) 41 pages text; 9 illustrations. Lexington, Virginia, 1939.

*GRANT, JULIUS: *Books and Documents: Dating, Permanence and Preservation.* 218 pages text; 35 illustrations. London, 1937.

*GRÜNEWALD, WILLY, and SENSENHAUSER, GEORG: *Papierhandel, ein Hilfsbuch für Papierhändler, Verarbeiter und Verbraucher.* 250 pages text; 49 illustrations; 42 specimens. Berlin, 1927.

HALLEY, R. A.: *Papermaking in Tennessee.* 9 pages text. Reprinted from the *American Historical Magazine,* July 1904. Nashville, Tennessee, 1904.

*HERRING, RICHARD: *Paper and Papermaking, Ancient and Modern.* 125 pages text; 4 illustrations; 25 specimens. First edition, London, 1855.

*HOFMANN, CARL: *Praktisches Handbuch der Papier-Fabrikation.* 2 volumes; 1769 pages text; 1730 illustrations and figures. Berlin, 1891–7.

HÖSSLE, FRIEDRICH VON: *Württembergische Papiergeschichte. Beschreibung des alten Papiermacher-Handwerks sowie der alten Papiermühlen.* 134 pages text; 54 illustrations. Biberach, Germany, 1910–14.

*HUNTER, DARD: *Old Papermaking.* 112 pages text; 88 illustrations; 10 specimens. Chillicothe, Ohio, 1923.

HUNTER, DARD: *The Literature of Papermaking, 1390–1800.* 48 pages text; 20 illustrations; 23 facsimile title-pages. Chillicothe, Ohio, 1925.

*——: *Papermaking through Eighteen Centuries.* 358 pages text; 214 illustrations. New York, 1930.

IONGH, JANE DE: *Van Gelder Zonen, 1784–1934.* 182 pages text; 35 illustrations; watermarks, etc. Haarlem, Netherlands, 1934.

JENKINS, RHYS: *Early Papermaking in England, 1495–1788.* 48 pages text. In: *The Library Association Record,* Volume II, Nos. 9 and 11; Volume III, No. 5; Volume IV, Nos. 3 and 4. London, 1900–2.

JONES, HORATIO GATES: *Historical Sketch of the Rittenhouse Paper Mill; the First Erected in America,* A.D. *1690.* (Read before the Historical Society of Pennsylvania, May 11, 1863.) 17 pages text; 1 illustration. In: *The Pennsylvania Magazine of History and Biography,* Volume XX, No. 3. Philadelphia, 1896.

*LABARRE, E. J.: *A Dictionary of Paper and Papermaking Terms, with a Historical Study of Paper.* 315 pages text; 45 specimens. Amsterdam, Netherlands, 1937.

LACROIX, AUGUSTE: *Historique de la papeterie d'Angoulême.* 516 pages text. Paris, 1863.

*LA LANDE, JOSEPH JÉRÔME LE FRANCAIS DE: *Art de faire le papier.* (The most comprehensive early textbook on the subject of papermaking.) In: *Description des Arts et Métiers,* published by the Académie des Sciences, Volume IV, Paris, 1761 (German edition, 1762; Spanish edition, 1778; Dutch edition, 1792).

LE CLERT, LOUIS: *Le Papier, recherches et notes pour servir à l'histoire du papier.* 2 volumes; 522 pages text; 23 illustrations; 366 reproductions of watermarks. Paris, 1927.

*LENZ, HANS: *La Industria Papelera en Mexico.* 121 pages text; 102 illustrations and reproductions of old Mexican watermarks. Mexico, D. F., 1940.

ONFROY, HENRI: *L'Art du papier et le papier d'art.* 64 pages text; 4 illustrations. Paris, 1906.

*——: *Histoire les papeteries à la cuve d'Arches et d'Archettes, 1492–1911.* 50 pages text; 16 illustrations. Evreux, 1912.

Papermaking as Conducted in Western Massachusetts, with a Brief History from the Earliest Ages. 71 pages text. Springfield, Massachusetts, 1874.

*PIETTE, LOUIS: *Traité de la fabrication du papier.* 492 pages text; charts, etc. Paris, 1831.

*PLANCHE, GABRIEL: *De l'industrie de la papeterie.* 312 pages text; folding charts, etc. Paris, 1853.

*POORTENAAR, JAN, HUNTER, DARD, and PELS, C.: *De Papier Wereld.* 244 pages text; 106 illustrations; 41 specimens. Amsterdam, Netherlands, n.d. (1939).

*PROTEAUX, A.: *Practical Guide for the Manufacture of Paper and Boards.* 292 pages text; 6 folding plates. Philadelphia, 1866.

RENKER, ARMIN: *Uber das Papier ein Dialog zwischen dem Papiermacher und dem Laien.* 30 pages text; 2 illustrations; specimens. Berlin, 1930.

*———: *Das Buch vom Papier.* 172 pages text; 46 illustrations; 14 specimens. Leipzig, Germany, 1934.

RIDDLE, E. C.: *Whatman Paper Mill: The Centenary of Springfield Mill, Maidstone.* 12 pages text; 26 illustrations. Maidstone, Kent, England, 1907.

SACHSE, JULIUS FRIEDRICH: *Die Papier Mühle der Brüderschaft zu Ephrata.* (Read before the Lancaster County Historical Society, March 5, 1897.) Lancaster, Pennsylvania, 1897.

SMITH, ALBERT BARTON: *From Spook Hill to Loveland in 1810. Historical Paper Mill Sketches by an Old American Papermaker.* 41 pages text; 12 illustrations. Trenton, New Jersey, 1938.

SMITH, J. E. A.: *Pioneer Papermaking in Berkshire. The Life, Life Work and Influence of Zenas Crane.* 55 pages text; portrait. Holyoke, Massachusetts, n.d.

*STEPHENSON, J. N. (editor): *The Manufacture of Pulp and Paper, A Textbook of Modern Pulp and Paper Mill Practice.* (Compiled by many writers prominent in American papermaking, the best work in any language on the technique of modern paper fabrication.) 5 volumes, exhaustive text; hundreds of illustrations, figures, etc. Third edition. New York, 1939.

*STEVENSON, LOUIS TILLOTSON: *The Background and Economics of American Papermaking.* 250 pages text; charts, etc. New York, 1940.

WEEKS, LYMAN HORACE: *A History of Paper Manufacturing in the United States, 1690–1916.* 352 pages text; 99 illustrations. New York, 1916.

*WHEELWRIGHT, WILLIAM BOND: *Printing Papers.* 133 pages text; 53 illustrations. Chicago, Illinois, 1936.

WILLCOX, JOSEPH: *Ivy Mills, 1729–1866. Willcox and Allied Families.* 139 pages text; 50 illustrations and portraits. Baltimore, Maryland, 1911.

WISWALL, CLARENCE A.: *One Hundred Years of Papermaking, a History of the Industry on the Charles River at Newton Lower Falls, Massachusetts.* 115 pages text; 13 illustrations. Reading, Massachusetts, 1938.

III. WATERMARKS

APCHER, LOUIS: *Les Dupuy de la Grandrive, leurs papeteries de la Grandrive et Barot; leur parent, l'Intendant du Canada Claude-Thomas Dupuy.* 150 pages text; 10 illustrations; reproductions of Dupuy watermarks. Paris, 1937.

BABINGER, FRANZ: *Zur Geschichte der Papiererzeugung im Osmanischen Reiche.* 9 pages text; reproductions of 12 watermarks. Berlin, 1931.

BAYLEY, HAROLD: *The Tragedy of Sir Francis Bacon, an Appeal for Further Investigation and Research.* 274 pages text; reproduction of watermarks, symbols, and emblems. London, 1902.

——: *Notes on Watermarks.* 8 pages text; 78 reproductions of watermarks. In: *The Book-Lover's Magazine,* Volume VI, Part II. Edinburgh, Scotland, 1906.

——: *A New Light on the Renaissance, Displayed in Contemporary Emblems.* 270 pages text; reproductions of more than 400 watermarks, printers' marks, devices, etc. London, 1909.

——: *The Lost Language of Symbolism, an Inquiry into the Origin of Certain Letters, Words, Names, Fairy-Tales, Folklore, and Mythologies.* 2 volumes; 763 pages text; 1419 reproductions of old watermarks, printers' marks, ornaments, etc. London, 1912.

BEADLE, CLAYTON: *The Development of Watermarking in Hand- and Machine-made Papers.* 15 pages text; reproductions of 28 watermarks. In: *Journal of the Society of Arts,* Volume LIV, No. 2791. London, May 18, 1906.

BOFARULL Y SANS, DON FRANCISCO DE A. DE: *Los Animales en las*

Marcas del Papel. 171 pages, with reproductions of 762 old watermarks of animals. Villanueva v Geltrú, Spain, 1910.

BRIQUET, CHARLES-MOÏSE: *Recherches sur les premiers papiers employés en Occident et en Orient du Xe au XIVe siècle.* 75 pages text. Paris, 1886.

——: *De la valeur des filigranes du papier comme moyen de déterminer l'âge et la provenance de documents non datés.* 13 pages text. Genève, Switzerland, 1892.

——: *Les Anciennes Papeteries du Duché de Bar et quelques filigranes barrois de la seconde moitié du XVe siècle.* 22 pages text, with 7 reproductions of watermarks. Besançon, France, 1898.

——: *Les Filigranes, Dictionnaire historique des marques du papier.* 4 volumes; 836 pages text; 16,112 reproductions of watermarks. Second edition, Leipzig, Germany, 1923.

CHURCHILL, W. A.: *Watermarks in Paper in Holland, England, France, etc., in the XVII and XVIII Centuries and Their Interconnections.* 94 pages text; 578 reproductions of watermarks. Amsterdam, Netherlands, 1935.

DENNE, SAMUEL: *Observations on Papermarks . . . in a letter to Mr. Gough.* 20 pages text; 64 reproductions of watermarks. In: *Archæologia,* Volume XII. London, 1795.

DEVAULX, T.: *Filigranes (Marques de papiers).* 8 pages text; 29 reproductions of watermarks. In: *Revue des Arts Decoratifs,* 18e Année, No. 1. Paris, January 1898.

DE WITTE, E.: *Comment il faut classer et cataloguer les filigranes.* 17 pages text. In: *Bulletin de l'Institut International de Bibliographie.* Bruxelles, Belgium, 1912.

——: *L'Histoire du papier et les filigranes.* 21 pages text; 8 illustrations; 135 reproductions of old watermarks. In: *Le Musée du Livre.* Bruxelles, 1912.

GACHET, HENRI: *Six Siècles d'histoire du papier.* 7 pages text; 9 reproductions of watermarks. In: *Le Courrier Graphique,* 3e Année, No. 14. Paris, April 1938.

GAUTHIER, JULES: *L'Industrie du papier dans les hautes vallées Franc-Comtoises du XVe au XVIIIe siècles.* 30 pages text, with reproductions of 62 watermarks. Montbéliard, France, 1897.

GRUEL, LEON: *Recherches sur les origines des marques anciennes qui se rencontrent dans l'art et dans l'industrie du XVe au*

XIXe siècle par rapport au Chiffre Quatre. 184 pages, with hundreds of reproductions of watermarks, emblems, ciphers, etc. Paris and Bruxelles, 1926.

HASSELQUIST, ALEXIS: *Vattenmärken i Handgjordt Papper.* 8 pages, with reproductions of 43 old watermarks. In: *Allmänna Svenska Boktryckare-Föreningens Meddelanden*, No. 7. Stockholm, Sweden, July 1905.

HAUSMANN, OBERBAURATH B.: *Albrecht Dürer's Kupferstiche, Radirungen, Holzschnitte, und Zeichnungen unter besonderer Berücksichtigung der dazu verwandten Papiere und deren Wasserzeichen.* 130 pages text, with reproductions of 57 watermarks used in paper employed by Dürer. Hanover, Germany, 1861.

HEAWOOD, EDWARD: *The Use of Watermarks in Dating Old Maps and Documents.* 22 pages text, with reproductions of 156 watermarks. In: *The Geographical Journal.* London, May 1924.

——: *The Position on the Sheet of Paper of Early Watermarks.* 10 pages text. In: *Transactions of Bibliographical Society,* Volume IX, 4th series. London, 1928.

HÖSSLE, FRIEDRICH VON: *Die Alten Papiermühlen der Freien Reichstadt Augsburg.* 39 pages text; 253 reproductions of watermarks. Augsburg, Germany, 1907.

HUNTER, DARD: *Handmade Paper and Its Watermarks: a Bibliography. Technical Association of the Pulp and Paper Industry.* 22 pages, listing 175 entries. New York, 1916.

——: *Watermarking Handmade Papers.* In: *Scientific American.* New York, March 26, 1921.

——: *Portrait Watermarking.* In: *Paper.* New York, January 11, 1922.

——: *Symbolism of Paper Markings.* In: *Paper.* New York, 1923.

——: *Romance of Watermarks: A Discourse on the Origin and Motive of These Mystic Symbols.* Cincinnati, Ohio, 1938.

HUNTER, JOSEPH: *Specimens of Marks Used by the Early Manufacturers of Paper, as Exhibited in Documents in the Public Archives of England.* In: *Archæologia,* Volume XXXVII. 8 pages text, with reproductions of 30 watermarks from the fourteenth and fifteenth centuries. London, 1858.

KEINZ, FRIEDRICH: *Die Wasserzeichen des XIV Jahrhunderts in*

Handschriften der K. Bayer. Hof- und Staatsbibliothek. 46 pages text, with 368 reproductions of watermarks. München, Bavaria, 1895.

——: *The Earliest Watermarks.* 8 pages text, with reproductions of 11 watermarks. In: *Literary Collector,* Volume VIII, No. 6. Greenwich, Connecticut, October 1914.

KIRCHNER, ERNST: *Die Papiers des XIV Jahrhunderts im Stadtarchive zu Frankfurt a. M. und deren Wasserzeichen technisch untersucht und beschrieben.* 35 pages text, with reproductions of 152 watermarks. Frankfurt a. M., Germany, 1893.

LICHAČEV, N. P.: *Le Papier et les plus anciens moulins à papier de l'État de Moscou* (in Russian). 106 pages of text, with reproductions of 783 watermarks. St. Petersburg, 1891.

——: *Paleographical Importance of Watermarks* (in Russian). 3 volumes and atlas; 758 pages text, with reproductions of 4,258 watermarks. (Next to the 4-volume work of C.-M. Briquet this is the most comprehensive study of old watermarks.) St. Petersburg, 1899.

MARMOL, LE BARON F. DEL: *Dictionnaire des filigranes classés en groupes alphabétiques et chronologiques.* 192 pages, with reproductions of 200 watermarks from the fourteenth to the eighteenth century. Namur, France, 1900.

MENA, LIC. RAMON: *Filigranas o Marcas Transparentes en Papeles de Nueva España, del Siglo XVI.* 29 pages, with reproductions of 20 watermarks. Mexico, D. F., 1926.

MIDOUX, ÉTIENNE, and MATTON, AUGUSTE: *Étude sur les filigranes des papiers employés dans le nord de la France aux XIVe et XVe siècles.* Text and reproductions of 600 watermarks. Paris, 1868.

MONTAIGLON, ANATOLE DE: *Filigranes de papiers du XIVe siècle.* 19 pages text, with reproductions of 53 watermarks. In: *Bulletin Archéologique du Comité des Travaux Historiques.* Paris, 1888.

NICOLAÏ, ALEXANDRE: *Histoire des moulins à papier du sudouest de la France, 1300–1800: Périgord, Agenais, Angoumois, Soule, Béarn.* 2 volumes, 361 pages, with 147 reproductions of watermarks. Bordeaux, France, 1935.

POTT, (Mrs.) HENRY: *Francis Bacon and His Secret Society.* Reproductions of about 550 watermarks. London, 1891.

RENKER, ARMIN: *Zweihundertfünfzig Jahre Papiermacherei in den Vereinigten Staaten von Amerika, Wilhelm Rittinghausen aus Mülheim (Ruhr) Begründer.* 8 pages text, 2 illustrations; reproductions of 7 watermarks used by William Rittenhouse, who established a paper mill in America in 1690. In: *Gutenberg-Jahrbuch.* Mainz, Germany, 1939.

SCOTT, REV. DR., and DAVEY, SAMUEL: *A Guide to the Collector of Historical Documents, Literary Manuscripts and Autograph Letters, etc.* 218 pages text, with reproductions of 138 watermarks from the fourteenth to the sixteenth century. London, 1891.

SOTHEBY, SAMUEL LEIGH: *Principia Typographica.* 3 volumes. The third volume is devoted to the papermarks found in books of the fifteenth century. London, 1858.

THOYTS, E. E.: *How to Decipher and Study Old Documents, Being a Guide to the Readers of Ancient Manuscripts.* 150 pages, with reproductions of watermarks, etc. London, 1903.

Watermarks of Early Rhode Island Paper. 3 pages text, with reproductions of 6 Rhode Island watermarks used in the eighteenth century. In: *Rhode Island Historical Society Collections,* Volume XXIII, No. 4. Providence, Rhode Island, October 1930.

WEISS, THEODORE: *Deutsche Wappenwasserzeichen.* 9 pages text, reproductions of 65 watermarks. In: *Der Deutsche Herold,* Nos. 8, 9, 11. Villingen, Baden, Germany, 1915.

WIBIRAL, F.: *Die Iconographie von Anton van Dyck nach den Forschungen von H. Weber.* 393 pages with reproductions of 94 watermarks. Leipzig, Germany, 1877.

WIENER, LUCIEN: *Étude sur les filigranes des papiers Lorrains.* 77 pages, with reproductions of more than 200 watermarks; plates, etc. Nancy, France, 1893.

IV. DECORATED PAPERS

*ADAM, PAUL: *Das Marmorieren des Buchbinders auf Schleimgrund und im Kleisterverfahren.* 73 pages, with descriptions of decorating by the moss and paste processes. Halle a. S., 1906.

*ARNETT, JOHN ANDREWS: *Bibliopegia; or the art of bookbinding* *in all its branches.* Pages 35 to 53 devoted to marbling and the surface colouring of paper. London, 1835.

BIERBAUM, OTTO JULIUS: *Künstlerische Vorsatz-Papiere.* In: *Dekorative Kunst,* Volume I, No. 3. München, 1898.

BOECK, JOF. PHILEAS: *Die Marmorierkunst. Ein Lehr-, Hand-, und Musterbuch für Buchbindereien, Buntpapierfabriken, u. s. w.* Contains thirty specimens of marbled and surface-coloured papers. Vienna, 1880.

*Bookbinding: The Whole Art of Bookbinding, containing valuable receipts for sprinkling, marbling, and colouring of paper. 60 pages text. Oswestry, 1811.

CLOUZOT, H., and FOLLOT, CH.: *Histoire du papier peint en France,* 272 pages text; examples of decorated paper. Paris, 1935.

**COCKERELL, SYDNEY M.: *Marbling Paper as a School Subject.* 16 pages; 1 specimen marbled paper. Hitchin, England, July 1934.

**CRANE, W. J. E.: *Bookbinding for Amateurs.* Pages 93–113 devoted to marbling and colours for paper staining. London, n.d.

**ERFURT, JULIUS: *The Dyeing of Paper Pulp.* Translated from the German by Julius Hübner. 175 pages text; 157 specimens of coloured papers. London, 1901.

**FICHTENBERG, M.: *Nouveau Manuel complet au fabricant de papiers de fantaisie.* 233 pages text; 34 specimens of coloured, decorated, and metallic papers. Paris, 1852.

**HALFER, JOSEF: *Die Fortschritte der Marmorir Kunst ein Praktisches Handbuch für Buchbinder und Buntpapierfabrikanten.* 224 pages text; 35 specimens marbled papers. Stuttgart, 1891.

**HALFER, JOSEPH: *The Progress of the Marbling Art from Technical Scientific Principles.* Translated by Herman Dieck. 224 pages text; 35 specimens of marbled papers. Buffalo, N. Y., 1894.

——: *The Art of Marbling and the Treatment of New Bronze Colours.* London, 1904.

**HASLUCK, PAUL N.: *Bookbinding, with numerous engravings and diagrams.* Chapter on marbling and the staining of paper. 160 pages text. London, 1907.

HENNIG, P.: *Sonderausstellung von Buntpapier in Kgl. Kunstgewerbe Museum zu Berlin*. Berlin, n.d.

HILDEBRAND, FRIEDRICH: *Die Buntpapier*. In: *Blätter für Buchgestaltung und Buchpflege*. Erstes Heft, n.p. 1932.

HONER, B.: *Die Geheimnisse der Marmorierkunst, nebst einer Anleitung zur Farbenbereitung*. Tuttlingen, 1870.

*KERSTEN, PAUL: *Das Färben und Marmorieren von Leder. Allgem. Anzeiger für Buchbindereien*. Stuttgart, 1912.

——: *Die Geschichte des Buntpapieres*. In: *Wochenblatt für Papierfabrikation*. 9 pages text; 15 specimens. 1938.

*KINDER, LOUIS H.: *Formulas for Bookbinders*. 115 pages text; pages 87–95 devoted to marbling of paper and marbling colours. East Aurora, N. Y., 1905.

Kunst und Kunsthandwerk: Austellung von Buntpapier in der Kunstgewerbeschule des österr. Museums. 319 pages. Vienna, 1910.

LOEBER, J. A.: *Bucheinbände und Vorsatzpapiere*. In: *Deutsche Kunst und Dekoration*. Volume IX, No. 9. June 1906.

*LORING, ROSAMOND B.: *Marbled Papers, an address delivered before the members of the Club of Odd Volumes, November 16, 1932*. 22 pages text; 12 specimens of marbled and paste papers. Boston, 1933.

*——: *Decorated Book Papers, being an account of their design and fashion*. 171 pages text; 25 specimens of decorated papers; 8 reproductions. Cambridge, Massachusetts, 1942.

MARTIN, T.: *The Circle of the Mechanical Arts: containing practical treatises on the various manual arts, trades, and manufacture. Bookbinding, papermaking, printing and surface colouring of papers*. London, 1913.

NASH, PAUL: *A Specimen Book of Pattern Papers Designed for and in Use by the Curwin Press*. 31 specimens. 145 copies. London, 1928.

*NICHOLSON, JAMES B.: *A Manual of the Art of Bookbinding*. 318 pages text; 6 specimens of marbled papers. Philadelphia, 1856.

PAZAUREK, GUSTAV E.: *Die Tapete Beiträge zu ihrer Geschichte und ästhetischen Wertung*. 6 specimens of decorated book papers. Stuttgart, 1922.

*PIETTE, LOUIS: *Essais sur la coloration des pâtes à papier sur la fabrication directe de papiers de tenture*. 357 pages text; 40

samples white and coloured rags; 428 specimens coloured papers. Paris, 1853.

*——: *Journal des Fabricants de Papier.* Numerous specimens of coloured and decorated paper. Château du Pont-d'Oie, près Arlon, Belgique, September 1854–December 1859.

*PLEGER, JOHN J.: *Bookbinding and Its Auxiliary Branches.* In: *Inland Printer.* In Part IV an account of marbling paper is given. Chicago, Illinois, 1914.

SACHS, H.: *Bucheinband und Buntpapier.* In: *Kunstwelt.* Berlin, 1913.

——: *Moderne Buntpapier und ihre Verwendung.* In: *Zeitschrift für Bücherfreunde.* Pages 73–80. 1909.

SCHADE, T. A. F.: *Die Marmorierkunst.* Berlin, 1845.

SCHRÖDER, H.: *Bücherpapiere und Einbandstoffe.* In: *Zeitschrift für Deutschlands Buchbinder und verwandte Gewerbe.* 221 pages text. 1911.

*SCHUBERT, MAX: *Die Papierverarbeitung.* Volume II contains description of the manufacture of decorated papers. Berlin, 1900–1.

SCHULHOF, W.: *Altere Buntpapier.* In: *Archi für Buchgewerbe.* Volume XXXVIII, pages 126–70.

*SEEMAN, THEODORE: *Die Tapete, ihre ästhetische Bedeutung und technische Darstellung, sowie kurze Beschreibung der Buntpapier Fabrikation.* 240 pages text; 42 illustrations. Vienna, 1882.

*SENF, B.: *Moderne Buntpapier und ihre Verwendung zu Bucheinbänden.* In: *Börsenblatt f. d. deutschen Buchhandel.* 1908.

STOLBA, LEOPOLD: *Vorsatz Papier.* In: *Dekorative Kunst.* Volume VII, pages 72–4. Munich, 1903.

*THRIFT, TIM: *Modern Methods in Marbling Paper, a treatise for the layman on the art of marbling for bookbinding and other decorative uses.* 38 pages text; 7 specimens of surface decoration. Winchester, Massachusetts, 1945.

VOGT, AD.: *Buntpapier und Tapetenfabrikation.* In: *Deutsche Kunst und Dekoration.* Volume X, pages 332–45. Darmstadt, 1918.

*WEICHELT, AUGUST: *Buntpapier-Fabrikation.* 329 pages text; 178 illustrations; 209 specimens of coloured and decorated papers. Verlag der Papier-Zeitung, Berlin, 1908.

*Weigner, Leop.: *Berevné a Pestré Papíry Jich Výrobní Techniky a Upotřebení.* 53 pages text; 24 illustrations; 56 specimens of surface decorated papers. Prague, 1909.

*Wolf, M. Mar.: *Marmorier auf Wasser.* Bremen, 1905.

*Woolnough, C. W.: *The Art of Marbling as Applied to Book Edges and Paper.* 80 pages text; 28 specimens decorated paper. London, 1853.

*——: *The Whole Art of Marbling as Applied to Paper and Book Edges, containing a full description of the nature and properties of the materials used and the method of preparing them.* 82 pages text; 38 examples of surface decorated paper. London, 1881.

Yamazaki, Akira: *Nihon Koyu Somoku Senshoku Fu. (Monograph of Plant-dyeing Peculiar to Japan.)* 57 pages, with specimens of paper dyed in the old manner. Tōkyō, 1933.

*Zaehnsdorf, J. W.: *Bookbinding.* 190 pages text; one chapter devoted to the surface decoration of paper. London, 1903.

*Ziegler, W.: *Zierformenerzeugung für Buntpapier, Vorsatz und Schnitt.* In: *Kosmos.* Volume VI, pages 205–23.

Notes

I

¹ Aside from my own observations of Mexican papermaking, the information has been based on the following works, and for further study these books should be consulted:

Christensen, Bodil: *"Notas sobre la fabricación del papel. . . ."* 16 pages text; 11 illustrations; map. In: *Revista Mexicana de Estudios Antropológicos*, Tomo VI, Nums. 1–2. Sociedad Mexicana de Antropología, Mexico, D. F., 1942.

Hagen, Victor W. von: "Mexican Papermaking Plants." In: *Journal of the New York Botanical Garden*, Volume XLIV, No. 517. 10 pages text; 8 illustrations. New York, N. Y., January 1943.

Hagen, Victor W. von: *The Aztec and Maya Papermakers.* 120 pages text; 77 illustrations. New York, N. Y., 1944.

Lenz, Hans: *La Industria Papelera en Mexico.* 121 pages text; 120 illustrations. Mexico, D. F., 1940.

León, Dr. N.: *"La Industria Indigena del Papel en Mexico."* In: *Boletín del Museo Nacional de Arqueología, Historia y Etnografía.* 10 pages text; 6 illustrations. Mexico, D. F., 1924.

Schwede, Rudolf: *Über das Papier der Maya Codices u. einiger altmexikanischer Bilderhandschriften.* 50 pages text; frontispiece and illustrations of fibres. Dresden, 1912.

Starr, Frederick: "Notes upon the Ethnography of Southern Mexico." In: *Proceedings of Davenport Academy of Natural Sciences*, Volume VIII, pages 81–3. Illustrations. Davenport, Iowa, 1900.

Starr, Frederick: "Mexican Paper." In: *American Antiquarian*, Volume XXII. 11 pages text, 8 illustrations. 1900.

Valentini, J. J.: "Mexican Paper." In: *Proceedings of the American Antiquarian Society, 1881*, pages 58–81. 15 illustrations. Worcester, Massachusetts, 1881.

² For detail relative to the making and decorating of tapa of the Pacific islands see: *Ka Hana Kapa*, by William T. Brigham (Honolulu, H. I., 1911); *Oceanische Rindenstoffe*, by Paul Hambruch (Oldenburg, 1926); *Primitive Papermaking* by Dard Hunter (Chillicothe, Ohio, 1927).

II

¹ *Sound and Symbol in Chinese,* by Bernhard Karlgren (London, 1923), page 62.

² *The Invention of Printing in China and Its Spread Westward,* by Thomas Francis Carter (New York, 1925), page 2, Part I.

³ For description of Chinese calligraphy see *Chinese Calligraphy,* by Chiang Yee (London, 1938).

⁴ *Chinese Written Language,* by J. C. Hepburn (Tōkyō, 1888).

⁵ *Chūsei ni okeru Seishigyō to Shishōgyō (The Paper Industry and the Paper Trade of Mediæval Japan),* by Ono Akitsugu.

⁶ For the histories and descriptions of more than 270 types of Japanese papers see *A Papermaking Pilgrimage to Japan, Korea, and China,* by Dard Hunter (New York, 1936), pages 87–118.

⁷ *The Paper Industry and Printing in Japan,* by P. D. Perkins (Japan Reference Library, New York, 1940), page 9.

⁸ *On the Origin of Paper,* by André Blum, translated from the French by Harry Miller Lydenberg (New York, 1934).

⁹ *Printing in Ancient China,* by Berthold Laufer (Chicago, 1931), page 24.

III

¹ *Kōko nichi roku* (1797).

² *On the History of Printing in Japan,* by Sir Ernest Satow. Transactions of the Asiatic Society of Japan, 1882, Vol. I, pages 48–51.

³ *The History of Printing of Early Buddhistic Sūtras (Nei-raku kan kyo shi),* (Tōkyō, 1923), pages 5–31.

⁴ *History of Japanese Printing (Nihon insatsu shi. Sekai insatsu shi),* edited by Kyūshirō Nakayama (Tōkyō, 1930), Vol. I, pages 29–41.

⁵ *Ichi wa ichi gen,* by Ota Nanpo.

⁶ *Hyaku-man-shotō sho-kō.*

⁷ *History of Ancient Printing in Japan (Nihon ko insatsu bunka shi),* (Tōkyō, 1932), pages 1–15.

⁸ *Kaigai kotsu shiwa.*

⁹ *Notes on Ancient Matters (Yūbun koji yoroku),* (Tōkyō, 1906), Vol. II, pages 532–55.

¹⁰ *On the History of Printing in Japan,* by Sir Ernest Satow. Transactions of the Asiatic Society of Japan, 1882, Vol. I, pages 48–51.

¹¹ "*Kōkoku kohan enkaku kō ho*" ("Supplement to the Evolution of Printing in Japan"), *Kōko kai (Journal of Archæology),* June 1901, Vol. I, pages 35–7.

¹² "On the Printing of the *Dhāranī of the Million Pagodas*" ("*Hyaku-man-tō dhāranī hankoku ni tsuite*"), *Journal of Archæology (Kōko kai),* July 1901, Vol. I, No. 2, pages 25–7.

¹³ "History of Old Japanese Printed Books" ("*Nihon kokoku-sho*

shi"), supplement to the *Kokusho Kanko-kai shuppan mokuroku* (Tō-kyō, 1909), pages 1–13.

¹⁴ *On the Printed Books of Japan* (*Nihon shoseki kan-kō*. *Kurokawa Mayori zenshū* (Tōkyō, 1911).

¹⁵ "Early Japanese Printing," in the *Japan Magazine*, October 1917, Vol. VIII, No. 6, pages 318–22.

¹⁶ "On Movable Type." Manuscript by Yasutaka Okamoto (1797–1878) (*"Kappan ko: Okamoto Yasutaka o jihitsu kohon"*) in *Journal of Archæology* (*Kōkō kai*), November 1901, Vol. I, pages 356–7.

¹⁷ "Evolution of Printing in Japan" (*"Kōkoku kohan enkaku kō"*) in *Journal of Archæology* (*Kōko kai*), June 1901, Vol. I, No. 1, pages 33–5.

¹⁸ (a) Charles Fabens Kelley: "Mr. Ryerson and the Department of Oriental Art," *Bulletin of the Art Institute of Chicago*, January 1933, Vol. XXVII, No. 1, page 16.

(b) James Murdock: *A History of Japan* (Kobe, 1910), Vol. I, Chapters v and vi, pages 142–205.

(c) G. B. Sansom: *Japan: a Short Cultural History* (New York, 1931), Part 2 on Nara, pages 105–73.

(d) Kenji Toda: "The Collection of Japanese and Chinese Books," *Bulletin of the Art Institute of Chicago*, December 1927, Vol. XXI, No. 9, pages 110–12.

¹⁹ *The Invention of Printing in China and Its Spread Westward*, by Thomas Francis Carter, Assistant Professor of Chinese, Columbia University (New York, 1925), Chapter vii: "The Empress Shōtoku of Japan and Her Million Printed Charms" (pages 33–8; note pages 206–7).

²⁰ "Printing Began in China in the Ninth Century," in the *Pacific Printer and Publisher*, December 1931, pages 33–4.

IV

¹ See *History of the Worshipful Company of Gold and Silver Wyre-drawers, and the Origin and Development of the Industry Which the Company Represents*, by Horace Stewart (London, 1891).

V

¹ For an analysis of Chinese characters relating to paper and bibliography see *Old Papermaking in China and Japan*, by Dard Hunter (Chillicothe, Ohio, 1932; limited edition).

² *Püchl von mein Geslecht und von Abentewr*, a manuscript diary compiled by Ulman Stromer in Nürnberg, about 1390. The original diary is in the German National Museum, Nürnberg. For an account of Ulman Stromer and his paper mill, see *Papermaking through Eighteen Centuries*, by Dard Hunter (New York, 1930), pages 7–16.

³ *Novo Teatro di Machine et Edificii,* by Vittorio Zonca (Padua, 1607).

⁴ *Theatrum Machinarum,* by Georg Andreæ Böckler (Nürnberg, 1662).

⁵ *T'ien kung k'ai wu* (天工開物), by Sung Ying-hsing (宋應星) (1634), a historical record of Chinese useful arts and industries and their manufacture, in 3 volumes. In 1927 a privately published edition of this work was issued in Tientsin. The text used in this edition was taken from a Japanese edition of 1771, which was collated with the text as found in the *K'ang-hsi* encyclopædia (圖書集成).

⁶ *Vollständige Mühlen Baukunst,* by Leonhardt Christoph Sturm (Augsburg, 1718).

⁷ *Ivy Mills, 1729–1866,* by Joseph Willcox. Printed for private circulation only. Baltimore, Maryland, 1911.

⁸ *Verschreibung und Abbildung meiner unweit Leipzig im Jahre 1801 durch den Zimmermeister Lüders erbaueten Windpapiermühle nach Holländischer Art* (Leipzig, 1820). (Eight pages of text, one folding plate showing the Hollander driven by a windmill.)

VI

¹ For complete details concerning papermaking in these countries see: for Burma: *Primitive Papermaking* (1927); for Nepal: *Papermaking by Hand in India* (1939); for Siam: *Papermaking in Southern Siam* (1936) — all by Dard Hunter.

² *Visible World: or, A Nomenclature, and Pictures, of all the Chief Things that are in the World, and of Men's Employments therein.* Written by the author [Johann Amos Comenius] in Latin and High Dutch. Translated into English by Charles Hoole. First edition, 1658.

³ For a detailed account of the forming of the sheets, couching, making the post, pressing, etc., in modern European handmade-paper mills, see "Handmade Papers," by Dard Hunter in *The Manufacture of Pulp and Paper, a Textbook of Modern Pulp and Paper Mill Practice,* Volume V (New York and London, 1939, third edition).

⁴ See *A Papermaking Pilgrimage to Japan, Korea, and China* (1936) for a detailed account of Oriental papermaking.

⁵ *The History of Silk, Cotton, Linen, Wool, and Other Fibrous Substances; including observations on Spinning, Dyeing and Weaving,* etc. (New York, 1845).

VII

¹ *Ch'ien Han Shu* (前漢書), compiled by Pan Ku (斑固).

² *Hou Han Shu.*

³ Privately printed in China, 1832–3, but the manuscript is thought

to date from as early as 1480. See *Certain Old Chinese Notes, or Chinese Paper Money*, by Andrew McFarland Davis (Boston, 1915). According to Dr. Paul Pelliot, the work *Ch'üan-pu t'ung-chih* is a forgery, but plates showing paper money from the T'ang to the Yüan Dynasties (618–1341) are reproduced as genuine by both H. A. Ramsden (*Chinese Paper Money*, Yokohama, 1911) and Davis.

⁴ The *Chronicles of the Old Book of T'ang* and the *New Book of T'ang* are the 16th and 17th of the 24 Dynastic Histories and cover the period A.D. 618–906. The *Old Book of T'ang, Chiu T'ang Shu* (舊唐書) was compiled by Liu Hsü (劉昫) and others; the *New Book of T'ang, Hsin T'ang Shu* (新唐書) was compiled by Ou Yang Hsiu (歐陽修) and Sung Chi (朱祁).

⁵ This book has appeared in many editions, the text being practically the same, as translated from the Arabic compiled originally by Abū Zaid Hasan al Sīrāfī, who lived about A.D. 916. The Arabic text may be found in: *Relation des voyages faits par les Arabes et Persans dans l'Inde et à la Chine dans le ix. siècle de l'ère chrétienne. Texte Arabe imprimé en 1811*, by M. Reinaud (Paris, 1845; 2 volumes). In this edition the reference to paper in French will be found on page 23, Volume I, with a note on page 15, Volume II. For translations into English of these voyages see: "*Ancient Accounts of India and China*, by two Mohammedan travellers, who went to those parts in the 9th century; translated from the Arabic by the late learned Eusebius Renaudot. With notes, illustrations and inquiries by the same hand. London: Printed for S. Harding, 1733." Also, "Travels of two Mohammedans in India and China, in the ninth century," in Robert Kerr's *A General History and Collection of Voyages and Travels* (Edinburgh, 1811), pages 47–95. This is in two parts, the first said to be taken down from statements made by a merchant named Sulaiman, the second a continuation of the first, by Sīrāfī, translated from an Arabic manuscript by Eusebius Renaudot (1646–1720).

⁶ For comprehensive accounts of ceremonial uses of paper in China see *Chinese Ceremonial Paper, a monograph relating to the fabrication of paper and tin foil and the use of paper in Chinese rites and religious ceremonies*, by Dard Hunter. Many original specimens of ceremonial paper. 1936. See also the following works: *The Moon Year*, by J. Bredon (Shanghai, 1927); *Chinese Birthday, Wedding, Funeral, and other Customs*, by Anne Cormack (Peking and Tientsin, 1928); *The Religious Systems of China*, by J. J. M. De Groot (Leyden, 1892–4; 6 volumes); *Social Life of the Chinese*, by J. Doolittle (London, 1868); *Researches into Chinese Superstitions*, by Henry Doré (Shanghai, 1914); *The General History of China*, by P. Du Halde (London, 1736; 4 volumes); "Some Account of Charms," by John R. Morrison, in *Journal of the Royal Asiatic Society*, Volume III (London, 1833); "Paper Currency of Fuhchowfoo," by H. Parker, in *Journal of the Royal Asiatic*

Society, Volume XIII (London, 1852); *Truth and Tradition in Chinese Buddhism,* by K. L. Reichelt (Shanghai, 1927); "Funeral Money in China," by J. J. Serebrennikow, in the *China Journal,* Volume XVIII, No. 4 (Shanghai, 1933); "Burial Customs in Sz-chuan," by T. Torrance, in *Journal of the North China Branch of the Royal Asiatic Society,* Volume XLI (Shanghai, 1910); "Some Chinese Funeral Customs," by W. Gilbert Walshe, in *Journal of the China Branch of the Royal Asiatic Society,* Volume XXXV (Shanghai, 1903–4); *Myths and Legends of China,* by E. Werner (New York, 1922).

⁷ *China Industrial Handbooks: Chekiang,* second series of the reports by the National Industrial Investigation. Compiled and published by Bureau of Foreign Trade, Ministry of Industry (Shanghai, 1935). (See "Handmade Paper," pages 631–48; "Joss-Paper Manufacture," pages 747–59.)

VIII

¹ *The Biography and Typography of William Caxton,* by William Blades (London, 1877).

² *Reminiscences,* by Charles Cowan, of Logan House (printed for private circulation, Wester Lea, Murrayfield, England, 1878), pages 66–74.

³ *The Centenary of Springfield Mill, Maidstone. A brief history of the firm, 1807–1907,* by E. C. Riddle (Maidstone, Kent, England, 1907), page 2.

⁴ "Description of the Process to be Observed in Making Large Sheets of Paper in the Chinese Manner, with One Smooth Surface," in *Transactions of the American Philosophical Society* (Philadelphia, 1793), pages 8–10.

⁵ *The Poetry of the Paper Industry* (Van Gelder Zonen, Amsterdam, n.d.), page 58.

⁶ "Historical Sketch of the Rittenhouse Paper Mill, the first erected in America, A.D. 1690," by Horatio Gates Jones, in the *Pennsylvania Magazine of History and Biography* (Philadelphia, 1896), Vol. XX, No. 3, pages 315–33.

⁷ "William McCulloch's Additions to Thomas's History of Printing," in *Proceedings of the American Antiquarian Society,* New Series, April 13, 1921, Volume XXXI, Part I, pages 89–247.

⁸ Although the poem was written in 1696, it was not printed until 1847, when it appeared in the *Bulletin* of the Historical Society of Pennsylvania, Volume I, No. 13, page 72.

⁹ *Ivy Mills, 1729–1866,* by Joseph Willcox (printed for private circulation only, Baltimore, 1911).

¹⁰ "Die Papier Mühle der Brüderschaft zu Ephrata," in *Lancaster County Historical Society Publications* (Lancaster, Pennsylvania, 1897).

[11] *Roslyn in the Olden Times,* by Alice C. Titus (?) (n.p., n.d.).
[12] *China Industrial Handbooks: Chekiang* (Shanghai, 1935), pages 631–48.

IX

[1] "Notes on Watermarks," in *Booklovers' Magazine,* Vol. VI, pages 65–71 (London, 1906); *A New Light on the Renaissance, Displayed in Contemporary Emblems* (London, 1909); *The Lost Language of Symbolism, An Inquiry into the Origin of Certain Letters, Words, Names, etc.* (2 volumes; London, 1912).

X

[1] *History of the Bank of England, Its Times and Traditions,* by John Francis (2 volumes; London, n.d.).
[2] *A Guide to the Collector of Historical Documents, Literary Manuscripts and Autograph Letters, etc.,* by John Scott and Samuel Davey (London, 1891), page 96.
[3] *History of the Bank of England,* page 178.
[4] *An Account of Forgeries on the Bank of England,* by Samuel Thompson (Manchester, 1860); *Charles Price, and His Forgeries on the Bank of England* (London, 1786).
[5] *The Gilbart Prize Essay on the Adaptation of Recent Discoveries and Inventions in Science and Art to the Purpose of Practical Banking,* by Grenville Sharp (London, 1854), page 242.
[6] *Report of the Committee of the Society of Arts, etc. Together with the Approved Communications and Evidence upon the Same, Relative to the Mode of Preventing the Forgery of Bank-Notes* (London, 1819).
[7] *The Story of Portals of Laverstoke, 1719–1925* (London, 1925).
[8] *Journal of the Society of Arts,* London, May 18, 1906.

XI

[1] "*Magnalia Dei in Locis Subterraneis oder unterirdische Schatzcammer aller Königreiche und Länder,*" in *Ausführlicher Beschreibung Aller, mehr als MDC. Bergwercke durch alle vier Welt-Theile, etc.* (2 volumes; Braunschweig, 1727–30).
[2] *Locupletissimi rerum naturalium thesauri accurata descriptio, et iconibus artificiosissimis expressio, per universam physices historiam. Opus, cui, in hoc rerum genere, nullum par exstitit. Ex toto terrarum orbe collegit, digessit, descripsit, et depingendum curavit Albertus Seba. Amstelædami, 1734–1765.* 4 volumes.

[3] *"Observations sur différentes matières dont on fabrique le papier,"* in *Mémoires de Paris* (Paris, 1741); *"Mémoire sur les différentes manières de fabriquer le papier,"* in *Histoire de l'Académie des sciences, année 1741; Journal économique* (July and August 1751); *"Recherches sur les matières qui peuvent servir à faire du papier,"* in *Mémoires sur différentes parties des Sciences et Arts* (Paris, 1768), Vol. I.

[4] "Inquiry concerning the Materials that may be Used in Making Paper, by Mr. Guettard, of the Royal Academy of Sciences, and Physician to his Serene Highness the Duke of Orleans," in *Select Essays on Commerce, Agriculture, Mines, Fisheries, and Other Useful Subjects* (London, 1754).

[5] "An Enquiry concerning the Materials that may be Used in Making Paper," in *Select Essays: Collected from the Dictionary of Arts and Sciences, and from various modern authors.* Printed by George Bell, Philadelphia, 1777.

[6] *Letter on the Origin of the Natural Paper of Cortona, with Other Observations Relative to the Uses and Excellent Qualities of the Conferva of Pliny* (Pisa, 1764).

Also see "An Account of an Essay of the Origin of a Natural Paper, found near the City of Cortona in Tuscany. A Letter from John Strange, Esq., F.R.S. to Mathew Maty, M.D., Sec. R.S.," in *Philosophical Transactions*, Volume LIX, pages 50–6 (read February 16, 1769), London, 1769.

[7] *Versuche und Muster ohne alle Lumpen oder doch mit einem geringen Zusatze derselben Papier zu machen* (6 volumes; Regensburg, 1765–71).

[8] In 1772 a combined edition of this work was issued with the six parts in one volume. In this edition there are 81 examples of paper, 13 coloured plates, and 8 engraved plates of appliances, etc. (Part I, 52 pp. text; Part II, 28 pp.; Part III, 32 pp.; Part IV, 24 pp.; Part V, 22 pp.; Part VI, 16 pp.). (Regensburg, 1772.)

[9] *Proefnemingen en Monster-bladen, om Papier te Maaken Zonder Lompen, of met een gering Byvoegzel, derzelven* (Amsterdam, 1770).

[10] M. J. H. Pelée de Varennes: *Les Loisirs des bords du Loing ou recueil des piéces fugitives* (Montargis, P. Prevost, 1784). 50 copies printed.

[11] *Œuvres du Marquis de Villette* (Londres, 1786). (a) *Volume est imprimé sur le Papier d'Ecorce de Tilleul.* (b) *Volume est imprimé sur le Papier de Guimauve.*

[12] *Die älteste Urkunde der Papierfabrikation in der Natur entdeckt nebst Vorschlägen zu neuen Papierstoffen von G. A. Senger, Prediger zu Reck. Dortmund und Leipzig, 1799.*

[13] *Historical Account of the Substances Which have been Used to Describe Events and to Convey Ideas, from the Earliest Date to the Invention of Paper.* Printed by T. Burton, No. 31, Little Queen Street, London, 1800.

XII

1 *Abridgments of the Specifications relating to the Manufacture of Paper, Pasteboard, and Papier Mâché* (Great Seal Patent Office, London, 1858). See the following patents: John Gamble, April 20, 1801, No. 2487; John Gamble, June 7, 1803, No. 2708; Henry Fourdrinier, July 24, 1806, No. 2951; Henry Fourdrinier, Sealy Fourdrinier, and John Gamble, August 14, 1807, No. 3068.

2 *Abridgments of the Specifications Relating to the Manufacture of Paper, Pasteboard, and Papier Mâché* (Great Seal Patent Office, London, 1858). See the following patents: John Dickinson, January 19, 1809, No. 3191; John Dickinson, May 21, 1811, No. 3452.

3 John Dickinson, January 14, 1829, No. 5754; John Dickinson, December 28, 1833, No. 6535; John Dickinson, October 17, 1839, No. 8242.

4 *The Firm of John Dickinson and Company, with an appendix on ancient papermaking,* by Sir John Evans (London, 1896).

5 *The Manufacture of Pulp and Paper, a textbook of modern pulp and paper mill practice.* See *Imitation Handmade Paper,* by Dard Hunter (first edition, New York, 1925).

XIII

1 *Bulletin of the New York Public Library,* Vol. XXXIII, No. 10, pages 743–9 (New York, N. Y., October 1929).

XIV

1 *Thomas Chatterton the Marvellous Boy, the Story of a Strange Life 1752–1770,* by Charles Edward Russell (London, 1909).

2 *The Confessions of William Henry Ireland. Containing the Particulars of his Fabrication of the Shakspeare Manuscripts; together with Anecdotes and Opinions of many Distinguished Persons in the Literary, Political, and Theatrical World* (London, 1805).

XV

1 For an account of amateur papermaking by hand see *Papermaking in the Classroom,* by Dard Hunter (The Manual Arts Press, Peoria, Illinois). 80 pages text; 47 illustrations.

Index